IAN WOOSNAM'S GOLF MASTERPIECES

IAN WOOSNAM'S GOLF MASTERPIECES

Classic tales from the clubhouse

Ian Woosnam with
Peter Grosvenor

SIDGWICK & JACKSON
LONDON

Cartoons by Roy Ullyett
Book design by Alan Chalk

First published in Great Britain in 1988 by
Sidgwick & Jackson Limited
1 Tavistock Chambers, Bloomsbury Way
London WC1A 2SG

ISBN 0 283 99676 5

Photoset by Rowland Phototypesetting Limited
Bury St Edmunds, Suffolk
Printed in Great Britain by
Butler and Tanner Limited, Frome, Somerset

Contents

Introduction

In this anthology I have tried to express some of my love of the game and just how much I owe to it. The more you play and think about golf, the more you marvel at the demands it makes not just on your physical skill but also on your temperament. The moment you think you have golf licked it comes up behind you and bites you in the rear. I reckon that a quick loss of temper to relieve your frustration – like the time when I snapped a 2 iron across my knee in the Majorca Open – is much better than brooding over disaster and letting it sap your morale. The game can be agony and ecstasy – the title of one of the sections in this anthology – and that's as true for the professional like myself as it is for the 28 handicapper. As one sage put it, 'Golf is like a love affair. If you don't take it seriously, it's not fun. If you do take it seriously, it breaks your heart.' What drives us on? No one expressed it better than that wise golf writer Bernard Darwin, several of whose pen portraits of the great players of the past you can read in these pages. He said, 'It is this constant and undying hope of improvement that makes golf so exquisitely worth the playing.'

Small is Beautiful

Severiano Ballesteros caused a few laughs after I had won the Suntory World Match Play at Wentworth in 1987 with his quip: 'Woosnam will be a great golfer when he grows up.' I have never seen my 5 feet 4 inches as a disadvantage. It certainly would be if I were a basketball player, but in golf the old adage 'A good big 'un is better than a good little 'un' is just not true. Look at Gary Player, barely 5 feet 7 inches; Hogan and Watson are no more than 5 feet 9 inches. Golf is very much a game of balance. The taller you are, the more you are liable to sway and create greater body movement. The smaller you are, the more turn you can get. That is why I am among the big hitters in the game. Sandy Lyle and I have been friendly rivals from the days of our Shropshire youth when he won the junior prize and I was runner-up. I vowed there and then that I was going to beat him one day. 'You'll have to grow a bit first,' Sandy told me. That's the least of my worries.

   The subject of my size came up when in March 1987 I was honoured to have lunch with the Queen and Prince Philip at Buckingham Palace. Though members of the Royal Family are not noted for their addiction to golf, the Queen, who is patron of the Royal and Ancient, watches it on television in the evenings. She asked me whether I found it difficult playing in the wind. 'It certainly helps to be small, Ma'am,' I replied, 'because you don't get blown about so much.'

When I turned professional in 1976 at the age of eighteen, I was christened 'the toy bulldog', although I'm also known as 'the mighty atom' and 'the little golfing wizard from Wales'. I am sturdily built for my height, weighing 11 stone, and I have the strength where it matters – in the legs, in the arms and above all in the hands, which is important because I'm a wristy player. As soon as I was old enough for my feet to touch the pedals, I was driving the tractor on my father's farm. There was no power steering then, and that gave me powerful forearms. I would also practise steering the tractor with just the index finger and thumb of my left hand, and in that way developed great strength.

My Back

The only cloud over my fortunes has been my back. I'm not the first golfer to suffer in this way. After years at the top Jack Nicklaus said, 'There has not been a day in the past twenty years when my back hasn't ached.' Like Seve, another back sufferer, he would hang from a trapeze that stretched his back, easing the pressure between the vertebrae. Langer also suffers periods of back pain and Lee Trevino has had surgery. I have had back trouble pretty much since I became a pro; it doesn't hurt when I'm actually playing, but I feel it afterwards. Sometimes the muscles go taut and I can't get to sleep, or I manage to sleep and wake up aching. And when I get up on the morning of a tournament it's sometimes so bad I can't even put my socks on.

One rheumatologist told me that I had spondylitis, a progressive disease of the spine in which the vertebrae start to fuse. It can be caused, or aggravated, by constantly leaning forward to hit golf shots. I was in real pain after all the rain in Hawaii where Dave Llewellyn and I won the World Cup for Wales at the end of 1987. It didn't seem like a happy omen for my trip to Sun City immediately afterwards for the Million Dollar Challenge. Happily, the weather was much warmer and the facilities laid on for us there were extensive. A chiropractor who specializes in muscle and joint problems gave me exercises to do, lying on a bed and lifting my feet up. I went on to win that week and to date his advice has worked wonders. Oddly enough, it is being so small that helps contribute to my back problem. If I sit up in an ordinary chair or even an aeroplane seat my feet sometimes don't quite touch the ground, and on aeroplanes especially I put a briefcase under my feet to give support to my back.

My Ambition

My ambition is to be number one golfer in the world and to be remembered alongside the real greats of the game – Tom Morris, Jack Nicklaus and my two special heroes, Tom Watson (who has such style) and Gary Player (because he's such a great fighter). I've had this competitive urge at sport ever since I can remember and I think it comes from my father, Harold. He's not a golf professional like Sandy Lyle's father, who gave Sandy a lot of painstaking tuition. Whereas Sandy always had a course outside his front door to play on, I had to make a 15-mile trek.

My own swing is more or less self-taught. What my father taught me was never to know when I'm beaten. He's so competitive at everything he does that he would spin a scrabble game out for two days to get the very best possible score if we let him.

My Early Days

At Rhyn Park School my main interest was sport, not study. I wanted to be the best at soccer, boxing, swimming, anything sporting. My father tells a story about a family holiday at Butlin's during which I earned the nickname Tiger for my ring heroics. 'They could never find anyone Ian's size, but he still beat them,' he recalls. 'He even won the swimming and we didn't think he could swim. It just shows how competitive he's always been.'

I had ambitions to play soccer for England, though never so strong as my ambitions in golf. When I left school I suppose it was touch and go whether I would opt for soccer or golf. I was in the local football team and used to play very hard, always getting stuck in. My father told me that if I carried on like that it wouldn't be long before I wasn't able to play football again or even golf. He says he just had to step in because he knew I would hurt myself.

So golf won, and anyway it's a sport in which you can go on longer. At the age of thirty I'd now be over the top as a footballer, whereas I know that the best of me is yet to come as a golfer.

I swung my first golf club when I was seven and my father says that even now he still

picks up the balls I hit on the farm when I was practising. He took up golf in his thirties and at one time played a very competitive game off a 5 handicap though nowadays it's nearer 8. We played at the Llanymynech Club where fifteen holes are in Wales and three in England. That's a bit like me. I was actually born on the border, just in England, at the village of St Martin's near Oswestry, but I regard myself as a Welshman through and through (as much of a Welshman as Lloyd George, who was born in Manchester).

I have two brothers and one sister. The eldest brother, Keith, a central heating plumber, is four years older than me and plays off 11. He was born in a hospital in Wales, as was my sister Julie who is two years older than me. My brother Gareth is nine years younger. He plays off 4 and could be a very fine golfer if he had more time to practise.

I played most of my early golf at Llanymynech and by the time I was thirteen I was down to a 6 handicap. I was always badgering the members to play me for £1, even though I hadn't any money in my pocket. Fortunately, I didn't often lose. Then I slumped a bit and was only down to a handicap of 1 when I turned pro in 1976.

When I was sixteen I left school and took a job with Albert Minshall at the Hill Valley Club near Whitchurch. First of all I helped in the pros' shop, but that was too quiet for me. So after a couple of weeks I joined the green staff, a 7.30 a.m. to midday job which gave me plenty of time for practice in the afternoons, though I probably spent more time playing than practising. Playing is the real way to improve your game, by which I mean getting round in fewer strokes. You can learn far more by playing than by practising, as I'll explain later.

Early Struggles as a Pro

I was eighteen when I turned pro in September, 1976.

I spent three seasons at the players' school at Foxhills, Chertsey, in Surrey. My first important win was in the *News of the World* Under-23 Match Play, when I beat John Hay in the final. I also acquired the nickname of Bertie because of the rather remote similarity of my surname to that of P. G. Wodehouse's famous character, Bertie Wooster. A special dinner was held for me to raise some money to get me to Portugal and we called it Bertie's party. The name has stuck.

I borrowed my father's old Volkswagen caravanette for the tour. It was white going off-white so I painted it blue to make it look a bit more respectable. It became a real home from home as we travelled round. We slept in it, dried our clothes in it, and ate our rather monotonous fare of crisps, soup and endless tins of baked beans.

I never had much trouble getting a good night's rest in the van, but moving around in it presented more problems. I just prayed it wouldn't break down because I had no money for repairs. I remember that it took me more than three days to drive to Milan. Once there, the old banger began to splutter and choke and slowed down to an embarrassing 10 m.p.h. crawl, its top speed. I hawked it about from one garage to another, fearing that the engine had broken up. How on earth was I going to find several hundred quid for a new one? No one seemed to be able to diagnose the trouble till at last I found a Volkswagen dealer. He fixed it in moments: a tube had come off the carburettor, and once it was back on the VW ran like a bird. I came ninth in the Italian Open so at least I had enough money for the petrol home.

I wasn't always so fortunate. Very often I didn't make eating money. Another time I was down to my last £2 after filling up in Lyons. Credit cards weren't generally accepted in France then – not that I had one anyway – and I just hoped and prayed that a full tank would get me all the way to Calais. Crossing the city boundary with the needle at empty I breathed a sigh of relief, only to have the van splutter to a dry stop just 1 kilometre from the ferry. If you've ever tried buying a couple of litres of petrol from a French garage with only £2 in English money in your pocket, you'll know just how difficult that can be. I trudged around with a can till finally I found a guy who would take English pound notes and I was spared the indignity of having to push my vehicle on to the boat.

Soon after that things got a little easier financially. I was still too poor to fly, but I could afford a bed and breakfast place. A group of us – David Russell, Joe Higgins, Martin Poxon, Mike Inglis and myself – took two cars, sharing petrol costs, to drive to the Italian Open. I shot an 87 and failed to qualify, as did Mike Inglis. The others, however, did qualify, and Martin generously lent us his wreck of a Triumph Dolomite so that Mike and I could seek our fortunes in the French Open.

This was another of those occasions when our driving troubles began well before we got to the tee. The wretched vehicle broke down in Nice and required a new head gasket. As usual, we had no money and were limited to drawing £50 a day each with cheques backed by cheque cards. Finally, after a couple of days, we scraped together enough to pay for the repairs and set off for Paris, only to have the shock absorbers go. Buzzing down the autoroute in that hair-raising old car which bobbed about like a cork on the ocean was not the ideal preparation for the French Open and not surprisingly we failed to qualify. The only consolation was that Martin Poxon agreed to pay for the repairs to the shock absorbers.

That was what life was like at the bottom end of the professional circuit. We had a lot of laughs and a lot of fun, but quite a lot of heartache too. No one would endure that kind of perdition and frustration for many months unless he was really determined to succeed, and I was. In 1979 I was 122nd in the order of merit and won £1,049. Often I had to quit the tour and get a part-time job as a barman or labourer to gather together enough money for another stab at it – anything to scratch a few bob together.

In 1980 I struck it rich: all of £3,481, and I was number 87 on merit. Then in 1981 it all fell apart when I slipped back to 104th and earnings of only £1,884. I couldn't seem to qualify and I felt like giving up the tour. I was going to apply for the pro's job at Oswestry Golf Club. I spent two weeks feeling very sorry for myself. Deep down I still wanted to be the best golfer in the world, but there were times when that objective became submerged. I got stuck: I couldn't even see what I was doing wrong; I could hit the ball as well as the rest of them, *but I wasn't scoring*. Yet something inside me told me to hang on in there.

The Breakthrough

In 1982 a chance encounter changed everything for me on the eve of the Nigerian Open. I was on the practice ground with Yorkshireman Gordon Brand Senior. While I was hitting the ball well, he looked awful: pushing one over the fence on the right, pulling the next one yards left. But while he got round in 68, I was taking 76. Suddenly it clicked: *bad shots didn't worry him.*

All he worried about was getting a good score on his card. I thought it was a great attitude. It changed my whole outlook on the game and also my life. I just went out and never worried about my bad shots again. I stopped putting myself under too much pressure by trying to hit perfect shots all the time, and adopted the oldest adage in the game: 'It's not how, but how many.'

By finishing third in the African Safari Tour money list in 1982 I became exempt from qualifying in Europe and that was the start of the big time. After that I got my temper under control: no more putters smashed in anger, no more clubs hurled in a rage. I went on to win the Swiss Open, my first big victory, and came second in the Italian Open. I didn't have to pre-qualify now; I won £48,794 and finished eighth in the European order of merit. I was on the road from golfing pauper to golfing millionaire, or so I hoped.

The other parts of my life began to come together as well. In 1983 I married my childhood sweetheart, Glendryth. Before we married she wanted to do her own thing and came to London to one of the teaching hospitals where she trained to become a State Registered Nurse. That gave me my first taste of London life. To be with her I bought a flat in Maida Vale which I later sold: it would certainly be worth a lot now. But I'm not a townee, though I wouldn't mind a place in the Wentworth area. I'm really still a country boy with no desire to give up my first home at Oswestry.

In 1984, in a thrilling head-to-head last-round contest with Sandy Lyle, I won the Scandinavian Open. When Glendryth gave birth to our son Daniel in the following year, that was another incentive to be successful. Winning is an infectious habit: it brings confidence. Success breeds success. I started with a win in the Zambian Open in March 1985, had ten top-eight finishes in the European tour and was placed fourth in final Order of Merit with earnings of over £80,000.

During the Ryder Cup of that year Paul Way and I beat Fuzzy Zoeller and Hubert Green by one hole on the first day, and then by four and three on the second to help Europe to their first victory in twenty-eight years, and that gave me as much pleasure as anything I'd done in golf up until then.

If I win in the early part of the season, I'm confident. If I start badly, I get a bit anxious. Although I don't have to worry financially, that doesn't mean I've lost the desire to excel, to be number one. I'm a good loser, I like to think, though I hate to lose. But every time I go out now, I feel that I can win.

Coping with the Pressures

1986 was a good year for me with winnings of £111,799, even though my putting was in poor shape for half the year.

At the Open at Turnberry I wasn't put off by the appalling conditions. Someone joked that at my height I operated 3 feet below the wind! I had a great first round of 70 to lead the field, then made 74, 70 and 72 on the final day when the weather had returned to normal. I finished third and won £35,000.

I was still struggling on the greens, however, until halfway through the third round of the Lawrence Batley TPC when I decided to line up my putts differently and promptly birdied four out of the next six holes to finish with a round of 66 and then 69 to win by seven shots, incidentally ending the Belfry's seven-year wait for a British winner.

Golf is full of hidden problems which can creep up on you unawares. But where there's a will there's a way.

Look at Bernhard Langer. He had the dreaded 'yips' – that involuntary jab or twitch that sends the ball wide on short putts – worse than anyone in the world; and the yips have driven other men out of the game, but not Bernhard. He conquered the problem by changing his method, adopting the reverse grip for close putts, and most of all by sheer guts and determination because he wanted so badly to overcome it.

There are lots of great players out there who have never won anything really big like a major. Maybe the pressure gets to them. Even now, when I'm close to winning, my heart is pounding and my hands are shaking, probably most of all on the greens. When you've learned to play through nerves like that, you've almost cracked it. Nerves can be a hindrance and nerves can be a help. But you can never play to the peak without some nerves. Nerves set the adrenaline flowing and get you pumped up. Great footballers like Sir Stanley Matthews used to be physically sick before a big game. The tempo of soccer is very different from that of golf, of course, in that once you're on the football pitch the game is so fast and so demanding you haven't got time to feel nervous (except during set pieces such as a crucial penalty). The player who is a bag of nerves before a Cup Final can go out and play the game of his life once he's on the pitch.

In golf, with long gaps between shots, the pace is obviously different, and that's where the other essential comes in: concentration. Because I need to concentrate I don't talk to my partners or opponents as I used to. When I played Sandy Lyle in the final of the Suntory World Match Play in 1987, I suddenly realized that I was in danger of blowing it because I was talking to Sandy too much. It was either him or me who would become the first Briton to win the trophy. So I kept quiet and the competitive edge returned.

Inevitably, after years of competitive pressure, there has to be a reaction at some point, as Tom Watson has shown. He's done everything and you can't last at the top for ever. Nicklaus, however, is different. His extraordinary win in the Masters in 1986 was a triumph of determination, as if to say, 'I want to win to prove that I still can win'. But I feel that maybe Jack should have retired at that point, going out right at the top. Jack and Tom Watson are both very nice guys. Usually the best players are the nicest, because they are at ease with themselves.

Money has changed my life to an extent, but for me the trophies of wealth are much less important than the success itself. I bought my five-bedroom house in Oswestry for a six-figure sum, that is peanuts by London or New York standards. Mind you,

Glendryth and I have put a lot into the house, with a specially built snooker room and bar, a jacuzzi and a sauna. The drawing room is bulging with Waterford crystal from various prizes.

I have a few of the badges of wealth, such as my Porsche with its personalized number plate – PRO IW. It has a car phone, which is a bit of a toy really and a damn nuisance when I leave it on by mistake and it runs the battery flat. I've got a compact disc player in the car and a TV dish in the garden to pick up those transatlantic golf programmes, because I'm addicted to watching golf. It can teach you so much. But extravagance will never come easily to me.

1987 saw me become the first player to top £1 million in tournament winnings. The year had got off to a whirlwind start when I won the Hong Kong Open with a four-round total of 275, four shots ahead of David Feherty and Sam Torrance who shared second place. I was the first Briton to win the tournament in its 29-year history, which pleased me a lot. After that came victory in the Jersey Open and the winning streak was well and truly on. In the Madrid Open at Puerto de Hierro I clipped one shot off the 270-stroke championship record set by Ballesteros seven years before. In July I had my third victory of the European tour by winning the Bell's Scottish Open at Gleneagles with seven shots to spare, having led from start to finish. The Lancôme Trophy gave me my fourth European win of the season and I was on the crest of a wave when I joined the European Ryder Cup team at Muirfield, Ohio. We were defending the trophy we had won at the Belfry two years before and playing in the four balls and foursomes with Nick Faldo we achieved 3½ points out of a possible 4. To be the first European team to win on American soil was a very emotional experience. Just as emotional was winning for Wales with David Llewellyn in the World Cup, where I had a 14 under par for the best individual score. The icing on the cake was victory in the $1 million 'Winner takes all' tournament at Sun City, the richest prize in golf. So what do I do for an encore in 1988? Win one of the majors, I hope.

Some Thoughts on Practice and Pacing Myself

This may shock generations of golfers but if things are going well I try to practise less, not more. Even today I don't like to practise more than forty-five minutes at a time unless there's some specific problem to work out. Practice sometimes leads to fiddling, to experimenting with different gimmicks and ideas, and that can be positively damaging. As the Americans say, 'If it ain't broke, don't fix it.' And that applies to a golf swing which is working well.

Before a big tournament I will arrive about an hour before tee-off and hit about eighty shots, largely just to loosen up. I then finish off with about half an hour's chipping and putting to get the feel and the pace of the greens.

Although I had some tuition in the early days – much of it was from the professional Cyril Hughes, a disciple of Henry Cotton – basically I'm a self-taught player. I learn from watching myself on video and from watching others whose swing I admire, notably Tom Watson and Gary Player. And, of course, I can always take a tip. Sam Torrance says, 'Clear your hips quicker on the down swing.' If it feels good and it looks good when I see it on video, I can believe in it. Sam's father, Bob Torrance, taught me to get my weight transference on to my right side on the back swing, which is very important.

If I'm not playing well, I settle down to watch myself on video: it usually works. In the European Open at Walton Heath in 1987, for example, I shot a poor 73 and then watched the television recording. I soon spotted the fault. My legs were too straight at the address. I was coming up on the ball too much and either pushing or hooking. Next day I made sure that I flexed my knees a bit and I shot a 65. The following week I went on to win the Lancôme Trophy in France. I know pretty well what works for me now and I generally know how to put myself right, though it's usually necessary to watch a video because that shows you exactly what you *are* doing rather than what you think or feel you are doing. I have a set method of addressing the ball, an identical set-up and stance, and I always grip the club in the same way. I usually hit the ball at 90 per cent power with woods and 85 per cent with irons. If I hit the ball more softly I can still put it off-line.

Many people are amazed to hear that I don't play regularly in the winter months and I don't want to either. In the winter of 1986–87 I played only seven times in three months. After Sun City in early December 1986 I didn't play again until mid-February, but last winter I had only three weeks off after Sun City before going to Australia. However, I still made some space for myself before that. For instance, after winning the World Match Play I had a good two weeks off before going to Hawaii for the World Cup, and after that I enjoyed a clear break, no play for five days, before flying to Sun City. After two practice rounds I was back in the game. Unfortunately, my stomach wasn't. The night before the last round my son Daniel, then not quite three, was up all night, and I had a tummy bug too. For the first nine holes of the last round I didn't know how to contain myself. I was hitting the ball everywhere but somehow managed a 35 for 1 under par. I felt much better on the back nine and thanks to an eagle 2 at the 17th I shot a 33 to beat Nick Faldo. I've seldom played better and seldom felt worse. It was a strange way to win the first million-dollar cheque in tournament golf.

I like to rest and I need to rest from golf. I believe it's very important to pace yourself. It's very easy when you have a big success to overdo it, to accept too many offers and engagements. Then you get tired and stale and lose your zest and enthusiasm for the game. That way lies premature retirement. You won't catch me making that mistake, nor Seve. He plays only about twenty times a year now and he still knows how to score.

Mind you, I swing the club quite often without the ball to make sure that I'm in the groove. Mostly I do it in the kitchen at our house at Oswestry, choosing the right time on a winter's evening when Glendryth is not cooking and Daniel isn't somewhere underfoot or demanding attention. I line myself up so that I'm reflected in the kitchen window (it's like a mirror at night-time) with the central strut of the window exactly bisecting my head. At the end of each swing I make sure that my head is still in the same place, bisected by the strut. If that sounds like rather a primitive practice facility for a man who won £1 million last year, I can only say that it suits me.

When I hit a bad patch in 1988 many commentators were saying that I shouldn't

CHIP PAN in the kitchen!

have changed clubs to the Japanese-made Maruman clubs in place of the ones that I had used during the great year of 1987. It's true that some adjustments had to be made to the new clubs – basically metal was shaved off the heels to flatten the lies – before I felt fully at home with them. But I never blamed the clubs for my loss of form. The real problem was in my swing. I went through what I can only call a nightmare and the problem was still not solved after I'd practised until my hands bled. After missing my second successive cut in America I spent three hours on the practice ground without learning a thing. Practising became like a drug that I couldn't stop, but I was only practising the wrong things. The solution came when I stood in front of the mirror in my hotel bedroom. I saw that my hips were in the wrong position when I addressed the ball. Consequently I was swinging the club from out to in. By putting more weight on my right foot and changing the position of my hips, the old rhythm started to come back.

Usually I know precisely what I want to achieve or correct. That is one of the things that distinguishes the professional from an amateur, who will often knock the ball around on the practice ground without much thought. But, and this may console the handicap golfer, just like an amateur the professional can hit a bad patch and not know the reason why. Sometimes it's a technical fault, sometimes a mental one. Then, as Seve says: 'It can all change. You wake up one morning and you feel different and know you're ready. Sometimes you just don't know when it will happen.'

A strong left hand and wrist is very important for control but I try to *hit* the ball with the right side. Being a wristy player, I want to feel my right side and hand coming into the ball. Seve tends to use the right side more now and to do that he's trying for a flatter swing. There's more to Seve than most people know. He's changing his swing so as to last longer and he doesn't hit the ball so hard now.

I am very precise about just how far I hit the ball with each club. In average conditions, I use a driver for 270 yards; a 1 iron for 235 yards; a 2 iron for 215 yards; a 3 iron for 200 yards; a 4 iron for 190 yards; a 5 iron for 180 yards; a 6 iron for 170 yards; a 7 iron for 155 yards; an 8 iron for 145 yards; a 9 iron for 133 yards; and a wedge for 125 yards.

I certainly haven't conquered putting but I'm probably unique among top golfers in not having a settled putting style. I keep changing my method, thinking I've found the secret, and it works very well for a while. Then, as with all such 'secrets' in golf, you go on doing it, exaggerating it perhaps, and quite suddenly it doesn't really work very well any more. So then it's time to turn to a new secret. At one time I used to line the ball up facing the hole square, then I'd move round, leaving the club face where it was. Another time I used to try reaching out for the ball.

Then David Llewellyn, my partner in the World Cup, said that I should lengthen my back swing. At the moment I favour a crouching style, right arm well bent, no wrist movement, hitting the ball on the up (so as to impart top spin and steady line) with the right hand. Next year it might be something different. Perhaps I should stick to one thing, but I've yet to pick the style that works well all the time, even though I've been a pro now for twelve years.

My Wobbly Friend

An essential part of my life is Wobbly. That's what we call Phil Morbey, my caddie, because of his rather unusual walk. He's a curly-haired 23-year-old Yorkshireman who used to stack goods in a Selby supermarket. Now he helps me stack up some good scores on the tour, having been with me for just over a year, and he's a real friend. When I won the Suntory World Match Play at Wentworth, we both had tears in our eyes. My achievements are his too. As he says, 'I'm involved in all the pressures and the action. It has all been happening to me as well as to Ian out there.'

Wobbly had a lot of experience working for David Jagger, David Russell, Ian Baker-Finch, Howard Clark and several others before joining me. He is very good at clubbing me. Quite often – as happened in the Match Play, for instance – Phil suggests a different club from the one I have chosen, and he is right. But he only volunteers information when I ask him. Sometimes I know just the right club and pick it for myself. We get together on the putts and usually we agree on the line. I want him to see the putt the way I see it. If he doesn't, I tell him to go and stand by the edge of the green.

They say that to be a great player you have to have a good golfing brain. In some ways because I've gone all out for golf I have a sort of tunnel vision. I don't want to clutter my head with information that doesn't help my golf career. I'd much rather listen to music on my car radio, Neil Diamond for preference, than to news or current affairs programmes, which I find mostly gloomy.

I can understand figures but big words fool me. I'm not much of a one for books, unless they are about golf. I'm proud of what I've achieved, but I don't dwell on it too much. In fact, I try to forget my scores, even the successful ones, because I'm concentrating on the future. I have to think if asked how many holes I've done in one: it's about six. The important thing in golf for me is now to win a major tournament.

If I had another ambition it would be to play snooker. I have a full-size table at home and spend a lot of happy hours on it already. The challenge is fantastic, the skills, the thinking behind a big break. The best I've managed so far is only 45, but I'm working on it. Challenge is what I thrive on. Perhaps in fifty years' time I'll be the fastest man in the World All-comers Wheelchair Race.

In the pages that follow I have tried to tell something of the history of golf through the personalities of the great players who have adorned it, from the Triumvirate of Vardon, Braid and Taylor at the turn of the century to the Big Three – Palmer, Nicklaus and Player – who dominated golf in the sixties and on into the seventies. Then come the younger giants including Greg Norman, Tom Watson, Bernhard Langer, Seve and Sandy. Of course, equipment has changed out of all recognition even since the war, so you cannot but marvel at, say, Henry Cotton's round of 65 at Sandwich when he won the 1934 Open (the round which gave the Dunlop 65 its name).

Despite developments in equipment and in the level of prize money the mental pressures are almost exactly the same: how not to choke when you're ahead, how not to let the bad shot get to you. This book, like the game of golf itself, is intended for

After 40 dedicate myself to snooker.

addicts of all abilities. And the long-handicapper can console himself or herself with the words of A. A. Milne: 'Golf is so popular because it is the best game in the world at which to be bad . . . at golf it is the bad player who gets most strokes.'

Ian Woosnam's Record

Country:	Wales
Born:	2 March 1958
Height:	5 feet 4 inches
Turned pro:	1976
Married:	Wife Glen, son Daniel (born 1985)
Hobbies:	Fishing, snooker and sports generally

Tournament Victories

1979	*News of the World* Under-23 Match Play Championship
1982	Swiss Open
1982	Cacharel Under-25s' Championship
1983	Silk Cut Masters
1984	Scandinavian Enterprise Open
1985	Zambian Open
1986	Kenya Open
1986	The Lawrence Batley Tournament Players' Championship
1987	Hong Kong Open
	Jersey Open
	Madrid Open
	Bell's Scottish Open
	Lancôme Trophy
	Suntory World Match Play
	World Cup (Wales)
	Sun City

Order of Merit Positions

1979	122	£1,049	1983	9	£48,164
1980	87	£3,481	1984	6	£68,126
1981	104	£1,884	1985	4	£82,235
1982	8	£48,794	1986	4	£111,799
			1987	1	£253,717

Miscellaneous

Ryder Cup	1983, 1985, 1987
Hennessy Cognac Cup	1982, 1984
World Cup	1980, 1982, 1983, 1984, 1985
Dunhill Nations Cup	1985, 1986
Nissan Cup	1985, 1986

1

IN THE BEGINNING
The Origins of Golf

Michael McDonnell

Till recently the Scots were confident that they had invented golf; now that claim is disputed by the Dutch. Certainly there is far more literature about the early game in Scotland. It was several times declared illegal there in the fifteenth century. 'Ye futball and ye golf be utterky cryt donne and nocht usyt,' said James II's ban of 1457. And Mary Queen of Scots made history as the first golfing widow – though not in the usual sense. She was severely criticised at her trial for heartlessly playing two days' golf after the murder of her unloved husband, Darnley. Here a distinguished golf correspondent gives his verdict on the controversy – by coming down on both sides!

I.W.

Even the Romans found a certain fascination in hitting a small ball with a curved stick. Their game was called *paganica*, referring to the leather ball stuffed with feathers, which in fact was to remain the form of the golf ball until the advent of the *guttie* in the mid-19th century.

Throughout the intervening centuries, variations of a game in which a ball was hit across open countryside have appeared in different countries, under different names and rules. The ancient French played a game called *jeu de mail* in which a wooden mallet (*mail*) hit a ball over a course about half a mile in length to a marker, the winner being the player who took fewest strokes.

Much later the Belgians and the French played a game called *chole*, clear evidence that the pastime was popular there in the mid-14th century, almost 100 years before any reference to the game in Scotland. However, there was a combative element to this form of play: it involved a team aiming to hit a cross-country target in a predetermined number of strokes, while their opponents were given specified opportunities to hit the ball in the opposite direction to any difficult hazard they could find.

The paradox is that golf, such an exact game in terms of skill and conditions of play, should have no verifiable record of its origins and has therefore become the subject of rival claims between the Dutch and the Scots as to who actually invented it.

While forms of stick-and-ball games were always popular in continental Europe, there is evidence that a game called *cambuca* – a feather-filled leather ball hit with a stick to a target – was also played in England in the 14th century and the stained-glass east window in Gloucester Cathedral depicts the figure of a man wielding a club at a ball.

When considering the game as we now know it, the main issue is whether 17th-century Scottish traders copied it from their Dutch counterparts along the seashore, while waiting for their ships to be unloaded, or whether in fact the Scots exported it.

The origins of the word do not help much either. The Scottish word *gouf* means 'to strike'. The Dutch word *kolf* means a club used to strike a ball.

That said, the Scottish parliament banned football and golf in May 1491 ('or uther sik unprofitabill sportis') because the populace was obsessed with those pastimes and not devoting enough time to archery practice. By 1513, Catherine of Aragon, Henry VIII's first wife, wrote to Cardinal Wolsey saying that the King's subjects seemed 'to be busy with the golf, for they take it for pastime, my heart is very glad to it'.

But the Dutch claim is strengthened by research work of historian Steven Van Hengel, who died while attending the 1985 British Open. Van Hengel traced a stick-and-ball game, using an iron-headed club back to 1300. It was popular with children and became such a nuisance in town that it was moved to open countryside.

The famous 1688 Adriaen van de Velde painting entitled 'A Frost Scene' clearly depicts a kilted man playing a form of golf in Holland. It adds to the debate about who invented golf, although there is no question that golf today owes its popularity to the Scots who taught the world to play.

From *The Complete Book of Golf*
by Michael McDonnell
(Kingswood Press, Surrey, 1985).

The Home of Golf

Pat Ward-Thomas

There's not much doubt that St Andrews and the Royal and Ancient are the home of the modern game. But there are rival views on this traditional old links course – modified though it now is. Sam Snead disliked it – and the icy wind, and even more the £150 prize money – despite winning the British Open at St Andrews in 1946. The late Pat Ward-Thomas, of the *Guardian*, was plainly a lover of this 'capricious mistress'; not so Peter Dobereiner of the *Observer*, in very acerbic mood in the second of these two pieces.

I.W.

The origins of golf are obscure. Whether it evolved from the Roman game of *paganica*, *kolven* in Holland or other pastimes few would dispute that St Andrews has long been the home of golf. For centuries the aged city has been renowned as a seat of learning and religion but to golfers the Royal and Ancient Club and the Old Course are the heart of its fame. No place on earth where a game is played has attracted more pilgrims and no other golf club has as many members from so many countries, nor as great an influence on the game.

The Royal and Ancient is a unique institution. It is a private members Club but has no course of its own. At the same time it is a governing body with supreme authority for the Rules of Golf, the organisation of the Open and Amateur Championships, and numerous other international affairs.

At any Autumn or Spring Meeting of the Club golfers gather from the far places of the world; the fires in the Big Room glow and the pictures of famous men look down upon the lively scene. The originals of the portraits might be surprised to find that claret is no longer a common beverage, and meals are not banquets.

On quiet days when nothing of moment is afoot and a few members drowse in their deep chairs one might look through the tall windows and dream awhile. So peaceful is the scene, so silent the room that it is hard to believe that almost every great golfer in the game's history has stood on the tee below and looked down the long fall of fairway to the hills beyond; and that on an upper floor the processes of guidance and government are constantly under way.

The Club's stature in the game was an accident of history. Had the Old Course not existed early in the 18th century, in whatever primitive a form, the Club might never have come to life. There would have been no cause for the historic meeting on 14 May 1754 when twenty-two Noblemen and Gentlemen assembled, doubtless over a substantial repast. Admiring the game as a healthy exercise, and having the interest and prosperity of their ancient city at heart, they decided to contribute five shillings each for a Silver Club to be competed for every year. The St Andrews Society of Golfers, subsequently the Royal and Ancient Club, was born, but the progenitors could not have imagined what would grow from the tiny seed of their inspiration.

For a hundred years and more after its foundation the Society had no particular powers. It was content to follow the original code of rules which had been devised in 1744 by the Company of Gentlemen Golfers in Leith, but when the fortunes of that Society fell into temporary decline in the 1830s there was a gradual growth of the Club's influence. Eventually, out of more than fifty countries, the United States and Mexico alone did not take their lead from the Royal and Ancient in matters of the Rules of Golf and of Amateur Status.

Of the millions who watch the Open Championship every year many are unaware that its promotion and organisation are solely the province of the Royal and Ancient. No professional golfing body is involved in any way. The Championship Committee, composed entirely of amateur golfers and assisted by a small club staff under the Secretary, bears the whole responsibility for the success or failure of an event which has become a substantial business undertaking.

The profit from the Open or other activities is devoted to the general welfare of golf and not shared among its members. For generations the Club has been a trustee for the game, its spirit and its customs. By using powers to guide rather than to dictate an effective form of democratic authority has grown. There have been no threats to the Club's stature from without, and no lasting turmoil within. It has moved peacefully into its third century, its foundations as secure as those of the grey stone Clubhouse.

The Old Course

For generations golfers have journeyed from afar to visit the Royal and Ancient Clubhouse and meet the timeless challenge of the Old Course. Throughout the ages it has tested the finest golfers, all save Hogan who, alone of the great masters, never competed there. And, particularly for golfers from overseas, there is a special satisfaction in being able to say that they have been in the Club and played the course, no matter how many strokes it may have cost them. For many the experience could match a garden party at Buckingham Palace or an audience with the Pope.

The visitor will not readily forget the first impression of the place – so intimate are its policies on the very fringe of the old university city. The clubhouse, massively implanted, sombre and yet serene, is at the crest of a quadrangle, encompassing the first and last holes, flowing down to the Swilcan Burn and the long ribbon of the links beyond. On the one hand shops, houses, hotels and golf clubs form a grey terrace; on the other a vast putting green rolls towards the curve of the bay where the tide trails its silver chains. The prospect could not fail to quicken the heart of any golfer as he faces a test the like of which he will find nowhere else.

The Old Course has no parallel anywhere because its fashioning owes more to nature than to the hand of man. In the beginning there was no plan, no architect; the holes simply evolved and by some miracle have stood the test of time with little need for change except for occasional lengthening here and there to counter the power of modern equipment.

The shape of the course is much the same as it was centuries ago when the citizens of St Andrews were granted the right to include golf among their pastimes. It runs over gently crumpled linksland out to the Eden estuary and then swings back along the 8th and 9th holes, giving it the shape of a billhook. Linksland, common to the coasts of Britain, was formed when the sea receded, leaving undulating wastes of sand.

These became resting places for birds whose droppings helped to fertilise seeds borne by the wind, and grasses, gorse and other vegetation grew. In time the links were an ideal breeding ground for rabbits and other animals who wore paths and burrows in the wilderness. Over the years the passage of man widened the paths and when the golfers appeared they found natural fairways, sites for greens and bunkers in profusion. At St Andrews the space between the arable land to the south with its protective banks of whins, and the whins on the other side was so narrow, about 40 yards, that the golfers had to share the same fairways and holes going out and coming home. At first they took the left-hand route going out and returned on the other side, changing about to add variety. The left-hand route was used for the Amateur championship in 1886 and occasionally in recent years for a winter competition at a time when the Course is being rested.

The early golfers started from a tee west of the present 18th green and played to the 17th. This must have been a formidable hole. The land which now lies to the north, with its embankment and putting courses, had not then been reclaimed from the sea wherein a sliced tee shot could easily vanish. The present first green was made in 1870, some years after Tom Morris had created the 18th, the green which now bears his name.

Long ago the gorse was thinned and cut back but the Old Course, running between the Eden and the New courses, rarely measures more than 100 yards across, and its total area must be the smallest of any championship course in the world. All the while golfers cannot help but trespass on each other's fairways and indeed on the seven double greens introduced in 1832. Only the 1st, 9th, 17th and 18th have a green to themselves; the remainder are huge, rippling surfaces, some almost an acre in area. Many are on plateaus, a providential blessing, starkly exposed to the elements and fearsome places for the man whose putting touch is amiss. As Nicklaus remarked once, 'You can feel so lonely out there, missing a short putt'. Nowhere does the classic excuse for an indifferent score, that of taking three putts, sound less convincing. The golfer may find green after green, although not always his own, and leave himself putting from 30 yards and sometimes much further. Judgement of distance is of the essence in scoring well unless the player can survive a great burden on his short game. However well a man may think he knows the holes there are times when he can be far out in his reckoning. The undulating land often makes the flags look much nearer than they are.

The legend of the 'Old' as a capricious mistress, all deceitful wiles, is less true than it was before the age of watering. When the ground was baked hard and the ball running fast, short approaches needed the utmost delicacy of touch, and the little slopes and falls had to be studied and known. There was too no question of firing approaches to pitch near the flags. The course still demands unceasing vigilance and rarely does it forgive thoughtless attack, faint-heartedness or lack of perception.

The winds can be flirtatious with the movement of the tides, so much so that it is possible to play out against the breeze and face it again coming home, but it is the subtler changes of angle that can alter strategy. Within the hour, or even minutes, what was a safe line can become a dangerous one mainly because of the bunkers. They are nowhere near as plentiful as when they were holes from which sea shells were dug or places for sheep to shelter, but they are numerous enough to dictate the strategy of play on every hole, save the first and last, and to tantalise the golfer. Many are not at once visible to the striker and can be totally unexpected hazards for those ignorant of their presence. Thus contentment can swiftly turn to fury and frustration. And yet, Thomas H. Peter, in his reminiscences was moved almost a century ago to declare that 'Bunkers which gave such interest in old times now scarcely form hazards at all'. They must have been fearsome.

From *The Royal and Ancient* by Pat Ward-Thomas
(Scottish Academic Press Ltd, Edinburgh, 1980).

Our Mother, that Sad Old Bitch

Peter Dobereiner

It was a matter of historical accident that decreed that a round of golf should be played over eighteen holes. In the early days of the game's development there was no standard number of holes. The available land was the governing factor. Holes were laid out according to convenience on the linkland; the waste common ground which bordered the sea. Some courses could accommodate nine holes only, others fourteen or more. It so happened that at St Andrews the players found it convenient to hole out eighteen times as they played out to the farthest promontory of their narrow strip of links and returned, using the same greens in many cases, to the starting-point. And as St Andrews developed as the most influential centre of the game so eighteen holes became accepted as the norm.

The reputation of the Old Course also set the standards for golf course layout and even today there are people who believe that links golf is not just the best but indeed the only true form of the game. It is a point of view with which I have little patience. Apart from the selfishness of denying that those who play inland are real golfers, it ignores the fact that golf is developing. New equipment has changed the game entirely and, in any case, St Andrews is no longer the course it used to be. This part of the coast of Fife is subject to silting and whereas the Old Course used to be right alongside the shore it is now nearly a mile inland. Changes in the character of the turf have been largely accelerated by modern techniques of course management. Artificial fertilisers have enriched (and coarsened the grass) and automatic water-sprinklers have softened the greens. These innovations have been introduced in the name of progress but the result, in my opinion, has been the destruction of the Old Course. Instead of being a monument to the pioneers of the game, St Andrews today is an unhappy mixture. The matriarch of golf has been tarted up in lipstick and mini-skirt. The dignity of antiquity has been lost and her character compromised. She is a sad old bitch of a golf course, grotesquely old fashioned by modern standards and hopelessly raddled to those who loved her as she was. The city of St Andrews is established as the home of golf and is the Mecca of enthusiasts from every corner of the world. The city fathers are conscious of their responsibility to the past and to the present, but in my view their compromising does a gross disservice to both.

How much more satisfactory it would be if they let the Old Course revert to as near her original condition as nature allowed. Take away the automatic-sprinklers and allow the greens to become as hard and fast as glass. Let the fairways be so that once again a golfer might be able, as the American Craig Wood once did, see his drive kick into a bunker some 400 yards distant down the wind. And, for good measure, provide pencil-case quivers of hickory clubs so that visitors could get an idea, if a sketchy one, of what the game was like during the genesis of golf. In other words, make St Andrews a living museum.

From *The Game with the Hole in it* by Peter Dobereiner
(Faber and Faber, London, 1970).

At no place but St Andrews would such hazards be acceptable; on the old course they are as natural as the grey stone of the houses which line the closing hole.

Robert Trent Jones, golf architect.

Say, that looks like an old abandoned golf course. What did they call it?

Sam Snead, on first seeing St Andrews in 1946.

Know what I really feel about St Andrews? I feel like I'm back visiting an old grandmother. She's crotchety and eccentric, but also elegant and anyone who doesn't fall in love with her has no imagination.

American Tony Lema, Open Champion at St Andrews,
in 1964.

Those greens on St Andrews used to be so crisp that you could hear the crunch your spikes made when they cut into the turf. Oh, they were fast!

Bobby Jones in 1968.

The Road Hole, the seventeenth, is the most famous and infamous hole. . . . As a planner and builder of golf holes worldwide, I have no hesitation in allowing that if one built such a hole today you would be sued for incompetence.

Peter Thomson, elegant Australian, five times winner of
the British Open, one of them at St Andrews in 1955.

The reason the Road Hole is the greatest par-four in the world is because it's par-five.

Ben Crenshaw in 1984.

My first impression of St Andrews was one of strange ambiguousness. I didn't like it, nor, for that matter, did I hate it. I've never been so puzzled after a first practice round in my life.

Tom Watson in 1984.

It finds you out. If there is one part of your game not right, no matter how you try to hide it – to protect it – the Old Course will find it during the championship.

Peter Thompson in 1984.

There is no place in the world that I would rather win a championship.

Jack Nicklaus in 1984.

Daniel, then two years old, celebrates his father's Suntory World Match Play win with Ian. (*Express Newspapers*)

Ian, at Sun City, becomes the first golfer to win a million dollar cheque. (*Associated Press*)

The putt that didn't get away. Ian explains how he narrowly beat Sevé Ballesteros in the World Match Play semi-finals in 1987 and then went on to win. (*Matthew Harris*)

Ian with Daniel
and his wife
Glendryth – a
typical close
family scene.
Not having his
family with him
in America
upset his form.
(*Phil Sheldon*)

The modern greats (Woosnam and Greg Norman) beat the ancient greats (Nicklaus and Trevino) in a sudden death play-off in the $300,000 Desert Scramble in Arizona. (*Associated Press*)

The victorious European Ryder team after their win over the USA in September 1987. From left: Sevé Ballesteros, Gordon Brand Jr, José-Maria Rivero, Ken Brown, Sandy Lyle carrying José-Marie Olazabal, Ian Woosnam carrying captain Tony Jacklin, Nick Faldo, Bernhard Langer, Sam Torrance, Eamonn Darcy and, kneeling, Howard Clark. (*Popperfoto*)

Sevé says it with bubbles, missing Jacklin's open mouth. No matter, a Ryder Cup win is champagne in itself. Torrance and Langer share the joy. (*Peter Dazeley*)

A million-dollar shot. With this 7 iron pitch which he holed for an Eagle 2 on the 17th at Sun City, Ian ensured his million-dollar victory over Faldo. (*Associated Press*)

Another triumph in his great year of 1987, Ian holds up one of the many trophies he won at individual and team competitions. Honours for Wales (with fellow Welshman Dave Llewellyn) in the World Cup tournament at Kapalua, Hawaii on Maui. (*Associated Press*)

Dave Llewellyn demonstrates a crisp follow-through. (*Peter Dazeley*)

The Best Game Man Ever Devised

Herbert Warren Wind

Herbert Warren Wind is one of the great American golf writers and a good enough golfer to have competed in the British Amateur at St Andrews in 1950. When he wrote this short perspective of the game in 1954, President Eisenhower was in the White House (on those rare occasions when he wasn't on the golf course) and the game was enjoying a spectacular post-war boom on both sides of the Atlantic which still shows no signs of diminishing.

I.W.

Ever since golf began – Scottish historians have settled on the year 1100 as a reasonable date of birth – the game has been an enigma. For those who have steered clear of its clutches, the devotion it commands from its followers looms as one of the great absurdities of the human race's supposed progress. There are moments when every golfer agrees with this verdict. If he could only have back in one lump all the time, money, energy, and anguish he has spent on golf and invest it towards some sensible goal, why, there is no knowing the heights of happiness he might reach. Then he plays a good round in congenial company on a sunny morning, and his golfer's balance returns. If there is one thing he is certain he has done right in his life, it has been to play golf, and his only regret is that he hasn't given the game more time. He might have become better.

Beyond the fact that it is a limitless arena for the full play of human nature, there is no sure accounting for golf's fascination. Obviously yet mysteriously, it furnishes its devotees with an intense, many-sided, and abiding pleasure unlike that which any other form of recreation affords. Perhaps it is, as Andrew Carnegie once claimed, an 'indispensable adjunct of high civilisation'. Perhaps it is nothing more than the best game man has ever devised.

In comparatively modern times, the spread of golf's popularity has come on by waves. The first big one broke just about a century ago – in 1848 – when the gutta-percha ball was introduced and rapidly replaced the 'feathery', the leather-cased ball packed tight with feathers, for centuries the standard equipment. Until the coming of the 'gutty', Scots living in Scotland had been the only golfers, but the new ball changed all that. It made golf a much better game. A player no longer had to be a technician of considerable skill to nudge the ball nicely off the ground and send it flying a good distance in a relatively straight line. The gutty required a powerful swing and a well-timed hit, but when it was struck cleanly, it could be propelled tens of yards farther than the feathery, and the essential thrill of 'distance' entered the game for the first time. This revitalised kind of golf swept south of the Scottish border into England, then to the European playgrounds of the international set of that day, and, by the turn of the century, it had made its way to every continent. Wherever golf was taken, it took. It arrived in the United States in 1888 – that, in any event, was the year the first American golf club was founded – and so instant was its contagiousness that twelve years later the number of American golfers exceeded a quarter of a million.

Golf – gutty golf – undoubtedly would have gained more and more adherents, but it is questionable if it would have made quite the conquest of man's leisure hours as did the rubber-core ball, the revolutionary modification of the gutty which made its appearance in 1898. This new ball – its core wound tightly with strips of rubber, the cover of gutta-percha – was the impetus behind golf's second great wave of popularity and ushered in the present version of golf, the game eight million people play today. The new ball was superior to the solid glob of gutta-percha in almost precisely the same respects which the gutty had been to the feathery: it would, on the average, go some fifteen yards farther when struck correctly, and, more important, it would go *someplace* when not struck right on the button. It was just what was needed to make the average player feel like a golfer and not like a well-dressed labourer. The invention of the rubber-core ball is usually credited to Coburn Haskell, of Cleveland, and for all that American ingenuity later did for the game, it undoubtedly stands as our outstanding technical contribution to the advancement of golf.

Then the waves began to come closer to each other. There was a mighty one in 1913. In our National Open Championship that September, an unknown home-grown amateur, Francis Ouimet, a remarkable twenty-year-old ex-caddie from a family of medium means, astounded the golf world as it had never been astounded before or afterwards by first tying with and then defeating in a dramatic play-off two acknowledged masters from Great Britain, Harry Vardon and Ted Ray. Until Francis' epochal victory, most non-golfers in America had viewed the game with hostility as the pampered pastime of the wealthy, the elderly, the would-be Continental, the unrugged – and they were welcome to it. After Francis' victory, this stigma was removed once and for all, and the base was laid for golf's development in this country as a genuinely democratic sport, whatever the inevitable social overtones of the clubhouse. Hundreds of thousands of reformed golf-haters rushed to the golf courses, and it was only a matter of months before they viewed with suspicion anyone who didn't play their game.

The majestic personalities of the 'twenties completed golf's ascendancy to the status of a major American sport. First there came Walter Hagen. Until Walter made the British Open his personal property – he won it first in 1922 and three times later – British golfers, despite Ouimet's one break-through, had continued to rule supreme in international competition. Walter's exploits abroad and at home eradicated our national inferiority complex, and they were achieved with a dash and bravado that captivated the Great American Sports Fan who had been bred on baseball, football, and boxing heroes. Hagen was a guy he could understand, and he took to golf through him. Another dimension was added when Gene Sarazen, the son of an immigrant carpenter from Italy, came bolting out of complete obscurity to win the

National Open in 1922, the first of his many championships. And then there was Jones – Robt. T. Jones, Jr., Atlanta, Ga. Even in the Golden Age of the 'twenties when every sport had its heroic-sized champion, its Ruth or its Dempsey or its Tilden, there was no other athlete who was consistently the champion that Bobby Jones was on and off the fairway. The beauty of it was that Jones's qualities were recognised by everyone instinctively.

Golf is presently on the crest of another wave, the first that has rolled in since Jones's Grand Slam. From the close of World War II on, the game has made tens of thousands of converts annually.

The increase in leisure time available to the average man and woman has been a major factor in this recent expansion. In a way, so has Ben Hogan, by all odds *the* dominant sports personality of the post-war world, the champion who came back after his near-fatal accident and had the stuff to make himself an even greater champion. In the process he became a national hero of such proportions that, during his assault on the British Open in 1953, non-golfers, so green about the game that they first confused Carnoustie with a new wax for motor-cars, followed his progress with the same proud concern that veteran golfers did. And, of course, a good measure of the game's increasing popularity derives from the presence in the White House of a man for whom golf is, no question about it, an 'indispensable adjunct of high civilisation'. Today well over five million Americans play some golf every year and there are not nearly enough courses to take care of everyone who would like to play.

Part and parcel of this upsurge of enthusiasm has been a burgeoning interest in what has been written about the game. A great deal has, which is not too surprising. Whatever else it may be, golf is the most ruminative of recreations. Play it and you will talk it endlessly and chew upon it at the oddest hours and, apparently, if you have the dormant urge to put your thoughts on paper, golf will bring it out. Over the years, as a result, a vast body of writing about golf has accumulated which far surpasses any other game's for sheer quantity. Forgetting the countless magazines and pamphlets, golf books alone run into the thousands – how-to guides, collections of short stories, poetry (usually of the class that leaves Milton's position intact), memoirs and biographies, diaries, critical essays, involved psychological disquisitions, formal histories, one-act and three-act plays, all varieties of humour, travel reports, over a score of full-length novels, and 'golf translations' of Shakespeare, Horace and Omar Khayyam. While a large part of this outpouring falls a good distance short of that standard of writing we call literature, no other game has acquired a literature that compares with golf's. Men write extremely well about it, and sometimes wonderfully.

From *The Complete Golfer* by Herbert Warren Wind
(Heinemann, London, 1954).

From Barefoot Caddie to Open Champion
Sandy Herd

Sandy Herd (1868–1944) was a great Scottish character, famous for his 'waggles' when addressing the ball. 'All the time the club waggles in my hand I am getting my wrists supple and shifting my feet inch by inch till I know everything is right for the shot,' was his explanation. He won the British Open in 1902, the first year in which the new American Haskell or rubber-cored ball was used. During practice before the championship, Herd tried a Haskell: 'That was the end of the gutty ball for me. The first drive I ever made with the Haskell was longer than any I ever made with the gutty.' He was the only player not to use the gutty and won by one stroke from Vardon and Braid. Perhaps fortune smiled on him then, as it certainly did not in 1895 after a hailstorm put paid to his championship chances.

Herd was a celebrated teacher, his pupils including Field-Marshal Lord Haig, who occasionally took time off from the mud and blood of Flanders to play golf, the Prince of Wales (later Duke of Windsor) and his brother, the Duke of York (later King George VI). He was a professional at Huddersfield, Coombe Hill and then for many years at Moor Park. But he made his start at St Andrews as a 'bare-fitted' urchin caddie, a golfer of the street who used sticks for clubs and champagne corks with screws (to give them weight) as balls. The lamp-posts on the cobble streets were the flags.

Apprenticed as a baker and then as a plasterer (his mother could see no future in golf which she saw as 'just a life for a ne'er-do-well'), Herd attributed his success to the advantages of a caddie's upbringing. He was one of the first golf professionals to think of making a real career in the game. Before him Jack Burns, Open Champion in 1888, actually preferred the 'security' of working as a platelayer on the railway. When asked how he was playing, Burns used to reply: 'Never better – I haven't been off the line for years.' He, like Herd, was also a plasterer, which made for a few pranks when they were youths.

I.W.

Three Plasterer Champions

It has often struck me as a wonderful thing that out of Andrew Scott's plasterer's yard, where I served my apprenticeship, should have come three Open Champions, Willie Fernie, Jack Burns, and myself. Fernie and Burns were a little before me.

When I was in St Andrews during the last championship week I met Jack Burns and asked him about his golf.

'Never better,' he said. 'I have not been off the line for years.'

The joke was that Burns had been working on the railway line as a platelayer. He won his championship long before I won mine. But Jack did not follow up his advantage. In fact, he played little competitive golf after that.

'I've done what I set out to do,' he used to say, 'and I am satisfied. Now all I want is a steedy job, and I've got that on the railway.'

The winning of a championship thirty-five years ago was not the great stroke of business it is to-day, when a champion is a 'made man,' with the wheel of fortune supposed to be throwing off Treasury notes and American dollars to him at every turn.

Burns probably got about £10 for his money prize. When I won the Open Championship in 1902 the first prize was £50. It is increased since. Throughout the year there were numerous other big prizes, of which at different times I have had my share.

Add to all this the amazing multiplication of golf clubs in this country and America since the beginning of the century, with all the expanding trade in clubs, bags, and balls and the demand for tuition – a profitable branch of the professional golfer's business – and it will be seen what gigantic strides the game has made.

Suppose some obscure young golfer were to come forward to-day and win the Open Championship – not a likely occurrence, I admit, but it might happen. He would wake up next morning to find himself in demand for exhibition matches at increased fees, and his club would find it hard to keep him at home.

The Americans, too, would be sure to want a look at him on a substantial guarantee basis, while clubs on both sides of the Atlantic might bid against each other for possession of him – if only as an ornament!

Anyhow, there would be no danger of his 'going on the line for a steedy job,' as Jack Burns thought it best to do long ago, before Edward Ray and George Duncan had started caddying, or Mr Cyril Tolley and Mr Roger Wethered were out of their nurseries.

James Braid was working in St Andrews as a joiner in my plastering days, but as he was three years my junior and a backward young fellow with little to say, we did not pal up much then. Three years' difference in ages around twenty means more than three years around fifty, where Jimmy and I find ourselves now, he 'daein' awful weel' at Walton Heath and I 'gettin' on fine, thank ye,' at Coombe Hill when telling this story, but at Moor Park when you are reading it.

Together we fought for the honour of Scotland in many a hard battle, mostly against those well-nigh unbeatable Sassenachs J. H. Taylor and Harry Vardon, who for twenty-five years probably won more foursomes than any two golfers in the world.

Not long ago the Americans wanted Braid and me to go across, but Jimmy could not 'gi'e up his business' for golf, and so it fell through. I have heard that when people have expressed surprise to him that he had never visited America, Jimmy's reply was: 'Neither has Mr Lloyd George.' Accompanied by J. H. Taylor, I paid my second visit to America in the summer of 1922. The Americans and I got on finely together.

There were no 'plus 4' knickerbocker suits for professional golfers in my young days. In fact, neither I nor Braid has ever departed from the 'lang breeks' – though now they are tailor-made and pressed, unlike the pair I wore at my first championship, which were mother-made and baggy.

You can imagine me going down to my first Open Championship at St Andrews wearing white fustian plasterer trousers, my working jacket, and a 'dooble peekit' cap, like that worn by Mr Balfour when he played himself in as captain of the Royal and Ancient Club in 1904, with old Tom Morris standing ready to clap his hands, as he did, when the great statesman, who has done more to spread the game of golf than any other amateur, made a very fine drive before a great ring of spectators that September day.

I was frightened to death when I tried my apprentice hand at winning a championship. As I stood up to address the ball on the first tee, I told myself to get well away at the start and the worst of the trouble would be past.

For the life of me I cannot remember now who I was drawn with. You may be surprised at this, but things are apt to get misty in one's memory with a long string of championships and a host of tournaments to sort out.

You see, it did not then dawn on my mind that ever I should come to this – relating my life for others to read. I wonder what my father and mother would say about it if they were alive, as I wish they were.

It may seem a thing hard to believe, but I do not remember having a handicap – I may have had one, but if so I cannot have taken any notice of it. Anyhow, it's a good thing to forget your handicap till the game's finished. I am speaking now of the time when I belonged to the St Andrews Club, not the Royal and Ancient, oh! dear no, the likes of me – a baker, or a plasterer, as I afterwards became – could not enter there.

As I showed no liking for baking I was next apprenticed to Andrew Scott as a plasterer. My parents were desperately anxious to make 'a decent working man' of me. As I had served four years as a baker so I served another four years as a plasterer, at which trade I worked some time as a journeyman. But whether mixing flour or cement my mind ran on golf all the while. At nights in bed I teed up an imaginary ball on the counterpane and drove off into the Land of Nod, where you may depend upon it I returned many wonderful scores, surpassing everything in real life.

Plastering taught me one trick that I laugh now to think of. I used to make a mould of the gutta ball and fill it with plaster of Paris. You could not tell the sham ball from the real. Then I'd get some caddie to tee up with one of my own make. The ball flew off in dust, and I'd watch the fun at a safe distance. I've seen angry old gentlemen chase caddies about the course for playing this trick on them, vowing vengeance on their heads with a club. We were wee devils aye up to some mischief or other.

Four Clubs and No Golf Bag

This much I can remember, that I had only four clubs – a driver, a spoon, a cleek and an iron – no putter and no bag! A younger brother carried my sticks to save caddie fees. Ten shillings a week as an apprentice plasterer put the idea of hiring a caddie clean out of the question.

Of course we played with the gutta ball. I made a very poor show, and went off my sleep for nights thinking that I had not done justice to myself. That is the galling reflection young professionals are often left to torment themselves with, calculating for weeks how many strokes were needlessly dropped.

Nothing but experience can put that right; and some are doomed never to play their best game when it is most wanted. I suppose I had less cause to complain on this score than many others; for I have generally figured pretty well, though my luck has not been of the best. There's aye been a lot of 'ifs' in it.

Had I won the championship of 1895 at St Andrews – as I must have done except for a hailstorm – there is no telling what the effect would have been on me as a champion at twenty-seven. The thought of it haunts me still.

I always flatter myself by thinking that that was the unlucky championship which ruined my chances of winning as many thereafter as Taylor, Braid, and Vardon.

The telling of my story now brings it all fresh to memory and some of the gall with it. Taylor was my conqueror and the first to acknowledge the trick the weather played on me, while it favoured him.

'You had me beaten, Sandy,' he said, 'but for that storm.' It blattered at me for ten holes and stopped when Taylor started out.

From *My Golfing Life* by Sandy Herd
(Chapman and Hall, London, 1923).

2

GOLF IS FUN – OR SHOULD BE

Sundered Hearts

P. G. Wodehouse

As I explained in the introduction to this book, my nickname on the professional circuit is Bertie, partly because of the resemblance of my surname to that of P. G. Wodehouse's famous character, Bertie Wooster. So I'm something of a Wodehouse fan. Certainly no one tells a funnier tale about golf addicts than 'Plum' Wodehouse. His memorable character, the Oldest Member, a venerable sage and clubhouse counsellor to young and old who gave up golf when the rubber-core ball replaced the gutty, regards golf as no laughing matter at all – and contrives to be hilarious in the process. Here is a typical story.

I.W.

In the smoking-room of the club-house a cheerful fire was burning, and the Oldest Member glanced from time to time out of the window into the gathering dusk. Snow was falling lightly on the links. From where he sat, the Oldest Member had a good view of the ninth green; and presently, out of the greyness of the December evening, there appeared over the brow of the hill a golf-ball. It trickled across the green and stopped within a yard of the hole. The Oldest Member nodded approvingly. A good approach-shot.

A young man in a tweed suit clambered on to the green, holed out with easy confidence, and, shouldering his bag, made his way to the club-house. A few moments later he entered the smoking-room, and uttered an exclamation of rapture at the sight of the fire.

'I'm frozen stiff!'

He rang for a waiter and ordered a hot drink. The Oldest Member gave a gracious assent to the suggestion that he should join him.

'I like playing in winter,' said the young man. 'You get the course to yourself, for the world is full of slackers who only turn out when the weather suits them. I cannot understand where they get the nerve to call themselves golfers.'

'Not everyone is as keen as you are, my boy,' said the Sage, dipping gratefully into his hot drink. 'If they were, the world would be a better place, and we should hear less of all this modern unrest.'

'I *am* pretty keen,' admitted the young man.

'I have only encountered one man whom I could describe as keener. I allude to Mortimer Sturgis.'

'The fellow who took up golf at thirty-eight and let the girl he was engaged to marry go off with someone else because he hadn't the time to combine golf with courtship? I remember. You were telling me about him the other day.'

'There is a sequel to that story, if you would care to hear it,' said the Oldest Member.

'You have the honour,' said the young man. 'Go ahead!'

Some people (began the Oldest Member) considered that Mortimer Sturgis was too wrapped up in golf, and blamed him for it. I could never seen eye to eye with them. In the days of King Arthur nobody thought the worse of a young knight if he suspended all his social and business engagements in favour of a search for the Holy Grail. In the Middle Ages a man could devote his whole life to the Crusades, and the public fawned upon him. Why, then, blame the man of today for a zealous attention to the modern equivalent, the Quest of Scratch! Mortimer Sturgis never became a scratch player, but he did eventually get his handicap down to nine, and I honour him for it.

The story which I am about to tell begins in what might be called the middle period of Sturgis's career. He had reached the stage when his handicap was a wobbly twelve; and, as you are no doubt aware, it is then that a man really begins to golf in the true sense of the word. Mortimer's fondness for the game until then had been merely tepid compared with what it became now. He had played a little before, but now he really buckled to and got down to it. It was at this point, too, that he began once more to entertain thoughts of marriage. A profound statistician in this one department, he had discovered that practically all the finest exponents of the art are married men, and the thought that there might be something in the holy state which improved a man's game, and that he was missing a good thing, troubled him a great deal. Moreover, the paternal instinct had awakened in him. As he justly pointed out, whether marriage improved your game or not, it was to Old Tom Morris's marriage that the existence of young Tommy Morris, winner of the British Open Championship four times in succession, could be directly traced. In fact, at the age of forty-two, Mortimer Sturgis was in just the frame of mind to take some nice girl aside and ask her to become a step-mother to his eleven drivers, his baffy, his twenty-eight putters, and the rest of the ninety-four clubs which he had accumulated in the course of his golfing career. The sole stipulation, of course, which he made when dreaming his day-dreams was that the future Mrs Sturgis must be a golfer. I can still recall the horror in his face when one girl, admirable in other respects, said that she had never heard of Harry Vardon, and didn't he mean Dolly Vardon? She has since proved an excellent wife and mother, but Mortimer Sturgis never spoke to her again.

With the coming of January, it was Mortimer's practice to leave England and go to the South of France, where there was sunshine and crisp dry turf. He pursued his usual custom this year. With his suit-case and his ninety-four clubs he went off to Saint Brüle, staying as he always did at the Hôtel Superbe, where they knew him, and treated with an amiable tolerance his habit of practising chip-shots in his bedroom. On the first evening, after breaking a statuette of the Infant Samuel in Prayer, he dressed and went down to dinner. And the first thing he saw was Her.

Mortimer Sturgis, as you know, had been engaged before, but Betty Weston had never inspired the tumultuous rush of emotion which the mere sight of this girl set loose in him. He told me later that just to watch her holing out her soup gave him a sort of feeling you get when your drive collides with a rock in the middle of a tangle of rough and kicks back into the middle of the fairway. If golf had come late in life to Mortimer Sturgis, love came later still, and just as the golf, attacking him in middle life, had been some golf, so was the love considerable love. Mortimer finished his dinner in a trance, which is the best way to do it at some hotels, and then scoured the place for someone who would introduce him. He found such a person eventually and the meeting took place.

She was a small and rather fragile-looking girl, with big blue eyes and a cloud of golden hair. She had a sweet expression, and her left wrist was in a sling. She looked up at Mortimer as if she had at last found something that amounted to something. I am inclined to think it was a case of love at first sight on both sides.

'Fine weather we're having,' said Mortimer, who was a capital conversationalist.

'Yes,' said the girl.

'I like fine weather.'

'So do I.'

'There's something about fine weather!'

'Yes.'

'It's – it's – well, fine weather's so much finer than weather that isn't fine,' said Mortimer.

He looked at the girl a little anxiously, fearing he might be taking her out of her depth, but she seemed to have followed his train of thought perfectly.

'Yes, isn't it?' she said. 'It's so – so fine.'

'That's just what I meant,' said Mortimer. 'So fine. You've just hit it.'

He was charmed. The combination of beauty with intelligence is so rare.

'I see you've hurt your wrist,' he went on, pointing to the sling.

'Yes. I strained it a little playing in the championship.'

'The championship?' Mortimer was interested. 'It's awfully rude of me,' he said, apologetically, 'but I didn't catch your name just now.'

'My name is Somerset.'

Mortimer had been bending forward solicitously. He overbalanced and nearly fell off his chair. The shock had been stunning. Even before he had met and spoken to her, he had told himself that he loved this girl with the stored-up love of a lifetime. And she was Mary Somerset! The hotel lobby danced before Mortimer's eyes.

The name will, of course, be familiar to you. In the early rounds of the Ladies' Open Golf Championship of that year nobody had paid much attention to Mary

Somerset. She had survived her first two matches, but her opponents had been nonentities like herself. And then, in the third round, she had met and defeated the champion. From that point on, her name was on everybody's lips. She became favourite. And she justified the public confidence by sailing into the final and winning easily. And here she was, talking to him like an ordinary person, and, if he could read the message in her eyes, not altogether indifferent to his charms, if you could call them that.

'Golly!' said Mortimer, awed.

Their friendship ripened rapidly, as friendships do in the South of France. In that favoured clime, you find the girl and Nature does the rest. On the second morning of their acquaintance Mortimer invited her to walk round the links with him and watch him play. He did it a little diffidently, for his golf was not of the calibre that would be likely to extort admiration from a champion. On the other hand, one should never let slip the opportunity of acquiring wrinkles on the game, and he thought that Miss Somerset, if she watched one or two of his shots, might tell him just what he ought to do. And sure enough, the opening arrived on the fourth hole, where Mortimer, after a drive which surprised even himself, found his ball in a nasty cuppy lie.

He turned to the girl.

'What ought I to do here?' he asked.

Miss Somerset looked at the ball. She seemed to be weighing the matter in her mind.

'Give it a good hard knock,' she said.

Mortimer knew what she meant. She was advocating a full iron. The only trouble was that, when he tried anything more ambitious than a half-swing, except off the tee, he almost invariably topped. However, he could not fail this wonderful girl, so he swung well back and took a chance. His enterprise was rewarded. The ball flew out of the indentation in the turf as cleanly as though John Henry Taylor had been behind it, and rolled, looking neither to left nor to right, straight for the pin. A few moments later Mortimer Sturgis had holed out one under bogey, and it was only the fear that, having known him for so short a time, she might be startled and refuse him that kept him from proposing then and there. This exhibition of golfing generalship on her part had removed his last doubts. He knew that, if he lived for ever, there could be no other girl in the world for him. With her at his side, what might he not do? He might get his handicap down to six – to three – to scratch – to plus something! Good heavens, why, even the Amateur Championship was not outside the range of possibility. Mortimer Sturgis shook his putter solemnly in the air, and vowed a silent vow that he would win this pearl among women.

Now, when a man feels like that, it is impossible to restrain him long. For a week Mortimer Sturgis's soul sizzled within him: then he could contain himself no longer. One night, at one of the informal dances at the hotel, he drew the girl out on to the moonlit terrace.

'Miss Somerset –' he began, stuttering with emotion like an imperfectly-corked bottle of ginger-beer. 'Miss Somerset – may I call you Mary?'

The girl looked at him with eyes that shone softly in the dim light.

'Mary?' she repeated. 'Why, of course, if you like –'

'If I like!' cried Mortimer. 'Don't you know that it is my dearest wish? Don't you know that I would rather be permitted to call you Mary than do the first hole at Muirfield in two? Oh, Mary, how I have longed for this moment! I love you! I love you! Ever since I met you I have known that you were the one girl in this vast world whom I would die to win! Mary, will you be mine? Shall we go round together? Will you fix up a match with me on the links of life which shall end only when the Grim Reaper lays us both a stymie?'

She drooped towards him.

'Mortimer!' she murmured.

He held out his arms, then drew back. His face had grown suddenly tense, and there were lines of pain about his mouth.

'Wait!' he said, in a strained voice. 'Mary, I love you dearly, and because I love you so dearly I cannot let you trust your sweet life to me blindly. I have a confession to make. I am not – I have not always been' – he paused – 'a good man,' he said, in a low voice.

She started indignantly.

'How can you say that? You are the best, the kindest, the bravest man I have ever met! Who but a good man would have risked his life to save me from drowning?'

'Drowning?' Mortimer's voice seemed perplexed. 'You? What do you mean?'

'Have you forgotten the time when I fell in the sea last week, and you jumped in with all your clothes on –'

'Of course, yes,' said Mortimer. 'I remember now. It was the day I did the long seventh in five. I got off a good tee-shot straight down the fairway, took a baffy for my second, and – But that is not the point. It is sweet and generous of you to think so highly of what was the merest commonplace act of ordinary politeness, but I must repeat, that judged by the standards of your snowy purity, I am not a good man. I do not come to you clean and spotless as a young girl should expect her husband to come to her. Once, playing in a foursome, my ball fell in some long grass. Nobody was near me. We had no caddies, and the others were on the fairway. God knows –' His voice shook. 'God knows I struggled against the temptation. But I fell. I kicked the ball on to a little bare mound, from which it was an easy task with a nice half-mashie to reach the green for a snappy seven. Mary, there have been times when, going round by myself, I have allowed myself ten-foot putts on three holes in succession, simply in order to be able to say I had done the course in under a hundred. Ah! you shrink from me! You are disgusted!'

'I'm not disgusted! And I don't shrink! I only shivered because it is rather cold.'

'Then you can love me in spite of my past?'

'Mortimer!'

She fell into his arms.

'My dearest,' he said presently, 'what a happy life ours will be. That is, if you do not find that you have made a mistake.'

'A mistake!' she cried, scornfully.

'Well, my handicap is twelve, you know, and not so darned twelve at that. There are days when I play my second from the fairway of the next hole but one, days when I couldn't putt into a coal-hole with "Welcome!" written over it. And you are a Ladies' Open Champion. Still, if you think it's all right – Oh, Mary, you little know how I have dreamed of some day marrying a really first-class golfer! Yes, that was my vision – of walking up the aisle with some sweet plus two girl on my arm. You shivered again. You are catching cold.'

'It is a little cold,' said the girl. She spoke in a small voice.

'Let me take you in, sweetheart,' said Mortimer. 'I'll just put you in a comfortable chair with a nice cup of coffee, and then I think I really must come out again and tramp about and think how perfectly splendid everything is.'

They were married a few weeks later, very quietly, in the little village church of Saint Brûle. The secretary of the local golf-club acted as best man for Mortimer, and a girl from the hotel was the only bridesmaid. The whole business was rather a disappointment to Mortimer, who had planned out a somewhat florid ceremony at St George's, Hanover Square, with the Vicar of Tooting (a scratch player excellent at short approach shots) officiating, and 'The Voice That Breathed O'er St Andrews' booming from the organ. He had even had the idea of copying the military wedding and escorting his bride out of the church under an arch of crossed cleeks. But she would have none of this pomp. She insisted on a quiet wedding, and for the honeymoon trip preferred a tour through Italy. Mortimer, who had wanted to go to Scotland to visit the birthplace of James Braid, yielded amiably, for he loved her dearly. But he did not think much of Italy. In Rome, the great monuments of the past left him cold. Of the Temples of Vespasian, all he thought was that it would be a devil of a place to be bunkered behind. The Colosseum aroused a faint spark of interest in him, as he speculated whether Abe Mitchell would use a full brassey to carry it. In Florence, the view over the Tuscan Hills from the Torre Rosa, Fiesole, over which his bride waxed enthusiastic, seemed to him merely a nasty bit of rough which would take a deal of getting out of.

And so, in the fullness of time, they came home to Mortimer's cosy little house adjoining the links.

Mortimer was so busy polishing his ninety-four clubs on the evening of their arrival that he failed to notice that his wife was preoccupied. A less busy man would have perceived at a glance that she was distinctly nervous. She started at sudden noises, and once, when he tried the newest of his mashie-niblicks and broke one of the drawing-room windows, she screamed sharply. In short her manner was strange, and, if Edgar Allan Poe had put her into 'The Fall of the House of Usher', she would have fitted it like the paper on the wall. She had the air of one waiting tensely for the approach of some imminent doom. Mortimer, humming gaily to himself as he sand-papered the blade of his twenty-second putter, observed nothing of this. He was thinking of the morrow's play.

'Your wrist's quite well again now, darling, isn't it?' he said.

'Yes. Yes, quite well.'

'Fine!' said Mortimer. 'We'll breakfast early – say at half-past seven – and then we'll be able to get in a couple of rounds before lunch. A couple more in the afternoon will about see us through. One doesn't want to over-golf oneself the first day.' He swung the putter joyfully. 'How had we better play do you think? We might start with you giving me a half.'

She did not speak. She was very pale. She clutched the arm of her chair tightly till the knuckles showed white under the skin.

To anybody but Mortimer her nervousness would have been even more obvious on the following morning, as they reached the first tee. Her eyes were dull and heavy, and she started when a grasshopper chirruped. But Mortimer was too occupied with thinking how jolly it was having the course to themselves to notice anything.

He scooped some sand out of the box, and took a ball out of her bag. His wedding present to her had been a brand-new golf-bag, six dozen balls, and a full set of the most expensive clubs, all born in Scotland.

'Do you like a high tee?' he asked.

'Oh, no,' she replied, coming with a start out of her thoughts. 'Doctors say it's indigestible.'

Mortimer laughed merrily.

'Deuced good!' he chuckled. 'Is that your own or did you read it in a comic paper? There you are!' He placed the ball on a little hill of sand, and got up. 'Now let's see some of that championship form of yours!'

She burst into tears.

'My darling!'

Mortimer ran to her and put his arms round her. She tried weakly to push him away.

'My angel! What is it?'

She sobbed brokenly. Then, with an effort, she spoke.

'Mortimer, I have deceived you!'

'Deceived me?'

'I have never played golf in my life! I don't even know how to hold the caddie!'

Mortimer's heart stood still. This sounded like the gibberings of an unbalanced mind, and no man likes his wife to begin gibbering immediately after the honeymoon.

'My precious! You are not yourself!'

'I am! That's the whole trouble! I'm myself and not the girl you thought I was!'

Mortimer stared at her, puzzled. He was thinking that it was a little difficult and that, to work it out properly, he would need a pencil and a bit of paper.

'My name is not Mary!'

'But you said it was.'

'I didn't. You asked if you could call me Mary, and I said you might, because I loved you too much to deny your smallest whim. I was going on to say that it wasn't my name, but you interrupted me.'

'Not Mary!' The horrid truth was coming home to Mortimer. 'You were not Mary Somerset?'

'Mary is my cousin. My name is Mabel.'

'But you said you had sprained your wrist playing in the championship.'

'So I had. The mallet slipped in my hand.'

'The mallet!' Mortimer clutched at his forehead. 'You didn't say "the mallet"?'

'Yes, Mortimer! The mallet!'

A faint blush of shame mantled her cheek, and into her blue eyes there came a look of pain, but she faced him bravely.

'I am the Ladies' Open Croquet Champion!' she whispered.

Mortimer Sturgis cried aloud, a cry that was like the shriek of some wounded animal.

'Croquet!' He gulped, and stared at her with unseeing eyes. He was no prude, but he had those decent prejudices of which no self-respecting man can wholly rid himself, however broad-minded he may try to be. 'Croquet!'

There was a long silence. The light breeze sang in the pines above them. The grasshoppers chirruped at their feet.

She began to speak again in a low, monotonous voice.

'I blame myself! I should have told you before, while there was yet time for you to withdraw. I should have confessed this to you that night on the terrace in the moonlight. But you swept me off my feet, and I was in your arms before I realized what you would think of me. It was only then that I understood what my supposed skill at golf meant to you, and then it was too late. I loved you too much to let you go! I could not bear the thought of you recoiling from me. Oh, I was mad – mad! I knew that I could not keep up the deception for ever, that you must find me out in time. But I had a wild hope that by then we should be so close to one another that you might find it in your heart to forgive. But I was wrong. I see it now. There are some things that no man can forgive. Some things,' she repeated, dully, 'which no man can forgive.'

She turned away. Mortimer awoke from his trance.

'Stop!' he cried. 'Don't go!'

'I must go.'

'I want to talk this over.'

She shook her head sadly and started to walk slowly across the sunlit grass. Mortimer watched her, his brain in a whirl of chaotic thoughts. She disappeared through the trees.

Mortimer sat down on the tee-box, and buried his face in his hands. For a time he could think of nothing but the cruel blow he had received. This was the end of those rainbow visions of himself and her going through life side by side, she lovingly criticizing his stance and his back-swing, he learning wisdom from her. A croquet-player! He was married to a woman who hit coloured balls through hoops. Mortimer Sturgis writhed in torment. A strong man's agony.

The mood passed. How long it had lasted, he did not know. But suddenly, as he sat there, he became once more aware of the glow of the sunshine and the singing of the birds. It was as if a shadow had lifted. Hope and optimism crept into his heart.

He loved her. He loved her still. She was part of him, and nothing that she could do had power to alter that. She had deceived him, yes. But why had she deceived him? Because she loved him so much that she could not bear to lose him. Dash it all, it was a bit of a compliment.

And, after all, poor girl, was it her fault? Was it not rather the fault of her upbringing? Probably she had been taught to play croquet when a mere child, hardly able to distinguish right from wrong. No steps had been taken to eradicate the virus from her system, and the thing had become chronic. Could she be blamed? Was she not more to be pitied than censured?

Mortimer rose to his feet, his heart swelling with generous forgiveness. The black horror had passed from him. The future seemed once more bright. It was not too late. She was still young, many years younger than he himself had been when he took up golf, and surely, if she put herself into the hands of a good specialist and practised every day, she might still hope to become a fair player. He reached the house and ran in, calling her name.

No answer came. He sped from room to room, but all were empty.

She had gone. The house was there. The furniture was there. The canary sang in its cage, the cook in the kitchen. The pictures still hung on the walls. But she had gone. Everything was at home except his wife.

Finally, propped up against the cup he had once won in a handicap competition, he saw a letter. With a sinking heart he tore open the envelope.

It was a pathetic, a tragic letter, the letter of a woman endeavouring to express all the anguish of a torn heart with one of those fountain-pens which suspend the flow of ink about twice in every three words. The gist of it was that she felt she had wronged him; that, though he might forgive, he could never forget; and that she was going away, away out into the world alone.

Mortimer sank into a chair, and stared blankly before him. She had scratched the match.

I am not a married man myself, so have had no experience of how it feels to have one's wife whiz off silently into the unknown; but I should imagine that it must be something like taking a full swing with a brassey and missing the ball. Something, I take it, of the same sense of mingled shock, chagrin, and the feeling that nobody loves one, which attacks a man in such circumstances, must come to the bereaved husband. And one can readily understand how terribly the incident must have shaken Mortimer Sturgis. I was away at the time, but I am told by those who saw him that his game went all to pieces.

He had never shown much indication of becoming anything in the nature of a first-class golfer, but he had managed to acquire one or two decent shots. His work with the light iron was not at all bad, and he was a fairly steady putter. But now, under the shadow of this tragedy, he dropped right back to the form of his earliest period. It was a pitiful sight to see this gaunt, haggard man with the look of dumb anguish behind his spectacles taking as many as three shots sometimes to get past the ladies' tee. His slice, of which he had almost cured himself, returned with such virulence that in the list of ordinary hazards he had now to include the tee-box. And, when he was not slicing, he was pulling. I have heard that he was known, when driving at the sixth, to get bunkered in his own caddie, who had taken up his position directly behind him. As for the deep sand-trap in front of the seventh green, he spent so much of his time in it that there was some informal talk among the members of the committee of charging him a small weekly rent.

A man of comfortable independent means, he lived during these days on next to nothing. Golf-balls cost him a certain amount, but the bulk of his income he spent in efforts to discover his wife's whereabouts. He advertised in all the papers. He employed private detectives. He even, much as it revolted his finer instincts, took to travelling about the country, watching croquet matches. But she was never among the players. I am not sure that he did not find a melancholy comfort in this, for it seemed to show that, whatever his wife might be and whatever she might be doing, she had not gone right under.

Summer passed. Autumn came and went. Winter arrived. The days grew bleak and chill, and an early fall of snow, heavier than had been known at that time of the year for a long while, put an end to golf. Mortimer spent his days indoors, staring gloomily through the window at the white mantle that covered the earth.

It was Christmas Eve.

The young man shifted uneasily on his seat. His face was long and sombre.

'All this is very depressing,' he said.

'These soul tragedies,' agreed the Oldest Member, 'are never very cheery.'

'Look here,' said the young man, firmly, 'tell me one thing frankly, as man to man. Did Mortimer find her dead in the snow, covered except for her face, on which still lingered that faint, sweet smile which he remembered so well? Because, if he did, I'm going home.'

'No, no,' protested the Oldest Member. 'Nothing of that kind.'

'You're sure? You aren't going to spring it on me suddenly?'

'No, no!'

The young man breathed a relieved sigh.

'It was your saying that about the white mantle covering the earth that made me suspicious.'

The Sage resumed.

It was Christmas Eve. All day the snow had been falling, and now it lay thick and deep over the countryside. Mortimer Sturgis, his frugal dinner concluded – what with losing his wife and not being able to get any golf, he had little appetite these days – was sitting in his drawing-room, moodily polishing the blade of his jigger. Soon wearying of this once congenial task, he laid down the club and went to the front door to see if there was any chance of a thaw. But no. It was freezing. The snow, as he tested it with his shoe, crackled crisply. The sky above was black and full of cold stars. It seemed to Mortimer that the sooner he packed up and went to the South of France, the better. He was just about to close the door, when suddenly he thought he heard his own name called.

'Mortimer!'

Had he been mistaken? The voice had sounded faint and far away.

'Mortimer!'

He thrilled from head to foot. This time there could be no mistake. It was the voice he knew so well, his wife's voice, and it had come from somewhere down near the garden-gate. It is difficult to judge distance where sounds are concerned, but Mortimer estimated that the voice had spoken about a short mashie-niblick and an easy putt from where he stood.

The next moment he was racing down the snow-covered path. And then his heart stood still. What was that dark something on the ground just inside the gate? He leaped towards it. He passed his hands over it. It was a human body. Quivering, he struck a match. It went out. He struck another. That went out, too. He struck a third, and it burnt with a steady flame; and, stooping, he saw that it was his wife who lay there, cold and stiff. Her eyes were closed, and on her face still lingered that faint, sweet smile which he remembered so well.

The young man rose with a set face. He reached for his golf-bag.

'I call that a dirty trick,' he said, 'after you promised –' The Sage waved him back to his seat.

'Have no fear!' She had only fainted.'

'You said she was cold.'

'Wouldn't you be cold if you were lying in the snow?'

'And stiff.'

'Mrs Sturgis was stiff because the train-service was bad, it being the holiday-season, and she had had to walk all the way from the junction, a distance of eight miles. Sit down and allow me to proceed.'

Tenderly, reverently, Mortimer Sturgis picked her up and began to bear her into the house. Half-way there, his foot slipped on a piece of ice and he fell heavily, barking his shin and shooting his lovely burden out on to the snow.

The fall brought her to. She opened her eyes.

'Mortimer, darling!' she said.

Mortimer had just been going to say something else, but he checked himself.

'Are you alive?' he asked.

'Yes,' she replied.

'Thank God!' said Mortimer, scooping some of the snow out of the back of his collar.

Together they went into the house, and into the drawing-room. Wife gazed at husband, husband at wife. There was a silence.

'Rotten weather!' said Mortimer.

'Yes, isn't it!'

The spell was broken. They fell into each other's arms. And presently they were sitting side by side on the sofa, holding hands, just as if that awful parting had been but a dream.

It was Mortimer who made the first reference to it.

'I say, you know,' he said, 'you oughtn't to have nipped away like that!'

'I thought you hated me!'

'Hated *you*! I love you better than life itself! I would sooner have smashed my pet driver than have had you leave me!'

She thrilled at the words.

'Darling!'

Mortimer fondled her hand.

'I was just coming back to tell you that I loved you still. I was going to suggest that you took lessons from some good professional. And I found you gone!'

'I wasn't worthy of you, Mortimer!'

'My angel!' He pressed his lips to her hair, and spoke solemnly. 'All this has taught me a lesson, dearest. I knew all along, and I know it more than ever now, that it is you – you that I want. Just you! I don't care if you don't play golf. I don't care –' He hesitated, then went on manfully. 'I don't care even if you play croquet, so long as you are with me!'

For a moment her face showed rapture that made it almost angelic. She uttered a low moan of ecstasy. She kissed him. Then she rose.

'Mortimer, look!'

'What at?'

'Me. Just look!'

The jigger which he had been polishing lay on a chair close by. She took it up. From the bowl of golf-balls on the mantelpiece she selected a brand new one. She placed it on the carpet. She addressed it. Then, with a merry cry of 'Fore!' she drove it hard and straight through the glass of the china-cupboard.

'Good God!' cried Mortimer, astounded. It had been a bird of a shot.

She turned to him, her whole face alight with that beautiful smile.

'When I left you, Mortie,' she said, 'I had but one aim in life, somehow to make myself worthy of you. I saw your advertisements in the papers, and I longed to answer them, but I was not ready. All this long, weary while I have been in the village of Auchtermuchtie, in Scotland, studying under Tamms McMickle.'

'Not the Tamms McMickle who finished fourth in the Open Championship of 1911, and had the best ball in the foursome in 1912 with Jock McHaggis, Andy McHeather, and Sandy McHoots!'

'Yes, Mortimer, the very same. Oh, it was difficult at first. I missed my mallet, and longed to steady the ball with my foot and use the toe of the club. Wherever there was a direction post I aimed at it automatically. But I conquered my weakness. I practised steadily. And now Mr McMickle says my handicap would be a good twenty-four on any links.' She smiled apologetically. 'Of course, that doesn't sound much to you! You were a twelve when I left you, and now I suppose you are down to eight or something.'

Mortimer shook his head.

'Alas, no!' he replied, gravely. 'My game went right off for some reason or other, and I'm twenty-four, too.'

'For some reason or other!' She uttered a cry. 'Oh, I know what the reason was! How can I ever forgive myself! I have ruined your game!'

The brightness came back to Mortimer's eyes. He embraced her fondly.

'Do not reproach yourself, dearest,' he murmured. 'It is the best thing that could have happened. From now on, we start level, two hearts that beat as one, two drivers that drive as one. I could not wish it otherwise. By George! It's just like that thing of Tennyson's.'

He recited the lines softly:

> *My bride,*
> *My wife, my life. Oh, we will walk the links*
> *Yoked in all exercise of noble end,*
> *And so thro' those dark bunkers off the course*
> *That no man knows. Indeed, I love thee: come,*
> *Yield thyself up: our handicaps are one;*
> *Accomplish thou my manhood and thyself;*
> *Lay thy sweet hands in mine and trust to me.*

She laid her hands in his.

'And now, Mortie, darling,' she said, 'I want to tell you all about how I did the long twelfth at Auchtermuchtie in one under bogey.'

From *The Golf Omnibus* by P. G. Wodehouse
(Barrie and Jenkins, London, 1973).

He overheard one guy say: 'I just got a new set of clubs for my wife.' The other replied: 'Now that's what I call a real good trade.'

Joe Chase, professional at Plantation Golf Club.

Golf Gamesmanship

Stephen Potter

The late Stephen Potter's *Gamesmanship* was one of the great humour books of the immediate post-war years. He then followed it up two decades later with the *Complete Golf Gamesmanship*, introducing yet more advanced psychological warfare techniques – the ploys and gambits which can sometimes displace skill with club and ball. Does gamesmanship exist at the top level of golf? Most certainly. There are some players who will murder your concentration with quips and chatter if you give them half a chance.

I.W.

The Swing

'Look out,' he said, just as Big Jim Dougan was about to drive. 'There's a fly on the ball. Stand back and start all over again.'

This ploy from an early gamesmanship school story may seem naïve yet it demonstrates well the truism that the first object of the gamesplay should be to break flow, and the second to introduce non-golf thoughts in the swing and the golfgame.

How many people realize that every part of the swing is associated with irrelevant and putting-off thoughts? It is these irrelevant thoughts, always latent, which the gamesman must try to bring to the surface, however buried and fleeting they may be.

Playing for Money

'What shall we play for?'
'You say.'

The man who says 'you say' is one up. It suggests that to play for half-a-crown would be amusing but that his ancestors, members of White's Club to a man, were equally prepared to stake an estate or a mistress on a game of shove-groat or 'Rock-i'-the-Ring'. Opponent is likely to suggest playing for something decidedly larger than is usual for him. May I tentatively suggest that for this occasion a new ploy I am provisionally calling 'To-him-that-hath-shall-be-givenmanship' may be tried? Let slip suggestions that there is wealth in your family. Say 'Have you got a car coming for you?' (suggesting chauffeur *milieu*) or 'Father has been asked to lend his Bernardino Taddi for next year's Quattrocento Italian exhibition at the R.A.' (picture worth £100,000). This will bring in the unbreakable rule of money play:

If stake is more than mother says
Ah then 'tis you it is who pays. *

The Drive

Of all the problems which face the golf gamesman, the problem of pure good play is the most difficult to fight. In particular, some of the best gamesmanship brains in America, many of them drained from England which drained them from Scotland, have been bent to the problem of how to be one-up on the man who hits the longer ball.

In normal circumstances it may be possible, for instance, to give advice to a man who is 2 or 3 up: but it is difficult indeed if he is outdriving you. A list of attempted ploys looks little better than a confession of failure. There is the driver from the head of which you unbutton a head cover marked with a large 'No. 4'. There is the remark, if your own drive of 150 yards happens just to have cleared the rough on the right, that 'position is the point here, not distance'.

Then there is the old ploy, first mentioned by me in 1947, of giving your Vast Distances man a caddy who never says 'good shot' but often points to a place, 30 yards ahead, which was reached by Byron Nelson when he played the course in 1946, or, better still, by J. H. Taylor, when he played there with a gutty in '98.

It is important to warn your female partner, in a foursome, especially if she is your wife, not to say 'Ooo' or give a little scream of female admiration. Tell her to say, 'Well, he got away with that one.'

The problem will be solved in time. Funds for our Long Ball Research Wing are welcome and needed. Meanwhile let me give one piece of general advice. Never, never comment on the fact that your opponent has got distance. Never say 'You certainly powdered that one'. Puzzled by your silence, long driver will try to outdistance himself until, inevitably, he ends up out of bounds.

But the important point to remember is that superiority in length is a myth, or is at any rate cancelled out by relativity. It depends on the standard of measurement. The man who is outdriven at Sandwich can always say 'when Sarazen won here he never used more than a 3 wood'. A following breeze may help you to make the 200 yard mark down wind at the 18th at St Andrew's. But if your opponent beats you by his usual fifteen yards it is usually safe to say:

'Amazing to think that in these conditions Nicklaus *reached the green* in all four rounds of the open.'

Safe unless you are up against a St Andrew's type gamesman who will probably say:

'Yes. I wonder what club he used from the tee. After all, two generations ago Blackwell reached the *steps leading up to the clubhouse* with a gutty.'

---

* My wife heard a celebrated version of this ploy when we were watching the pro–amateur at Seminole, Fla. There was a new young professional, Mike Souchak, under whose huge frame and footballer's feet the earth trembled. 1952 was a successful year for him on the circuit 'because he had learned to reduce the length of his drive'. We passed this on to Wiffley, J., (16) of our Club.

It might be added here that the inferior player should never, never in any way behave differently, let alone apologize, because he is inferior. In the days when I was genuinely young and had muscles like whipcord I used to drive nearly 210 yards on the downhill hole at Redhill. My father's best was 140 yards. As soon as he had struck one of these hundred-and-forty-yarders, he would stand back still gazing after the ball till it had stopped and then pace the distance, counting out loud, and ending in a crescendo 'a hundred and thirty-eight, *thirty-nine*, FORTY'.

It is worth noting here that if Long Handicap is playing Short – 14 playing 4, for instance – never must 14, if he wins, admit, recall, apologize, or refer in any way to the fact that he has received 8 strokes in the round; and it is most unusual to refer to this when telling the story to family, particularly wife.

Tickler, having won the Doverbridge Tea-tray playing off 16, used to like putting on the special Tea-tray tie, particularly when he was playing against men whom he had just beaten in this competition, men who had given him perhaps as much as nine strokes.

This situation and its handling shows yet once again the deep relationship between life and golf, of which life is so often the metaphor or mime.

Style

This is the place to say something not about the style of gamesmanship but the gamesmanship of style. A perfect, flowing, model style can be alarming to an opponent. The teaching of golf is not our domain: but the teaching of style comes very much into our orbit. An appearance of a strong effortless style, flowing yet built on a stable foundation, can be alarming to an opponent even if it has no effect on one's shots.

'Right, let's have a game then!' says Jeremy Cardew to comparative stranger after a dinner party.

'I haven't played for ages,' he goes on. Though in full evening dress, he may pluck a bamboo stick from a pot in the conservatory and begin to take a practice swing, left hand only.

'My, what a wide arc to that swing,' thinks Wiffley, who is already wondering if he, too, ought to have worn a white tie instead of a black. We recommend the suggestion of great width, on this back-swing, and long relaxed follow-through.

Above all we recommend practising a practice swing which ends with the body turned correctly square to the direction of the ball, the hands held high, an expression of easy confidence on the face, a touch of nobility, as if one were looking towards the setting sun. Students who find themselves unable even vaguely to simulate a graceful finish may do well by going to the opposite extreme. It is possible to let go of the club almost completely at the top of the swing, recover it, and by a sort of half-paralysed jerk come down again more or less normally. Opponent will find himself *forced to stare at you*, and may lose his rhythm.

Straight Loft Arm: A Personal Confession

I am sometimes asked which, of all the gambits I have invented, do I personally find most useful. Here, exclusively and for the first time, let me reveal the answer to this question.

In *Lifemanship* it is either 'Yes, but not in the South' (when Man who has Actually Been There is holding forth as if he alone, therefore, had any right to speak about the subject). Or perhaps it is the use, in motoring, of 'Plaste's Placid Salutation' (recorded in *One-Upmanship*).

In golf I have no doubt. Described in *Gamesmanship*, it is for use against the man who is driving further and less erratically than yourself.

'I see how you're doing it,' you say, 'straight left arm at the moment of impact, isn't it? Do you mind if I stand just *here* and watch?'

In spite of the fact that the left arm is always straight at the moment of impact, this used to cause a pull in the old days. Now there is a well-developed counter. (Driver says, 'Do you mean like this?' and if drive is unsatisfactory takes out another ball and drives again as if first drive was for demonstration only. 'Now let's watch *your* arm,' he then says.) But I am still finding it useful.

Later History of the Frith-Morteroy

Long before gamesmanship was invented, competitors in any sport used to use game leg play – 'my leg is troubling me a little today'. Gamesmanship described its use in lawn tennis and produced the famous Frith-Morteroy counter – the pause, half-way through the second set, the grave smile, the reference to the 'ticker', and the 'I'm supposed not to hit the ball too hard'.

All this was almost immediately taken up by golfers, as we hoped it would be. Equally predictable was it that ripostes suitable for golf were found to the Morteroy counter. Indeed a splendid gamesfield was at once exposed and I was lucky enough to be within earshot of one match played between experts in this technique.

The venue was in the Isle of Mull, with its delicate colouring, dignified coast line, and views of Gaelic place names, superb fishing and a distant sight of nervy looking stags, for we always played golf in the stalking season.

The golf-course, at Tobermory, is 9 hole; it is typically Highland – i.e. equal in effort to the playing of 27 holes in Leeds Castle Park. Two or three holes involve driving across a vast valley or *druchaid*. In this foray I saw it was Seligmann against Saxe. So far as golf was concerned, Seligmann was better than Saxe, as one would expect from their handicaps, Seligmann being a clicketty-click 14 and Saxe a soft-centred 12.

Climbing up to the second tee to play up to the Hole o' Crest, Seligmann began to use his club as a stick. By the time he had reached the green he was limping. Saxe might at this point say:

'OK?'

'Yes – yes, perfect,' Seligmann replied: though a hundred yards further on he would give a curious sideways kick with his left leg.

'They tell me I've got to have this op,' Seligmann remarked to Saxe, who was taking no notice.

Thus was the scene set for the counter to Game Leg Play; and sure enough, at the top of the second hill Saxe said classically:

'Sorry, I've got to stand still for two seconds. Nothing to worry about.'

Seligmann kept his head.

'Yes, well,' he went on at once, 'as I was saying, the end of the hip bone fits into the socket or acetabulum. While we're waiting I'll draw it for you . . .'

At first Seligmann did well simply by taking no notice of Saxe's troubles – did well that is until yet another deer-stalking man joined our little party at Knock. This was Boyce, a red-hot 10, and it was he who, in our 4-ball, all against all, out Seligmanned Seligmann. Boyce had never held down a job for more than a year but Boyce had this remarkable pet subject, knowledge of medical terms. His study was full of pale blue piles of the *British Medical Journal*. He had Gray's *Anatomy* and the nineteenth-century edition of Stedman's *Medical Dictionary* which Tickler and Odoreida – both of them, rather surprisingly, part of Seligmann's circle – liked to look at because it was illustrated, rather thrilling if one was a layman, which speaking personally one wasn't.

I first noticed Boyce for his deft treatment of our (5) man Cardew, a bit of a hero at Old Soaking, who was having lessons from Campion, then the pro at Royal Hampton. 'How's it going?' Boyce asked him.

'Marvellous. Campion really gave me an *image*; for a bit I knew what hitting was all about.'

'Oo – I bet you did.'

'How do you mean?'

'I only mean that Campion plays every day and he's a man of *immense strength*. He can break your back, you know. That full professional swing puts a huge strain on the deep muscles of the back, especially the *transverso-spinalis* system with the – what's it called – *semispinalis capitis*?'

At Tobermory I remember that at the 4th, second time round, Seligmann, finding himself 3 down, was glad to get one back by holing a long putt.

'I say,' he said, 'somebody pick that ball out for me. Suddenly I can't stoop.'

He only vaguely knew Boyce, who was on to the situation like a knife. However Boyce said nothing.

On the next tee Seligmann reiterated his point by slowly sinking on to both knees to fix his peg into the hard ground.

'Afraid I shan't be getting any distance,' he said.

'You were always pretty short,' said Boyce.

'I can't turn my hip,' said Seligmann, smiling as if not complaining though in pain. He had never pivoted in his life. 'Maybe a slipped disc.'

'So *that's* turned up again, has it?' Boyce said. 'Probably it's just O.A.'

Seligmann didn't get it.

'Forgive me; it's just a technical term for Old Age. Anybody over the age of 45 suffers a slight disintegration of the bone structure and the joint mechanism. Splendid view.'

Round the corner below there was a huge chunk of sea, which was just beginning to roughen up.

'The wrinkled sea beneath him crawls,' said Saxe, always a bit of a quotesman.

'And there's a slight diminution of the intervertebral spaces,' Boyce continued as they walked to their respective drives. 'Staggering isn't it?' he went on, gazing out to sea. 'In the distance you can see McCoutinglass's Mouse-trap.'

'Criminy,' said Seligmann with his smile, but he was being out-gambited and he knew it. Boyce was well ahead, on the other side of the fairway.

'Your spine begins to SHUT UP LIKE A TELESCOPE,' Boyce called out in a high, cheerful, carrying voice, rather throaty. 'They call it the CONCERTINA EFFECT.' Seligmann looked round to see if anyone was listening. Boyce was pointing to an uninteresting rock which he said was called Coolie McCoulin's Collar-stud.

'No, actually,' Boyce went on quietly when they had to wait on the next tee. 'You're rather a marvel. Let me look at your spine. Very little kyphosis. Think of Lionel – on two sticks now.'

'Hooray,' said Seligmann: but he never played with Boyce again.

Boyce certainly did well with his medical knowledge. Three or four members of his Club – we all know who – began to suffer from hypochondria. It was said that Wiggs, now, never touched spirits before 10.30 a.m.

'Have you noticed?' Boyce would begin. 'Strang is developing quite a tremor of the right hand.'

'How do you mean?'

'I simply just mean it trembles slightly. Watch it when he's bending down to put his ball on the peg, first thing.'

Boyce went through six members of the Club in the same way. 'Look at that walk,' he would say. In the end he was bound to describe some hitherto unsuspected weakness of his opponent, or better still, create an imaginary one.

In the twenties the average age at Mid Surrey was high, and they knew it. There was said to be a Death Expectancy Chart above the Secretary's desk. I do know that in the doorway, only half hidden, was a hand ambulance in wickerwork for collecting coronaries in the summer months.

As our techniques get nearer to the ultimate margins of human character, as the psychologies merge with the psychoses, we may have to pass forwards towards, or perhaps we should say fall backwards on, one of the most questionable questions in Gamesmanship.

It is this: 'Do you yip?'

Readers are reminded that the word 'yip' was invented by T. D. Armour the great teacher of golf and a fine teacherman as well. I once watched him working his way through what I hope and believe was a very profitable morning's instruction near Palm Beach. Comfortably seated in a shady arbour, with a large glass at his elbow, he sat relaxed while pupil after pupil twisted and turned in the heat of the Florida sun.

Armour defines 'yips' as a 'brain spasm which impairs the short game.' 'Impairs' is a euphemism. Since Hogan has stepped down from the throne, thousands of spectators have suffered with him as he stands motionless over his putter unable to move it. The disease seems to affect men of highly strung and subtle temper who have practised an art too long or with too dedicated a concentration. There is our own Peter Alliss, with his putts; Dave Thomas with his short chips. Control of that complex joint, the elbow, seems to be lost. A great snooker player has been a victim, and a famous violinist.

No need to point out to the gamesman the uses to which these facts may be put, nor which of them to choose. No need – and on my part small desire. This is for a last resort only. There is even a possibility that during play any mention of yips, however indirect, may be banned at the next meeting of WOGG (World Organisation of Golfing Gamesmen). The necessity of some such law was made clear when H. Longhurst reported the case of the gamesman (if indeed the man deserves such a title) who revealed before a match that he did not suffer from yips himself but 'was a carrier'.

Complete Golf Gamesmanship by Stephen Potter
(William Heinemann, London, 1968).

It is a law of nature that everybody plays a hole badly when going through.
Bernard Darwin, *Playing the Like*
(Chapman and Hall, London, 1934).

Golf in a Dinner Jacket

Walter Hagen

Walter Hagen not only ended the American inferiority complex about golf by winning the British Open four times, starting in 1922, he also did a lot to create the British inferiority complex – only now coming to an end. More than that, Hagen was the playboy hero with style. Who else could turn up on the first tee after a night's revelling still dressed in his dinner jacket? Have tux – will drive.

I.W.

My tendency to stay up late at night was another little bit of business that bothered a few of my fellow golfers. I usually managed to get eight hours sleep, but there were a few times when I stepped up to tee off with an hour or less spent on my cool white pillow. Every athlete needs plenty of sleep and rest during strenuous competition. But few actually get it. This is particularly true of golfers in a championship tournament. I was able to get what I required because I knew I was going to need steady nerves and good physical co-ordination the next day. I never hurried. This goes for both on and off the golf course. People have written that I've no regard for time. I respect time highly and I try to make the most of it. There is just as much in saving time as there is in spending it properly. It fits the old Army gag about 'Hurry up and wait'. That's pretty much my idea. I don't hurry, therefore I'm not bothered with waiting.

From the minute I rose in the morning, I kept on an even keel until I reached the first tee. I got up in plenty of time to dress and breakfast leisurely and to arrive at the golf course just when I was due to play. There's a certain sort of rhythm in such a smoothed-out routine that carried over to my game . . . a rhythm that helped me avoid the jerky, gear-shifting movements which characterised the game of many easily upset or nervous golfers.

There were a few times when I stepped up to tee off with not even one hour of sleep. One such occasion has been narrated incorrectly so often that I'm going to set it straight. When I was president of the Pasadena Golf and Country Club at St Petersburg, Florida, we made it a point to have exhibition matches over every week-end and on holidays to interest the public in the home site possibilities of the place.

These exhibitions were bread-and-butter promotions for us and the main reason for building the course. This particular exhibition was scheduled for New Year's Day, at ten in the morning. My wife and I had been on a round-robin party on New

Year's Eve and had ended up at the home of Gene Elliott for breakfast. Gene's place was a good half-hour drive from the club. My chauffeur, James Randall, came in and reminded me of the exhibition match.

The sun had been up so long I'd no idea of the correct time. Checking my watch I found I had slightly less than thirty minutes to motor across to Pasadena. I arrived at the first tee wearing my dinner clothes and patent leather pumps. The few hundred people in the gallery thought that was great fun. I was sliding in all directions trying to tee off in those slippery-soled shoes and after several attempts I got my drive away. I gave the gallery the impression that I intended playing the entire match in those clothes. Then, after taking my second shot, I made my excuses and explained that I'd go into the clubhouse and dress for the game. Looking over the gallery I remarked that I thought a number of them hadn't been up too long, either. They laughed and agreed I had a lot of company.

In the clubhouse I changed to regular golf clothes and spiked shoes. Even then, for the next several holes, I noticed that the fairway was much more slippery than it had ever seemed the dozens of times I'd played it. I managed to keep my footing and balance and went on to win my match with a 68.

From *The Walter Hagen Story* by Walter Hagen
(William Heinemann, London, 1955).

The Wit and Wisdom of Sam Snead

Talk to the ball: 'This isn't going to hurt a bit.' I tell the ball under my breath: 'Sambo is just going to give you a nice little ride.'

Is that right? How long are decades nowadays?

> (When told he had won tournaments in six different decades.)

The valleys are so narrow that the dogs just have to wag their tails up and down.

> (On his Virginia birthplace in the mountains.)

Many a golf course and many a gambler would have eaten me up if I hadn't eaten them first by having a mean frame of mind.

No matter what happens, *never give up a hole*. In tossing in your cards after a bad beginning you also undermine your whole game, because to quit between tee and green is more habit-forming than drinking a high-ball before breakfast.

> From *The Education of a Golfer*
> (Cassell and Co., London, 1962).

Lay off for three weeks and then quit for good.   (Advice to a pupil.)

You've got one problem. You stand too close to the ball – after you've hit it.

> (Advice to a pupil.)

I'm only scared of three things – lightning, a side-hill putt, and Ben Hogan.

You're Supposed to Enjoy Golf – Even with a Pain

Peter Dobereiner

Whatever your handicap, whether it's 28 or plus 5 like mine, golf is what you make it. And yes, Peter Dobereiner, whose golf reports in the *Observer* give me a lot of amusement, is right – a pain or an ailment, real or imaginary, can aid your concentration because it can divert your mind from self-doubt and needless worries. When I won the world's first million-dollar cheque at Sun City in 1987, I had the most fearful stomach cramps – and they weren't imaginary!

I.W.

People take up golf for a variety of reasons, all of them more or less harmless. Ambitious business types sometimes turn to golf as another professional skill, like doing a fast-reading course or computer studies, and very useful it can be too, now that so many deals are negotiated on the course and birdie talk has become the *lingua franca* of the commercial world.

Doctors frequently prescribe golf for patients who are running to fat in sedentary occupations although the medical profession is by no means unanimous on the value of once-a-week golf. At least one medical report has branded golf as a killer in certain conditions and certainly for people of uncontrollably volatile temperament it is, as they say, contra-indicated. Tournament players are prone to backache and a lifetime of intensive golf sometimes results in a rounding of the shoulders, a natural consequence of a crouching posture and as much an occupational disease as the elongated arm of a fast bowler. The main condition associated with golfers, however, is chronic hypochondria. Many of them play better when they are suffering from some slight ailment and if they don't have one they invent it. It is an interesting delusion, arising I suppose from the need to have a ready-made excuse to hand in case of failure, although there is a school of thought which holds that an ailment makes a golfer swing more slowly and therefore better. Or perhaps a nagging pain, real or imaginary, prevents the mind from wandering into distracting areas of speculation about the prize money or how they are swinging the club. Whatever the reason, the history of famous golfing victories reads like a medical dictionary – Ben Hogan, limping heavily from the car crash which nearly ended his golf career, as he won the US Open in 1950; Ken Venturi in the last stages of exhaustion and supported by a doctor as he took the 1964 US Open; Doug Sanders with his foot gashed open after stepping barefoot on a piece of broken glass and yet spreadeagling the field in the Peniscola Open in 1962.

Bruce Devlin won the biggest prize of his or anyone else's career by lifting the record Carling first prize of 35,000 dollars when he was convalescing from a varicose vein operation. Many players do not sleep, or eat, properly during big events but neither fatigue nor hunger prevents them from winning. There are many more examples of invalid supermen; Billy Casper, the most successful golfer of them all, suffers from allergies so obscure that at one time he had to live on a diet of rattlesnake and buffalo steaks.

The favourite standby is bursitis, a condition related to housemaid's knee. When all else fails, and a golfer is enjoying apparently perfect health, he can usually rely on a few psychosomatic twinges of bursitis to boost his confidence. Golf must be the only sport in which the discerning punter is encouraged by the sight of his selection receiving a pain-killing injection or bandaging an inflamed wrist. For most of us the pressures of golf will never bear heavily enough to force us into the esoteric realms of beneficial disabilities. We can enjoy the game and good health at the same time. And I suppose that the commonest reason for taking up golf is not to make a fortune or to clinch deals, but simply because of its intrinsic appeal.

It looks like a pleasant game, specially for those who have grown too old for more athletic sports. And it looks easy. The ball is not moving; it sits there waiting to be hit and you can take as much time as you like over the hitting. The novice takes club in hand, addresses the ball and takes a swing at it. Nine times out of ten he misses by about a foot. Now is the chance, if he wants to escape an obsession which may well transform his whole life, for him to say 'What a bloody silly way of spending your weekend', cast the club aside and dismiss the subject of golf from his mind for ever.

Human nature, however, is a ruthless slave-driver. The would-be-golfer undergoes a bewildering sequence of emotions. Astonishment, embarrassment and frustration are submerged by determination. He tries again. And again. And again. By now the challenge is overpowering; he *must* hit that ball, his self-esteem is seriously threatened. It is absurd that a perfectly normal human being should be unable to hit a stationary ball which is fast turning into an enemy with an insolent sneer and hypnotic powers.

The novices' attitude, which started as faintly amused contempt and turned to blind anger, now changes again. He realizes that he is getting nowhere and if he is to keep his sanity he must approach the problem in a coldly rational manner. The ball is a doughty adversary, the trick is to match cunning with cunning. He takes the club back slowly, with as much care as approaching a sitting bluebottle with upraised fly-swot. The club descends, not very fast but with intense deliberation. There is a click, not unlike the sound which Hollywood would have us believe is made by John Wayne's clenched fist on a villain's jaw. The shock wave being absorbed by the shaft of the club is transmitted to the player as a sensuous tingle in the hands and forearms. And the ball, as it is picked up in flight by the wide-eyed gaze of the striker, is soaring straight and true into the far distance. At that moment a golfer is born. The memory of his first accidental good shot may have to sustain him through a tiresome period of learning. The pro makes him hold the club in a manner which is uncomfortable, unnatural and clearly ill-suited to the purpose. He hits a thousand shots that go scooting off along the ground to the left, or curl feebly into the right rough, or miss altogether with the head of the club burying itself into the ground behind the ball.

He learns the most complex set of rules known to sport, spends a small fortune on equipment and gives assurances about the religious persuasion of his ancestors in applying for membership of a club. All the while the memory of that one golden shot fortifies his ambition. And, in due course, there are other shots, raking drives, chips from 100 yards that run into the hole, miraculous recoveries from bush or bunker. There are plenty of bad ones as well but the glory of golf is that they are forgettable and forgotten.

It would be nice to be able to say of this type of novice that he takes up golf and lives happily ever after. Unfortunately, happiness is by no means automatic. Once a golfer is established in the game he should take stock of himself and decide exactly what it is about the game which he enjoys. There are several satisfactions from which to choose. The deepest joy is to improve and with sensible application and good instruction everyone can enjoy reducing his handicap. After a certain point, however, the graph of improvement which has been rising like a well-struck nine iron flattens out and the player must accept that unless he is prepared to devote an inordinate amount of time and energy to the game, his future progress will be considerably slower. We may live in hope that next time we shall find the secret: it is a harmless and indeed healthy delusion but most people have to work or raise families. Golf can claim only a small proportion of time; enough perhaps for a couple of games at weekends. If so, it is only sensible to take a rational view, spend the available time in playing for enjoyment and accepting improvements, if any, as extra bonuses.

In that case, with pleasure as the main aim, a distinction should be made. Some people like to wallop the ball. Fine. Let them wallop it. There are players who take four strokes at a short hole while their opponents take three but nevertheless enjoy the smug satisfaction of a moral victory at having got up with an eight iron while the lower-handicap opposition took a six iron. To such people three-putting is an irrelevance; length is all and golf is a trial of strength.

Another type of player gets his kicks from stylish golf. He is a perfectionist, more concerned with hitting good shots than effective ones. This attitude is normally a symptom of ambition, commonest among younger players who are working hard to improve. I must say I find it slightly tiresome when an opponent lays his ball stiff, three feet from the hole, with a full seven and slams his club down in anger because he hit the shot a bit thin.

But if scoring is what you enjoy then it is necessary to recognize the fact and adjust your attitude to this end. A correspondent, a retired engineer, who suffered a serious disability as the result of a car accident, wrote to me with details of his personal system which I consider is worthy of general application. He objectively assessed his own capacity with each club, on the modest basis of what he was confident of achieving rather than blue-moon exceptions. With this information he translated the card of his home course and set himself a new set of par figures.

As he put it, a beneficent committee had given him a number of handicap strokes to use as wisely as he could. The long par-fours, the most difficult holes to score in regulation figures, he made par-fives. On such a hole he could just about reach the green if he hit his best drive followed by his best fairway wood. The odds against hitting two such wonder shots in succession were fantastic. However, by making the hole a par five he could take an easy four wood off the tee and then an easy five iron. That left him with seventy yards to cover in three more strokes, a push-over. And he only needed to hit one of those shots better than usual, pitching close or sinking a good putt, and he had a personal birdie.

The psychological advantage of picking up shots on par instead of dropping them was considerable. Obviously you cannot use this system of setting yourself a target and playing to a plan and at the same time indulge in heroics of enormous hitting. The two approaches are not compatible.

When I received this letter I indulged in an orgy of self-criticism and analysed my motives on the course. I decided that what I had been trying to do was not only to birdie every hole but with technically perfect strokes. No one in the history of the game has ever come within a mile of achieving that sort of standard. I felt thoroughly absurd at my own vainglorious fantasies. Since then, however, I like to think that my ambitions have been trimmed to something nearer my capabilities and certainly I have enjoyed my golf more.

And that, after all, is what golf is all about. It may be a banality but it is all too often forgotten. Golf should not be a battle in the lifemanship war, or a virility test, or a social asset or an excuse in gambling, or a character-building hobby, or an excuse for not taking the family out on Sundays, although it may contain elements of all of them. Essentially it is for amusement only. If it is played in that spirit it can be the most rewarding and satisfying game of them all and its fascination will endure for a lifetime.

From *The Game with the Hole in it* by Peter Dobereiner
(Faber & Faber, London, 1970).

Celebrity Quips

I have always found it to be the hole in one.

> Groucho Marx, asked what he thought was the most difficult shot in golf.

Give me golf clubs, the fresh air and a beautiful partner and you can keep my golf clubs and the fresh air.   Jack Benny.

Golf is a funny game. It's done much for health, and at the same time has ruined people by robbing them of their peace of mind. Look at me: I'm the healthiest idiot in the world.   Bob Hope.

And the name that is synonymous with Ford – Fore!   Bob Hope.

I know I'm getting better at golf because I'm hitting fewer spectators.

> Gerald Ford, 1984.

Jack Lemmon has been in more bunkers than Eva Braun.   Phil Harris.

I would rather play Hamlet with no rehearsal than play golf on television.

> Jack Lemmon.

3

THE GREAT TRIUMVIRATE

Bernard Darwin

At the turn of the century people talked about the Great Triumvirate of golf – Vardon, J. H. Taylor and Braid – who from the mid-1890s till the outbreak of the First World War dominated golf as surely as the Big Three of Nicklaus, Palmer and Player did in the 1960s. Between the three of them they won sixteen British Opens.

I.W.

Harry Vardon

The greatest member of the Triumvirate – for a period in a class by himself – was Jersey-born Harry Vardon (1890–1937), one of seven sons of a gardener. Harry's brother Tom was also a pro. Like many great golfers of that (and this) era, he started as a caddie, only seven years old at the time. Vardon won the British Open a record six times, in 1896, 1898, 1899, 1903, 1911 and 1914. He won the US Open in 1900 when he also went on a 20,000-mile tour of the USA playing exhibition matches to popularize the game there. In those pre-aviation days the strain of all that travel helped contribute to his breakdown in health from TB, causing him to spend many months in a sanatorium. He came back to go on winning and only lost the US Open in 1913 after a tie with the then unknown American amateur Francis Ouimet.

He is credited with the invention of the Vardon overlapping grip, now almost universal. Here is the first of three pieces on the Big Three of yesteryear by Bernard Darwin, grandson of the great Charles Darwin of Evolution fame; he was, as the anonymous golf correspondent of *The Times* for many years, still just about the most famous golf writer of his day.

I.W.

In the case of each of the other heroes of the past of whom I have tried to write it is easy to say in effect that he was in his day a great golfer and to leave it at that. In the case of Harry Vardon it is not easy to resist comparisons.

When he was in his prime, the question was constantly debated whether or not he was better than the now almost mythical young Tommy Morris had been. To-day people will insist on wondering how he compares with Bobby Jones. Such comparisons are tempting, but essentially futile, and I am going resolutely to resist them. But this much I will say: I cannot believe that anyone ever had or ever will have a greater genius for hitting a golf ball than Harry Vardon.

Courses and clubs and balls change; it is of no use to compare his scores with those either of his predecessors or his successors. But with anyone who ever saw him at the zenith of his game that impression of supreme genius will abide.

What is, in a few words, the general belief to-day about Vardon? I should say it was this, that he was a grand player up to the green and a very bad one when he got there. That belief is, I venture to say as regards the second part of it, false.

Until his illness, now thirty years ago or more, Vardon was not a bad putter. He was not in the class of great putters such as Hagen or Bobby Jones. He lost on the green something of that air of supreme grace which distinguished the rest of his game.

He did not make putting look absurdly or hopelessly easy, but he was a really good approach putter and at least a perfectly competent holer-out.

He gave himself probably less putting to do than any other man, and he did it something more than adequately. As one very small illustration, I remember going to Ganton and seeing Vardon play for the first time, soon after he had won his first championship. I talked to a good local amateur, who played with him constantly, and the point that he emphasized then was not Vardon's wonderful wooden club play up to the pin nor his mastery of all irons, but his relentlessly good putting.

Possibly the amateur had suffered from some particularly long putts and exaggerated a little, but I am quite sure I have not invented what he said.

After his serious breakdown in health, Vardon admittedly became a misser of short putts. He remained a sound approach putter, but there used to attack him some curious 'jump' in hand or wrist which made him stab at the short ones more quickly than he meant. It not unnaturally got on his nerves, and he became capable of putting very badly indeed, but this had not been so in his prime. Indeed, how could a man have beaten the heads off everybody in the way that Vardon did and yet have been the deplorable putter than he has been painted? The supposition refutes itself.

Vardon's greatest golf was undoubtedly played with the gutty ball – the ball he has never ceased to regret. He was a magnificent wooden club player with a unique power – due in some degree to his upright swing – of hitting the ball high and clean from almost any sort of lie. The brassy was not almost atrophied as it is to-day, in the times of the gutty, and it was Vardon's brassy shots that broke the hearts and backs of his competitors.

He was very long, so that he could reach in two wooden club shots holes at which most other people needed two and a chip. He was so accurate with those high-floating, quick-stopping brassy shots that he would put the ball as near the hole in two as his toiling, sweating adversaries would put theirs with their third, the chip. What hope was there against such a man? In truth, in his great years, nobody had any real hope.

'I played my game, sir, I played my game,' said Taylor after a memorable match at Newcastle in Ireland, and so no doubt he had, but Vardon had beaten him 13 up and 12 to play.

Vardon was certainly as good an iron player as any other of his contemporaries, and I do not exclude J. H. Taylor. At one time he was hideously long with a driving mashie and could use it at anyone else's brassy range, but it was not the length of his iron but its accuracy that was so devastating. He was as good with a short mashie pitch as he was with his famous push-shot with the cleek, and no man ever played iron shots more prettily. He merely shaved the turf and did not take cruel divots out of it.

Everybody has agreed from his first appearance as to the beauty of his iron play, but it is odd to remember now that by no means everybody admired his style with wooden clubs. It was so exceedingly unlike the big, sweeping St Andrews swing which had been deemed almost necessary to salvation; it had such a perceptible 'lift' in it, the club went up so straight, that at first there were cavilling critics.

It certainly seemed to me very strange and heterodox when I saw it. Perhaps it was something of an acquired taste, in that, at first, one looked at the things that did not matter and so did not perceive the perfectly beautiful rhythm which was so much more important.

The more triumphant Vardon became, the more utterly he routed his rivals, the more his style became admired. The overlapping grip was not exclusively his own, for Taylor had found it out for himself at Westward Ho, and Mr Laidlay had used it years before either of them. But it was Vardon that made it popular, and, when he was making victorious progresses up and down the country, 'Have you tried the Vardon grip?' was almost as common a greeting amongst golfers as 'Good morning.'

In the end, Vardon won our Open Championship six times, as compared with the five apiece of Braid and Taylor, but it is not unfair to the others to suggest that but for his illness, his total would have been considerably higher. People to-day are apt to forget how completely for a time he dominated the golfing world. Perhaps I had better very briefly set out his record.

He was born in Jersey in 1870, and when he was about twenty-five he became professional at a good inland course at Ganton in Yorkshire. In 1895 some of the leading professionals were bidden to play in a tournament at Pau in France. Somebody knew something and Vardon was included in the party. He did well and the golfing world began to say, 'Who is this Vardon? He seems a good player.'

In 1896 he came into his kingdom. Taylor was then king of the castle, having won the championship two years running. He went to play Vardon at Ganton and came away heavily beaten, declaring that this conqueror was a great player. The Open Championship at Muirfield proved it. Taylor and Vardon tied, and on the play-off Vardon won by four strokes. He was now, of course, one of the elect, but his most dominating time had not yet come.

In 1897 he did nothing very notable in the championship which was won by Harold Hilton. Then came the overwhelming years. In 1898 he won again, just beating Willie Park at Prestwick. Park challenged him to their historic seventy-two-hole match – North Berwick and Ganton – and Vardon made mincemeat of him. In 1899 at Sandwich nobody so much as dreamed of anyone else being champion, and he won, easing up, almost as he liked.

And during all those two years, he was winning nearly all the other tournaments there were to win and murdering his enemies in exhibition matches. He made a triumphant tour through Scotland, and that dour country had to admit that England had the best of it. His play was as Andrew Kirkaldy said, 'Enough to break the heart of an iron horse.' The only way in which Vardon could be beaten was by the better ball of two of the very best amateurs, Mr Laidlay and Mr Balfour-Melville at St Andrews, and St Andrews was never Vardon's course.

Next came his first triumphal tour through America and his winning of the Open Championship there. It was an amazing programme alike in the hard work it involved and the almost unbroken success of his play. There is, I take it, no doubt that he gave a wonderful stimulus to golf throughout the United States, and there is very little doubt that he left just a little of the fine edge of his game behind him there. Great as he was for years afterwards, he was never again – and this is, I think, his own opinion – quite the same player, never again quite so conquering and untiring and confident.

There were splendid things, of course, yet to come. In 1903 he won the Open

Championship at Prestwick and won it easily, although he was so 'done' in the last round that he several times thought he would be unable to finish. In 1905, with Taylor as his partner, he administered a fearful drubbing to Braid and Herd in a foursome match over fast greens. He played superbly, but he was wholly unfit for such a strain. Serious illness had him in its grip and soon he was in a sanatorium. He recovered, but it was some time before his golf recovered.

It was not till 1911 that he came back to something very like his greatest game, when he won the championship again after a tie with Massy. Finer wooden club play has never been seen than his on the play-off of that tie, and he played Massy to a standstill; the Frenchman gave up on the thirty-fifth green.

In 1913 there was another historic play-off and Mr Ouimet's victory at The Country Club, and then in 1914 Vardon won his sixth and last British championship at Prestwick. He and Taylor were leading the field with the last day to come and they were drawn together. Never was there so near an approach to pandemonium on a golf-course, and it was truly astonishing that the two men could play as they did. After that came the war years, and, when they were over, Vardon's championships were over too. He remained for a long time, and remains now, a model for all golfers, a true aesthetic joy to watch, the old master of old masters, but as far as championships go, time has won the match.

Harry Vardon has kept not all his old untiring energy, but all his old enthusiasm for golf. He loves playing it and teaching it and watching it. He is not given to saying very much, but very little escapes his eye and he is an acute and stern critic. While he is always ready to help young players, he is essentially a praiser of the time that is gone. He has never ceased to regret the coming of the rubber core and the passing of the gutty. He liked the old ball, which required clean and perfect hitting; he dislikes the new one, which he thinks enables many an imperfect hitter 'to get away with it.'

Neither is he in favour of some modern doctrines. He says he is constantly having to cure patients who have been ruined by the 'stiff left arm.' Who shall blame him if he is inclined to look back at the end of the nineteenth century as the golden age of golf? At any rate golf was a great game then, and how he could play it with the gutty!

From *Playing the Like* by Bernard Darwin
(Chapman and Hall, London, 1934).

J. H. Taylor

John Henry Taylor (1871–1963) won the British Open five times, in 1894, 1895, 1900, 1909 and 1913. He was also runner-up six times. A leading light in the founding of the PGA in 1901, he did much to boost the professionals' lot. He was renowned for his play with the mid-iron – the mashie, or what is now the 5 iron – a club which he virtually invented. He was professional at Burnham and Winchester but his name will forever be associated with Royal Mid Surrey from 1899 until his retirement.   I.W.

No greater or more characteristic figure has ever appeared in the ranks of professional golf than John Henry Taylor.

He was a very great golfer indeed; he won five Open Championships and was second so often that his record for consistency is unique. He is still a very, very good golfer, but he is first of all a man of character. Whatever walk of life he had chosen, it is safe to say that he would have made his mark in it, for he possesses in a remarkable degree enthusiasm, imagination, resolution.

When he had emerged from the caddie stage to that of working on the greens at Westward Ho! he wanted, I believe, to be, in turn, first a soldier and then a sailor, and by a curious irony was rejected for some defect of eyesight. What he would have done in either of those professions it is impossible to say, since peace-time in his young days gave no great opportunity of rising from the ranks, but it is certain that everyone who served him would have remembered him.

He is, as far as I know, a conservative in politics; if his life had been cast in other ways, he might have been a trade union leader who swayed crowds by his fierce oratory, for he is a natural speaker. I have often heard him speak and always well, but there is one little speech of his in particular that I recall. It was when his eldest son, J. H., junior, was on the Oxford Golf Team and he, together with some other fathers, came to the dinner after the university match. He spoke very shortly and simply and I do not remember exactly what he said, except that he thanked people for being kind to his boy, but it will always stick in my head as one of the best and most moving speeches I ever heard.

Because he was born by a famous golf-course and had a natural genius for the game, J. H. became a professional golfer and, being so, he has now inevitably become the leader of his profession, respected by everybody, *the* man who instantly comes to mind when there is needed someone to represent professional golf, to express its views or to negotiate on its behalf.

He has not only played hard but worked hard. He has for many years been the professional (he is now an honorary member) at the Royal Mid Surrey Club at Richmond, where there are probably more rounds played in the year than on any other course except St Andrews. He has in addition a flourishing club-making factory unconnected with that club, and he has done a good deal of work as a golf architect. Yet he has found time to take interest in many things and to read many books, and, I believe, his favourite book is Boswell's *Life of Johnson*.

It strikes me as eminently characteristic of J. H. that of the illustrious four – Vardon, Braid, Taylor and Herd – he has been the first to give up playing in championships. No one of the four was keener or perhaps so keen as he was; no one of them took the game so much to heart. I am sure that he hated giving up, and as long as he played he played with all his fiery might, because he was incapable of doing anything else.

Yet, once he made up his mind that the years had become too much for him, he would have no lagging superfluous on the stage, no playing 'just for fun'; he stopped there and then and he had his reward in that the game no longer tortures him, and he is as happy as can be looking on and encouraging the younger ones. When at last he saw a Briton win our Open Championship again, I thought he would explode with happiness.

I use the words 'tortures' and 'explode' deliberately, because they are appropriate to Taylor's temperament. I do not believe that anyone, not even the great Bobby himself, suffered more over championships than he did. Like Bobby, he had great control and might appear outwardly cold, but the flames leaped up within. Vardon had a naturally gay courage, Braid a dour and stoical calm. J. H. was a man on wires, having to choke down his temper and often suffering agonies.

Now and again perhaps he could not wholly master himself. Then he would say with that shake of his head which everyone knows so well, 'He didn't beat me, sir, I beat myself, I beat myself.' On the other hand, if he had a bad time and got over it, he was neither to hold nor to bind, there was no stopping him then.

I remember one championship at Deal in 1909. He had been playing superbly in practice, but for the first nine holes or so everything went wrong. The score was piling up horribly, he was palpably at the boiling point, and I felt in watching him that not for a hundred pounds would I dare speak to him. Then on about the ninth or tenth green he holed a good putt for a three and from that moment his cares dropped from him; he came home in one long-drawn-out burst of inspiration, and remained inspired for the rest of the championship, which we won easily. It is a maxim of his that the only way to win a championship is to win it easily, and he has lived up to it, for at least three times out of his five he won by large margins.

There can hardly be a doubt that his best win of all was his fifth and last at Hoylake in 1913, and it had an even more touch-and-go start than did the one I have just mentioned at Deal. He made terribly hard work of it in the qualifying rounds and was in the gravest danger. At long last he seemed in the haven of safety, for he had only to do a five at the last hole to qualify; he had hit a fine drive and had a straightforward iron shot for the green. He half hit it, was caught in the cross-bunker, got out too far and finally had to hole a putt of fully six feet to save his neck. Down it went and those who knew him exclaimed in chorus, 'It would be just like J. H. to win the whole thing now.'

'Win' proved a most inadequate word, for he ended eight strokes ahead of Ray, who was second, and his total of 304 in sheets of rain and a tearing wind will always remain one of the outstanding feats in our championship. How he did stick his chin out and pull his cap down over his nose and bang that ball right through the gale! It was the greatest of all golfing victories of man over nature.

Taylor was always at his best on such a day of tempest as that was, not merely on account of his pugnacious turn of mind, but because of his methods. 'Flat-footed golf, sir, flat-footed golf.' Thus I have heard him several times proclaim his faith, and no man ever lived up to it better. He was as firm as a rock, as if his feet were positively entrenched, and his swing was a marvel of compactness with his elbows close in to his body throughout. It needed a strong man to play in this style and he was and is a very strong man.

No doubt he could have hit the ball farther with something more of freedom – his club never came through very far after the ball and he seemed to punch it away with a little grunt rather than swing it away with lazy grace as did Harry Vardon. It was, however, his natural method, and, if he lost something in power, he was a miracle of accuracy. The old joke that the only hazards for him were the guide-flags was well justified.

Taylor's reputation has always been that of a supreme mashie player up to the pin. He was, to be sure, extraordinarily good and accurate, and was a master of the low flying shot with backspin when the art of backspin was not perhaps so generally understood as it is now. Yet he was no better a player of this shot than was Harry Vardon; indeed, I incline to think Vardon was the better of the two.

To my mind his undeviating accuracy in full shots, whether from the tee or up to the pin, has been every bit as big an asset to him as his pitching. In the days of the gutty, when there was far more brassy play than to-day, his wooden club shots, played right up to the flag, came as something of a revelation. He was likewise a magnificent player with the cleek, and, once he is within reach of the green, he is almost as accurate now though not quite so long, as ever he was.

As a putter he was eminently sound without being brilliant. He was not in the class of great putters with, let us say, Bobby Jones or Hagen; he did not hole a great many long putts, but he could be relied on to lay the ball dead and he did not miss it when it was dead. Vardon and Braid had their bad days on the green; Taylor was always there or thereabouts.

Finally, in J. H. and his illustrious contemporaries we have to salute men who raised the whole status of their profession in their own country. When they first made their appearance, the professional golfer here was apt to be a rather shiftless, feckless person – a pleasant enough fellow, but living from hand to mouth and not always to be relied upon. That he is to-day a respected and self-respecting, prosperous member of society is largely due to the generation of professionals which arose in the early nineties with J. H. as their natural born leader.

From *Playing the Like* by Bernard Darwin
(Chapman and Hall, London, 1934).

James Braid

James Braid (1870–1950) won the British Open five times, in 1901, 1905, 1906, 1908 and 1910. Renowned for the 'divine fury' of his drives, he was not always a long-hitter. 'It was as if I went to bed a short-driver one night and got up a long-driver in the morning . . . the greatest golfing mystery I have ever come across,' he once recalled. Professional at Walton Heath for forty-five years, he was also a golf architect of repute, designing or restyling Gleneagles, Carnoustie, Royal Blackheath and Forfar among other courses.

I.W.

It has been said of some celebrated person – perhaps of several of them – that nobody could be so wise as So-and-so looks. As regards golfers, I feel inclined to transpose the aphorism and say that nobody could look so wise as James Braid is. There is nobody whose every word and action is so redolent of sagacity. He has a great twinkle of humour, too, humour such as the Scots call 'pawky,' and many other admirable qualities, but one thinks of him first and foremost as a man of extraordinarily cool, wise judgment.

Certainly no man ever played golf with a cooler head, though I have heard him say that he liked to feel just a wee bit nervous before starting. Oddly enough, he combined with this quality a power of hitting at the ball with an almost reckless abandon as if he meant to kill it. He would march along the course with a long, slow, almost sleepy stride, and then, when he came to the ball, he would lash at it with what Mr Horace Hutchinson well called a 'divine fury'; and indeed, though one must write of his triumphs in the past tense, he can still do so.

He was a superb iron player, famous especially with the now departed cleek, a master of every kind of running shot, and though not naturally a good putter, he made himself for one period of his career almost a great one. A better player out of difficulties I am sure was never seen, for not only could he by pure strength remove tons of sand and acres of heather, but he was as skilful and resourceful as he was strong. In fact at his best, he was almost impregnably armed at all points, but it was his driving that delighted people when he first appeared, and it is still his driving, more especially against the wind, that they remember best. It was at once so appalling in its ferocity, so rhythmical in its majesty.

Braid may almost be said to have inherited long-driving, since he was a cousin of Douglas Rolland who came, like him, from Elie in Fife, and was the legendary long-driver of the eighties and early nineties. He himself has given to the world the mysterious piece of natural history that he went to bed one night a short-driver and woke up next morning a long one. We must take his word for it, but I never heard of anyone who remembered him as a short-driver, and he assuredly was a long one, when, with something of the suddenness of a meteor, he flashed upon the golfing world about 1895.

Everybody thinks of him now as one of the famous three – Braid, Vardon and Taylor, who were known as the 'triumvirate' and for years almost monopolized the Open Championship. But we are apt to forget that in point of fame though not of age (he was born in 1870), he began a little later than they did. He started life as a joiner, first at Elie, then at St Andrews and at Edinburgh, and was working at his trade while Vardon and Taylor were already budding professionals. Braid's own desire was always for golf, but his family thought nothing of it as a career and so he worked away as a joiner and played his golf when he had time as an amateur, and a very good amateur, too, at St Andrews or on the Braid Hills course, near Edinburgh.

It was almost at the end of 1893, the year before Taylor won his first championship, that Braid crossed the Rubicon and became a club-maker. The manner of his doing so was rather odd. A friend of his, C. R. Smith, was a club-maker at the Army and Navy Stores in London. He wanted help and offered Braid the job, and Braid accepted it, though he had never in all his life made a club. His trade had taught him, however, all about the use of tools, and he had golf in his blood, so all was well.

Even so, he had very little time for playing, and I well remember, when I was an undergraduate at Cambridge, hearing rumours that there was a wonderful golfer (name to me unknown) at the Stores, who would do terrific things if he could only get the chance.

The chance was bound to come and it actually came in 1895, in the form of an exhibition match which somebody got up between Braid and Taylor, then reigning champion, on a suburban course. After a great struggle the match was halved, the newcomer's fame was established straightway, and he became not only a regular professional, but one of those at the top of the tree.

Braid was second in the championship of 1897, beaten by Mr Hilton by a single stroke, but he did not win till 1901 (at Muirfield), the last year before the coming of the rubber-cored ball. It always seemed strange that of his five championships, Braid won only one with the gutty ball, for there was surely no one better calculated to fog that comparatively unresponsive and stony-hearted ball. I remember that a good many years after the coming of the Haskell there was staged an exhibition between Vardon, Taylor, Braid and Duncan in which one side played with the gutty and one with the rubber core. Braid's play with the gutty that day was something to remember, and one had the impression that if that ball could be restored, there would never be any other champion but he.

How, then, was it that he did not really come into his kingdom till the rubber core was established? I think the answer can be given in a single word – putting. Braid's putting was for several years almost the despair of his supporters. I recollect that the first time I ever saw him was in the late nineties, when I went down with a friend to Romford to match our best ball against his. Up to the green he was overpowering, but I am almost sure we won one round because of those putts, and Braid remarked, more in sorrow than in anger, that he had putted 'like an auld sweetie wife.'

In those days he putted with a cleek and had a great deal of that 'knuckling' movement of the knees, as it was called, which then marked the caddie-bred putter. It tended to a movement of the body and a pushing out of the ball and had nothing whatever to recommend it. Braid toiled away at his putting with but varying success, and I think it was when he got to Walton Heath and played with that fine putter, Mr Herbert Fowler, that he really improved. He took to an aluminium club, he curbed that 'knuckling' and developed a smooth movement with a noticeably slow take-back of the club.

Putting never looked as if it came quite naturally and easily to him, but – artificial or no – he undoubtedly became a highly effective putter and, if he remained just a little vulnerable over the short ones, he holed the most inordinate number of middle length and downright long ones. The putts won championships for him, and once he started he did win them with a vengeance.

I said he won in 1901. In 1904, for the third time in his career, he had a putt to tie and did not hole it. Then at St Andrews in 1905 he won for the second time, despite some desperate adventures at both the fifteenth and sixteenth holes, where he put his ball on the railway line (not then out of bounds) and had to batter it back to the course from amongst metals and sleepers. Now that he was fairly started he won again in 1906, 1908 and 1910.

At the same time he made a not infrequent practice of winning the *News of the World*, the unofficial match-play championship, and it may be said that from 1905 to 1910 he ruled the roost. Of all his wins that in 1908 at Prestwick was the most impressive. Not only did he hole the four rounds in 291 – magnificent scoring – and win by eight clear strokes, but in the third round he took eight to the third hole, the dreaded Cardinal.

Never shall I forget the ghastly silence that reigned as he tried to get out of the big bunker with his mashie and twice in succession the ball glanced off the boarded face and went out of bounds into the burn. Neither shall I forget, when at last he got clear, the utter impassivity alike of countenance and of gait with which he advanced towards the green. Those that awaited him there had not a guess that anything untoward had happened.

It was much argued at the time whether first of all Braid ought to have played short of the big bunker, and second whether he ought to have been content to get out and no more with his niblick. Perhaps he ought, but despite all his coolness and dourness Braid was always a bold player and went out unhesitatingly for the big shot. Sometimes he got into trouble, for he had not quite the machine-like accuracy of Vardon and Taylor and could at rare intervals hit a devastating hook. In a sense one of the greatest compliments I ever heard paid him was by an illustrious contemporary, who said that he ought to have won more than he did and that the hook was responsible.

Well, he won a very great deal and, moreover, there never was such a recoverer. A friend of mine once took a charming lady to Walton Heath to play a foursome with Braid as her partner. At hole after hole she toppled the ball off the tee into heather and Braid with terrific blows of the niblick put her ball far down the course. At last came a lie too much even for him. He removed the greater part of a young tree, but the ball moved only a few yards – nobody else could have moved it at all. Then said the lady with a sweet smile, 'Oh, Mr Braid, I am glad to see that even you can make a mistake sometimes!'

After 1910 Braid won no more championships, partly, I think, because his eyesight troubled him, but he remained a great player not only up to the war but after it. He reached the final of the *News of the World* Tournament when well on in his fifties, and even to-day, when he accepts the inevitable gliding of the years with entire placidity, he is perfectly capable of a sixty-nine or so in a friendly round at Walton Heath. At that noble course he has now been the professional for some thirty years, and reigns there an undisturbed monarch.

If all monarchs had been as sage and suave, as imperturbable and as far-seeing as he is, what a lot of crowned heads there would be in the world to-day! He has done much work as a golfing architect, and, though the kindliest of men, is rather ruthless in the matter of bunkers. His old friend, J. H. Taylor, once got into one of Braid's creations at Prestwick and remarked that the man who made that bunker ought to be buried in it with a niblick through his heart.

Alone of our great professionals, Braid has never visited the United States, having, I believe, a well-grounded apprehension of sea voyages. I am afraid he never will now, and if it is his loss it is also America's. Every American golfer who comes here should make a pilgrimage to Walton Heath to see this monument of a man.

From *Playing the Like* by Bernard Darwin
(Chapman and Hall, London, 1934).

Sam Snead's legendary career spanned five decades. Here he gets in some practice at Wentworth for the 1956 Canadian Cup watched by 12-year-old son Jackie. (*Keystone Collection*)

Harry Vardon did not believe in the straight left arm, and with the cumbersome jackets worn in those days it must have been difficult to achieve. But his results spoke for themselves. (*Keystone Collection*)

James Braid is well-jacketed, as was the custom of the day. Braid drives off at Walton Heath in the professional golfers' tournament in 1927. (*The Photo Source*)

At 86, J. H. Taylor had lost none of his appetite for demonstrating the game. On the extreme left, George Duncan, and next to him, the Open Champion Alf Padgham. (*Keystone Collection*)

Walter Hagen, otherwise known as 'the Haig', four times winner of the British Open, twice winner of the US Open and five times winner of the USPGA. The flamboyant Haig dominated professional golf after the First World War. (*Topham Picture Library*)

Bobby Jones, majestic, graceful, the true amateur, here drives off in the Walker Cup at Sandwich. (*The Photo Source*)

Ben Hogan survived a near-fatal car crash and came back greater than ever to win his only British Open at Carnoustie where he is pictured driving at the second tee. (*The Photo Source*)

Henry Cotton in 1985.
(*Peter Dazeley*)

Cotton in his younger years
(this is a 1938 picture) was
ruggedly handsome. Ian
Fleming said he was the
physical prototype for James
Bond. (*Popperfoto*)

Henry Longhurst as commentator. 'He looks like W.C. Fields in drag. But he happens to be the best in the business,' said a CBS producer. *Below:* The tricky 16th at Augusta. The hole that Henry made his own as a commentator. (*Peter Dazeley*)

4

THE IMMORTAL BOBBY AND THE INDOMITABLE BEN

Bobby Jones

Bernard Darwin

Nerves are an inseparable part of golf at the top level. Without them you are nothing and with them you are nothing until you learn to play through them. Nobody had a more nervous temperament than Bobby Jones, one of the truly heroic figures of the game from the Golden Age of golf in the 1920s – four times winner of the US Open and three times winner of the British Open, the last in 1930. That was his greatest year when he brought off what was then called the Grand Slam or Impregnable Quadrilateral, winning the American and British Open and Amateur Championships. He was still only twenty-eight but found the strain so great that he gave up competitive golf. He played big-time golf only once again, in 1934, the opening year of the Augusta National Invitation Meeting, later, of course, to be known as the Masters. He returned a respectable 294. The Augusta Club was the brainchild of Bobby and his friend Clifford Roberts. Stricken by a disease that confined him to a wheelchair, Bobby died in 1971. Here a master writer, Bernard Darwin, who elevated golf writing to the level of literature (as well as being good enough to win in the Walker Cup of 1922), looks at the nervous tribulations of a master golfer who learned to tame his wilder habits like club-throwing but who could still lose a stone in weight during a championship.

I.W.

As far as the United States is concerned the Bobby Jones era began, I suppose, in 1916 when at the age of fourteen-and-a-half he reached the third round of the American National Championship at Merion and went down after a hard match before an ex-champion, Robert Gardner. From this time onward till he retired full of honours if not of years, he was a great figure in American golf. For us, however, his era began somewhat later, since he came here first in 1922 and did not show us his full powers till 1926 when he had reached the immense age of twenty-four. He then won our Open Championship for the first time and perhaps this is the best place to set out his record in the barest and briefest outline. In his own country he won the Open Championship four times (he also tied for it twice and lost the play-off) and the Amateur Championship five times. Here he won one Amateur and three Open Championships. In 1930 he established what has been picturesquely called 'the impregnable quadrilateral' by winning the Open and Amateur Championships of both countries in a single summer. He played against Britain in six International Matches, five of them for the Walker Cup; he won his single every time, sometimes by immense margins, and he won his foursome five times and lost once by a single hole.

Bobby's first appearance here was in the International Match preceding the Amateur Championship at Hoylake in 1921. He won both his single and his foursome handsomely, and impressed everybody, as he could not fail to do. Then came anti-climax. His career in the Amateur Championship was short and rather chequered. He began well enough against a good Scottish player, Mr Manford, and there followed that rather farcical encounter with Mr Hamlet of Wrexham. Whatever he might be at Wrexham it is pardonable to say that Mr Hamlet was not of the stature to face Hoylake, even though it was made less formidably long than usual by the hard ground. Yet with the match all square going to the Royal, which is the seventeenth, it really seemed as if he were going to beat Bobby, which, as Euclid might remark, would have been absurd. This was not due to any great golf of his but to a sort of general futility and paralysis on the greens on Bobby's part. However, the crisis passed, Bobby scrambled through with a score nearer ninety than eighty and proceeded to play devastatingly well in his next match against Mr Robert Harris. He had got his bad round over, he was going to win – and then he relapsed again and was beaten by many holes by Mr Allan Graham. There was a chance of redeeming himself in the Open at St Andrews but all went ill; he felt a puzzled hatred for the links which he came afterwards to love and at the eleventh hole in the third round he picked up his ball. Legend declares that he relieved his feelings by teeing it up and driving it far out into the Eden. If he did it was a gesture deserving of sympathy, and if he did not I am very sure he wanted to.

In 1921, at the age of nineteen, Bobby was already a magnificent golfer, as great a hitter of the ball though not as great a player of matches or medal rounds as he ever was. Several years before Mr Walter Travis had said he could never improve his strokes, and that was true enough; there was, humanly speaking, no room for improvement; it was simply a matter of stringing them together more successfully. There could be no more fascinating player to watch not only for the free and rhythmic character of his swing but for the swiftness with which he played. He had as brief a preliminary address as Duncan himself, but there was nothing hurried or slapdash about it and the swing itself, if not positively slow, had a certain drowsy beauty which gave the feeling of slowness. There was nothing that could conceivably be called a weak spot. The utmost that could be said – and this may be a purely personal impression – was that he did not seem quite so supremely happy with a mashie-niblick as when playing approaches with longer irons.

People liked Bobby at once, and that not only for his natural pleasantness of manner; they discerned in him a very human quality; he was no cold machine but took his game very much to heart as did humbler people. In his almost infantile days he had been inclined to throw his clubs about. This we were told since the American Press had once emphasised it rather unkindly; otherwise we should never have guessed it, for he had already tamed his naturally fiery temperament into betraying no outward signs. Those indeed how knew him well professed to know the symptoms which showed the flames leaping up within. I remember once watching him at an Open Championship, it may have been at St Anne's, in company with that fine American golfer, the late Mr J. G. Anderson; Bobby missed a shortish putt and 'Now, he's mad,' said my companion. I could detect nothing, but doubtless Mr Anderson knew his man and Bobby did hate missing a shot. Perhaps that was why he missed so few, for in the end that highly-strung nervous temperament, if it had never been his master, became his invaluable servant. In his most youthful and tempestuous days he had never been angry with his opponent and not often, I think, with Fate, but he had been furiously angry with himself. He set himself an almost impossibly high standard; he thought it an act of incredible folly if not a positive crime to make a stroke that was not exactly as it ought to be made and as he knew he could make it. If he ever derogated from that standard he may even in his most mature days have been 'mad' in the recesses of his heart, but he became outwardly a man of ice, with the very best of golfing manners.

How much other people have suffered over their golf we do not always know; the light of fame has not beaten on them so fiercely. Of Bobby we do know that he suffered greatly. How he could scarcely eat anything till the day's play was over; how on occasion he felt that he could not even button his shirt collar for fear of the direst consequences; how he could lose a stone in weight during a championship; how he was capable of breaking down to the point of tears not from any distress but from pure emotional overstrain – these things are now well known and may be found in Mr O. B. Keeler's admirable and Boswellian pages. No doubt his capacity for an emotional outlet was at that time a relief and a help to him, but there must be a limit. I was in his company soon after he had finished his fourth round when he won the last of his three Open Championships here in 1930, and seeing him nearly past speech I thought that the time had come for him to call a halt and that his game could not much longer be worth such an agonising candle. He had great courage and ambition, and these not only pulled him through but probably made him a more successful player than he would have been had he been gifted with a more placid temperament. There is much to be said for the stolid, phlegmatic player, but the great golfers have never had what I once heard Jack White call a dead nerve. It is worth remembering that James Braid, most rock-like and apparently impassive of men, has said that he 'liked to be a wee bit nervous' before a big game. The steady-going and unimaginative will often beat the more eager champion and they will get very near the top, but there, I think, they will stop. The prose labourer must yield to the poet and Bobby as a golfer had a strain of poetry in him. He stands for ever as the greatest encourager of the highly-strung player who is bent on conquering himself.

In 1926 we saw Bobby on his second visit. Four years had passed since he had been here before and he had now, as the Americans called it, 'broken through'; the lean years were over. In 1923 he had won the American Open after a tie with Cruikshank, thus emulating Mr Hilton here in winning the Open before the Amateur. In the following year he had put this to rights by winning the Amateur with triumphant ease and had been runner-up in the Open. In 1925 he had won the Amateur again and had tied in the Open, to lose rather surprisingly after a protracted play-off with Willie Macfarlane. He was in the plenitude of his powers and who should stand before him? And yet there was a moment when it seemed as if his second visit, like his first, would end in disappointment. All went swimmingly in the Amateur Championship at Muirfield till he reached the fifth round and then out he went and that with a resounding crash, for he was well and truly beaten by Mr Andrew Jamieson who was then hardly known outside Scotland. I believe that Bobby woke with a stiff neck that morning though he was most anxious to conceal it. Certainly he seemed to lack something of his usual ease, but Jamieson, a very neat, unobtrusive, efficient golfer, did play uncommonly well, well enough to beat anybody if anybody gave him, as Bobby did, the very slightest opening. What was more, having got away with a lead he never grew frightened of it but played with victorious confidence. I saw only odd holes of the match but I remember one vividly. This was the short thirteenth called 'The Postage Stamp', though whether it or the hole at Troon has the prior right to the title I do not know. The hole as it then was, had a long narrow green with a drop to perdition on the right, and on the left a high rough bank. Jamieson, with victory firmly in his grasp, if he could keep steady, had the honour and he made a slip; he hooked his tee-shot and the ball lighted on the top of the left-hand bank. Would it stay there? It hovered for a moment and then, audibly encouraged by the crowd, began to topple downward by stages, almost coming to rest and then moving on again till at last it ended its rather nefarious career on the green. That was the final blow and Jamieson, having had his little bit of luck, went on to win calmly and easily by 4 and 3.

Mrs Gamp has remarked how little we know 'what lays before us'. If Bobby had won that championship he has said that he would have sailed straight for home after the Walker Cup match. As it was he decided to give himself another chance in the Open at St Anne's. So, after duly doing his deadly stuff at St Andrews in the Walker Cup – he beat Cyril Tolley by 12 and 11 – he went to Sunningdale for the qualifying rounds of the Open and proceeded to play there what was by common consent as nearly flawless a round as ever had been played. He went round in 66 and he may be said to have holed only one putt worthy of mention, one of eight yards or so for a three on the fifth. Otherwise if he missed nothing short – and there were one or two putts missed to be called shortish – he holed nothing that could conceivably be called long. He simply went on and on with exact perfection. There was indeed one slip, an iron shot pushed out into a bunker at the short thirteenth, but it cost the player nothing since he chipped the ball out dead. It probably brought relief to him as it did to the spectators, who had been feeling that they must scream if perfection endured much longer. It was Mr Keeler, I think, who once wrote, 'They wound up the mechanical man of golf yesterday and set him clicking round the East Lake course.' All great golfers at their best are more or less mechanical, for they do the same thing over and over again, but I doubt if any of them save perhaps one has given quite such an impression of well-oiled, impeccable machinery as Bobby did from tee to green. The notions of beauty and machinery do not go well together; the word 'clicking' may suggest something done 'by numbers' and so far it is inappropriate; but Mr Keeler's was nevertheless an apt and memorable phrase. Harry Vardon and Bobby Jones combined exquisiteness of art with utterly relentless precision in a way not quite given to any other golfers.

Few joys in this world are unalloyed, and though Bobby was naturally and humanly pleased with that 66 he was a trifle worried because he had 'reached the peak' rather too soon before going to St Anne's. His second round of 68, with, if I remember, one innocuous misunderstanding with a tree, did nothing to reassure him on this point and he was so far right that, though he won at St Anne's, his play there was not quite of the same unrippled smoothness as at Sunningdale. The game was by contrast 'aye fechtin'' against him and he had to work hard for his scores. That was as exciting a championship as any between the wars, save only for this, that from the very start it seemed that no Briton was likely to win it. Mitchell ended fifth but he only accomplished so much by two very fine rounds on the last day; as far as winning was concerned he had put himself out of court by beginning with two 78s. So to the narrowly patriotic this championship was merely a brilliant, alien exhibition contest.

The invaders went off with a bang: Hagen had a 68 and the powerful, broad-backed, rough-hewn Mehlhorn, said to have graduated as hod-carrier to the champion bricklayer of America, had a 70. Then came McLeod, an expatriated Scot, and Al Watrous with 71 and then Bobby in the position he liked, lying well up but not prematurely leading, with a 72. It was a good round but he had to fight for it, since at each one of the last four holes he made some sort of a slip and had, in Mr Laidlay's phrase, to 'trust to a pitch and a putt' to get his four. In the second round Hagen had a compensating and disastrous 77 and at the end of it Mehlhorn with 70 and 74 and Bobby with two 72s led the field. Watrous, 71 and 75, was two shots behind them.

On the last day Bobby and Watrous were drawn together, and as it turned out this chance involved just such a strain on them and just such a terrific duel for first place as Vardon and Taylor had endured at Prestwick ten years earlier. Watrous was a very good player who had left no very distinct image on my mind; he had no tremendous power, but he had all the American virtue of smoothness and rhythm and he was a very fine putter, bang on his putting. Bobby was two strokes ahead when they set out and he had a 73 in a good fresh wind, but Watrous playing perfectly had a 69 and so – again this brought back memories of Vardon and Taylor – turned the deficit of two into a lead of two. Hagen took 74 and Mehlhorn began to fade. So the battle was to be fought out between these two and they were fully conscious of it as they went back to their hotel together, lunched together and even lay down to rest in the same room – a pleasant picture of friendly rivalry.

When it was all over and Mr Topping, who had been in charge of this couple, gave away the prizes he declared that Bobby had made but one remark to him in the course of the last round, 'My golf is terrible.' In fact it was terribly good except in one important respect; he was taking too many putts. By his own account he took thirty-nine of them and what he gained on Watrous in length he certainly threw away on the greens. The short ninth which had consistently bothered him beat him again

and he was still two down with five to play; in what was in effect a match the language
of match play may be used. Then at last the strokes came back one at a time and the
pair were all square with three to play. At the seventeenth came Bobby's historic
second, which I must presently describe yet again, but before that on the sixteenth
came an incident of which a friend has lately reminded me; it gives force to the
ruthless doctrine that someone ought to murder a photographer *pour encourager les
autres*. Watrous had played his second to the green and Bobby had got half-way up
with some pitching club when a fiend with a camera stepped out and tried to snap
him. Bobby stopped and began again, and again the photographer tried. This time he
was metaphorically lynched; he was shooed out of the way, and Bobby, by a
considerable display of control, pitched safely to the green and the hole was halved in
four.

Now for the seventeenth, a hole a little over 400 yards in length. The course of the
hole bends to the left and the line is well out to the right, in order to get a clear view of
the hole and avoid the sandhills guarding the left-hand side of the green. Nor is that
the only reason for keeping to the right, for on the left of the fairway is a wilderness of
sandy, scrubby country dotted here and there with bunkers. Bobby with the honour,
drew his tee-shot, not badly but badly enough to be obviously in some form of
trouble; Watrous went straight and playing the odd reached the green; he was some
way from the hole but he was on the green and that looked good enough. Bobby's ball
lay in a shallow bunker and it lay clean, but he was 170 yards or more from the flag
and between him and it were the sandhills. He took what I think he called his
mashie-iron (it now reposes a sacred relic in the St Anne's Club) and hit the ball
perfectly clean, playing it somewhat out into the wind so that it came in to finish on
the green and nearer the hole than his opponent. Admittedly the ball lay as clean as
clean could be and this was the kind of shot that he might very well have played in a
practice game, but in the circumstances, when a teaspoonful too much sand might
have meant irretrievable ruin, it was a staggering shot, and it staggered poor Al
Watrous. He took three putts, Bobby got down in two and everybody felt that that
shot had settled it. Watrous was bunkered at the home hole, Bobby nearly bunkered
but not quite; he got a four against a five and finished in 74 against 78, 291 against 293.

There still remained Hagen and George Von Elm, both of whom were rumoured
to be doing well. Hagen arrived on the last tee wanting a four for 74 and a two to tie.
He could doubtless have tied for second place with Watrous but Hagen was never
interested in second prizes. After a fine drive, he walked some way forward and then
with a characteristic gesture had the flag taken out. His ball very nearly pitched into
the hole and ran on into the bunker behind the green. *Aut Caesar*, etc. His effort had
failed and he took four more to get down, so that Von Elm coming with a wet sheet
and a 72 tied with him for third place. Let me add as a postscript that the Council of
the Royal Lytham and St Anne's Club have now decided to mark, as far as it can
exactly be done, the spot at the seventeenth from which Bobby played his shot. This
is a precedent that could not often be followed, but here the geographical conditions
are favourable and if now and then someone has to lift a drop from behind the
monument he will do so in a reverent rather than an exasperated spirit.

I have written at perhaps excessive length about the St Anne's Championship both because it was Bobby's first and because it was so dramatic. When he came back next year to defend his title at St Andrews, having in the meanwhile won the American Open at Scioto, he played unquestionably better; he enjoyed the greatest single triumph he ever had here, but there seems much less to say about it, for the reason that it was 'his' championship, he was winning all the while. By this time St Andrews had taken a thorough hold on him. He was amused by its problems; he knew whereabouts were its hidden bunkers and was not annoyed by them, as some people never cease to be, because they are hidden; he has devised some three different ways of playing the Long Hole In according to the wind; he had realised that for a player of his parts the Road Hole need hold no excessive terrors, unless he is over-ambitious. In short he had proved the truth of Mrs Malaprop's saying that, ' 'Tis safest in matrimony to begin with a little aversion,' for he was now thoroughly in love with the Old Course and played it as if he loved it.

Bobby's four rounds were 68, 72, 73 and 72 and he led from the start. I do not know that he played any better for his 68 than in any of the other three rounds; it was simply that everything came off for him, as for example a putt holed for three at the Hole o' Cross going out. It is by far the biggest green in the world and if this was not the longest putt ever holed it must have been very nearly so. Mr Keeler's brow was a little knitted, for he was not sure how his man would like to be 'in the lead' straight away instead of lying a stroke or two behind, but the general impression was that there would be no holding Bobby. After two rounds he only led Hodson by two strokes, but good player as Hodson was he could scarcely hope to give the leader two strokes; in fact the third round destroyed him as far as winning was concerned and those who were more likely to hold on were several shots further behind. At the end of the third round Bobby led Fred Robson, who had just done a splendid 69, by four shots and Aubrey Boomer by six, and it was for him to set the pace.

Only at the beginning of the last round was there a moment's doubt, for Bobby frittered away a couple of shots in the first four holes, and so with an orthodox five at the fifth his score was three over fours – a definitely vulnerable start. At that point I left him to look at other people, meaning to pick him up again at the thirteenth on the way home. Some bursts of clapping from the neighbourhood of the 'loop' suggested that he was doing well, but how well no one of us waiting on the big double green knew. The advance guard of his crowd came towards us, in the van one who trotted briskly, as if big with news to impart. I have a well-grounded distrust of spectators' tales but this one looked a man of good counsel, sober and unimaginative; so I button-holed him and asked his tidings. When he said that Bobby was now two under fours I thought he was only the usual liar, but what he said was true, for Bobby had done the holes from the sixth to the twelfth in twenty-four shots. After that the round was a triumphal procession. His second to the last hole was a little cautious and ended in the Valley of Sin. Thence he ran it up dead and as he scaled the bank the crowd stormed up after him and lined the edge of the green, barely restraining themselves. He holed his short one and the next instant there was no green visible, only a dark seething mass, in the midst of which was Bobby hoisted on fervent shoulders and holding his putter, 'Calamity Jane', at arm's length over his head lest she be crushed to death. Calamity Jane had two pieces of whipping bound round her shaft where she had been broken, not we may trust in anger but by some mischance. When some years later the market was flooded with exact models of her, each of them duly bore two superfluous black bands. Did ever imitation pay sincerer flattery than that?

Only once more, in 1930, were we destined to see Bobby here in battle array, though he has returned once since his retirement and in playing a friendly round of the Old Course took the major part of St Andrews round with him. It was at St Andrews in 1930, the year of the 'impregnable quadrilateral', that he realised almost his last unachieved ambition and won our Amateur Championship. He did not win it without his bad moments, for he had never concealed his dislike of eighteen-hole matches. In the American Championship the first two rounds, which were of eighteen holes only, had at least once brought him to grief and he had had, in the words of old Beldham the cricketer, 'many an all but'. Once safely through them and in the haven of thirty-six holes, where he felt that he had space to manoeuvre, he had crushed his men one after the other by murderous margins. Thus in our championship he could never feel really at ease until in the final and he had never yet reached the final. He set out on the enterprise strung up to a high pitch and no one who saw the beginning of his match against a good Nottinghamshire golfer, Mr Roper, will forget it. On the first green he holed a long putt for a three, the ball going in with an almost suspicious rattle against the back of the tin. Bobby looked a little apologetic and made several little practice movements of his club. I remember Mr Hilton whispering to me that he was trying to get the swing of his putter smooth; that first putt, successful as it was, had shown signs of tension. After a four at the second he holed another and shorter putt for a three at the Cartgate and then at the fourth hit a very long tee-shot rather to the left into the Cottage bunker. Thence, a culminating atrocity, he holed out, a full shot of 150 yards or so, with some sort of iron, for a two.

After this astonishing display Bobby became comparatively quiescent and had to struggle as hard to get through as many less gifted players have done. Two of his most close-run things were against compatriots, Mr Harrison Johnston and Mr George Voigt. Mr Johnston, after being several holes down, chased him to the last gasp and Mr Voigt, if I may permit myself an 'if', ought to have beaten him. Bobby was obviously struggling and when Mr Voigt, very cool and steady and putting beautifully, stood two up with five to go, he looked like a winner. And then he committed what the onlooker, who has nothing to do but criticise, felt inclined to call a gratuitous folly. With the broad space of the Elysian Fields to drive into he cut his tee-shot over the wall and out of bounds. It was a heaven-sent reprieve; Bobby took it and fought his way home to win by a hole.

Yet even this paled before his battle with Cyril Tolley. Every man, woman and child in St Andrews went out to watch it, and Mr Gerard Fairlie was quite right to set the scene of the murder in one of his stories on the afternoon of that match. There would have been ample opportunity to commit several murders and escape undetected through the lonely streets, though stained with the marks of crime. Never was there more perceptible the silence of expectation, that lull before the storm in which men speak instinctively in whispers, and Cyril gave it, if possible, a more thrilling emphasis, since he began with a full-blooded top from the first tee. It was ominous but it was no presage of disaster for he played finely afterwards and a dog-fight on a magnificent scale ensued, which delighted everyone save other poor wretches who were trying to play their own insignificant matches. Each man seeing the mighty flood approach him must needs crouch over his ball guarding it as best he might and pick himself up again when the torrent has swept over him. The most discussed shot in the match was Bobby's second to the Road Hole, as to which hundreds are prepared to take their oath that the ball would have been on the road if it had not hit a spectator and an equal number of witnesses are quite certain that it would not. I was there but was running for my life with my head well down at the moment and can offer no opinion. The hole was halved; so was the last and Bobby won at the nineteenth, where his adversary played a rather loose second and was punished by a stymie. Exactly how good the golf was I cannot now remember for there are occasions when that is of secondary importance. It was the devil of a match.

At last Bobby was in the final – against Mr Wethered; his chance had come and he did not mean to waste it; he was on his favourite long trail of thirty-six holes. At the very first hole a shudder of surprise went through the crowd as he entirely missed his pitch and stayed short of the burn, but from there he chipped dead and got his four; nor did he ever exceed that figure till he put his second into the Road bunker at the seventeenth. I can see him very clearly now, as the stewards are moving away the crowd at the back of the green. He is gently smiling a protest to the effect that he does not mean to go on to the road. In fact his explosion shot gave him quite a good chance of a four but the putt did not drop; there was to be no fiveless round for him. His opponent fought manfully but without avail and Bobby won by 7 and 6.

Now for the last lap, the Open at Hoylake, which was won in the end as had been that at St Anne's by sheer, hard fighting. As at St Andrews Bobby jumped away with the lead with a 70 which was equalled by Macdonald Smith. He added a 72 while Mac Smith took 77 and his nearest pursuer was now Fred Robson with 143. The third round was sound enough, 74, but meanwhile another British hope had arisen. Compston, who had begun with 74 and 73, added to these a tremendous 68 and led Bobby by a stroke. Diegel was not far behind with a 71, giving him a total of 228; but Diegel, though having an astonishing game in him, has been in championships one of those unfortunates who can never quite do it. He has said bitterly himself that however hard the other fellows try to give it him he will not take it. This may be partly due to his highly artificial method of putting, 'contorted almost to anguish', as was written of a fine putter of a much older generation.

Such styles are always apt to break down under strain, and apart from this Diegel was cursed with a temperament the most highly strung possible. Walter Hagen, once sitting up cheerfully late before a final against Diegel, was told in a tone of mild reproach that his adversary had been in bed for hours. 'Ah,' said Hagen, 'but he's not asleep.' I have seen Diegel, as 'crazy' as ever was Duncan, and as brilliant as anyone I ever did see, but somehow he did not quite seem the man to stop Bobby, and in any case it was with Compston that were all British hearts.

I went out to see him play the first hole in the last round. His drive was perfect; his iron shot inadequate, to the edge of the green, and he took three putts. One five meant nothing to be sure but there came other fives and the final 82 was heart-breaking. So out again in search of Bobby. All went if not perfectly according to plan at least reasonably well until he came to the eighth or Far Hole, which measures according to the books 527 yards, two shots and a pitch for Bobby in ordinary conditions with the ground fairly fast. The two shots were entirely satisfactory but the pitch was weak and the ball rolled back from the plateau; the next was nothing to boast of and at the last he missed a shortish putt; result, a horrid seven without touching a bunker. As Ben Sayers might have said, 'It was no possible but it was a fact.' The news of that seven quickly spread all over the links bringing consternation or encouragement. To Bobby himself it must have been a cruel blow but he pulled himself together and fought his way home, much, I imagine, in the frame of mind of a runner running himself blind, not seeing the tape but determined to get there. He was round in 75 and now we knew what had to be done. Compston was dead and buried; Diegel did a 75, good but not quite good enough for he had started two strokes behind. Those of us who were with him in one of the smaller rooms of the clubhouse united in assuring Bobby that all was well, as he wandered restlessly about holding a glass in two hands. And then there came a suggestion that all might not be well since Mac Smith was doing great things. To be sure he had to do a 69 to tie and that to an impartial judgment seemed very unlikely, but at such moments judgments can scarcely be impartial.

I remember very well going out to meet him. I could not go far for I had to broadcast and time was getting hideously short, but I *must* know. He holed out at the Dun taking to my jaundiced eye a very long time over it, and then we knew; two threes to tie. It was almost but not quite impossible. I saw him play the Royal – I was to broadcast from a house not far off – and his putt for three did not go in. Two to tie and that was surely impossible, but with an obstinate fidelity to duty I waited till his second had pitched on the home green and had palpably not holed out. Then I ran and ran and arrived just in time to announce in breathless tones to an expectant world that Bobby had won again.

I will not follow him home to America. He won the Open at Interlaken and the Amateur at Merion where he had played in his first championship at fourteen and won his first Amateur Championship at twenty-two. But as far as this country is concerned he departed in a blaze of glory from Hoylake.

He retired at the right time and could say with Charles Lamb, 'I have worked task work and have the rest of the day to myself.' After Tom Cribb had beaten Molineaux for the second time in the great battle of Thistleton Gap it was decided that he need never fight again but should bear the title of Champion to the end of his days. I think that most golfers in their hearts grant the same privilege to Bobby Jones.

From Golf Between Two Wars by Bernard Darwin
(Chatto and Windus, London, 1944).

Ben Hogan

Geoffrey Cousins and Tom Scott

I'll always admire a gutsy fighter. Ben Hogan overcame a near-fatal car crash in 1949 to win six more majors (out of a career total of nine). He won the Masters twice (in 1951 and 1953), the US Open four times (in 1948, 1950, 1951 and 1953) and the US PGA twice (in 1946 and 1948). But perhaps his greatest achievement was to win the British Open at Carnoustie at the first attempt in 1953. He believed that no golfer could regard himself as one of the all-time greats unless he could master a British links course. The Scots christened him 'the Wee Ice Man'. He was a perfectionist who once shot a round with half a dozen birdies – and promptly went out on to the practice ground. His friend Jimmy Demaret said: 'For Christ's sake, Ben, nobody ever played better than you today. You can't birdie every hole.' 'Why not?' demanded Hogan. He once had a dream in which he played 17 holes in one and woke up angry to have missed on the other one. At almost 5 feet 9 inches, the tough Texan was no midget, but it's proof nonetheless that size is not vital in golf – thank goodness. Here's an account of that memorable Carnoustie triumph.

I.W.

This chapter – and the 1953 Championship at Carnoustie is well worth a chapter all to itself – is not so much about the competition as about the man who won it, Ben W. Hogan from Fort Worth, Texas.

On February 2nd, 1949, Hogan was driving with his wife Valerie back home to Fort Worth when a huge bus loomed out of the fog into the path of the Hogan car. A collision was certain and Hogan threw himself in front of his wife in order to save her from the inevitable impact. In doing so, he saved her life and also his own, for in a flash his car was a heap of twisted metal and the steering wheel had been forced back into the seat he had occupied a split second before.

But his injuries were severe: a broken collarbone, a fractured ankle, a smashed rib and a broken pelvis. He was taken to hospital at El Paso, where doctors struggled for hours to save his life. Thrombosis developed, and his life was despaired of. In the end the doctors and Ben Hogan won. He lived, but the general opinion among medical men and laymen alike was that he would never play golf again. Hogan had different ideas on the subject. He did play again, and so became a legend.

The road back was long and hard. For before his accident Hogan had been a 'loner', a man not easy to understand, a man with whom even his closest friends found it hard to communicate and who liked to work out his own problems. After his accident he mellowed to some extent, but even then he kept himself to himself. There was no change in his outlook on golf; his dedication to the game became, if possible, greater than ever. His recovery from the accident was slow, very slow; there were some who thought he would lose the uphill fight, and more who thought his dream of playing golf again would never come true. Then came the electrifying news that he had entered the 1950 Los Angeles Open. In his first round he scored a 73. Then he tacked on a 69 and then another 69, and in the last round it was another 69 to tie with Snead. True, he lost the play-off, but the 'little man', the 'hawk', the 'ice man', was back in business.

His next test was the US Open. He still required treatment for his legs, but his courage and ability triumphed. He tied with George Fazio and Lloyd Mangrum, then romped home in the replay to prove to himself and to the world in general that he had regained his place as the top man in golf.

In 1951 he won the Masters and also his third US Open. The following year was not so good for him, but in 1953 he surged back and again won the Masters with a tournament record of 274, including a never-to-be-forgotten round of 66. He followed that with a sweeping win in the US Open, beating off all the opposition with apparent ease and winning by six strokes from Snead, the man who despite all his greatness was to find the national title beyond his reach.

There was only one world for Hogan to conquer – the British Open. To some of the old-timers in American golf, men like Sarazen and the great amateur Chick Evans, the British title still meant a great deal and it was such men who let it be known that if Hogan was to be the King he would have to win the British Championship. Hogan succumbed to the persuasion and decided to go to the great golf centre at Carnoustie in Angus to try to win the British crown.

As with everything that Hogan did, his preparation for the event was meticulous. He came over early, settled himself into a suite in an hotel and spent hours and hours practising on a nearby course. The only onlooker was his caddie, Cecil Timms. When Hogan did appear on the course at Carnoustie it was mostly by himself. He was closely watched by the knowing locals, who after they had seen him in action declared that there was no way he could lose the Championship – and that, from the dour Scots, was praise indeed. Seldom had they been so much impressed by a visiting golfer, and not even the fact that few men had ever succeeded in winning the title at the first time of asking deterred the Carnoustie experts from plumping for the little Texan. To them he was the epitome of golfing perfection, not because he was the best stylist they had ever seen – Hogan was no Snead in that respect – but because of the amazing accuracy of his shots. Even on the long, testing links and in the wind which blows there so often, Hogan showed a complete mastery in placing the ball. And that, thought the locals, would be the decisive factor in the Championship. How right they were. The question was whether Hogan would rise to the occasion and win what was for him 'The little slam' – the US Open, the US Masters and the British Open.

But Fate stepped in and attempted to halt the great bid that thousands of golf enthusiasts had gathered to see, for just before the event Hogan developed a feverish cold and the opening day of the Championship was wet and miserable, so the American set out swathed in sweaters. His long shots were as they had always been, as fired from a rifle, but his putting on the slow greens was no more than ordinary. A

73 went down on the card, and the man who stole the limelight was the amateur Frank Stranahan who had so nearly won at Hoylake six years before. Stranahan returned a 70. Eric Brown, much to the delight of his fellow-Scots, was only one stroke more than Stranahan and there were other strong contenders like Thomson, Rees, Locke and de Vicenzo. If Hogan was going to win it was going to be by the hard way, or so it seemed.

A second round of 74 put Stranahan out of the way, but Rees, whose favourite course is Carnoustie, produced a brilliant 70 and Brown repeated his 71 of the first round to share the lead. Hogan's round was 71 as well, so at the halfway stage he was two strokes behind.

We can forget now about Brown, who, to the great misery of his many admirers, scored 75, a figure he was to repeat in his last round. Rees had 73 third time out and de Vicenzo, the tall Argentinian, who in the last two or three years had been building up a formidable record in the Championship, moved up with a 71 to challenge Hogan who had 70. That meant de Vicenzo and Hogan were level with one round to play.

Things were shaping well for the Texan after his modest start and there wasn't a man or woman in Carnoustie that night who would not have staked their all on a Hogan victory. The others had had their chances, and thrown them away.

Hogan's cold had got no worse, but after that first round in the wet his back had been giving him some concern. And so had his putting. True, in the first round it was patchy, but after that almost any golfer would have been pleased enough with it. Not so Hogan. But in the end it was not his putting which was to play a vital part in the proceedings. It was his woods and long irons. Time and again he placed his wooden shots exactly where they should be placed, and those shots made up for any deficiency with his putter, and such deficiencies, may it be said, were few. So on he went relentlessly. He was still out on the course while those who were his challengers were finishing. They were Dai Rees, who had won the Match-Play title at Carnoustie, and who was desperately anxious to win the Open there; Peter Thomson, still chasing his first British title; the incredible Stranahan who finished with a 69, and Tony Cerda who had followed Faulkner home at Portrush. And all were on the same aggregate, 286.

It seemed too high a total to cause Hogan any grave concern for now one of the biggest-ever crowds in the history of the Championship was seeing Hogan at his thrilling best. True, on the outward journey he had twice been over par, but to counter that he had made three birdies. Only at one hole did he fail: the seventeenth, where he cut a No. 4 wood into sand. Then he three-putted and a six went down on the card. By then, however, he could afford the luxury of a six and still win by two strokes. But as it happened he finished with a flourish worthy of the occasion, a birdie 4 at the long last hole which had been the graveyard of hopes on more than one occasion at Carnoustie. His round was a 68 for a total of 282, four strokes ahead. The quality of his golf throughout can be judged from the fact that his aggregate was eight strokes better than Cotton's total in 1937 and fourteen strokes better than Armour's in 1931. In fairness to Cotton, however, it must be said that in his Championship on the great links the weather conditions were deplorable.

Still, Hogan's feat in winning at the first time of asking was something for every golf enthusiast who saw it to cherish for the rest of his days. He had won as he had set out to do, and the only regret was that he was not to play in the Open again. British spectators were, however, to see him show his brilliance once more, when along with Snead he won the Canada Cup for the United States at Wentworth in 1956.

On returning to the United States after his victory at Carnoustie Hogan was accorded, just as Bob Jones had been accorded, a hero's welcome in New York, when the ticker tape showered down on to his car. And after, as he stood on the steps of New York's City Hall, the man of iron all but broke down with emotion. 'I owe it all,' he said, 'to God and my wife, Valerie.'

Carnoustie was the climax of his greatest year. He was still to be in the limelight in several big events, and he so nearly won the US Open and the US Masters once again. He narrowly failed, but what did it matter? He had been acknowledged to be the greatest golfer of all time in the eyes of many. A film, *Follow the Sun*, had been made of his life, honours were showered on him, and he continued to make appearances in Championships and leading events for a long time afterwards. Wherever he appeared the crowds flocked to see him, and to enjoy some of the magic that was still his.

The legend of Hogan still lives on. There will always be arguments as to whether he was greater than Vardon or Nelson or Palmer, but the American golf writers at least had no doubt as to his stature in the game. In 1965 they voted him the greatest professional golfer of all time.

One thing is certain – Hogan in his era was the undisputed king of the links.

From *A Century of Opens* by Geoffrey Cousins and
Tom Scott
(Frederick Muller, London, 1971).

The answer to Hogan is, I fancy, that if Hogan means to win, you lose.
Henry Longhurst in 1953.

Hogan came as near to dehumanising golf as anyone ever has done.
Pat Ward-Thomas.

5

HENRY THE GREAT

Banned from Cricket – So I Take Up Golf

Henry Cotton

Many successful golfers will acknowledge the debt they owe to their father – I know I do; not for bequeathing me his swing (though it isn't a bad one) but because he gave me encouragement and that essential competitive edge. You can have all the natural talent in the world but without the overwhelming urge to win it will come to nothing great. In *This Game of Golf* Henry Cotton describes how his father started him on the road to golfing fame. Like me, Henry had a keen golfing brother, Leslie, who (like my own brother Gareth) didn't have quite the dedication to reach the top. Like me, Henry, as a young man, was torn between two sports, in his case golf and cricket. It was a disciplinary offence at Dulwich School and his refusal to be caned for it which led to his being banned from cricket. So he filled in the time playing golf instead. With me it was my father's fear that I would do my limbs a permanent injury at soccer, because of my whole-hearted 'get stuck in' attitude, that switched me over to golf. Like me, Henry developed a competitive spirit as a teenager by playing with older golfers and going all out to beat them . . .

I.W.

How did I come to be a professional golfer? Although I can claim to have chosen this profession for myself, I suppose I must have been guided in some way to pick one in which I could succeed, if my achievements entitle me to use such a word.

My father was a keen golfer of the week-end type, with a very ugly style which, as I realised later, was caused because he had a 'gammy' left knee and had to do a sort of hop in his downswing to prevent too much strain going on to the delicate joint.

He encouraged my brother and me by every means in his power and to the limit of his financial ability, and was very proud of his 'little boys.' One of my proudest days was when I beat him on level terms for the first time. I was about eleven or twelve years old at the time and he was about 59 years old and had a 16 handicap, but allowing for this, he was very good in his own way. He was an enthusiastic member of the Honor Oak and Forest Hill Golf Club, and then of the Dulwich and Sydenham Hill Golf Club, and on this particular day I insisted on playing him level. He had been giving me a gradually diminishing number of strokes for some months previously and I had been beating him regularly and, parent-like, he hesitated to let me play him with no handicap. I beat him, and he later recalled my telling him very seriously at the time, 'Father, you will never beat me again.' He never did.

My brother and I were made full members of the Aquarius Golf Club, a nine-hole course belonging to the Metropolitan Water Board, and this privilege we enjoyed until we both became professionals, I at 16 and my elder brother at 17. I think the encouragement I got from the golfers at this little nine-hole golf course did much to build up the competitive spirit which I expect it will be conceded I possess.

It almost goes without saying that I love golf, and long before I had really set my mind on being as good as the professionals I saw playing in the various tournaments around London, which could be seen in the holiday periods, I used to spend every moment I could chipping a golf ball about in the garden.

My brother and I both played cricket well and got our colours at Alleyn's School, and we used to take it in turns to 'bowl' to one another with a golf ball played with a golf club, the batsman playing cricket strokes back with a cricket bat. We thought this a good way to practise two games at once! Original, anyhow.

Although I have had a better golfing temperament than my brother Leslie and perhaps more ambition, I have been a more accurate striker all along. When we only had one ball left between us, we used to practise hitting the ball to and fro, one to the other, with all sorts of clubs up and down a fairway, and it was always I who had to do all the running about at my end. I used to grow annoyed at some of my brother's wild shots and so, brother-like, to get even with him, I would hit some of my shots off the line on purpose to make him run too!

When my father played regularly at Dulwich and Sydenham, we were allowed to be schoolboy members there. During our summer holidays we used to go to the club early in the morning, play 27 holes before lunch, eat the lunch we had taken with us, have a short rest, play 27 holes again after lunch and then feel we were all ready to take on my father and his partner, whoever it was, in his evening round. These four rounds a day carrying our own clubs seemed to be no bother at all in those days, but just good practice.

When my brother, who was not as good at the three 'Rs' as I was, left school, he decided to become a professional golfer. At this moment he was almost as good a player as I was, within a stroke or two anyhow, but had less power of concentration. He went to George Oke, professional at the Fulwell Golf Club, as assistant. In his younger days before going to Fulwell, George had been professional to the Honor Oak and Forest Hill Golf Club, so we knew him well.

I was determined to stay on at school and pass my Matriculation examination, and then decide whether or not to try for a University scholarship, and go then for Civil Engineering, which I always had in mind to do. However, an incident in what turned out to be my last term at school, the summer term of 1923, decided my future.

I was in the school first eleven, having worked my way up as 'under 14' Captain, and a good first-wicket bat and was definitely a better cricketer than golfer. We went to play at Marlow, and the match finishing early, the six prefects left the five non-prefects, of whom I was one, all the cricket gear to take back to the school that same night. So with four other boys I dragged the three large school cricket bags and two private cricket bags all the way to Dulwich by train and bus. We arrived late and very tired, and wrote a very pointed note to our prefect team-mates telling them it was a bit hot to expect us to do all the dirty work.

A lot of fuss was made over this note by the prefects, and the headmaster ordered the prefects to cane us. I refused to be caned by other boys for an offence against them and said an apology, which I would give, should cover our bad taste. This case developed into quite a serious affair, and I was banned from further cricket until I had had my caning. When the headmaster told me this, I suppose my seemingly innocent answer to his question as to what would I do with myself when the other boys were playing cricket, must have sounded very insolent. I said: 'I'll play golf, sir.'

That is just what happened; I played golf whenever I could, and from that moment decided I would become a champion.

When J. H. Taylor, whom I succeeded as professional at the Royal Mid Surrey Golf Club in 1946, was presented with a testimonial and the honorary life membership of the club after 46 years' service, he recalled, in his speech after the presentation, a day when my father took my brother and me to play with him many years before. I was 13, I suppose, at the time, and J. H. was asked to give a written report on his impression of us both. He said he remembered writing to my father, who died in 1941, aged 81, that he thought I would be the better player ultimately as I apparently had much more determination than my brother and more power of concentration.

After matriculating, my mind was made up to become a professional and my taregt was the 'stars.' I do not quite know what influenced me finally to become a professional, the incident at school, my brother being already a professional, or just the love of the game. But, having taken this decision, I tried hard with all I had got. A golf net built in the garage adjoining our house was pounded far into the night by my brother and me till we were exhausted, in an endeavour to perfect our swings.

I feel that it was the love of the game that kept me at it, and the competitive spirit.

From *This Game of Golf* by Henry Cotton
(Country Life, London, 1948).

My Three British Opens
Henry Cotton

It comes to only the very great in modern times to win the British Open three times. Henry Cotton was one of those. Henry died at the end of 1987, just days before the news was announced that he was to have been knighted. But he knew about the accolade just before his death and this is my salute to Sir Henry. Though I never really saw him in action – just in the odd clip on TV – I'd love to inherit his mantle as 'the finest British golfer of modern times'. I may have inherited some of his swing – one of my early tutors was Cyril Hughes, who was a disciple of Henry's.

When he was forty-one, Henry wrote the story behind his three Open triumphs of 1934, 1937 and 1948, from which I quote below. He did much to revive the lowly fortunes of British golf after years of American dominance (a very similar state of affairs to that in 1985 when Sandy Lyle broke a sixteen-year largely American monopoly of the Open).

One big difference between Henry's time and mine was in the professionals' pay. He says that in his early days the caddies sometimes earned as much as the players. Part of Henry's achievement in golf was vastly to improve the status of the British professional.

I.W.

Golf is a wonderful game. It is more than a game to me; it is a life's work, a career, a profession. Whether it is a science or an art I do not know – it is probably half and half – but it is a noble occupation all the same.

Nobody can pick a profession and make good at it without having some flair for it – at least that is as I see it. I came into golf fully aware that it was a hard game, but with the maximum amount of enthusiasm, which led me to burn up more energy than I possessed; and this is where I nearly failed. As the years have passed I have learned to place a greater value than ever on my health, which in general has been below the average, but I am grateful in every way for my earthly state today.

To say I have fought ill health is to some extent an exaggeration, but I might have had a stronger stomach. On the other hand I have only myself to blame for some of its weakness, as I did not for some years count meals as of sufficient importance to warrant the waste of an hour on them, and so ruined my digestion. Now I am very French in my outlook, and vote for a two-hours break for the world at midday. I feel I am getting the proportions right – perhaps values is a better word.

I owe everything to golf. This is a fact I cannot or would not deny, and I only hope that as far as it has been in my power, I have been able to put something back into the game to help others. Many of my actions have been wrong, I know, and many must have been right, though sometimes misunderstood. I may sum it all up by saying that while trying to please everyone, I have finally learned that a parady of Lincoln's famous saying might finish, 'You can't please all the people all the time.' So I said I would please myself as a start – that must be mostly right, surely!

I have always received, or rather patiently listened to, much unsolicited advice on how to run my career. This topic has interested many people – in fact, so many people that at times I have forgotten my rule to be polite to everyone, and let go. This gratuitous advice extends often to the golf course, and even on occasion to the final round of a major competition, when surely one can be excused for being cutting, for the same person would never walk in on, say, a most important conference or interrupt a private conversation; he would be too polite.

Naturally, the big slice taken by the war out of the best part of my golfing life has caused me to revise my plans, for from one with much future and little past, I became, as it seems now almost overnight, one with much past and a little future, in the tournament sense at least. This I know applies to nearly everyone in our Islands, but I am here putting my own case.

I have enjoyed my life as a professional golfer and still do, for it is a great life. To travel, to meet the world and his wife, and to live in the open air, what more can one ask?

Teaching golf is great work. It means helping people to enjoy themselves more, and with my temperament, it means suffering with them when they are tortured by failure and sharing their elation when they touch their high levels. Many people, often those who do not know me at all, think I enjoy teaching and playing only with scratch players. How wrong they are! I spend more time with the good players because they feel they can get the best value from my lessons, but I get much pleasure from enlightening the golfer who is doing everything wrong. 'Oh! I am not good enough to play with you.' I get tired of hearing this remark, and of explaining that I do not mind whom I play with so long as he is a decent fellow and enjoys his golf.

The person I cannot bear on the links is the grumbler, the person who is never satisfied and thinks he is only getting 25 per cent value for the money he is spending, and who never plays his real game. If he only knew it, his real game is his ordinary rotten stuff. He could remember with advantage the story of the old golfer at St Andrews, who after a round was sitting with his partner in the famous bay-window looking down the course, when a friend approached and asked him how he had played.

'I played rotten stuff,' he said. 'Nothing like my real game.' Then, after taking another sip at the glass of whisky at his elbow, he added very slowly, 'Come to think of it, I have never played my real game.'

I have, like many other players, done only two holes in one. I have had many very 'near ones,' but there were nearly 20 years between these flukes of flukes. I have had disappointments by the score, but they have taught me lessons; some I have learned, I suppose, and of course these disappointments have made success all the sweeter and more appreciated.

I have always tried to better myself, and as soon as I was old enough to appreciate the difference between the good and the shoddy, I went for the good all the time, for I think it is not a bad thing to hold that 'the best is just good enough.'

I have had a go at nearly everything in golf, from shoes with running spikes to 47-inch long drivers with deep faces, in order to try to do something a bit better than before. There is still much more I want to do in golf for myself, and the game, and I hope I shall be forgiven for trying to do it my own way.

My attempt to win the Open always started from the moment the preceding one was over, and I kept setting my target 12 months ahead to achieve a certain result on a certain course. I suppose this obsession to win the greatest title of them all made it all the more difficult for me, but it was foremost in my mind for years. I do not pretend I am not ambitious now, but the same burning desire has cooled off with the passing years and three successful attempts to my credit.

I was taken by Cyril Tolley to Prestwick for the 1925 Open when an assistant at Rye, and I played badly, or rather putted badly. The next year when regional qualifying was tried out I failed to qualify at Sunningdale. I was partnered by George Gadd, who was a really extraordinary putter at that time. George did 70 and 71 and I did 80 and 81, and I, childlike, worked out afterwards that if I had putted as he did and not taken any three-putt greens, I would even have beaten his score.

The following year, 1927, at St Andrews, I was well up after two rounds with 145, but slipped up on the greens again, on the final day especially.

In 1928 I qualified well but did not do anything to remember.

In 1929 I reached the last day after having the interesting experience of playing the first two rounds with Walter Hagen, who played beautiful golf to win, for the fourth and last time, his most esteemed title.

In 1930 at Hoylake, I did well in a way, for after the first round Bobby Jones and I were on the 70 mark with Macdonald Smith. On the morning of the second day I woke up and found my right wrist was set so stiffly that I could not bend it either way without great pain. I remembered jarring it badly against a tuft on the fairway playing to the old 12th hole the previous day. I was in a panic, and I chased around trying to find someone to help me; I finally got an early appointment with a famous Liverpool bone specialist who for my three guineas told me to get it massaged. I then chased off to find a masseur, had 30 minutes' massage and then chased to the station to get the train, for the road tunnel was not yet open, barely arriving on the first tee in time to drive off. Naturally I was upset by all this and with my wrist still worrying me I played the first nine holes badly; 43 out. I was back in 36, however, when I got the feel of the club again, though 79 was too many. I could have cried when I read, 'Cotton blows up' for it was no use telling the world my wrist was not normal *after* 79. Before, yes! – one might get some sympathy; but after all it was not sympathy I wanted but results, at least that is what the public wanted. So it meant cutting out the squealing and getting on with the practice.

At Carnoustie, in 1931, I did well again, better in fact than before. I was leading the field with Jurado after two rounds at 147. Looking back on this Open I am not sure that I was really good enough to win it, but I think that 'my adviser' did not understand me well enough, or he would have left me alone. Eliot Cockell, who ran *Golf Illustrated* for many years until his death just before the war, arrived at Carnoustie, having travelled overnight from London, to help me win the Open.

His plan was, 'Take no risks this morning, then get the "whip out" in the afternoon and go for everything.' So he walked around as my bodyguard and saw me endeavour to carry out his schedule. In so doing I took 79 strokes, which ruined my chances for this Open, though I lost by only six strokes.

In golf there is no playing safe; the ball can still run against you wherever you hit it, as I realised, and there is no whip to take out, unless to beat yourself after the round for making a mess of things.

In 1932 I had a sharp dose of 'flu' after the qualifying rounds and played the first round on half a bottle of champagne, because I was so weak after a night's perspiration in pulling down my temperature that I could scarcely walk at all. It did seem as though I would never win this event, and to take champagne, which I had very rarely tasted, though I had been ordered red Bordeaux wine by a French specialist, was considered my last chance of being able to play at all.

I did the first nine at Prince's in 32, and then on the longer homeward half, with the effect of the champagne already worn off, I did 42 back. I have often wondered whether another half-bottle would have 'done the trick' or put me out of action altogether. Sarazen won with 283, which stood as the lowest total ever put up in the Open. I always thought the Prince's course of 1932 just about as perfect a links as I ever played on.

This same year I did my usual summer trip to the Continent, where I have always felt at home; it might be because of some distant link with the French in me, because my sweet mother was Alice Le Poidevin, from Guernsey in the Channel Islands. Anyhow, whilst I was playing in Belgium, I was asked by Major J. C. Symonds, secretary of the Waterloo Golf Club, near Brussels, if I knew of any well-known English professional who spoke French and would like to come to his club.

Some six weeks later I had a sudden impulse one morning to send him a telegram offering to go to the Waterloo Golf Club myself. Not that I was unhappy at Langley Park, but I felt that it was, at the moment, necessary to be a visitor to our shores to receive any appreciation from both the Press and the public.

I suppose the long years of American domination had made everyone lose confidence in our golf. Anyway, that was how I felt about it.

Also, I could not see the way to get better fees for playing and teaching where precedents existed for caddies to receive as much for carrying the clubs of a golfer as the professional received for teaching and playing – and he might be Open Champion or an International player. I thought I was worth more than this poorly paid tariff, but it seemed that no one else did.

I made this decision alone, and it turned out to be a complete surprise to the golfing world and to my friends, but I went to a club where I felt very much at home, and where I spent four very happy years; it turned out to be a very good decision, one of the best I have made in my life. I had for a year or two now been suffering from gastric trouble. I expect the continual tournament strain was telling on me, and I was paying the price of trying to subdue an excitable temperament.

I found it much easier to follow a diet on the Continent for one thing, and for another, I think the variety of life appealed to me. As I have already mentioned, I had been ordered red wine by a famous French specialist. In Belgium I could afford to enjoy my wine, as it was well within my pocket.

During the first two years in Brussels, where I lived for the best part of each year, my health improved greatly, and I began to get fitter and stronger, and this led up to my winning the Open, which I did in the middle of my second year as professional at Waterloo.

One of the letters I treasure and which is stuck in one of my many scrap-books is from 'Sandy' Herd, a great friend of mine until he died. It is dated in December, 1932, when I was being criticised for going away from England. Sandy wrote as an old man to a young one, telling me to keep my chin up. I have never forgotten Sandy's words, and I was delighted to receive and acknowledge his congratulations in 1934, and on many a later occasion, too!

In 1933 I paid another visit to St Andrews. Like all golfers who keep going back to this old grey city, I found that it grew on me. The Old Course, which I hope is never altered any more, is always wrongly and severely criticised because it is – well, just different and *difficult*.

This particular year it was presented to us dry and fast, and, although it is just as playable and just as good a test under these conditions, it is trying to players used to hitting them up to the pin to have to 'bumble' them along. Yet two American members of the Ryder Cup team tied with 292, Densmore Shute beating Craig Wood on the play-off.

I was sharing the lead on this occasion after three rounds with several other players and yet, although I started well enough on my final round with my four, I said to a friend on the second tee, 'I cannot win. I have just had a feeling it is not my year again.' I did my best, but without inspiration, and although I was well in it till the 13th, where I played safely on to the 6th fairway and got an impossible stance and took a stupid six, I felt I was pulling against the collar all the way. I finished only three shots out, but that was another Open gone. This year was Walter Hagen's last big try for the Open. He led the field after two rounds and then just faded out.

In 1934 I won. I led all the way and played really good golf during the whole week, including the qualifying rounds. Yet, curiously enough, after again beginning my training right after St Andrews the previous year, and working at my golf as never before, I arrived on the eve of the Championship week at Royal St George's, Sandwich, not knowing which of four sets of clubs I had with me to use, and I almost felt like scratching, for I had practised till I was dizzy, tried all the swings I knew and still could not get the ball to go properly. So, with a sort of feeling 'I might as well play now I am here, but I ought to quit,' I put my clubs in my bags on Saturday afternoon and threw them in behind the seat of my red Mercedes cabriolet and decided to forget golf, if I could, till Monday morning, when I was due to play my first qualifying round at Royal St George's.

I was out very early on the Monday and, accompanied by a marker and a couple of friends, I played 18 of the most perfect holes I have ever played and holed the course without a long putt going in, in 66. I did a 75 at Deal the next day, on a course I did not know very well, and then came back to play on the Championship course on the Wednesday. I did 67 for my first round, then finished my second round with three threes and did a 65 this time, and I knew this virtually gave me the Championship if I could hang on, as I had a seven-stroke lead. On the final day – I remember it well, it was a lovely day at the seaside, bright sun and with a nice breeze – I did a 72 for my third round, which gave me a further two strokes lead. So here I was with my life's ambition within my grasp, having only to finish the 18 holes in decent figures to win by a 'street.'

People, meaning to be kind, kept congratulating me prematurely, and although I was feeling like the 'King' but uncrowned, I kept asking them to wait till afterwards, saying, 'one never knows' with my lips, when my heart was telling me 'It can't be otherwise, unless you are too stupid for it to be believable.'

I had a light lunch. It would be not telling the truth to say I was not excited, but I did eat enough to sustain me, and I judged I had timed my arrival on the first tee just right when I got there five minutes before I was down to drive off. The starter, however, to my disappointment, informed me that my time had been delayed fifteen minutes to help the stewards to control the crowds better. I did not know what to do with myself; I was unprepared for this and, not wishing to talk to anyone, I went and sat alone in an empty tent by the first tee, whilst my closer friends stayed outside talking to my well-wishers, keeping them away from me. Those fifteen minutes dragged by; here I was waiting to see my life's ambition realised and I was powerless to get on with it.

I cannot remember all the things that flashed through my mind. All my dreams had come true in one instant, then in another instant I had gone all cold with the thought of what would happen if I slipped up. This anxiety proved more than my delicate stomach could stand and I had a terrible stomach cramp. I could hardly stand up. I must have looked pretty ill, for I could hear the comments of the crowd on my 'green' colour as I teed up. There was nothing to do but play and get on with it. I knew how little any excuses would help me: the crowd expected results. My long game was dreadful. I was all limp and perspiration was cold on my forehead. I seemed powerless to pull myself together whilst this stomach cramp continued. Luckily, I putted well, otherwise I dread to think what would have happened.

I had not eaten too much ice-cream or spaghetti, as has been suggested, for I was on a diet and had been for a long time. Anyone who has followed a strict diet for a time and who knows what it means in the way of self-control regarding food, will realise that at such an important moment I would be most unlikely to break my rules of diet. I got out in 40, and with three short holes in this half, too! I continued to struggle and looked like taking yet another five at the long 13th (which would have been the fourth in succession on the homeward nine) when I holed a ten-foot putt for a four. This seemed to cheer me up and I relaxed a little for the first time for over two hours, and from that moment I played as I had done all the week, and came back in par figures to finish the round in 79 and a 283 total, equal to Sarazen's record at Prince's in 1932. When the time came to step forward and get this most coveted of all golf trophies from the Hon. Michael Scott, Captain of the Club, I had no jacket with me, so I borrowed Henry Longhurst's camel-hair overcoat to wear over my pullover for the big occasion.

I saw quite a lot of Harry Vardon during that week, for he was also staying at the Guildford Hotel, Sandwich. On the final day, Harry was ill in bed and so could only follow the play from reports. When I took up to his bedroom the old Cup he had so gloriously won on six occasions, tears came into his eyes, and he could not say a word;

nor could I, for I was crying, too! Harry was always most encouraging to me, and on the rare occasions that I got talking golf with him in a serious way I was most impressed with his knowledge of the game. I learnt a lot from the old master; more, in fact, than I ever learned in America.

That year, the year of the first British win for eleven successive years, I had the friendly encouragement of all the 'Old Brigade' who wanted once again to see our golf on top. James Braid, J. H. Taylor, and Ted Ray were always on hand to give me a word of encouragement.

The 65 I did stands as the lowest score ever done in the Open, and what was unusual was to do 66 and 67 as well, during the same week on this great golf course. I look back on this week at the Royal St George's Golf Club as one of the highlights in my career.

There was no relaxing after this, for it was just as necessary to keep practising to hold the crown as to win it, and as I was only 27 I was now set on winning it again.

In 1935 we went to Scotland again, this time to Muirfield. I was favourite and did, I think, 141 in the qualifying rounds and was either first or second. This means nothing, though to read some reports of the play it might be considered almost a junior title. I then led the first round with a 68, a course record for the altered course. I never know why they keep altering these classic courses. They are still doing it, for they altered Hoylake in 1946 even.

My 68 left me very unhappy. I will tell you why! I was playing beautiful golf, as can be imagined by my scoring, but in this round I wanted a four for a 66. It was a drive and a No. 4 iron only, that day, for me, and things were going so well that I was even looking for a three to do another 65. I hit a long drive which curled dangerously towards one of the bunkers on the left, and although I could not see if the ball had dropped in I felt very uneasy about it. As I left the tee, a well-wisher, whom I could have slain on the spot without turning a hair, came up to me and began talking about my brother, whom he had not seen for a while, and enquired about his health, etc. My look did not deter him, nor could a hastened step shake him off. He clung like a leech, pouring out light stupid conversation into my ear, all the way to the bunker.

When I arrived there I was quite angry with myself for getting into the sand. I stupidly decided to go for the green, to get a No. 4 length shot with my number 7, which meant pressing like the dickens! I hit the top of the bunker with a powerful shot, and the ball fell down, and there I lay nearer the face than before, for two! This time shaken out of my anger by this other blow, my brain began to work coolly. I must cut my losses now. So I played out safely but a little too well, and my ball plugged into soft sand in another bunker 50 yards from the green. The ball was so deep down that I could not reach the putting surface even though I hit the ball with all my strength. So, out in four and still well short of the green. I got down in two more for a six. Sixty-eight was a fine round, but I was very uneasy. I felt the championship had already gone, although I was the holder and in the lead after the first round.

I played the rest of this championship with my tail down somehow, and finished poorly; Alfred Perry who won, also took my record with a 67.

Hoylake again, 1936. I have always liked this course despite the old-fashioned, very formal air about the club itself. I did 68 in the first qualifying round and then 67 at Wallasey, both course records, but rain washed out the second day's play and it meant another round that week. I played beautifully every day and yet could not score. My putts refused to drop and yet I was only two strokes out in the end, in spite of having two penalty strokes in my final round of 74. I hit the ball better and straighter all the time there than I had done before in my life.

Raymond Oppenheimer, a life-long friend of mine, who was my head gallery-steward during several rounds that week, was asked by a newly arrived spectator to the gallery, how Cotton was playing; he was overheard to remark in a way that only he can, 'Sir, he is driving so straight, it is impossible to tell whether his ball is on the left or right half of the fairway.' It was quite near the truth as well!

At the end of 1936 I decided to come back to England, and Lord Rosebery, the president of the Ashridge Golf Club near Berkhamsted, asked me if I would like to help the Ashridge Club get ahead. We got to terms and I joined the club in January, 1937.

I built a house in the beautiful Ashridge Park on a spur of the Chiltern hills, and called it 'Shangri-la' after the valley of that name, which plays a big part in the James Hilton book *Lost Horizon* – a valley in which 'no one grows old and happiness reigns.' The film of that name, in which Ronald Colman played the lead, I can still remember most vividly. I saw it several times as I enjoyed it so much.

From Ashridge I entered for the 1937 Open at Carnoustie, and with America's strongest Ryder Cup team also in the field, I won for the second time this treasured trophy.

I was playing well that year, and spent a week at Carnoustie in May, when I found the course in a very rough condition – as most of these public links usually are to be found, out of championship time – but I got a good idea of the layout as I did not know the course prior to this visit.

I did not play outstandingly better than other players in the field during the week, though I was in the running all the time, but on setting out for the final round in one of the most consistent downpours I remember, I told an intimate friend of mine, as we left the first tee, I had a feeling I could win.

I played one of the best rounds of my career, 71, one over the course record, and won by two strokes. I putted very well on the water-sodden greens and when I came to the last hole, which crosses two burns, with a four for a 70, I did not play safe, short of the burn, as I might have done, but concentrated on hitting the ball hard and as far from the 'out-of-bounds' on the left as I could. My No. 2 iron shot finished in a sand bunker, hole-high to the right of the green. Then I took my ordinary niblick, for, from the hard, wet sand, I figured 'one a bit thin with my blaster could go over the fence,' and I played out safely, short of the pin, got down in two putts and felt that unless something unusual happened I was 'home' – as the crowd also considered, judging from the reception I received.

The unusual nearly did happen, for the rain continued steadily and pools of water lay everywhere. If any holes had got under water things would have been awkward, but as it turned out, all was well, and my name went on the cup a second time.

One of my best friends, Leonard Crawley, later golf correspondent of the *Daily Telegraph* and a great supporter and demonstrator of the 'Cotton system,' was staying with us in our boarding house at the time, but after a week's practice with the American players he was of the firm opinion that we had 'had it.' He had seen our play at Southport, where we lost the Ryder Cup for the first time at home.

Leonard, for some unaccountable reason, failed to qualify and returned to London feeling very disappointed and anxious to get away from the sight of the inevitable American victory.

However, when I won and R. A. Whitcombe was second, I received one of the most appreciated telegrams, for Leonard was big enough to be humble over his mistake. This win is considered my best performance.

In 1938 the Open went to Royal St George's again, and, after two rounds, I was seven strokes behind the leader with 147. I seemed to have no chance, but the weather decided otherwise.

During the early hours of the morning of the final day, it started to blow a gale, and the gale increased as day dawned; the exhibition tents were blown down, and when we arrived the clubhouse surrounds looked like a battlefield. Naturally the scoring went up sky-high; my rounds of 77 and 74 gave me the best total of the day, and my round of 74 after lunch, which was three strokes better than any other, was nearly the best of my life, for I was level fours on the 16th tee.

The wind was so strong that afternoon that I drove the 2nd green, 370 yards, and holed my putt for a two. I drove also the 384 yards 11th hole, and got a three.

This was Reggie Whitcombe's 'year,' and his two rounds on the final day, 75 and 78, represented wonderful golf. He always is at his best when the going is tough.

My third championship visit to St Andrews was in 1939 and, while I appeared to play soundly, I was not, in fact, striking particularly well, though I was confident with a card and pencil.

I did a 69 in the qualifying rounds on the Old Course, the only time I broke 70 there until 1947 in the Spalding Tournament, when I had a similar score. Then after a 74 to open with, played during a foul thunderstorm, for a third part of the round I fell behind gradually. 'Dick' Burton won with 290 that year.

In my second round I stood on the 14th tee for 25 minutes waiting for the huge crowd (I was nearly last on the Thursday afternoon, and so picked up everybody's crowd) to cross from the 13th green to beyond the wall. This long wait ruined my round, for I was five under fours at this point and the strain of watching and thinking of that 'out-of-bounds' on one side, and the 'Beardies' on the other, was too much for me, and I finished weakly in 72.

It was from that moment that I really saw the necessity for making St Andrews a golfing arena completely, and my suggestion, carried out as far as possible under existing conditions in the 1946 Open, has proved to be the solution.

Then came the war, which completely stopped British golf of all sorts, and, except for the charity games and some weekend play, the British Isles thought little about the small white ball.

After the second World War the first Open Championship was at St Andrews in 1946, and the golfing public thought that this was a sign that at last the world was on the way to normality. So it was, but very slowly indeed as it turned out.

'Slamming' Sam Snead from USA flew over to Scotland a few days before the

Open and took the old Trophy back with him. My part in this event was a conspicuous one, for I led after two rounds with two 70s, but on the last day I gradually faded away. In the final round I could hardly walk the distance and realised how far from 100 per cent fit I was, for the strain of holding on in the last holes was too much for me and I finished absolutely exhausted. My long period of ill health in the RAF, which caused my discharge from the service and finished with a serious abdominal operation, plus the one year's convalesence during which period I was not allowed to hit a shot, and the absence of adequate rebuilding food, prevented me from making a complete recovery.

Then came 1947 at Hoylake. A great course in perfect condition; no Snead to defend his title, but Stranahan, Ghezzi and Bulla came to collect the cup. I led with a 69 with Laurie Ayton, but fell to second place on the next day with a thoroughly bad 78; then I recovered to a decent position, for with nine holes left to play I found myself in the lead again, but on the home stretch, battling against a gale of wind which had suddenly sprung up, I failed and finished tamely in 76. Fortunately for Britain, Fred Daly won, and a worthy champion he proved to be, for he won the *News of the World* PGA Championship the same year.

I realised that it was no good training hard for 1948 unless I could get really fit, and the only way to get proper food was to go abroad. My sincere American friends, R. A. Hudson, William Danforth and Ed. Lowery, were most encouraging and felt sure that even after our Ryder Cup failure another trip to America would set me up physically, so after a brief visit to Monte Carlo, I returned in the Spring of 1948 to USA, where I played better and returned fitter and more confident.

At Muirfield I found that the course for the Open was my course – narrow fairways and lots of rough. I played well all the week, scored 69 + 69 to lead the qualifying rounds by 2 strokes, and then won the Title for the third time with 284, to lead Fred Daly by 5 strokes.

My 66 in the second round, played in part before His Majesty the King, who followed the play keenly, was a course record and paved my way to success.

From *This Game of Golf* by Henry Cotton
(Country Life, London, 1948).

The Master and a Modest Case of Forgery

Henry Longhurst

Though Henry Cotton had won the British Open in 1934 (and had been presented with the trophy wearing my overcoat – which I still possess), this year, 1937, really represented his prime. There had been no Americans when he won at Sandwich in 1934. In 1937 at Carnoustie there had been the whole American Ryder Cup team and with a stupendous final 71 in driving rain, almost the best individual round I ever saw, he beat them all. We all tend to inflate the heroes of our early days but I have seen them all since that time and cannot believe that any of them, Hogan included, hit the ball better than Cotton. Nor do I know anybody who did not himself automatically hit the ball better when playing with him, though this is no place in which to be tempted into the technicalities of golf. It was a great advantage in my own line of life, however, to be his contemporary and to be good enough to play occasionally in his company, albeit not on level terms. He won his third Open after the war, fourteen years after his first, and, when King George VI came to Muirfield to watch, he put on a 66 for his benefit.

I myself have basked in Cotton's reflected glory and still do. On coming off the last green at St Andrews not long after the war I was surrounded by autograph-hunting children and, making the elementary mistake of thinking they knew who I was – whereas all they do is to rush up to all and sundry, thrust their books under his nose and then see who they have got – I signed a good many books. I was cut down to size by hearing a freckled, fang-toothed, ginger-headed boy round at the back exclaiming, on seeing my signature, 'Och, he's no' anyone!' All right, I thought, but he bloody well will be in future. Since that day I must have signed *Henry Cotton* in at least a couple of hundred books, thereby giving much innocent satisfaction to both parties. Furthermore, I still produce the most excellent specimens, whereas the Maestro himself has been getting a little slack in latter years.

From *My Life and Soft Times* by Henry Longhurst
(Cassell and Co., London, 1971).

6

HENRY THE COMMENTATOR
Augusta in April
Henry Longhurst

Nothing to date has equalled the thrill of my first invitation to the Masters at Augusta – though having been disappointed the year before, I still didn't believe that it was really going to happen (despite several journalists' confident predictions) till I'd actually got the written invitation in my hand. Augusta has so many memories for so many people. For Gene Sarazen it's that incredible albatross which virtually won him the Masters at the fifteenth hole of the fourth round. For Gary Player it's that amazing fight back in 1978 when he came from nowhere in the last nine holes to clinch the title. For Henry Longhurst of the sonorous voice and wry wit, it was being made the best-known TV commentator on both sides of the Atlantic. As he relates here, he got on to American TV pretty much by accident and unwittingly caused a sensation just by being himself.

Our Henry was good enough to win the German Amateur Open in 1936. His post-war golf column in the *Sunday Times* was a must for every keen golfer of whatever ability. His rubicund nose was testimony to his robust drinking, though never to the detriment of his performance, not even when it came to climbing to perilous heights up what ABC TV christened the 'Longhurst ladders'. For all his fame in other directions, to the American in the street he was 'the guy that does the sixteenth in the Masters'.

I.W.

CBS (the Columbia Broadcasting System), who were televising the 1965 Carling Tournament at a course called Pleasant Valley outside Boston, wondered if it would interest me to go up one of their towers, it being their rehearsal day, and 'see how they did it'. I was naturally intrigued and did so, joining one of their announcers, as they call the commentators, John Derr. So far as I remember I only said a few words into their microphone, but to my astonishment I got a note from the producer, Frank

Chirkinian, inviting me to do the 16th hole next day. This turned out to be a long short-hole of some 210-odd yards, where the players drove from an elevated tee down between two bunkers and onto a huge green, behind which we sat under a big parasol on a tower no more than twenty feet high.

I did all I was called upon to do, which heaven knows did not seem very much, naming the players and their scores correctly as they came up to the tee, which one could hardly fail to do in view of the fact that a very efficient young fellow had already put a piece of paper in front of one's nose containing the information, and occasionally adding some commonplace comment before being told to 'throw it to 15'. It transpired, however, that completely unwittingly I had managed to cause two minor sensations in our limited little world. One was when towards the end a young Mexican called Homero Blancas came to the 16th hole with the prospect looming before him of picking up, if everything went right, the equivalent of some £12,000. It proved to be a little much for him, and taking a 2-iron, he hit the shot that a good many of us would have done in the circumstances; in other words he hit it right off the sole, half topped, and it must have stung like the devil. 'Oh, that's a terrible one,' I said instinctively. 'Right off the bottom of the club.' In fact, it scuttled down the hill and finished on the green, but that wasn't the point. I had said it was a bad shot – which of course it was – but no one, it transpired, had ever said such a thing before, at any rate in such downright terms. This, though it took some time for the penny to drop and I can sometimes scarcely believe it still, was the first 'sensation'. The second took even longer to dawn on me. Golf being, like billards, a 'silent' game, that is to say that silence is expected while a man is making his stroke – unlike, say, the Cup Final, when both viewer and commentator are conscious of being one of a vast vociferous crowd (though even so, compare the silence that comes over them when a man is to take a penalty and therefore to make a single individual stroke) – it had never occurred to me from the very beginning that one should do other than remain silent while the golfer was actually playing his shot, so that 'talking on the stroke' had always seemed to be one of the cardinal sins of golf commentating, even though, heaven knows, I have found myself often guilty of committing it. This had not been, up to that time, the accepted principle in America which it has since become and the 'brilliant flashes of silence' turned out to be the second 'sensation'.

Also, of course, the most commonplace little expressions in one man's country may seem strange and catch the attention in another's. Towards the end of this (for me) momentous day, for instance, I announced that the eventual winner, Tony Lema, later so tragically killed in a private plane accident, had a very 'missable' put. This, I was told, was greeted with much applause by the crowd watching in the locker room. 'You hear what the old guy said? He said, "He's got a *missable putt*!" ' For some extraordinary reason this commonplace and self-explanatory expression seemed never to have become part of golfing language in America.

Anyway, it was all good for trade and not only was I invited again by CBS, this time to the Masters at Augusta, but also by ABC (the American Broadcasting Company), who handle such 'prestigious' events as the US Open and the US PGA championships.

In a modest way, too, my name has gone into the language of television, for by the time we all met in America I had already grown portly enough to wonder what I was doing, climbing these ladders at my weight and age, and made so bold as to wonder whether it would not be possible to somewhat civilize this mode of ascent. From that time onwards a form of staircase, complete with handrail, has been the order of the day, for which I and all my successors may be truly thankful. What I am really proud about, though, is the fact that, in the directions to the scaffolders who erect the towers, these staircases are ordered by ABC under the name of 'Longhurst Ladders'.

Such is immortality!

As a result of the pleasant episode at Pleasant Valley CBS, as I have said, invited me the following April to cover a hole at the Masters at Augusta, Georgia, and for the past five or six years I have had the honour, to say nothing of the aesthetic pleasure, of sitting on a little tower at the back of the 16th there too, once again a short hole and clearly, I should have thought, among the first half-dozen in American golf.

Augusta in April is heaven. The course itself was a nursery and many of the original trees and shrubs were left to grow on when in 1930 Clifford Roberts, a New York investment broker, persuaded the one and only Bobby Jones, who had completed his Grand Slam (the Open and Amateur Championships on both sides of the Atlantic in the same year) and was himself from Atlanta, to join him in creating a national golf course – 'a retreat of such nature and such excellence that men of some means and devoted to the game of golf might find the club an extra luxury where they might visit and play with kindred spirits from other parts of the nation'. This they certainly succeeded in doing.

I shall never forget my first visit to the property [*Jones later recorded*]. The long lane of magnolias through which we approached was beautiful. The old manor house with its cupola and walls of masonry two feet thick was charming. The rare trees and shrubs of the old nursery were enchanting. But when I walked out on the grass terrace under the big trees behind the house and looked down over the property, the experience was unforgettable. It seemed that this land had been lying here for years just waiting for someone to lay a golf course upon it. Indeed, it even looked as thought it were already a golf course, and I am sure that one standing today where I stood on this first visit, on the terrace overlooking the practice putting green, sees the property almost exactly as I saw it then.

Year by year I myself have sat in the same chair on the same little balcony, upstairs, looking through the wisteria down at the same scene, while the same coloured waiter comes out and says, 'You like the same as last year, sah? Beefeater on the rocks?' Everything indeed, is the same and it is only by looking down at the huge scoreboard that you can tell which year it is – a Palmer year or a Nicklaus year or whatever it may be. The same people come, decked out in every colour of the rainbow – ridiculous under the grey skies of Britain but exactly right for the spring sunshine of Georgia. They bring the same folding chairs, take them to the same places as last year, and, many of them, sit there all day every day each year. One year we had a three-way play-off starting at one o'clock. This made it inconceivable that the game should reach the 16th hole before five, yet when I went down there to be 'taped' at about mid-day, many of the regulars, whom I had come to know by sight over the years, were already in their places, with no prospect of a shot being played before them for five hours.

The Masters, though it may have envious critics, is something special. A strong sense of traditional decorum is preserved, and woe betide the man or woman who did not observe it when Clifford Roberts's eye happened to be upon them. The spectators never run – would you mind! – but they do love to shout, and from time to time a colossal yell reverberates between the pines as someone holes a putt which, from the roar that greets it, might have been the winning goal in a Cup Final.

It all started in 1934 when the select gentlemen who had formed the Augusta National club, in a part of the world where the climate hardly permitted tournaments in the heat of summer, conceived the idea of inviting some of the leading players of the day to a tournament in the spring, when it was perfect in Georgia and the players were not engaged elsewhere. This was a great success and at once became an annual event. Who christened it 'the Masters' no one seems quite to know, nor is it certain that the pious founders would ever have started it at all if they had known what eventually they would be letting themselves in for. However that may be, the tournament they created remains unique. No advertisements are allowed to disfigure the scene either inside or outside the grounds – except when some supporter of Arnold Palmer (not, we may be sure, the great man himself) hired an aeroplane to fly noisily over the scene all day trailing a banner with the words GO ARNIE GO – nor is any mention of filthy lucre permitted, and this really is something when you consider that the 'leading money-winner' seems to be the chief focus of interest in American golf. All the television directors and commentators have to submit to a solemn lecture forbidding mention of any tournaments other than the US and British Open and Amateur championships and the American PGA (other tournaments on the professional tour simply do not exist) and especially forbidding them to mention money in any form. No prize money is announced beforehand and none presented at the time, it being held sufficient for the winner to have won the Masters and to have been invested with the traditional green blazer which thenceforward, even though he be a millionaire, he wears with justifiable pride. Only later is it revealed that the first prize this year came to $25,000 or whatever it may be.

From the side of the town on which I am usually billeted, one drives to the course through avenues of elegant houses whose gardens – open to the road, as always in America, not hedged in – are ablaze with azalea, rhododendron and dogwood. On the course itself two holes stand out and on a sunny afternoon they really take your breath away: the 13th and 'my' hole, the 16th, of which I will let the picture tell the story, except to add that on the 13th you may imagine the great Georgia pines a hundred feet high and the bank at the foot of them a solid mass of vivid scarlet, orange and yellow azaleas. At both holes the water is liable to remain an equally vivid blue, even on a cloudy day, due possibly to the fact that, if you get there early enough, you will see a gang of dusky workers, each with a watering-can full of blue dye! It was in this that I once said that Doug Sanders's ball had 'found a watery grave'. This appears to have given much innocent pleasure, since I am still reminded of it.

Augusta National, rare among the more prosperous clubs in America, is a golf club pure and simple, like Pine Valley and Cypress Point, with no swimming-pool nor gigantic locker room complete with barber, masseurs and the rest – an old porticoed plantation-style house with an unspoilt air of elegance and peace. Among the pines on the left are a number of white cottages, or 'cabins', as they call them, in the same style, one of them a gift from the members to President Eisenhower, and behind these, discreetly secluded by a hedge, is what is probably the best 9-hole, par-3 course in the world, again enclosed by a background of spectacular colour. Here they hold a tournament on the day before the Masters, the record for which is held by Art Wall, who, believe it or not, had two 3s and seven 2s for a 20. So altogether, as you may gather, the Augusta National is not a bad place for us scribes and commentators to earn our living in, especially those of us who arrive, in April, fresh from an English winter.

Perhaps I may add one final comment on my own modest operations in television, namely that, whatever you may say, it is nice to be recognized, even if only by one's voice. This is not vanity. It adds much to the pleasure of a taxi ride, for instance (as well as to the tip!), if the driver says, 'I'd know your voice anywhere,' and starts talking about golf. Only the other day, hailing a cab opposite the American Embassy in Grosvenor Square, I said, 'I wonder if you could take me to Cricklewood Broadway?' to which the man at once replied, 'I'd take *you* anywhere.' Like so many London taxi-drivers he was an avid golfer – they have a golfing society of their own – and actually had a golf magazine beside him in the cab, open at a picture of Arnold Palmer, who once, he said, the biggest day of his golfing life, he had driven in this very cab. All this is not, however, the irrelevance of the subject of the Masters that it may seem, for my peak was reached, and you can hardly blame me for relating it, when, on handing in my baggage at Cape Town airport in South Africa, I had had time to say only, 'I wonder if you could check in this shooting-stick as well as the suitcase?' when a transatlantic voice behind me said, 'Hey! Aren't you the guy that does the 16th at the Masters?'

From *My Life and Soft Times* by Henry Longhurst
(Cassell and Co., London, 1971).

I just don't know about the guy. He looks like W. C. Fields in drag. But he happens to be the best in the business.

CBS TV producer Frank Chirkinian on
Henry Longhurst as commentator.

On Augusta National Golf Club, Georgia

The only difference is at Augusta the divots tear loose on dotted lines.
John Updike, 1980.

The greens *are* the course. . . . They are faster than a fart in a hot skillet.
David Mill, 1977.

7

THE BIG THREE

The Million-dollar Shot – How Arnie Palmer Made Boldness His Friend

Arnold Palmer

Of the Big Three of golf in the 1960s – Player, Palmer and Nicklaus – it was Arnie who commanded the biggest following because of his spectacular 'go for broke' style. Many top-class golfers play the percentage game and handicap golfers always should. But that has never been Palmer's style. He says: 'You must play boldly to win. My whole philosophy has been based on winning tournaments, not on finishing a careful fifth or seventh or tenth.' Here he explains how he turned that philosophy into a glorious winning streak, starting with his victory in the US Open in 1960. In a way it all began with his first shot at what he called 'that maddening first hole'. International golf is so competitive now that it isn't enough to 'keep shooting par and the other guy will crack', as Bobby Jones used to say. Now the winner of a major needs an Arnie-type charge in at least one of the four rounds.

I.W.

There was a sharp bite and sparkle in the mountain air. The Rockies loomed clearly in the distance – immense, clear, barren. I remember on the first hole at Denver, the sun was so bright that it hurt your eyes to look down the fairway. Standing on the tee, it was difficult to see the green without a pair of dark glasses. It took me four rounds to find it – but when I did, the whole thrust of my life was altered.

The time was 1960. The place was Cherry Hills Country Club. The event was the US Open.

On the fourth round of that tournament, I tried a shot that I'd missed three times in three rounds. I tried it again not because I'd failed – or because I like failure – but because I was convinced that it was the shot necessary to win the tournament.

A bold shot?

Yes.

But you must play boldly to win. My whole philosophy has been based on winning golf tournaments, not on finishing a careful fifth, or seventh, or tenth.

A reckless shot?

No.

In eighteen years of tournament golf I feel that I've never tried a shot that I couldn't make.

On that summer day in 1960, I was young in what the world calls fame, but I was ripe in golfing experience. I'd been a professional golfer for five years, and up to then I'd won twenty tournaments. In those years, I'd learned something about the strategy of the game and its psychology and rewards. If there was any reward I treasured most, it was the way that the game responded to my inner drives, to the feeling we all have that – in those moments that are so profoundly a challenge to man himself – he has done his best. That – win or lose – nothing more could have been done.

My own needs were deeply driven ones: I could not retreat from a challenge. If the chance was there and if – no matter how difficult it appeared – it meant winning, I was going to take it. It was the 'sweetness' of risk that I remembered, and not its dangers.

In looking back, I feel that in these years I was learning something of the subtle dimensions of all this – I was learning the *meaning* of boldness as well as its feeling.

For boldness does not mean 'recklessness' to me. Rather it involves a considered confidence: I *know* I'm going to make the shot that seems reckless to others. I also know the value of the risk involved: A bold shot has to have its own rewards – winning or losing the match, winning or losing the tournament.

But perhaps it was not until the US Open at Cherry Hills that I put it all together, philosophically as well as physically. For not until that summer day in 1960 did it become apparent to me how boldness might influence not just a hole but an entire round, an entire tournament, and even an entire golfing career.

It began, really, on the first tee of the last round at Cherry Hills. On the face of it, there was nothing terribly subtle about this hole: You could see every mistake you made. It was downhill to the green; the tee was elevated perhaps 150 feet above the green. It was only 346 yards long, not a terribly long par 4 – and a terribly tempting birdie 3 . . . to me. It was guarded on the left by an irregular line of poplars and pines and on the right by a ditch that the membership had practically paved with golf balls. A nice direct hole for the strong driver, somebody who could – in that thin, mile-high air – get the ball out there 300 yards or so.

But there *was* one nasty little afterthought that had been provided for the US Open: The grass was allowed to grow very long and become a 'rough' right in the fairway, about 50 or 60 yards in front of the green. Moreover, the hazard was heightened by a treacherous bunker guarding the gateway to the green. It had grass in it that looked like it was three feet deep. If you got in there, you might never be found again. I mean it was the kind of place where you hunted buffalo – not par.

The idea, of course, was to penalize the strong driver, to threaten him with capture by the rough – and a difficult second shot – if he played to his own best game (a powerful drive) on his first shot.

The safe way to play that hole, for most golfers, was not to invite trouble – not to challenge the rough or the bunker in the first place. In that sense, the first hole was an authentic mirror of the entire course. For Cherry Hills was long in yardage (7004) but not in reality: The thin air gave most tee shots a much longer carry than on a sea-level course. But its greens were small and well guarded by bunkers and water hazards; there was an added danger that under the hot, direct sun and the afternoon winds they would become so dried out that it would be all but impossible to get the ball to stop on them. If you hit those greens with power, the ball would roll right over and off them on the far side. So it was a course that took accuracy, touch, and an unflagging concentration. It *looked* to many like a course whose yardage beckoned to power – Mike Souchak, a powerful golfer, led at the halfway mark of the 1960 Open with a remarkable 68–67 for a thirty-six-hole score of 135. But it was, in reality, a course that catered to placement more than to power – in that opening round of 68, Souchak had only twenty-six putts, nine or ten short of normal for an eighteen-hole round. So he wasn't up there scattering power shots; he was getting good placement with everything he did.

To focus on the first hole: It was the kind of hole that shaped your entire approach to the course in that it could reward you for power or for placement.

To the pretty good amateur golfer, it was an opportunity for a par 4. He might put the ball out in the fairway pretty much where he could – far short of the rough – and then hope to get close to, or onto, the green with his second shot.

To the venturesome pro, it was an opportunity for a birdie. He'd use an iron to hit his shot off the tee, expecting to get enough accuracy from it (which he would less likely get from a driver) to drop the ball precisely in the fairway, where he'd have the ideal second shot. In short, he intended to place his first shot so that he could hit his second shot precisely to the cup – not just any old place on the green but *specifically* to the cup. For this was the kind of shot where the pro prefers – where he *intends* – to get his second shot so close to the cup that he'll need only one putt to 'get down.' So if he emphasized placement over power, he hoped to wind up with a birdie 3, not a par 4.

From my angle of vision – somewhat singular, I'll admit – this was an eagle hole, not a birdie hole. I figured that, with boldness, I could get down in two strokes, not three or four.

That meant being on the green in one shot, not two.

That meant getting into the cup in one putt, not two.

That meant emphasizing power over placement.

That meant using my driver, not my iron.

My intention was simply to drive the ball hard enough and far enough so that it would bound through the rough in front of the green and run up on the putting surface to a good position near the cup. To get a ball to stop precisely on a green, you must give it backspin, so that it bites into the grass when it hits and then stops short, or even hops backward. That's fairly easy to do when you're using an iron from the fairway that is fairly close to the green; you merely strike straight downward at the ball, taking a divot after making contact with the ball, and take a normal follow-through. But it is difficult to do while driving off the tee and ramming the ball through the rough. For one thing, on tee shots you may be hitting the ground a microsecond before you make contact with the ball. At least that's what I was doing with my driver back in 1960 (though since then I've changed my style somewhat). Then you normally give the ball a considerable overspin when you hit the ball dead centre (or thereabouts) and make the big follow-through. Normally you want to give the ball some overspin when hitting off the tee with a driver. Overspin will cause the ball to roll a little farther after it hits the ground. So my tee shot would, I expected, be hitting those small greens without backspin. And if the greens were dry and hard, as I expected, the ball might never stop rolling this side of the Continental Divide.

So I was proposing to use a power club – the driver – rather than a placement club – the iron – on a hole that demanded placement as well as power. And I was accepting overspin, not backspin, on a green that threatened to be faster than the Indianapolis Speedway on Memorial Day.

'Boldness' is what my friends called it. 'Insanity' is what they meant.

But I figured to have two things going for me when the ball hit the green:

If the ball went through the rough, not over it, the thick grass would cut down significantly on the ball's momentum, and very likely on how far it would roll, once it hit the green. Also, I'd be playing this hole relatively early in the morning on the first three rounds. (On the fourth and last round – because of the way the US Open was run in those days – I'd be playing it in the early afternoon.) I knew that every green was being heavily watered at night, simply because the tournament officials were afraid that otherwise the greens would be hard and dry by the afternoon. So in the morning, the first green – obviously the first to be played – would likely be heavily laden with the water from the all-night sprinkling, and the water residue would slow down any ball hit onto it. That's another reason why the roll of the ball would be reduced.

(You didn't *really* think that I just went out there and hit the ball hard, without giving any thought to what would happen to it once it came down – now did you?)

The way I looked at it, all I had to do was pound the ball bouncingly through the rough and onto the heavily watered green. Then I'd one-putt and have an eagle. I'd have that course by the throat, and – as my fellow pro, Jerry Barber, once said – 'shake it to death.'

Only it didn't happen. Not on the first three rounds. That green was tough to reach with a rifle, much less a driver. In my first round I sent my tee shot into the ditch on the right. I didn't get an eagle or a birdie or a par on the hole. I didn't even get a bogey, for that matter. I got a double-bogey 6 – two over par, instead of the two under par that I'd aimed for. After that, things got better – but not much. I got a bogey 5 on the second round and a par 4 on the third round. So in the first three rounds, I'd taken fifteen strokes on that hole, instead of the twelve strokes that playing it safe might have given me. And instead of the six strokes that – in wild flights of genius – my boldness might have given me.

More than that, starting off every round with a deep disappointment damaged my whole pattern of play. After three rounds, I had a total of thirteen birdies in the tournament, but they were so scattered that I'd never gotten any momentum out of them – no 'charge,' so to speak. The result was that I was in fifteenth place with a 215 after three rounds.

Just before lunch, and the start of my last round, I paused outside the vast white scoreboard outside the rambling, neo-Tudor clubhouse at Cherry Hills. There in the elaborate black and red numerals of golf, written in a manner as highly stylized as medieval script, I saw how the field lay. I was seven strokes behind the leader, Mike Souchak. But Mike wasn't the only hurdle. Between me and the leadership lay such great golfers as Ben Hogan and Sam Snead, Julius Boros and Dow Finsterwald, Dave Marr and Bob Goalby, and a twenty-one-year-old amateur named Jack Nicklaus.

By the time I sat down to a sandwich in the clubhouse, my mood was about as black as a witch's heart. Ken Venturi and Bob Rosburg, who also seemed to be out of contention, joined me, and a couple of newsmen stopped by our table to offer solace to the newly bereaved.

One of them was an old friend, Bob Drum, then of the Pittsburgh *Press*. He knew of my tribulations with that first hole and of my conviction that it was an eagle hole that would unlock the entire course to the player bold enough to attack it. He also knew that my failure in a daring power approach had – in an era of golf when meticulous precision was most admired – given a certain satisfaction to a few older hands around professional golf. 'There are some guys out there who think you're just an upstart, a flash-in-the-pan,' he'd told me. So when he began to console me, and hint that maybe it was time to play it safe and try to pick up some good also-ran money in the US Open – since it was obvious I couldn't go from fifteenth place to first place in one round – the chemistry began working in me. Explosively.

'What would happen if I shot a 65 on this last round?' I asked, perhaps more aggressively than in the thirst for pure knowledge.

'Nothing,' said Bob. 'You're out of it.' He was an old friend but a realistic one. Only one man had *ever* shot a 65 in the final round of the US Open: Walter Burkema in 1957.

But that got to me. And to my pride. Realism – and pessimism – I did not need.

'Well,' I said, my voice lowering into my don't-tread-on-me tone, 'the way I read it is that a 65 would give me 280 for the tournament. And 280 is the kind of score that usually wins the US Open.'

Bob gave me a startled look, as if he just noticed I had two heads.

'Sure,' he said, 'but you won't do it by taking another double-bogey on the first hole.'

So there it was: I still looked at the first hole as a chance for triumph; Bob – and a great many others – looked at it as a place for patent disaster. I suppose they were right. If I'd played it safe on the first hole and teed off with my iron, instead of the driver, and gone for placement and par, I'd be three shots closer to the leaders after the first three rounds. If I'd picked up a birdie or two along with it, I might even be right on their necks. So the thing to do now was admit that the first hole had me beaten and go back to playing it like the other pros did – with an iron off the tee – and figure that by placing the ball and playing it safe, I might pick up enough strokes in the standing to avoid further shame.

But that's not the way I saw it. I wasn't playing golf to avoid shame. I was playing it to win championships. And the last round of a National Open is no place to start changing your whole style and philosophy of golf.

The way I looked at it, being fifteenth made it more *imperative* that I play boldly. It couldn't cost me much: The difference between being fifteenth or twenty-fifth or fifty-fifth is not terribly meaningful – at least to me. It's the difference between first and second that has meaning. And a considered boldness might – I was sure – still win me the tournament.

So when I got to the first tee, I reached for my driver. Even though it was now one-forty-five in the afternoon and the green figured to be dried out and it would take incredible accuracy to hit the green and hold it. One of my luncheon companions (not Bob Drum) had come along, and he looked as if there were nothing wrong with me that brain surgery couldn't cure. I addressed the ball as if it were my enemy – or my slave – and hit it with everything I could get into it. The ball went up and hung in the sharp, clear air as if it had been painted there. When it came down – with overspin – it leaped forward and ran through the rough and right onto the middle of the green.

Twenty feet from the hole.

Three hundred and forty-six yards and I'd not only driven the green but drilled it right in the heart!

Just like I'd been planning it all along.

Right? Right!

Okay – two putts. A birdie, not an eagle. But that didn't much depress me. For I'd shown that my idea *did* work – that boldness could conquer this hole. And that if it made the first hole yield, then the whole course could be conquered with boldness.

Suddenly my whole spirit, my entire attitude changed.

I charged onto the second hole – a 410-yard par 4 with an elevated green and trees right in the fairway. In two shots I was not quite on the green. But I chipped the ball from off the green right into the cup for another birdie 3. I charged onto the 348-yard third hole and birdied it. I charged onto the fourth hole and birdied it with a twisting 40-foot putt. Four holes: four birdie 3s. A par on the fifth, a birdie on the sixth, a birdie on the seventh: six birdies on seven holes. I finished the first nine holes in 30 strokes, just one short of a record.

'Damn!' I said to Bob Drum when he finally caught up to us. 'I really wanted that 29.' Bob exhibited deplorable self-control: 'Well,' he murmured consolingly, 'maybe next time.'

By the tenth hole, I was tied with Mike Souchak. By the twelfth, I was ahead of him. But it was not all over: There had been fourteen men between me and the lead, and before the afternoon was over, a half dozen or more held or challenged for the title. 'This was, to put it mildly, the wildest Open ever,' said *Sports Illustrated*. For me, the birdies disappeared, but the pars survived. The final five holes at Cherry Hills are a punishing finishing stretch: Ben Hogan, then forty-seven, felt it, and he faded here; Nicklaus was twenty-one, and so did he. I managed to play each of those last five holes in par and to come in with a 65 for the eighteen-hole round. Boldness had paid off: That surge at the start was, in the words of golf writer Herbert Warren Wind, 'the most explosive stretch of sub-par golf any golfer has ever produced in the championship. . . .' I finished the tournament with a seventy-two-hole score of 280. That was enough to give me the US Open championship and, as it developed, a certain hold on history.

For the 'charge' didn't stop there. It was not, in the long perspective, to be confined solely to one round or one tournament. It became a sort of phenomenon that marked my career: In the period 1960–63, I was to win thirty-two tournaments – and go on to become the first million-dollar winner in golf history.

From *Go For Broke!* by Arnold Palmer with Barry Furlong
(William Kimber, London, 1974).

The Genius of Nicklaus – Greatest of Them All?

Herbert Warren Wind

Nicklaus was determined to be the greatest golfer that ever lived from the time he was a teenager. He has won twenty major tournaments in a career that has spanned a quarter of a century, including five Masters over three decades from 1963 to 1986. He was the prodigy who didn't burn himself out. He could falter in sight of victory as he did in the 1963 Masters against the main contender Sam Snead, and then come scorching back to regain the lead, which is the hardest way to win any tournament. The first time we played together he didn't say much, his game was off. But there's always a great atmosphere playing with him. His unique blend of temperament and will to win, of technique plus deep golf thinking about the course and shot, is analysed by Herbert Warren Wind, writing in 1963.

I.W.

When golf authorities rank the great golfers of all time, a sizeable percentage of them place Nicklaus on the top level, along with Harry Vardon, Bobby Jones, and Ben Hogan, who were as preeminent in their eras as Nicklaus has been over the last two decades. While I am inclined to go along with this point of view, I can readily understand why many people close to the game consider Nicklaus nothing less than the greatest golfer ever. To a large extent, a golfer's place in history has traditionally been determined by his achievements in the major championships. Played on long, rigorous courses that require expert shotmaking, these championships are the British Open (established in 1860); the British Amateur (1885); the United States Open and United States Amateur (1895); our Professional Golfers Association (1916); and the Masters (1934). Professional golfers, of course, cannot play in amateur championships, and amateurs cannot play in the PGA. Before Nicklaus came along, the highest number of major championships any golfer had won was thirteen. This mark was set by Jones in the eight-year period between 1923 and 1930, and was thereafter believed to be out of reach. Nicklaus, who should be competing for several years to come, has already won nineteen [now twenty with the 1986 Masters].

   To my mind, the most effective way to convey what Nicklaus has done is simply to set down the dates of those nineteen victories, championship by championship. Before turning professional, in 1961, he won the US Amateur twice, in 1959 and 1961. He has won the British Open three times, in 1966, 1970, and 1978; the US Open four times, in 1962, 1967, 1972, and 1980; the PGA five times, in 1963, 1971, 1973, 1975, and 1980; and the Masters five times, in 1963, 1965, 1966, 1972, and 1975.

Moreover, Nicklaus has been close to victory in these events on many other occasions. He has finished second or in a tie for second three times in the PGA, four times in the Masters, four times in the US Open, and no fewer than seven times in the British Open. It is hard to believe, but for fifteen straight years, from 1966 to 1980, he finished among the top six players in the British Open. Altogether, in a total of eighty-four major championships he played from 1962 through 1982 he failed to finish in the first ten only twenty-three times. And Nicklaus has been as all-conquering and consistent in tournaments other than the majors. A golfer who travels well, he has, for example, taken the Australian Open six times. He has won sixty-nine tournaments on the PGA tour – a total approached by none of his contemporaries. He was the first to win more than $4 million.

Golf may be the most difficult of all games to play well. For one thing, it is the only major outdoor game in which the player must generate his own power as he strikes a stationary ball from a stationary position. To do this and at the same time hit the ball accurately toward a target requires mastery of a very sophisticated technique. For another thing, since the game is played on natural terrain the player must continually adjust his hitting action to the lie of the ball, not to mention the wind and weather. All the great champions have necessarily been extremely sound shotmakers, but what really separates them from the talented golfers on the level just below them is their deep, unshakeable belief in themselves. This engenders the determination and the self-possession that enable them, in this game where the slightest faulty movement can lead to a costly error, and even to disaster, to rise to the occasion and produce their finest golf at the most important moments. For all the gracefulness of his swing, Jones was a high-strung young man who felt the stress of tournament play so acutely that during one championship he lost eighteen pounds. He had the ability, however, to gather his concentration as he prepared to play each shot. Hogan, from the beginning to the end of a round, could insulate himself from the world and go about his golf with white-hot intensity. He was oblivious of everything else. Nicklaus's mind works unceasingly during a tournament round, but at the same time he appears to be cooler and calmer than any other golfer of the modern era. He seems to actually thrive on pressure. Out on the fairway, surrounded by thousands of exuberant fans, he wears the tournament golfer's invariable frown of concentration, but he seems completely relaxed – as much at home as if he were taking a solitary walk in the country over a pleasant stretch of land he has known all his life.

In a word, Nicklaus has the ideal temperament for a golfer, and, combined with his physical stamina and phenomenal will to win, it helps to explain the miracles he has performed at many critical moments. Let me briefly describe three that come to mind. In the playoff for the 1970 British Open at St Andrews, he held a one-shot lead over Doug Sanders as they came to the eighteenth, a straightaway par 4 only 354 yards long. When there is a good following wind, as there was that afternoon, a big hitter like Nicklaus can drive the green. Sanders, with the honour, played a fine tee shot that ended up a few yards short of the green. Nicklaus then removed the sweater he was wearing – he did not mean this action to be as dramatic as it was – and swatted a huge drive dead on line for the pin. He had, in fact, hit the ball too well. It bounced onto the green and rolled over the back edge into some fairly high rough. Sanders had his birdie all the way, so it was up to Nicklaus to get down in two to win. From a difficult downhill lie in the rough, he played a delicate wedge chip that stopped eight feet from the hole. His putt looked as if it might be slipping a shade too much to the right, but it caught a corner of the cup and fell in. By and large, Nicklaus has been a very solid putter throughout his career – an invaluable asset.

In the 1972 US Open, at Pebble Beach, Nicklaus, with two holes to go, apparently had the championship won, for he led the nearest man by three strokes. Still, anything can happen on the last two holes at Pebble Beach. The seventeenth, a par 3, 218 yards long, is tightly bordered on the left by Carmel Bay, and the green is severely bunkered. With the wind in his face, Nicklaus chose to play a 1-iron. He ripped a beautiful shot through the wind which almost went into the hole on the fly. The ball landed inches short of the cup, bounced up and struck the flagstick, and came to rest inches away. He tapped it in for his birdie, and that was that.

Three years later, in the Masters, Nicklaus was involved in a tremendous battle in the fourth, and last, round with Johnny Miller and Tom Weiskopf. Throughout the long afternoon, all three played some of the most spectacular golf shots imaginable, and the outcome was not decided until the final green, where both Miller and Weiskopf, who were the last twosome, missed makeable birdie putts that would have tied them with Nicklaus. In retrospect, Nicklaus had played the winning shot on the sixteenth. When he came to that hole, a 190-yard par 3 over one of the largest and loveliest water hazards in golf, he trailed Weiskopf by a stroke. The pin was set that day, as it usually is on the fourth round of the Masters, in the hardest position – near the front of the narrow terrace at the back right-hand corner of the green. It takes a superlative shot, with true backspin on it, to hit and hold that terrace, because there is little margin for error: a large bunker sits in wait just beyond the green. Nicklaus, going with a 5-iron, played a so-so shot that ended up on the left side of the green well below the slope of the terrace and some forty feet from the pin. He took a long time studying his putt, to make certain he had read the line correctly. He then rapped the ball firmly up the slope and watched it break some eighteen inches to the left in a gradual curve and dive into the cup. That birdie put him in a tie for the lead with Weiskopf, and when Weiskopf three-putted the sixteenth for a bogey 4 Nicklaus was out in front to say.

Nicklaus is unquestionably the best fourth-round golfer there has ever been. Even when he starts the last eighteen so many strokes off the pace that his chances seem hopeless, it is not his nature to think for a moment of conceding the tournament to anyone else. He is never more dangerous than at these times, and it takes a stout-hearted competitor, such as Lee Trevino or Tom Watson, to stand up to the threat that Nicklaus poses. For most golfers trying to protect a lead on the last day, there is nothing more rattling than to look up at one of the leaderboards positioned around the course and see that Nicklaus, who has slowly mounted one of his celebrated rushes, has picked up three birdies in a row and, now in full flight, is within striking distance of overtaking them.

Nicklaus's awesome career impresses on one how valuable it is in golf, or anything else, to start with the proper fundamentals. His father, Louis Charles Nicklaus, Jr, a warm, companionable man who was a successful pharmacist in Columbus, Ohio, made his home in the suburb of Upper Arlington, and was a member of the nearby Scioto Country Club, the scene of Jones' victory in the 1926 Open. His son began golf at ten. Jack played some with his father; he joined the Friday-morning class for junior members that Jack Grout, the Scioto professional, held in the summer; and every two or three weeks he took a private lesson from Grout, a gifted student of the golf swing.

As Grout saw it there were three main fundamentals. First, the head must be kept still throughout the swing. It is the balance centre, and if a golfer allows it to move it throws everything else off: the movements of his body, his arc, his timing. Second, balance also depends on footwork. The basis of footwork is rolling the ankles correctly. On the backswing, the left ankle and heel roll in toward the right foot, and the right foot remains firmly planted. On the downswing, the left ankle and heel roll back to their original position, where they remain planted, and the right ankle and heel roll in toward the left foot. Golfers with analytical minds, such as Jones, realized early that good golf is played on the inside of the feet. Third, when a golfer is young and limber he should try to develop the widest possible arc by making a full shoulder turn and fully extending his arms on the backswing, downswing, and follow-through. That way, he will be able to utilize all his latent power. The boy who learns to hit the ball hard and far can work on improving his accuracy when he is older. Nicklaus learned very quickly from Grout. The two not only communicated well but liked and respected each other, and they became fast friends.

Like Jones, who was only nine when he won his club's junior championship and only fourteen when he first played in the US Amateur (and won his first two matches), Nicklaus was a prodigy. At twelve, after shooting eight straight rounds of 80, he broke the barrier with a 74. At thirteen, he broke 70 at Scioto for the first time. To do this, he had to eagle the eighteenth, a good par 5, which he did by reaching the green with a drive and a 2-iron and holing a thirty-five-foot putt. That was also the year he made his début in the US Junior Amateur championship. At fifteen, he qualified for the US Amateur. He played well in his first-round match but lost on the last hole to Bob Gardner, a golfer of Walker Cup calibre. At sixteen, he won the Ohio State Open from a field of experienced professionals after take the lead on the third round with a 64. At seventeen, he qualified for the 1957 US Open, which was held at Inverness, in Toledo. He played two loose 80s and failed to make the thirty-six-hole cut by ten strokes. In the summer of 1958, he strengthened his chances of making the Walker Cup team the next year by winning the Trans-Mississippi Amateur, a top tournament, and finishing twelfth in his first PGA tour event – the Rubber City Open, in Akron, in which he was paired with such stars as Julius Boros, Tommy Bolt, and Art Wall. Many boy wonders in sports fade away when they are still young men. Sometimes they lose the precocious skill that had set them apart. Sometimes they lose their enthusiasm – they have had enough of the spotlight and wish to lead an altogether different kind of life. When Nicklaus, at nineteen, was named to the American Walker Cup team for the 1959 match in this biennial series against a team representing Great Britain and Ireland, it was as clear as could be that here was one young man who, given his background in golf and his ardent and justified ambition, would almost surely mature into a much more proficient player and possibly go on to become an authentic champion. In that Walker Cup match, which was played at Muirfield, outside Edinburgh, he adjusted splendidly to the demands of linksland golf and won both his singles and his foursomes.

That summer, he captured his first national championship, the US Amateur, at the ease course of the Broadmoor Golf Club, in Colorado Springs, beating the defending champion Charlie Coe on the last hole by sinking an eight-foot birdie putt. He was on his way.

Grout is the only teacher Nicklaus has had. Since boyhood, Nicklaus has understood the workings of his swing extremely well, and as a rule he has been able to take care of small adjustments himself. He is one of the few golfers who can often do this even during a vital tournament round. There have been times, though, when he has accepted knowledgeable friends' suggestions, and these have proved helpful in correcting some faulty movement of a minor nature which he had been unable to pinpoint himself.

But down through the years, whenever something basic about the way he was hitting the ball was bothering him, or if he simply wanted to have his setup at the ball or his swing checked out, he has always gone to Jack Grout. When they are on the practice tee together, it generally takes Grout no time at all to spot the minutest departure from Nicklaus's customary swing pattern, suggest a remedy, and begin to work on it with Nicklaus.

In 1975, Nicklaus asked Grout to become the professional at the Muirfield Village Golf Club, in Dublin, Ohio, outside Columbus. Muirfield Village is a real-estate development in which Nicklaus has an interest; he was a co-designer of its golf course, the venue each May of the Memorial Tournament. Grout has been at Muirfield Village since 1975, except in the wintertime, when the course is closed.

When old golf hands discuss when it was that it first occurred to them that Nicklaus might turn out to be not just a first-class golfer but a rare champion, more often than not they cite his performance in one or another of three events that took place early in his career: the 1960 World Amateur Team championship, at Merion, an exacting course near Philadelphia, in which his four-round total of 269 (66, 67, 68, 68) was thirteen strokes lower than the runner-up's; the 1960 US Open, at Cherry Hills, outside Denver, in which he was second, only two strokes behind Arnold Palmer, then the premier golfer in the world; and the 1962 US Open, at Oakmont, outside Pittsburgh, where he caught Palmer with an almost flawless last round of 69 and defeated him the next day in their playoff. While I concur that this cluster of events was significant, I would like to add some personal comments. At Merion, Nicklaus hit the ball so squarely and sweetly over the seventy-two holes that I thought he must be having one of those improbable streaks in which people play way over their heads – no one could be that good at twenty. I failed to appreciate the significance of Nicklaus's showing at Cherry Hills, because a large share of my attention was appropriated by Hogan's gallant bid for a fifth Open title and by Palmer's dashing last round of 65. And I must confess that Nicklaus's victory at Oakmont also surprised me. It was as if it had happened a bit ahead of schedule: I'd thought that it would take even a Nicklaus a year or two to win the Open. I had underrated not only his skill but his fortitude.

After winning the 1963 Masters, Nicklaus had established himself as a golfer who could play all the shots, but, understandably, it was his thunderous power off the tee that attracted the most attention. He was the Snead of his generation – the longest driver among the players who were regularly in contention in the big events. He lacked the ineffable rhythm and tempo that made Snead an aesthetic treat, but he was thrilling in his own way. Watching him unload on the ball and smash it three hundred yards down the fairway packed an excitement that never lessened, no matter how often an admirer had been in his gallery. Until 1969, when he went on a diet that radically altered his appearance, Nicklaus, who stands five feet eleven and three-quarters inches, weighed about two hundred and ten pounds. This young Percheron had especially heavy legs and thighs, which helped to explain his power, but the distance he hit the ball was not the result of brute force. Growing up under Grout's guidance, he understood from an early age the four main sources of power. He listed them like this in his book *The Greatest Game of All*, which was published in 1969: '1. a club of proper weight and balance; 2. a long, wide arc; 3. speed of movement from the right side to the left at the start of the downswing; 4. the speed with which the left hip, having stopped its move forward, spins to the rear in the hitting zone.' As goes without saying, the body movements involved in a power swing are infinitely complicated, and few players succeed in mastering them. Nicklaus was able to because of his extraordinary talent and his willingness to put in the untold hours on the practice tee that finally made the synchronization of the multiple movements almost instinctive.

When Nicklaus's colossal power comes up in conversation, golf fans tend to recall different tournaments. Some go back as far as the 1960 World Amateur Team championship. (It was then that people started to speculate about Nicklaus's possibly being the longest driver in the game.) Others immediately think of the 1965 Masters – perhaps the most popular choice. That April, Nicklaus flew the ball such great distances that he made the Augusta National, which measures 6,905 yards from the back tees, seem like one of those little nine-hole courses that used to be operated at old summer hotels in New England. He broke the previous Masters record total of 274 by three strokes, with rounds of 67, 71, 64, and 69, and finished nine strokes ahead of his nearest competitor. On his third round, in particular, he was driving the ball so far that on the ten par-4 holes – only two are under four hundred yards long – he had only a pitch left on his second shot: he used his 6-iron once, his 7-iron once, his 8-iron three times, his pitching wedge four times, and his sand wedge once. Jones, the founder of the Masters, and its host, summed up Nicklaus's performance perfectly when he said at the presentation ceremony, 'Jack is playing an entirely different game – a game I'm not even familiar with.' When I think of his power, as a veteran Nicklaus watcher, I think of the shots he tore through a bitter wind off the North Sea when, in a losing cause, he chased Gary Player down the final holes at Carnoustie in the 1968 British Open.

Nicklaus's victory in the 1966 British Open, at Muirfield, also comes vividly to mind. This takes a little explaining. That summer, Muirfield was modified a bit to keep the big hitters in check. At about the 250-yard mark, the fairways, which were narrow to begin with, were gradually pinched in so that at the 275-yard mark they were scarcely twenty yards wide. Furthermore, the rough bordering the fairways was allowed to grow almost two feet high. Nicklaus made the adjustments called for. Over the seventy-two holes of the championship, he used his driver only seventeen times. He drove with his 3-wood ten times, and the rest of the way he went with either his 1-iron or his 3-iron off the tee, depending on how the wind was blowing. His decision to put accuracy ahead of distance and his discipline in refusing to stray from this strategy was the basis of his victory. At the same time, from the point of view of power the most sensational single hole I have ever watched Nicklaus play was the seventeenth hole of the 1966 British Open. The seventeenth at Muirfield is a 528-yard par 5 that bends sharply to the left about two hundred and twenty yards from the tee and then runs more or less straight to a smallish green tucked in a hollow beyond a daunting mound. As Nicklaus stood on the tee, he knew that he would have to birdie either the seventeenth or the eighteenth to win. With the wind blowing from right to left, he drove with a 3-iron, to make sure the ball didn't carry too far and end up in the rough on the right-hand side of the twisting fairway. On his second shot, with the wind directly behind him, he selected a 5-iron. He played a superb shot. The ball landed on the small front apron about fifteen feet short of the green, as he had planned; it then hopped up and rolled to within eighteen feet of the pin. He was down in two for the crucial birdie. Even allowing for the helping wind and the lively British ball, imagine reaching a 528-yard hole with a 3-iron and a 5-iron!

While Nicklaus has a genius for hitting a golf ball, it should be brought out that he possesses uncommon physical coordination for sports in general. He got his size early: at thirteen, he stood five feet ten and weighed a hundred and sixty-five pounds. In junior high school in Upper Arlington, he was the quarterback, punter, and placekicker on the football team; the centre on the basketball team; the catcher on the baseball team; and, surprisingly, a sprinter on the track team, who could run the hundred-yard dash in eleven seconds flat. He might well have had a career in baseball or football, but in high school he gave both of them up and concentrated on basketball, his favourite team sport.

In college – he went to Ohio State, his father's school – he limited himself strictly to golf. His range of sports interests is wide. He has been a devoted fisherman since boyhood. In conjunction with his golf travels, he has fished the world over. (For example, before playing in the 1978 Australian Open he fished for black marlin off the Great Barrier Reef, and last summer he stopped off in Iceland after the British Open to fish for salmon.) At his home in North Palm Beach, he has two grass tennis courts – a rarity in Florida. They are part of a grassed-over plot adjoining his house which serves Nicklaus, his wife, Barbara, and their five children as a playground. After the golf season ends, he plays a lot of tennis. The workout he gets from a couple of sets helps to keep him in shape, but, in addition, he is fascinated by the game, and he plays it well. (On most Saturday mornings in the autumn and early winter, Nicklaus and seven middle-aged friends, each wearing a special 'Day Camp' T-shirt, assemble at his courts for doubles and singles.) At the side of the house, attached to the garage, are a basketball backboard and hoop. When the spirit moves him,

Nicklaus still goes out and practises shooting by himself or with his kids. He also still enjoys throwing and kicking a football. He can be called, with no exaggeration, a brilliant passer and an astounding punter. (I have seen him boom kicks that were forty yards high and carried sixty yards.) During the last decade, he has developed one new sports passion – skiing. Since 1975, the Nicklaus family has spent nearly every Christmas holiday skiing at Vail, Colorado, or Park City, Utah. All seven Nicklauses are of one mind: skiing is the ideal family sport.

Nicklaus inherited both his love of sports and much of his athletic ability from his father. In high school, Charlie Nicklaus – he was always Charlie to his friends – starred in football, basketball, and baseball. From the start of Jack's career, his father was always on hand at major events. His greatest joy was to watch his son play golf. Until his death, in 1970, he was a familiar figure at the championships, his name purposely removed from his tournament badge as he hurried along in Jack's gallery with his pals from Columbus. Of all the stage mothers and sports fathers I have met, I would put Charlie Nicklaus right up at the top. He was careful, for instance, to inculcate a deep sense of sportsmanship in his son. 'My dad knew how to get his points across,' Nicklaus recalled not long ago. 'One day when I was eleven, I was playing with him at Scioto. We were on the fifteenth, and I had an 8-iron to the green. I put the shot in a bunker, and then I threw my club almost to the bunker. My father turned to me and said, very clearly, "Young man, that will be the last club I'll ever see you throw or hear of you throwing, or you're not going to be playing this game." I've never thrown a club since.' He was silent for a moment, started to laugh, and added, 'I must admit that I've tossed a few over to the bag, but never with any kind of force behind them.'

Nicklaus has given more and more time in the past decade to building courses. He has found it stimulating and fulfilling. When he elects to retire from competitive golf, the bulk of his time and energy will undoubtedly go into golf-course architecture.

He has expanded his vistas in many directions, developing a good mind, through exercise, into an excellent one. His memory can be astonishing. He has learned to understand other people better, and has become more generous of spirit. All in all, he has matured very well – particularly when one takes into account how long he has been in the spotlight and the disruptive effect that this kind of thing has had on many celebrities. My guess is that Nicklaus has always been a much more complicated man than most of us recognized. A profoundly private person of considerable sensitivity, he prefers to keep his problems to himself. He has had his share of them. To name only one, he could not have picked a worse time to burst onto the golf scene. The reigning hero in 1962, Nicklaus's first full year as a professional, was Arnold Palmer, the most popular golfer since Bobby Jones' heyday. A handsome, magnetic man who approached golf with a dramatic boldness, Palmer, who is ten years older than Nicklaus, had the gift of communicating his feelings to his galleries. He had another extraordinary gift: He was at his best when the going was hard, and would come charging down the stretch on the last round with a barrage of birdies that often carried him to victory. Small wonder that his galleries were so immense they became known as Arnie's Army. After winning his first major championship, the Masters, in 1958, Palmer won the Masters and the US Open in 1960, the British Open in 1961, and the Masters and the British Open in 1962. In between these feats, he had torrid streaks on the tour, during which he performed his magic almost on a weekly basis, cheered on by his army and by the enraptured millions who watched him on television. Palmer continued to play fine golf for many seasons, but by 1965 it was clear, if it hadn't been before, that, remarkable as he was, he was not as good a golfer as Nicklaus. In the eyes of Palmer's fans, Nicklaus, the corpulent, expressionless kid who had supplanted their hero, was an unwelcome usurper. Nicklaus took all this in, stoically, and got through it. For several years, even when he stood alone at the top, he had a limited appeal for the average golf fan. Most of the regulars in his galleries were people who had been close to golf all their lives and could appreciate the beauty of his shotmaking. Then, slowly, starting in about 1970, the situation began to change. Nicklaus not only earned an ever-increasing esteem at home and throughout the world but also emerged as one of the most popular figures in modern sports. I can remember no occasion in golf quite like his victory in the US Open at Baltusrol in 1980, eighteen years after he won his first Open. The upstart kid had become a venerated champion among champions. In Nicklaus's own opinion, he has never played a better nine holes than the second nine on the final round of that 1980 Open. The ecstatic, roaring thousands who greeted his sure progress down the last few holes seemed to me at the time to have something of the quality of the worshipful multitudes in Cecil B. De Mille's motion-picture extravaganzas about the heroes of the Bible and early Christian Rome.

On reflection, the comparison is not inapt. If ever there was what has come to be known in sports jargon as a 'living legend,' it is Nicklaus. At Baltusrol that June afternoon, three generations of golf fans – most of them had often watched his exploits on television, but only on television – were ecstatic at being present to witness Nicklaus, in all his glory, once again outplaying and outscoring a strong field of challengers.

Since we live in the age of the 'image' as well as the 'living legend,' it is perhaps not surprising that one factor in the new popularity Nicklaus gained was a drastic change in his appearance. In 1969, he let his blond hair, which he had worn rather short, grow longer, as other young men were doing. The reaction was very favorable, and this naturally pleased him. That autumn, when he and Barbara were flying home from London after the Ryder Cup match, the last event on his schedule that year, he began to think about his weight. He had always had a hearty appetite and had steadily become heavier. He now weighed two hundred and ten pounds or thereabouts. To his admirers, he was the Golden Bear, but to the claques of his rivals he was Fat Jack or Ohio Fats. He had let things go too far and too long, he told his wife on the plane, and he was determined to do something about it immediately. Once back home, he went on the Weight Watchers diet, and he stuck to it. The results were startling. In little over four weeks, he dropped twenty pounds, and in just the right places: He lost six inches around the hips and an inch and a half around the waist. The extra weight around his chin and neck also disappeared. The new Nicklaus was a younger-looking and much more attractive man. Realizing this, he watched his eating habits as vigilantly as a ballet star, and has continued to. The rise in Nicklaus's popularity rested on some things more meaningful than his new look, however. During his first years as a professional, when he sensed that the loyal followers of Palmer and other established stars begrudged him his sudden prominence, his reaction when he was playing tournaments had been to go into a sort of shell. In the nineteen-seventies, he began to relax more on the course and, at length, to be entirely himself. Watching him work on a round became an enchanting experience: one could follow his thinking practically step by step as he prepared to play each stroke, and this made the brilliant shots he brought off all the more spectacular. (Nicklaus believes that setting up correctly at the ball is ninety percent of golf.) As the years passed and the pressure of tournament golf became more and more intense, most of the new young stars flashed for only a brief period. Nicklaus continued to roll on and on, though. His longevity has been the product of his pertinacity no less than of his skill. He has been able to endure several long, discouraging slumps and play his way out of them. Four times, he has done this by winning a major championship – the 1967 US Open, the 1970 British Open, the 1978 British Open, and the 1980 US Open. There is nothing like carrying off one of the four majors to renew a golfer's confidence, and, apparently, there is nothing like confidence to restore the timing in a golfer's swing.

Few golfers know their swing as well as Nicklaus knows his. 'In 1961 and 1962, I was very pleased with the way I hit the ball,' he said the evening of my visit, when he was reflecting on his play during different phases of his career. 'I hit it long and straight those two years. In the middle sixties, I wasn't quite as good with the driver, but I was very sound with the irons. Then, toward the late sixties, my iron play went off. I played on power for several years. In the nineteen-seventies, I had some new problems. When I lost twenty pounds in 1969, I lost twenty yards. Being lighter was only incidental – I lost distance because my swing was starting to deteriorate. I got too upright. During the seventies, I wasn't a good striker of the ball at all. Oh, I won a lot of tournaments. In both 1972 and 1975, I won two major championships – my game happened to be at its best in those important weeks.'

By working on his swing he got back the twenty yards he lost. 'Of course, I practise now more than I used to. You have to when you get older. But I'm more excited about playing golf than I've been in a long time. I suppose the real reason for this is that I know I'm not going to play tournament golf that much longer. I don't want to go out of golf having let my game just dwindle away. I want to make sure that each year that I play I give it everything I've got. As long as I play tournaments, I'm going to work at it, I'm going to make it happen, and if I can't make it happen then I won't play.'

When the day comes that designing courses replaces playing tournament golf as Nicklaus's chief occupation, he will be remembered for his sportsmanship as well as for his achievements. Considerate and gracious in victory, he stands alone in his time as a golfer who is able in defeat to go out toward his rivals with warmth and a genuine understanding of what winning means to them. Nicklaus's father instilled high precepts in him, but there is also something at the core of Nicklaus's character which underlies his attitude and conduct. He believes that there are definite ways a golfer must act in specific situations, and that if he fails to, the failure detracts immeasurably from the essence and worth of the game. There have been many examples of this in his career, but I will note just three. In the 1969 Ryder Cup match, at Birkdale, in

England, the three-day competition came down to the last singles – Nicklaus vs. Tony Jacklin. All even as they played the eighteenth, a short par 5, Nicklaus lay 3 five feet from the cup, and Jacklin 3 two feet from the cup. Nicklaus's putt was a testing one. He took his time over it and holed it. He then turned to Jacklin and told him his putt was good – he was conceding it. This halved singles made the final score of the team match 16–16. Some people thought that Nicklaus should have made Jacklin hole out, but Nicklaus felt that what he did was the right thing in those exceptional circumstances.

In the 1977 British Open, at Turnberry, in Scotland, the championship turned out to be a two-man fight between Nicklaus and Watson, who, as it happened, were paired together on the last two rounds. Nothing in the history of golf quite matches their scoring and shotmaking over those thirty-six holes. Tied for the lead at the start of the third day, each was around in 65, six under par. On the fourth day, Nicklaus, despite a heroic birdie on the last hole, took 66 strokes – one stroke too many, for Watson had another 65. As they walked off the last green, Nicklaus flung his arm over Watson's shoulder and, smiling broadly, told him how wonderfully he had played. The two were involved in a similarly unforgettable moment at the close of the 1982 US Open, at Pebble Beach. Playing three twosomes ahead of Watson, Nicklaus moved into contention on the last round with a string of five birdies on the front nine. Coming down the stretch, they were tied for the lead, but on the par-3 seventeenth Watson played what proved to be the winning shot: he holed a little wedge pitch from the greenside rough for a birdie. When Watson completed his round, there was Nicklaus, waiting off the eighteenth green to greet him heartily and congratulate him. Golf is one of the rare sports in which there has been no drop in the level of sportsmanship over the last decade, and I imagine that the example Nicklaus has set has had something to do with this happy state of affairs.

From *Following Through* by Herbert Warren Wind
(Macmillan, London, 1986).

Mind Over Matter

Gary Player

Gary Player is three times winner of the British Open, in 1959, 1968 and 1974. He and Vardon are the only two players to have won it in three different decades. He is three times winner of the Masters, winner of the US Open and twice winner of the US PGA. Player is the doughtiest fighter in the game of golf, which is why I admire him so much – and, of course, he is another little 'un (5 feet 7 inches tall) who hits the ball a long way. I don't subscribe to all of Gary's habits, such as not drinking alcohol, tea or coffee. Nor do I wear black to absorb the heat of the sun, or do lots of hard-graft exercises from press-ups to running which he reckons enabled him to summon the extra strength to hit the par 5s in two. His attitude to practice is more rigorous than mine. But his 'never say die' spirit is exactly what I believe in. He also believes, as I do, that medal play is better than match play because in medal every shot counts and it makes for better golfers.

To the purist Gary's swing may seem a bit flat. When, on his first trip to Britain in 1955, he asked one well-known player his opinion of his golf, the man advised him to go back to South Africa! Gary, of course, thrives on adversity and on adverse comment. When he went seven down to Tony Lema in the World Match Play in 1965, he heard a spectator say: 'Player has really had it now.' That was enough to spark one of the most spectacular recoveries in golf which, he said, 'contains my whole life story'. Here's how he puts his philosophy of mind over matter.

I.W.

In the make-up of a professional golfer, I would say that only seventy per cent of his success is due to his ability to hit the ball – the rest comes from his superior mental approach to the game, his ability to relax and to out-think his opponent on the course.

How often have you heard it said of an athlete: 'He would be the best of them all, if only he would train harder,' and of a golfer, 'He is undoubtedly a great player, but he takes the game far too seriously.'

I have learned that in sport there are no 'ifs' and 'buts.' It is very simple to me: the fact that a certain athlete does not train hard enough is the reason why he is not as good as others who do. The grim-faced golfer would not be half as good if he went round the course laughing and joking with everybody. It is very much a matter of temperament, and you can no more ask a champion to change his mental approach than you could tell him to alter his style. Both are very much a part of him and both are responsible for his success.

In other words, the athlete who trains hard can be thankful for that capacity for hard work that might be denied his opponents. A man without this gift, or whose nerve cracks under strain, must accept this as a basic weakness in his make-up, for in many cases no matter how hard he tries to overcome these handicaps, he cannot succeed completely.

Temperament is very much a matter of birth I feel, although, like many other aspects of the game, when it is applied to golf it can be cultivated to an extent.

Still, I doubt if the man afflicted with nerves under pressure can ever really be taught to control his emotions. I might add that everybody feels pressure, even Bobby Locke and Ben Hogan, who have the best temperaments I know, although they are totally different in character: Hogan grim and often scowling, with determination written in his every action, Locke expressionless, unruffled and patient but no less determined to win.

These men, like Bobby Jones and Byron Nelson, although the latter's progress ended sooner than one would have expected, had the ability – perhaps gift is a better word – to remain apparently calm and force themselves to function normally even with their nerves screaming.

There are also examples at the other end of the scale, good golfers in every other respect but who fail in the moment of crisis. These attacks of nerves are apparent even in amateur golfers, who find themselves hooking the last putt that would have won them a couple of balls, or breaking down after playing the first few holes in par or better. When this happens in America they say the player 'choked.'

It is perhaps rather a callous way of putting it, but it describes the action aptly. These players do in fact choke on the surge of emotion that in the end overwhelms them.

If I have not exactly choked, I have come pretty close to it in my early days, so I know what the feeling is like. And I won't easily forget missing a three-foot putt on the last green to lose the 1959 South African Open to the then amateur Denis Hutchinson. So unexpected was the lapse that there were those who said I missed the putt on purpose to avoid a play-off, because I was due to leave the next day for America.

Perhaps I should have been flattered by these views, but in fact I always play golf to win: I tried for my life on that putt and when it missed I was as shocked as anybody.

Afterwards I was not as upset as I might have been, for when I looked back on the tournament I realised it was not the putt that had lost me the title but the fact that I had scored seventy-five in my last round, compared to Hutchinson's seventy. When I score seventy-five in perfect conditions I reckon I deserve to lose. Perhaps that does not sound so nice in print, but I have set myself a high standard in this game and when I fall below it I really hate myself for it.

I think one must always be greedy in golf, even in amateur golf. If you are not always striving might and main for the biggest win or the best possible score, your thinking must be negative.

I found this out in a 'challenge' series in my own country against the former American Open champion Tommy Bolt. I had Bolt's temperament in mind when we met in the first match in Johannesburg, where conditions of nap on the greens and altitude are almost unique in world golf. I got two holes up on Bolt very quickly and I began worrying that if I went too far ahead the American might stop trying to fight the strange conditions and allow me too easy a victory, thus spoiling the series.

You might say at this stage that I was presumptuous in thinking that I had a walk-over on my hands when my opponent was a man who had proved himself to be one of the best golfers in the world. In many ways you might be right, but let me assure you that my misguided reasoning was not the result of an exaggerated opinion of my own capabilities. Rather was I overconscious of the fact that all previous visitors to South Africa, including Sam Snead and the British Open champion, Alf Padgam, not to mention a host of others, had floundered in the conditions and had never really shown their home form.

Anyway, that is how I thought and, walking along with my two-up lead, I began telling my friends that it might be a good thing for Bolt's confidence and the match if he were to take a lead. I began hoping that his game would improve. For the first time I did not want to crush my opponent into the ground.

I was not feeling too friendly at the end of the match after I had congratulated Bolt on his one-up victory, nor at the end of the series which the American won by four games to one.

I will admit that Bolt's victory in my own country and within months of my winning the British Open, took me down a peg or two, and I am not making any excuses now, but I am convinced that I contributed towards my own defeat by my negative thinking in the first match. I never at any stage attempted to pull a shot to allow Bolt an advantage he might otherwise never have won, but in feeling sorry for him as it were, I allowed the devil to go out of my own game. Instead of exerting all my concentration upon each and every shot, so that they drove like arrows into Bolt's failing confidence, I became subconsciously content with the not-so-good shot. When it became apparent that Bolt needed no encouragement to play better in South Africa than any previous visitor had done, and my lead began to slip away, I fought as hard for victory as ever I have, but I never again in that match recaptured the 'killer' instinct which I consider necessary to winning golf.

In other other matches of the series Bolt beat me fair and square, but I have often thought since what the result might have been had I hammered away at Bolt when I had the best chance of gaining mental and practical superiority – when he was still new to the conditions.

Like a boxer who wades into a helpless opponent against the ropes, or a Rugby captain who orders his flankers to harass the opposing fly-half, a golfer is also entitled to take the greatest possible advantage of any weakness in his opponent's game.

I have mentioned this incident against Bolt at some length as I want to stress the importance of playing to win, especially if a golfer hopes to improve his game. Also, the killer instinct, which this attitude is sometimes dramatically called, helps to cultivate temperament, the subject with which we began this chapter, and it certainly helps to overcome those periodic fits of choking I mentioned.

A golfer who plays one round light-heartedly, knocking up putts without taking proper care, or who does not mind hitting a bad shot because he is so far ahead of his opponent that it does not really matter, cannot logically expect to sink crucial putts or play his best when he really needs to.

Winning golf, like everything else in the game, has to be practised and, I advise all club golfers to strive as hard as possible at all times for victory, even if they are playing with members of the handicapping committee. Obviously, an amateur golfer does not want to become known around the club as a pot-hunting, ball-grabbing so-and-so, always on the make, or even as a fanatic with whom it is no pleasure to play. One can still play the game hard and pleasantly. One can still win graciously, although you will find that if you win often enough you are bound to excite some criticism.

I have another reason for saying you should always play hard to win, apart from the fact that it improves your golf. I think you owe it to your opponent. For my own part I should feel insulted if I found out that my opponent had purposely eased up because he felt sorry for me. If I am in for a six and five hiding, then that is the way I would like it to be. I want no quarter and I expect none. Anyway, a man who cannot take a thrashing in good part is usually intolerable when he is doing the thrashing.

I do not recall a really good player who does not play the game seriously. The top tournament players who blow up during a round very rarely do so through careless-ness or because they funk a particular shot or situation. They are not suddenly overawed by the prospect of victory, because they have trained themselves to accept it, even to expect it. With them it is not so much a case of nerves as imagination, and this applies to nearly all amateurs. I have often heard it said that to be a great golfer you must be just a little stupid – no brains, no imagination. When I hear this I know that the speaker is merely embittered at the success given to others.

Still, I am always reminded of the story told about Hogan. Somebody asked him if it was necessary for a champion golfer to be stupid. He replied: 'No, it is not necessary, but it helps!' What Hogan perhaps meant was that if a golfer cannot control his imagination it would be better that he had none at all.

This applies particularly to amateurs, who generally think too far ahead. If they play the first couple of holes well they immediately begin thinking of how best they can pick up more strokes on par on holes still to come. The standard joke of the golfer who throws away shots towards the end of his round, that he forgot to play the shots because he was thinking of what to say at the prize-giving, is much nearer the truth than many of his listeners realise.

Many amateurs never realise what most professionals learn early in their careers: that a golf-course must be played as it comes, that your score should be recorded faithfully on each hole and then forgotten. It is bad enough trying to sink a four-foot putt or to hit a straight drive without torturing yourself with the fact that 'this putt means another birdie,' or 'if I make the rough now I'll never reach the green.' However hard it may seem at first, forget about such things. Remember what I said earlier. If you always try hard to sink the putts and hit straight drives, you have no reason to panic when a very important shot comes up.

I know when I was younger and had been practising putting without much success, I used to say to myself: 'All right, so you've missed. Now this one is to win the British Open. If you don't sink it now you never will.' But for all the boyish determination and gritting of teeth, I don't think I ever got one of the putts that was going to win me the British Open. When I really had a putt to achieve my greatest ambition, I will not say that I regarded it as just another stroke, but my previous determination to hole every putt, no matter what the circumstances, certainly helped me overcome the worst attack of nerves I have yet experienced.

If it is essential for a golfer to accept the good scores without them turning his head with visions of glory, when such glory has not even begun to be deserved, it is perhaps even more important that he accept bad scores calmly, for just a few indifferent strokes at isolated holes never completely ruined a card yet. It is when these few lapses eat into the soul, creating the ill-tempered or defeatist or don't-care golfer, that the game is lost.

Even I as a professional, who is supposed to have reached greater proficiency than any amateur, expect two bad shots in every round. A scratch golfer is entitled to have five bad shots without cursing his form, and a handicap golfer many more. I reason this way. The same scratch player is entitled to expect two good chip shots, a good bunker shot, and two putts that drop but could just as easily have stayed out. In this way the balance is restored to his game. If he keeps his head and does not become upset at his lapses, he will be in a position to take advantage of his luck. If he allows his game to disintegrate, however, all the luck in the world later on will not help him.

If I had to give just one definition of a good golfer it would be: *the man who has the determination to win and the patience to wait for the breaks.*

Locke is the living proof of this maxim, and if ever I needed convincing of the truth of it, I had it in the East Rand Open in South Africa against Locke in 1959. At the turn in the last round I led Locke by seven strokes, and I think you will agree that I was entitled to feel confident of victory. Not even Locke's many ardent admirers gave him a chance, and who could blame them, either? I would have had to crash like a novice to allow anyone to make up seven strokes on me in only nine holes.

I did not crack. In fact, I did not drop a shot to par on any hole, yet as I stood on the last tee my lead of seven had been cut to one! I think Locke's bid for victory that day in the face of seemingly overwhelming odds is the greatest I have seen. In the end he needed a three-footer for a par four to be home in six-under-par twenty-nine. That he missed the final putt was due more to the fact that I was assured of a four and victory by a stroke than anything else. To me, that tremendous recovery at a time when most golfers would have been inclined to give up the ghost proved Locke's greatness just as conclusively as his four victories in the British Open, or his fine record in America, had done earlier. During all the time I had imagined myself cruising to an easy victory, Locke had never given up hope, so that when the breaks started to come his way in the end, he was mentally equipped to take advantage of them.

This ability to fight is really more the hall-mark of a champion than any technical excellence in the swing. It is apparent in all the best golfers to-day, and never more so than in a man like Doug Ford, who at first sight would hardly excite comment until one had studied the determination and grit with which he plays every shot. In fact, the amateur purists should see in the flesh many of the great players they know only through the cold statistics published in the record books. They would be in for a shock. Perhaps then they would realise that the 'sweet singers' in their own countries for whom they have so much misplaced respect are completely lacking in many of the other, more important, aspects of a champion.

If this were not so and temperament played no part in golf, a player like the Italian, Aldo Cæsera, or the Englishman, Peter Alliss, would have achieved far greater success, for certainly very few golfers I have seen strike the ball better than they do. In Cæsera's case he suffers like many other Europeans on account of his Latin temperament, which is not easy to apply to a cold, calculating sport like golf. I can never mention Cæsera without thinking of the time I saw him carrying no fewer than three putters in his bag – such was his mental approach to putting.

An excitable person, no matter that he becomes that way through success or failure, is immediately at a disadvantage. At all times one should be relaxed, both in mind and body.

I know that I have drawn heavily upon Bobby Locke as an example to the reader, perhaps because I have had more opportunity to study this great player, but also because he possesses nearly all the qualities I consider necessary for success. I have no option but to mention him again now, because of all the great players I have met, none has been more relaxed on the course than Locke. With Locke this studied relaxation, his refusal to do anything in a hurry, is almost exasperating. I know his leisurely ritual after a tournament has been the despair of many a club official who has urgently sought him for the prize-giving.

Yet it is one of the secrets of his success. No man could be as relaxed without a conscious effort to be so. No doubt it is now second nature with Locke, but it could not always have been so. I think even if Locke was dying of thirst, he would stretch out slowly and unhurriedly for the water that would save his life. When he ties his shoes, his actions are those of a surgeon attempting a difficult operation. On the course his movements are so deliberate as to be almost aggravating, and often when playing with him I get a strong urge to creep up behind him and shout 'boo!' Although Locke is not a slow player once he decides on his club, his lagging gait between shots has often been the subject of controversy. But who is to say that Locke is wrong? This tremendous ability to relax of Locke's is part of him as a man and a champion golfer, and as such must be taken into consideration whenever his success or technique is examined, just as certain other players' tantrums are part of their golfing character. I do not believe either Locke or Bolt is very conscious of his actions on the course, or that they are done deliberately as part of an act. I don't say that Bolt has not found his natural bad temper to be a wonderful 'gimmick,' but he cannot be too conscious of it on the course, or his concentration would be divided between the necessity to act and to play golf. His golf would be the first to suffer – and the same goes for Locke and every other golfer with some pecularity which spectators are all too quick to criticise.

In order to relax properly, a golfer's mind should be completely at ease. Before a round or during a tournament nothing should be allowed to upset his tranquillity or to intrude upon his singleness of mind. Because of this, most top golfers I know appear self-centred without really meaning to be – and I include myself in this. They have set routines and they allow nothing to interfere.

Confidence, too, plays a big part in learning to relax; confidence that one has the right equipment and the right clothes. One of the most miserable rounds of golf I have ever played was in borrowed trousers in an exhibition match with Peter Thomson and Locke very early in my career. My own trousers were not good enough, yet the ones I borrowed were miles too big for me round the waist and far too long in the legs. I had to hitch them up with a tie for a belt and I wore a jersey to hide the folds, even though it was the middle of summer. I know people remarked on the jersey and although I felt uncomfortably hot, I dared not take it off. Throughout the round I was conscious of my borrowed pants and could not concentrate as I should have.

I was often criticised in the Press for my slovenly dress when I first began to play the circuit, but in those days I could not afford anything better. Now my golfing wardrobe is bigger than most and my critics say that I am too ostentatious. Even so I would not dress the way I do if I did not feel confident and relaxed. Incidentally, I wear black often because in the hot South African and American sun, it gives me the feeling of strength.

As with clothes, so with clubs. If you are not confident that your clubs are absolutely right for the job, you can hardly expect to hit the ball well with them. That is why I never agree with beginners who suggest that they need only a few clubs to start with. The feeling of inadequacy is bad enough when they make their first clumsy attempt to hit the ball without the feeling that they have not all the necessary implements.

For the same reasons I never harp on the necessity of a matched set of clubs. Confidence should always be the main consideration in golf, and if you feel confident with an odd driver salvaged from the attic, or an ancient mashie-niblick, then you hang on to it, for that is all that matters. In other words, if you feel that a club is right for you, it usually is. If you feel it is wrong, it most definitely is wrong.

Although I am a strong believer that only bad golfers blame their tools, one cannot overlook the part played by the mind in golf. Because a round takes three hours and more to play, the mind gets plenty of exercise. Obviously, much depends on how the mind works. If you are given to dreaming and imagining, you will not play very well. On the other hand, if you mind is a blank – a popular misconception of professionals among amateurs – you will play worse still. Perhaps a professional does not give much thought to the execution of a shot, but he has to think very hard in his preparation for it. And that is another big difference between the good and the average golfer. I personally think that I play better in major championships and on difficult courses because I think harder than at other times.

It is for a similar reason that the doyen of South African golf professionals, Sid Brews, is reported to have purposely used a driver from a very bad lie at a crucial stage in a tournament. He said afterwards that by choosing his driver, the most difficult club in such circumstances, he forced himself to think and concentrate harder than was actually necessary.

It is for this reason, too, that I always play medal golf, even if I am in a match play event. Medal forces you to think all the time, match play does not, because the value of a stroke is not as important. Only a couple of strokes separates the near-champion from the champion, the good golfer from the not-so-good golfer, and in match play this difference is often not apparent. The costly lapse on one or two holes is swallowed up in the course of the match and in the end the fives and the sixes are not reflected in the result. Being brought up to regard medal as the premier form of competition is one of the big reasons why Americans are better golfers than we in the Commonwealth, where match play has always been said to be more in the spirit of the game. Perhaps it is, but then we must accept that it does not make for better golf. The Americans prove this time and again when they play us at our own game in the Walker and Ryder Cup matches.

Obviously, there are times in match play when it would be plain foolish to try for a score, or play safe, when your opponent is much better placed. Then you can be forgiven for trying the impossible, or having a go to sink the only putt that matters. But remember this. The bad shots that one sometimes plays in the enthusiasm of match play are not always easy to overcome, to wipe from your mind. In fact, *the swing should never be jolted out of its groove in an effort to achieve something spectacular*.

Funnily enough, although match play produces many dramatic happenings in golf, spectacular scoring is seldom required for victory. All too often match play contests are reduced to the level of a dog-fight, with the better golfer subconsciously being pulled down to the standard of his lesser endowed opponent. I know that in the normal course of events, if I can score a medal card of sixty-eight, or just a couple under par for that matter, I can win most match play contests in which I compete.

I would go so far as to say that a golfer who hopes to improve his game, and train himself to think, should *never* play without religiously keeping his score: golf is a constant battle against par, and if you play it any other way, you are encouraging sloppy thinking and sloppy strokes. Ignore the social or business engagement on the golf-course, therefore, and play medal whenever possible: play against lower handicaps than yourself when you can and play in as many serious tournaments and on as many different courses as you can.

There is nothing like a change of course to make you think. Familiarity with your own course undoubtedly breeds contempt, and a two-handicap at 'home' is some-times nearer a seven or eight when he is invited out.

The competitive argument should speak for itself. In tournaments you train yourself in all the things we have spoken about in this chapter – temperament, determination and concentration. Golfers who have burned up courses in practice and then scored in the eighties in the first round of the tournament will know exactly what I mean.

From *Play Golf with Player* by Gary Player
(Collins, London, 1962).

Player's Incredible Last Nine Holes in the Masters

Herbert Warren Wind

Even when he was in his forties, Gary Player was equal to the very best. In 1978 he surprised the golfing world as much as Nicklaus did in 1986 by winning the Masters when all seemed lost.

I.W.

Ever since Gene Sarazen holed out a 4-wood shot for his double-eagle 2 on the fifteenth hole in the last round of the second Masters tournament, in 1935, and went on to tie Craig Wood for first and to defeat him in a play-off, the Masters has been known for the high number of dramatic finishes it has provided. At the same time, a certain law of averages has obtained, and golf fans have learned that, after they have been treated to an especially thrilling Masters, more likely than not a few years will follow in which the tournament will probably be relatively placid, like the PGA Championship or a George Eliot novel. For example, after the 1975 Masters, which was perhaps the most exciting three-man battle in the history of the game – as you may remember, on the last day Jack Nicklaus holed a twisting, uphill birdie putt of some forty feet on the sixteenth green to edge out Johnny Miller and Tom Weiskopf by a stroke in a four-hour struggle crammed with the most dazzling kind of golf, which was not concluded until the last green, where Miller and Weiskopf barely missed birdie putts – no one was really surprised when the 1976 Masters proved to be one of the most soporific tournaments ever: Ray Floyd took the lead on the opening day and was never seriously challenged thereafter. In 1977, however, most Augusta regulars, conditioned by the percentages, were unprepared for that year's Masters' tremendously stirring stretch duel, in which Tom Watson, playing half a hole behind Nicklaus and watching all the marvellous strokes that Nicklaus summoned, managed to stand up to the man who is the most awesome competitor in golf (and possibly in all of sport) and, finally, carry the day by sinking a curling birdie putt on the seventeenth green. And certainly none of us expected yet another historic tournament this April, but for the third time in four years we had an extraordinary Masters – one that will be discussed and dissected as long as the game is played.

The 1978 Masters had a different pattern from any of its predecessors. Four men, each with a chance to win, were bunched during the final hour and a half. I am not sure, but I don't think that there has ever been a four-horse race quite like it anytime, anywhere. During most of the afternoon, the interested centered on whether or not Hubert Green, the current United States Open champion, could hold off the challenges of Watson and Rod Funseth, both of whom had started the round three strokes behind him.

Very little attention was paid to Gary Player, of South Africa – the ultimate winner – since he had started the final round seven shots off the pace. Slowly, quietly, almost indiscernibly, Player, the fourth horse, crept into contention. He was out in 34, two under par. This put him five under par for the tournament, and his name then went up on the leader boards, but he was still so far back that no one thought that even Player, a nerveless man who thrives on pressure and the big occasion, could mount a serious challenge on the last nine. Well, he did. In an incredible display of solid shotmaking and some fantastic clutch putting, he proceeded to birdie the tenth, the twelfth, the thirteenth, the fifteenth, the sixteenth, and the eighteenth holes while parring the other three. This gave him a 64, eight under par, for the round, and a seventy-two-hole total of 277, eleven under par. When he posted that score, there was no assurance that it would hold up and gain him a third Masters title, since Watson, Green, and Funseth were still out on the course with a chance to beat his total or tie it and send the tournament into a sudden-death play-off. While it would be completely wrong to say that Player did not *win* the forty-second Masters – I don't remember any previous golfer's playing the last nine holes of a major tournament in thirty strokes, as he did – Watson, Green, and Funseth also had, in effect, to lose it. For the most part, the decisive shots were played on the last hole, before an enormous horseshoe-shaped gallery that watched the drama in hushed silence. This, it should be noted, was one of the best-run Masters tournaments ever.

Of the men with a chance to tie or defeat Player, Watson, a twenty-eight-year-old Stanford graduate who is probably the most literate golfer on the pro tour, was the first to come to the eighteenth, a 420-yard par 4 on which the fairway swings to the right and runs steadily uphill to a two-level green that slopes from back to front and is protected by two bunkers – a shallow one on the right, and a deep one before the green.

Watson, in trouble with a hooked drive could only make a 5, his eight-foot putt for par slipping by just above the cup. What a hard way to lose after all the fine shots he had played throughout the tournament, and all the course he had shown!

Then Green and Funseth, who were the final twosome, came to the eighteenth. Both needed birdies to tie Player. Both failed. Funsett lipped the hole from eight feet. Poor Green, after a superb 8-iron second to within two and a half feet missed to the right without touching the rim. He had been distracted by the voice of a radio announcer.

It seemed like ages before Green walked over and made the tap-in that didn't count. While he did this, the gallery remained transfixed. Then it slowly dawned on the vast assembly that what they had seen had actually occurred: The tournament was over, and Gary Player had won it.

In most record books, Player is listed as standing five feet eight, but he may be nearer to five-seven. He does not, however, give the impression of being a small man. He has a splendid physique, which he has built up and maintained by constant attention to diet and exercise. He weighed a hundred and fifty pounds when he turned professional, in 1952, and he still does. In 1957, when I first saw him play, I was terribly disappointed. He had an ugly swing, for he was intent on hitting the golf ball as far as the big men did, and in his pursuit of length he set up in an overly wide stance, wrapped the club around his neck going back, and practically jumped at the ball at impact. Besides this, he had a defective grip, and on many rounds he was all over the course. Nevertheless, he contrived to bring in some surprisingly good scores, for he used the wedge well and putted like an angel. (In those days, he employed a locked-wrist method of putting, with the movement of his shoulders controlling his stroke.) He was also aided incalculably by his persistence: Success at school sports had convinced him that he had athletic co-ordination, and he was determined to be a golf champion. When I saw him in action the next year, 1958, I barely recognized his swing. I don't know how he managed the change so quickly, but he had transformed it completely. He now had a good-looking orthodox American-type swing, and he hit the ball nicely and far. Over the last decades, he has had his hot streaks and his slumps, but he has never stopped working on the technical nuances of hitting the golf ball as well as he can. Since he understands clearly what the proper movements should be in the vital part of the swing – when the golfer moves into the ball and hits through it – he has been able to remedy bad habits (all golfers fall into them periodically) and come back ready for the next big event.

Today, when practising, he works mainly on tempo. Unquestionably, he has long been and still is the best bunker player in the world. In temperament, he is somewhat like Arnold Palmer, in that he can concentrate during the heat of tournament play on at least three different levels simultaneously. There is also a helpful theatrical streak in his personality, which enables him to respond well to the strident galleries, the spur of competition, and the dramatic moment.

Player lives with his wife, Vivienne, and their six children in a suburb of Johannesburg called Honeydew, where he raises race horses. He has won the South African Open eleven times. There has never been a golfer who has performed outside his own country as well as Player. This is an index of his remarkable talent, for the game is played under subtly different conditions in every land, and so requires the ability to adjust and readjust. Player has won more than a hundred tournaments around the globe. He has won the Piccadilly World Match Play Championship, at Wentworth, outside London, five times. Teamed with Harold Henning, he won the World Cup for South Africa at the Club de Campo, in Madrid, in 1965; that year, too, he won the trophy for the lowest individual total score, and he won it again last year, at the Wack Wack course, in Milana. He has taken the Brazilian Open twice. He has won in Egypt and in Japan, and he has carried off the Australian PGA Championship twice and the Australian Open no fewer than seven times. He looks much younger than he is, possibly because he has never been out of top condition. 'I believe that if a man takes care of himself, then, all things being equal, he should be as competent a golfer at fifty as he was at thirty,' he said at the conclusion of the Masters.

From *Following Through* by Herbert Warren Wind
(Macmillan, London, 1986).

8

THE AGONY AND THE ECSTASY

When Just One Shot Can Make or Break a Career

Angus MacVicar

I can't resist another look at Gary Player and his great comeback against Tony Lema in the World Match Play in 1965, here described by journalist Angus MacVicar, a self-confessed Fairway Fanatic. Sometimes, of course, a medal game comes down to virtual match play as in that contest of the titans, Nicklaus versus Watson, at the British Open at Turnberry in 1977 where not even a defiant birdie was good enough to save Jack at the last hole. In that game there was probably one crucial shot that shattered Nicklaus when Watson holed a putt of 'obscene length up and down the hills of short fourteenth for a 2'. Similarly, one shot changed the life of poor Doug Saunders at St Andrews in 1970. He missed a 3½-foot putt at the eighteenth to win the Open – and then lost the play-off to Nicklaus the next day. He was never the same player again and nor was Tony Jacklin after the 1972 Open at Muirfield when Trevino's chip into the hole at the seventeenth caused Tony to three putt and cost him the title.

I.W.

In a chapter mainly about heroes – and remembering that heroes do not always win – it would be unthinkable to leave out Gary Player. Pound for pound, Gary is the greatest golfing competitor who has ever lived. He is never more lethal than when he is down.

Some doubt his sincerity at times because of his insistence upon talking in glowing terms about players, courses, in fact anything that catches his fancy at any particular moment. But this is part of the Player philosophy of black and white. In his mind there are no greys.

The little man has never been more positive than in the 1965 semi-final of the World Match Play Championship at Wentworth. It was a thirty-six-hole match and after eighteen holes he was six down to the American, Tony Lema, who, in the previous year, had won the Open Championship at St Andrews.

Lema had come home in 32 over the treacherous Burma Road, and Player looked a forlorn figure, particularly when he lost the first hole after lunch to go seven down with seventeen to play. This was surely the end for Gary against a thoroughbred like Lema. But the South African birdied the 2nd and 3rd holes to win both, halved the 4th with another birdie, and promptly birdied the short 5th as well to be only four down with thirteen holes to play.

When he missed a short putt on the 6th green, however, to slide five down again I was sure it was all over. The pendulum had swung back again. But Gary has never been one to follow an old script. He was determined to write a new one for himself.

He was still five down with nine to play. But he won the short 10th with a 3, then birdied the 11th. Three down with seven to play: Lema's beautiful swing was beginning to quicken ever so slightly. The 12th was halved. Then, at the 13th, the American hooked his drive, could only hack his second a few yards along the fairway and barely reached the edge of the green with his third.

After great deliberation, Lema holed his putt, from fully 30 feet, for a miraculous four. Now Player, on with two great woods, had to hole a ten-foot birdie putt to cut Lema's lead to two when only seconds earlier two putts would have been good enough. It was a curly putt, a nasty putt, but Gary gave it every ounce of concentration he possessed and in went the ball. Two down, with five to play.

The next two holes were halved, but at the 16th Lema snap-hooked his drive into the trees. One down, with two to play.

The 17th was halved with birdies, and so on to the 18th, with the light fading fast. Both hit good drives, but Lema was short with his second and Player slammed into a 4-wood, which he struck so hard that he almost swung himself off his feet. The ball, however, soared away with a slight draw and landed in the heart of the green, rolling to within ten feet of the flagstick. Gary reckons it was one of the best shots he has ever hit, and Lema failed to respond with a pitch and a putt. All square and on to the 37th.

Thousands of spectators, spellbound by the drama, charged towards the first fairway, anxious not to miss one second of this awesome struggle. The light was now almost gone, and it looked to me as if Lema, too, was almost gone, in a physical sense.

And indeed he was. Whereas Player found the green in two shots, Lema drew his second into a bunker and failed to get up and down to match his opponent's 4.

A match that is now a legend was over. Player sank to his knees on the edge of the green and wept. He told me later he had had a sudden vision of his farm near Johannesburg, his family, his farmhands, his horses, his home. It had inspired him. His resolute will to win had defied a mountain that had looked impossible to scale.

I have witnessed a great number of memorable moments in golf, both amateur and professional. Some were uplifting, others involved players in the crushing disappointment of having the prize whipped away in the cruellest of circumstances.

Two such occasions stand out especially for me: the 1970 Open Championship at St

Andrews and the Open Championship two years later at Muirfield. Perhaps I did not quite appreciate it at the time, but in those two championships two strokes of a golf ball completely changed the lives of Doug Sanders and Tony Jacklin.

The scene at the 18th in the last round of the 1970 Open remains as clear in my mind as if it had happened yesterday. Thousands had gathered round the historic setting to witness Sanders edge out Jack Nicklaus for the most coveted title in golf. I had squatted down at the top of the clubhouse steps as the colourful Georgian prepared to play his second shot. Doug's personality was as sparkling as his attire. But this time I did not need binoculars to see the tension on his face. He required only a par 4 to beat Nicklaus, but in front of him was the Valley of Sin. I could almost hear him telling himself not to be short. Inevitably he was too strong, and the ball scampered up to the back of the green.

Nicklaus had no hope of getting a birdie 3. Sanders, therefore, had two putts for his first major title and lasting fame.

The downhill putt from the back of the 18th green at St Andrews is notoriously difficult to gauge for speed, and Sanders made the classic error. He left his first putt short by about three and a half feet.

The old grey town waited in silence. Sanders, his face now pale and drawn, hunched himself uncomfortably over his second putt. Suddenly, however, he stood up again, and picked an imaginary impediment from his line. The tension was killing him. It seemed that he couldn't bring himself to strike the putt that meant so much to him.

Finally, his concentration gone, he made contact. It was a diffident putt; his right hand came off the putter grip and the ball trundled to the right of the hole and remained above ground. Though he accepted the bitter disappointment with a dignity few others could have mustered and fought to within a stroke of Nicklaus in the play-off the following day, Sanders was never the same player again.

Two years later Tony Jacklin was within two holes of capturing the Open for a second time when his playing partner, Lee Trevino, perpetrated the most stunning – and the luckiest – shot I have ever seen in championship golf. It was lucky because, as Trevino admitted later, he had not given it his full concentration after bunkering his drive at the 17th, blasting his second shot out sideways, hitting his third into rough and his fourth over the green.

Meanwhile, Jacklin was not far short of the green in two and required only a pitch and two putts for a par 5, followed by a par at the last to beat Jack Nicklaus, who had charged in with a final round of 66. Tony elected to play a chip and run shot, expecting the ball to move quickly on the firm, fast green. But it didn't: it stopped 16 feet short of the hole.

Trevino, obviously angry with himself, then pulled a wedge quickly out of his bag, had a cursory glance at the flag and struck his chip from behind the green. To everyone's amazement the ball went straight into the hole.

'By tenfold that was the worst shock I've ever had on a golf course,' admitted Tony afterwards. Concentration ruined, he took three putts. The title had been snatched away from him.

It was a shattering mental blow from which he has never fully recovered. 'I went into a state of shock, and it definitely took me a long time to get over it, if I ever did get over it,' he admitted some years later.

In the autumn of that year Jacklin again found himself face to face with Trevino in the semi-final of the World Match Play Championship at Wentworth. Tony was four down at lunch, but with a fine exhibition of precision golf, he hauled Lee back in the second round with an outward half of 29. He got round in 63 but still lost the match by a hole. Truly the talkative Texan was Jacklin's executioner.

If the Hollywood moguls had been there they would have bought the film rights of the 1977 Open Championship at Turnberry Hotel, the Open in which no one can ever remember who was third. This was a championship about two players. Tom Watson and Jack Nicklaus. They stalked each other for four rounds, through blistering heat and a thunderstorm. Neither gave an inch. All that was missing was John Wayne, a saloon bar and a musical score by Dimitri Tiomkin.

The final act, had it been scripted, would have been returned to the writer for being too corny, for having gone over the top. But it did happen, and Opens in the years that followed suffered by comparison.

I tipped Watson that year in the *Express*. In fact, half the press tent had put money on him, and so the final hour was doubly tense for us. After all, it was our chance to be right at last!

One shot, more than any other, won it for Watson. This was his putt of obscene length, up and down the hills and valleys of the short 14th, for a 2. When the ball vanished into the hole Nicklaus winced.

If it is possible to break Nicklaus, he was broken then, though he summoned up a miraculous birdie 3 at the last hole in a desperate attempt to catch the man whom he had always regarded the most likely to replace him. He was inches from destruction in the bushes after coming off his drive. But he found the green with his second and holed an enormous putt that owed more to his extraordinary will than to technique. Watson never looked like missing his tiddler, but in retrospect the 18-incher *was* in the missable range, considering the circumstances.

But even before the ball disappeared we in the press tent were congratulating ourselves for an all too rare success in the forecasting business. Next morning, when I caught up with Watson at Prestwick Airport on his way home to Kansas, he was wearing a large pair of dark glasses. Obviously, like ourselves, he had spent little of the night in bed.

From *Golf in My Gallowses* [Scots for braces]
by Angus MacVicar (Hutchinson, London, 1983).

The Long and the Short Handicapper

Given that he understands the game's customs and courtesies, the bad player can play with acceptance alongside the good, because golf so lends itself to handicapping.

Norman Mair.

Tony Jacklin – the Price of Success

Liz Kahn

After winning the British Open in 1969 and the US Open in 1970, Tony Jacklin was the hero the British golfing public had been awaiting for so long. He was still in the forefront for two or three more years – and then it all went wrong. My own feeling is that Tony didn't pace himself after his extraordinary success, that he did too much off and on the course, got stale and lost his real hunger for success in the game. This surely was an element of his failure, but Tony, in the soul-searching book he wrote with Liz Kahn, narrows down the possible causes to that traumatic episode at Muirfield when Trevino chipped in at the seventeenth. Jacklin promptly three-putted and turned what looked like a certain lead into a deficit. Arnie Palmer told a dejected Tony as he came off the last green: 'Whatever you do, try not to let it affect the way you think.' But it did. Triumph turned to dejection and despair. Jacklin tried Valium to help him sleep and he tried Scientology, but he rejected hypnosis. 'Drink and pills dull the senses, and if you think they will change the way life is, you're an idiot.' Ultimately the enjoyment of the big-time game left him. 'Normally you only get so nervous at a tournament and you control it but to be nervous and out of control as I was, that's the end of the world – there's no future in it.'

I.W.

After winning the 1970 US Open at Hazeltine, Tony was on a high. His next major event was the Open Championship at St Andrews, where he was defending his title.

By now, Tony was a household name, an international star, shining bright. He was also heavily involved with all sorts of promotions and commitments, which kept him on a hectic schedule round the world, and which gave rise to plenty of criticism that he was far too stretched to be able to give of his best on the golf course.

The first round of his defence at St Andrews began in amazing fashion: 'I played magical golf. The putts started going in – it was as though I had a hot-line to the hole. On the first three holes I drew back the putter and those three putts, two from 15 feet and one from five feet, went straight into the hole and I was three under after three holes.

'I had a par at the 4th, birdied the 564-yard 5th, where I was on in two and had two putts: I just missed a birdie at the 6th, birdied the 7th from six feet, and had a par at the 8th. At the 9th, I hit a one iron off the tee, pulled it slightly into the rough, and had just over 100 yards to the flag. I took a wedge, and the ball bounced slightly short of the flag, then hit it and dropped right into the hole. I was out in 29 and seven under par for the first nine holes.

'I went eight under as I birdied the 10th from six feet. I just missed chances to birdie the 11th and 12th, and had a par at the 13th. I drove well at the 14th, then, as I swung the club back on my second shot, I heard someone in the crowd shout out "fore" – I don't know why but my concentration wavered and I heaved off the ball and hit it into a gorse bush.

'It had been terribly sultry and quiet, and the sky was looking really threatening. Suddenly, there was thunder and great flashes of lightning, and by the time I reached my ball, after my second shot on the 14th – the course was under water. The greens were unplayable and there was no question of going on, it was a freak storm.

'It was a significant moment when you consider that finally I missed a putt of 10 feet on the 72nd hole and came fifth – if I'd made it I would have tied Lee Trevino and Harold Henning in third place. I was on 286, three shots behind Nicklaus and Sanders.

'I had to go back at 7.30 am the next day to finish my round. I had to drop out of the bush and on the 14th and I made six on that hole. I dropped two more shots on the last four holes, but whereas the day before it had been a drive and pitch to the 15th and 16th, and it had been possible to drive the 18th, now it needed a four and five iron for the second shots, and it was impossible to hit the 18th with a driver. I finished with 67, which was disappointing when something like a 62 had seemed possible.

'I continued with ever-increasing scores in the Championship, taking 70 in the second round that same day; then 73 in the third round to tie me with Nicklaus and Sanders, two strokes behind the leader, Lee Trevino.

'I was in with a chance on the last day, until I bogied the 16th by three-putting, then found myself in loose stones near the Road at the 17th and took five on that hole. I finished in 76, with a par at the last hole, and it was just not good enough.

'It was awful to have your momentum going as I did on that first day, and then not be able to finish your round. People say the whole round should have been wiped out and that I was lucky. Many people think that because it was me we were brought back the next day, when in fact it is the tournament ruling.

'Obviously if I could have finished that day, even in 65 . . . but there I'm dreaming – it's all castles in the air.'

That Open Championship ended not only in disappointment for Tony, but with Doug Sanders becoming a tragic figure, missing his short putt to win on the 72nd hole, followed by the anti-climax of a play-off and victory for Jack Nicklaus.

The following year Tony's schedule was no less hectic, and in June he defended his US Open title at Merion but missed the half-way cut.

He went to the Open Championship in July at Royal Birkdale, where he put up a strong challenge to finish third, two shots behind winner, Lee Trevino, who had just won the US and Canadian Opens, and one shot behind the smiling, hat-doffing Liang Huan Lu from Formosa.

Tony had been fighting a hook all week, and after the third round he was tied with 'Mr Lu' just one shot behind Trevino. Pulling his shots the last day, Tony dropped three shots in the first nine holes, but managed a birdie spurt on the inward half that gave him a creditable round of 71, a total of 280, but not quite good enough to win.

Tony's record in the Open Championship at Muirfield was to prove one of the most devastating moments of Tony's life, and of his golf career. The 1970 and 1971 Open Championships had been major disappointments in not providing Tony with another victory, but they paled in comparison to the shattering experience of 1972.

Earlier in the year Tony had achieved a further milestone in his career by winning a second Jacksonville Open, showing the talent was still there, giving his status in golfing terms another boost and doing wonders for his natural self-confidence. He knew he still had it in him to make the effort for the big occasion, to stand up to the pressure of another Open win, and at Muirfield the scene was set for what so nearly became his second Open win. But in reality it turned out to be a nightmare and a turning point for Tony, which to a great extent undermined that wonderful self-confidence. 'Nothing really good ever seemed to happen after Muirfield,' he claimed.

Tony's constant source of worry with his golf was his putting. He began the first hole of the Open Championship at Muirfield by three-putting for a bogey and ended the round in similar fashion, as he charged a 30-foot putt at the 18th for his birdie, went four feet past, and missed the return. But he played some great golf between the first and 18th, reflected by the five birdies in his round of 69, where he holed some very good putts which prompted him to comment, seemingly forgetting Jacksonville: 'They were the sort of putts I haven't been holing this year, and the sort a winner must hole.'

Tony's opening round in the Championship put him one shot behind Yorkshireman Peter Tupling, one ahead of Jack Nicklaus, and two ahead of Lee Trevino.

After a second round of 72 Tony shared the lead at the end of the day with Lee Trevino who had scored 71, 70, for his 141 total. It had been a scorching hot day at Muirfield but only one person had broken 70, and that was Johnny Miller whose five under par 66 set a new course record and put him one shot behind the leaders. Jack Nicklaus said he had not played well for his 72, and he was tied two shots behind the leaders.

On the third day Tony was paired with Lee Trevino and they were last out in the field. Tony was three under par at the turn, having holed some magnificent long putts to keep abreast of Trevino who was slotting them in from all over the greens.

At the short 13th Tony hit his ball into the bunker on the left of the green. He left it in the sand with his next shot, then hit it out into the bunker across the other side of the green: he got that out and finally two-putted for a three over par six. 'In the third round of the God-damned tournament, I'm in contention and I take a triple bogey and you know what that's going to do to anybody. Well, I was fantastic – I really was. I'm not talking about what anyone else thinks, that's from my own point of view. I can remember saying to myself, somehow you're not going to let that worry you, it's nothing. It was a six on one hole, but it's finished and it's not going to help worrying. I had a great attitude towards it. I can say I was fantastic because I know how I've been since, in letting things affect me.

'I went on to the next hole. Trevino birdied the 14th and I birdied; he birdied the 15th and I birdied; he birdied the 16th, thinned the ball out of the trap, where it hit the bottom of the flag and went in the hole, and I parred. We both birdied the 17th – Trevino nearly eagled the hole. At the 18th we were both five under par. Trevino hit a fantastic drive straight down the middle and put a five iron through the green. I drove into the left rough, then took a six iron and hit it on the front of the long green. It was me to putt as I was further from the hole. But it's a dumb thing to do in professional golf, to let the other player off the green play first, usually you offer him the option, but on this occasion Trevino said, "I'll come up" and I agreed. Then he chipped the damned thing in the hole again for another birdie. By now I was wishing I hadn't let him play – but the guy had asked and you don't like to refuse. I putted up to six feet and made it for a four, and it really was a big putt to make.

'So he finished with five successive birdies for a 66, holing two wedge shots and I think I'd done pretty damned well to stay with him for my 67, especially after my six on the par three. You can only do so much and I really did a good job there that day – I hung right in and felt good about it, and I'm saying to myself, patience lad – your time will come.

'We were out together again the next day and I was one shot behind Trevino who was on 207. It was the most fantastic Open – with Nicklaus six shots behind me, seven behind Trevino, and he was going for the Grand Slam having already won the Masters and the US Open that year. On the first tee Trevino said to me, 'Well, Nicklaus might catch one of us but he ain't going to catch us both.' When we were playing the 9th and Nicklaus stood on the 11th, he had passed us both.

'We both eagled the 9th where we were on the green in two. Trevino holed from 35 feet and I followed him in from 20 feet. There were two tremendous roars, and the film of the 1972 Open shows Nicklaus on the 11th tee backing off for Trevino's roar, then for mine. I continued to play very well, concentrating hard, and when we reached the tee at the par five 17th – we were both six under and needing level par to beat Nicklaus, who had finished with a 66, putting him on 279, five under par for the Championship.

'Trevino hooked his drive off the 17th tee into a bunker. I hit a perfect drive and then put my second just short of the green with a three wood. Meanwhile Trevino had played sideways out of the bunker, hit his third into the left rough, his fourth over the green, and he had given up.

'It was then my turn to play from a good position in the short rough on the left in front of the green. When I hit it, I thought it was a good chip. I know that some long time after, Tom Weiskopf was being questioned about dumb shots in golf, and he said that that chip was one of the dumbest shots he had ever seen. I was mad about that and I never said anything to him, but I thought how little he knew, and that he had never asked me about it.

'The course was very dry at that stage after a week of good weather and the green looked very hard, very fast and very brown. I had a lot of green to go over before I got to the hole, as the pin was tucked in near the back on the right. I played a chip and run with a pitching wedge, and honest to God I thought it was good, I truly did. I expected it to run forwards but instead it slowed down quickly and stopped about 16 feet short. I wasn't too worried, however, as Trevino had played four and was through the back to the green.

'Then he simply took a club out of the bag, never lined it up – took one look and hit the chip just like you would when you want to get the job over. And incredibly it went into the hole.

'My immediate reaction after all the events of the day before was that he'd had all the breaks up to that point but I thought it could be my turn next. When he chipped in, I reacted by thinking I'm not going to let him beat me that way, I'll hole this and still go to the 18th one up. So I gave my ball a bit of a dunk and it went two and a half feet past. I wasn't worried by the one coming back, but I just got quick on the putt through lack of concentration – though really the circumstances were more to do with it than anything – and I missed it. Once I'd three-putted he played the last hole perfectly, while I hit my second shot in the right-hand bunker and took five. The wind had gone out of my sails by then.

'It was one of those incredible situations that happen in life and one hopes that one is always on the doing and not the receiving end. I'm sure if you play long enough most everything can happen to you. But by tenfold that was the worst shock I've ever had on the golf course. It was such an important event, it was in the one tournament that means more to me than any other in the world, and the only saving factor was that I'd already won an Open. If I'd never won one, then it would have been even worse.

'I went into a state of shock and it definitely took me a long time to get over it, if I ever got over it. I was just numb. I didn't weep or cry, knowing that nothing was ever going to change it, knowing that when I awoke the next morning it was still going to be the same. It took a week to realise it, and it was certainly the biggest shock I ever had. Losing that Open to Trevino was like Muhammad Ali must have felt when Henry Cooper knocked him on his arse.'

At the time in 1972, Trevino admitted that he was not giving the chip he holed at the 17th his full concentration. It was for Jacklin, he said, 'the straw that broke the camel's back.' Now, Trevino looking back, comments: 'What a lot of people don't realise is that Tony didn't finish second to me at Muirfield, he finished third and I beat Nicklaus. When I chipped in at the 17th I was aiming at the hole – when you putt and chip, that's exactly what you aim for. If you're saying was I mad when I got over the chip, yes, I was upset at having hit the ball over the green, but you are still trying to hole it. Maybe my chipping in the ball did deflate Tony, but then he bogied the last hole. It's happened to me and I know how he feels about it. But there has to be a winner and there has to be somebody who finishes second. It just happened that I won, that's all.'

For Tony it was obviously not something he could take in his stride. To put so much store by one championship increases the tension to pressure-cooker level. He had given out so much in time, energy, motivation and achievement: the effort and the strain over the years must have been enormous, and when it looked like the reward was there once again the shock of having it snatched from your very grasp must mean that you begin to experience feelings of self-doubt.

'It was the most significant thing that happened in my career and it sure as hell had a big effect. Anything after that may be insignificant, it was a crazy, incredible thing. Anyone who plays sport knows that it can happen, and when I came off the last green Arnold Palmer was there and said to me, "Whatever you do, try not to let it affect the way you think." I knew what had happened to him in the 1966 US Open when he lost seven shots to Casper in the last nine holes, tied, and then lost the play-off. And I think that affected him because he only won odd tournaments after that. Some people can play a whole career and not have that happen to them in a major championship.

'You can say, that's the way it is, you've never won until the last ball is in the hole. But I felt bloody sick. Everyone had talked to me about the law of averages but they don't exist – that confirmed it, there's no such thing. Nothing's fair. Life and golf are for the takers, you've got to take it, grab it and keep it. Never give anything away, it's for taking – there's no question in my mind about that. It may be a hard outlook but life is that hard. There's no room for sentiment while you're doing it. You can like a person but it's very important to have a straightforward outlook because it is dog eat dog whether it's Nicklaus or whoever you're playing against. Nicklaus wants to win so badly and he wants it for himself.

'Of course it can be a matter of who does what and when, but I've never felt a lucky player over the years. I've never won anything without winning it – no one has ever missed a putt on the last green to let me win. If you miss a putt on the last green it's talked about for ever more, if it's the first no one remembers. Doug Sanders will never be forgotten for the putt he missed in the 1970 Open at St Andrews at the 18th, yet in his own heart maybe he thinks about another shot that cost him it more, but he's left looking foolish on the last hole. People play on that sort of thing and you start to believe it – like Oosty (Peter Oosterhuis) believes he's going to flash one to the right under pressure – he's read about it so often and done it so many times, that in the end he expects to do it.

'Until you've won a major championship you don't realise what it means, that the majors are really the only ones that matter. For a British player there's no greater tournament to win than the Open Championship for making money – and that's my profession. I was lucky to win the Open as a young British player with everything going for me. No one could have made more money out of winning one single tournament than I did out of winning that one.

'With the Open being played on links courses and thus having the factor of the consistent bounce, the player who wins is the player who can accept adversity the best – which is what I feel I did that week at Muirfield. When I said to myself, you've made six, let's get some birdies now, when you don't let little things or big ones affect you, realising and putting yourself above them, that's what it's all about.

'There are not many players around who are capable of doing that. There are players who are capable of winning golf tournaments, but very few who can do it when it matters. There always have been very few. Even now in the last 15 years there have only been a handful – and it has nothing at all to do with hitting a golf ball. It's purely and simply an attitude of mind. I think I react well to a crowd. It was always the case in the Open where the crowd would turn me on. I used to expect to hole a long putt because I would anticipate it through the crowd. I didn't have to work at getting up, I was up.

'Motivation and circumstances are crazy things. Winning can be as simple as a putt going in at the right time, or a chip, and thinking, I needed that. Inwardly you always know if it's a lost cause or not – you're honed in to the happenings. When you're on that level, when you know you're going to win, it's like corridors and lots of people banging into each other below you, and the higher the level you reach the more you concentrate and the better you are in control of yourself.

'It's like flying at 45,000 feet where there are no other 'planes and there's nothing to stop you. It's just a question of making your destination. You're not dodging around.'

From *Tony Jacklin: The Price of Success* by Liz Kahn
(Hamlyn, London, 1979).

I thought I'd blown it at the 17th green when I drove into a trap. God is a Mexican.
Lee Trevino, who went on to win at Muirfield in 1972.

How to Lose the US Open

Sam Snead

Sam Snead was the best player never to win the US Open though he was runner-up no less than four times, in 1937, 1947 (after a tie with Lew Worsham), 1949 and 1953. However, he probably came closest to winning in 1939 when the wheels came off in extraordinary fashion, as he relates here. He was only twenty-two with plenty of time ahead of him in which to try for victory, but it was not to be. In 1947 after the eighteen-hole play-off with Worsham, Snead needed a shortish putt for a sure half. He was about to slot it when Worsham queried whether Snead was indeed farther from the hole. It was decided he was, so Snead putted – and missed. Worsham then holed to win.

Snead viewed his win in the British Open in 1946 with scant pride, hated the icy wind at St Andrews and reckoned that the £150 prize money was such a joke he decided there and then not to defend the title. But perhaps he views it with more pride now. He played forty-four years on the US tour, aided by the smoothest of swings, and in 1979 became the first player to equal then break his age in a full US tour event with a 67 and a 66 at the age of sixty-seven.

I.W.

Going into the final eighteen holes, it looked like I just might win my first [1939] National Open. My 212 score tied me with Denny Shute, Clayton Heafner, and Craig Wood, 1 stroke behind Johnny Bulla's first-place 211.

I was loose as a goose, mentally. The night before the final day of play, I did some catsprings and some other calisthenics around the hotel-room floor. My roommate, Gene Sarazen, was already in bed and thought my exercises were tomfoolery.

'This stuff helps me to relax,' I told him.

'Yes, and you can sprain your back,' said Gene, snapping out the lights and practically ordering me to bed.

I finished my sit-ups in the dark and then slept like a possum in his mother's pouch. I felt another 68 or 69 coming on when I woke up. Couldn't wait to get out there and win me that $100,000 Open.

With seventy holes played, it looked like I'd make it. Two pars on the finishing holes would give me a 69 for the final round and a seventy-two-hole total of 281. A 281 seemed good enough, as it would tie the all-time Open record. I went for the first par on the par-4 seventy-first, where I hit a beautiful 300-yard drive. My second shot was over the green into thick clover grass. Chipping out short, I missed a 5-foot putt by an inch and took a bogey 5.

Right there is where my most famous 'blowup' began.

For some reason, nobody wanted to tell me the facts of the situation I was up against – which wasn't anything to worry about. As matters stood, I needed only a par on the last hole to beat the best score registered so far, Byron Nelson's 284, and win. A bogey would tie Nelson. No one else still playing the course was in shape to beat Nelson.

But I didn't know any of this, and my bogey on the seventy-first had made me nervous. Ed Dudley, my playing partner, and others around me knew what Nelson had done, yet not one of them spoke up. When you're in the dark, your fears close in on you. I felt I had to gamble on a birdie on the par-5, 558-yard closing hole.

People were swarming the fairways and I had a thirty-minute, nerve-racking wait while the marshals cleared the way to build up the decision to play that last hole wide open.

The tee shot was hit squarely, but my right hand turned a bit too quickly and the ball started to hook. I said, 'Whoa, ball, whoa' – but it hooked into trampled rough anyway. The lie was in sandy soil. Up ahead were traps, short of the green and around it. Normally you'd use an iron to make sure of getting out and up. It was still 275 yards to the pin, however, and I still had the idea that the only way to win was to gamble.

Taking a custom-made 2-wood, with several degrees more loft than a driver, one of my favorite sticks, I went for the pin instead of playing safely out. Hit badly, the ball had no height. It was a low liner pushed down the fairway, and I said, 'Giddyap, giddyap,' when I saw it failing near a trap 160 yards away.

It fell into the trap. It was partly buried.

Every expert I've read claims that I played the trap shot before I thought it out. That's not true. With 2 shots used up, I had to reach the green with the next (or believed I did) and the green was still 110 yards away. My bunker lie wasn't too bad. Half the ball was visible. Above me the collar of the trap had been resodded with squares of soil topped by rough grass. This lip had to be cleared at a height of about 5 feet. A heavy sand wedge would get me up but wouldn't give me the needed distance. I asked the caddie for a shallower-faced club. 'Give me the 8-iron,' I said.

Even in 1939, when I was only a two-year touring pro, I knew how risky it can be to use a semilofted iron from a semiburied lie. The danger is that you'll catch the ball too clean. If you don't take enough sand, you don't get it up. Weighing that against the need to reach the green in 3, I gambled.

The ball went 4 feet, slammed into the collar, and struck in a crack left by the resodding. The moans and groans that went up were nothing to my feeling when I caught it too clean and saw it plug in there. In hitting too clean, you don't get under the ball; you hit too high on it and lose the lofted effect of the club. Now I had to chop sod, grass, ball, and all, while standing on sand below the ball.

To cut it out required a sideswiping blow, and she slashed out to the left 40 yards into another bunker. I was sick all over. Still thinking I needed a birdie on No. 72 to win, all my hopes were gone. In landing in that second trap, I'd used up my birdie shot. And now I was shooting 5 from another tough lie in sand.

Just then somebody stepped out of the gallery and said, 'Nelson finished at 284. You've got to get down in two more to tie him.'

I thought I'd explode at this news. All those gambling shots had been needless. 'Why didn't somebody tell me that back on the tee,' I snarled, 'so I could play it safe?' I was mad enough to plow through that crowd, swinging a club right and left. People will give you nine million miles of advice when you don't need it, but here in the clutch, they had dummied up on me.

If there's anything in this story I'm not ashamed of, it was the 9-iron recovery I made then. I was shaking all over. But I was still thinking. My ball rested 4 or 5 inches below my feet at the bunker's edge. In any situation where you must stand in the trapside grass with the ball below you, the danger is 'falling into' the shot and slicing it. Unless you're careful, because you body is tilted forward, you tend to shift weight too soon from your right leg, on the backswing, to the left leg, on the downswing. Which gives you a push or slice. A photo I have of this Spring Mill explosion shows how I avoided that. I bent my knees more than usual, 'sitting down' to the ball. My weight was back on my heels to prevent overshifting. I choked down on the club, to make sure I stayed down to the ball throughout the swing. If you rise up even a little bit on a lie like this, you're ruined. The clubface was closed slightly to counteract any slice. And I scraped the ball onto the green, 40 feet from the cup.

To tie Nelson, I needed the putt, and again I'm not ashamed – the 40-footer came close. It lipped the cup and twisted 3 feet away.

After that, I was an awful sight. I didn't give a damn anymore. The collapse was complete when I missed the 3-footer. One more putt gave me an 8 – the most talked-about 8 ever taken in golf, I guess. Some women were crying and men were patting me on the back as I walked to the locker room. It was worse in there. There was dead silence. The other pros avoided looking at me, to spare me embarrassment. The sportswriters stayed far away, too. All except one, George Trevor of New York, who walked up with a pencil and notebook in hand and asked, 'Sam, what happened on that last hole?'

The boys led Trevor away before I did something I'd regret.

From *The Education of a Golfer* by Sam Snead
(Cassell & Co., London, 1962).

After an abominable round of golf a man is known to have slit his wrists with a razor blade and, having bandaged them, to have stumbled into the locker room and inquired of his partner: 'What time tomorrow?'

Alistair Cooke.

If profanity had an influence on the flight of the ball, the game would be played far better than it is.

Horace G. Hutchinson (the first Englishman to captain
the Royal and Ancient).

I've thrown or broken a few clubs in my day. In fact, I guess at one time or another I probably held distance records for every club in the bag.

Tommy 'Thunder' Bolt.

If you are going to throw a club it is important to throw it ahead of you, down the fairway, so you don't waste energy going back to pick it up . . .

Tommy 'Thunder' Bolt.

Every day I try to tell myself this is doing to be fun today. I try to put myself in a great frame of mind before I go out then I screw it up with the first shot.

Johnny Miller, the devout Mormon who, from being the most successful golfer in the world (US Open in 1973, British Open 1976 by six clear strokes), plummeted from superstar to also-ran (111th) by 1978. Like the mayfly he shone brilliantly for a brief season and was the best in the world. But unlike Nicklaus he did not have the motivation (or perhaps confidence) to be the best who ever lived. However, he was still a good player.

Arnold Palmer demonstrates bunker power. (*Peter Dazeley*)

Bunker power by Lee Trevino. (*Peter Dazeley*)

Bunker power by Sevé Ballesteros. (*Peter Dazeley*)

Nicklaus at the 18th at Augusta – another Masters almost won for the Golden Bear. (*Peter Dazeley*)

Palmer at the 4th hole of the Burma Road, Wentworth. (*Peter Dazeley*)

Player personifies mind over matter; here he comes to terms with a near impossible lie. (*Peter Dazeley*)

Now comes the triumph. Player's putter holes another long one. (*Peter Dazeley*)

Battle of the giants. The never to be forgotten clash between Nicklaus and Watson, when Watson won the 1977 Open at Turnberry. (*Peter Dazeley*)

They used not to drop . . . But now they do. Bernhard Langer at the 1981 Open. (*Peter Dazeley*)

9

MY FAVOURITE COURSES
Wentworth

Ronald Heager

I first played the West Court or Burma Road at Wentworth in 1977. I got four birdies in the first six holes, and since that includes the 452-yard par-4 third, which demands an accurate tee shot to avoid the bunkers and an equally accurate second to avoid the perils of the two-tier green, I was well pleased. The greens at Wentworth are marvellous – like a snooker table. The course has had happy memories for me ever since and my 1987 win against Sandy Lyle in the World Match Play was a personal pinnacle – so far. The seventeenth, with its sharp dog-leg left, is one of the great par 5s – 571 yards long for tournament purposes. Go too far left and you land up in the trees; too far right and there are trees on the other side. The eighteenth is a left-to-right dog-leg. Greg Norman eagled the eighteenth hole to beat Bernhard Langer by a single stroke in the 1981 Martini International after a birdie on the seventeenth.

The late Ronald Heager, former golf correspondent of the *Daily Express* and *Sunday Express*, tells us about the history and attractions of what must be the best-known course to all British TV viewers.

I.W.

The Americans have a satirical story about the archetype TV watcher who possesses the blinkered view that Arnold Palmer invented the game of golf and everything flowed from there with the aid of the television studios. It was, however, another legendary American, Walter Hagen, who was captivating an awakening golfing public at the time Wentworth's East Course was opened in 1924. It was laid out by H. S. Colt, who became the first secretary of Sunningdale in 1900 and went on to become one of the greatest of golf architects.

The Club was just an infant of two years when it first earned a place in golf history, playing host to the unofficial match between Britain and the United States in 1926. This fixture had been tried out at Gleneagles in 1921 and this time was to implant the idea of the Ryder Cup in the mind of millionaire seedsman Samuel Ryder. Britain – believe it or not – won 13½–1½. Another Wentworth 'first' was the launching of the Curtis Cup between Britain and the US women's teams on the East Course in 1932. This time the Americans won 5½–3½.

Through the 1930s the longer and more exacting West Course began to build a reputation that still stands as one of the supreme inland tests of golf in the whole of the British Isles. When the fighting Servicemen were demobilized from 1945 onwards the West Course renewed its climb to international stature. It is easy to visualize a suffering campaigner, having at last reached the haven of the '19th', likening his ordeal to the 'Burma Road', a name so eloquent that it stuck.

The 'Burma Road' received its international hallmark in the 1950s when first the Ryder Cup and then the Canada Cup – now World Cup – were staged there. The legendary Ben Hogan and Sam Snead formed the US team for the 1956 Canada Cup contest. The Americans inevitably won, with Hogan as the individual winner. When golf moved into the age of Palmer, Player, Nicklaus and beyond, Wentworth was ready. The World Match-Play brought the modern giants there and a new chapter of golf history unfolded. Palmer, appropriately, was the first winner. The next year saw Player's epic fightback from seven down and 17 to play, still five down and nine against Tony Lema before winning their semi-final at the 37th.

But even if the Club had never opened its doors to a single tournament it would still possess a special place in golf simply on the merit and the charm of its courses, on the subdued grandness of the clubhouse, and for all the accompanying amenities.

The West Course was also laid out by Harry Colt in collaboration with his partners John Morrison and Charles Alison. No layout has better stood the test of time: the only changes came with the building of super 'tiger' tees for the 1953 Ryder Cup, making the course the exacting test it is today.

The West Course has had so much exposure that even a first time visitor could hardly feel a stranger. You would already know that Arnold Palmer ranks the 17th as one of the world's greatest par five holes and that Bobby Locke includes the par four 11th in his gallery of the best 18 he has played round the world.

The course winds in a vast hairpin through the first six and last seven holes, with a loop of five holes in an undulating clearing of heathery slopes. Neil Coles names the 3rd as one of the supreme holes, as does Bernard Gallacher, the Club professional and latest in a line of distinguished Ryder Cup players to hold the office, with Archie Compston, Jimmy Adams and Tom Haliburton preceding him. The continuity of the World Match Play has provided a fascinating spin-off of statistics and if anything can be proved by figures there is confirmation that the 3rd is Wentworth's toughest hole: it has had the highest aggregate of strokes over par and the lowest yield of birdies.

By the same yardstick the professionals have found the downhill, dog-legged 4th the most rewarding of all the Burma Road stages, for it has the highest birdie yield together with the 12th, and the biggest aggregate sub-par total. But then few can make birdies in the manner I recall Gary Player once achieving here: after a pernicious hook had put him in the trees, he came out sideways, hit a 4-iron to the green and holed a long putt!

Player, as you would expect, was defying the first rule of Wentworth – if you miss the fairway, you are dead; it is certain to cost you one shot, if not more. That is a fact of golf as you thread your way through the trees, heather, sand, gorse and water to the turn, tangling with a well-bunkered 5th green, a tee shot that demands restraint and accurate placement at each of the 6th, 7th and 8th, and the most formidable par fours at the 460-yard 9th.

SCORE CARD: West Course

Hole	Yards	Par	Hole	Yards	Par
1	471	4	10	186	3
2	155	3	11	376	4
3	452	4	12	483	5
4	501	5	13	441	4
5	191	3	14	179	3
6	344	4	15	480	5
7	399	4	16	380	4
8	398	4	17	571	5
9	460	4	18	502	5
Out	3371	35	In	3598	38
			Total	6969	73

Now the 'easy' half is over and one of the most intimidating of par threes starts the par 38 back nine, so difficult as almost to be unfair – unless you have hit the green with a high tee shot. The 11th has its dogleg and two ditches to negotiate, the 12th a line of conifers defying the tee shot and the 13th dog-legs left with a fairway that falls away to the jungle on the right. There just is no respite as you face not only an uphill tee shot but a terraced green again at the par three 14th as the preliminary to the finish of three par fives in the last four holes.

One of the tests of a golf course is how easily the holes are remembered after a casual acquaintance. By this standard the East Course rates as highly as the West. The East possesses five short holes, and such is their quality that it is not one too many. Though measuring only some 6,200 yards, the challenge and variety measures up to the West. Holes particularly to savour are the 2nd – for the glorious panorama from the tee – the 11th and the three finishing holes.

But it is not the courses alone that make Wentworth Club, it is the whole ambience of one of the game's Meccas.

From *AA Golf Guide to Great Britain* (London, 1977).

A Course to Make a Welshman Proud

Peter Allen

I had just turned pro at the age of eighteen when I played my first international against the French at Royal Porthcawl in South Wales and the course has remained a favourite of mine ever since – second only to Wentworth among British courses. In this piece Sir Peter Allen, a former Chairman of ICI and a keen amateur golfer whose business happily took him travelling in the neighbourhood of many fine courses all over the world, describes the special attraction of this Welsh seaside course.

I.W.

I didn't get to Royal Porthcawl in South Wales until late in 1966 and more's the pity, for it is a mighty fine seaside golf course. However, I *did* get there in the end and so completed my tally of all the championship courses of the British Isles, a pursuit which had begun at Deal forty-one years before. True, Porthcawl joined the select band late in the day in 1951 and so became the last but for Ganton to be used for one or other of the major events, but it had its reputation made long before then.

I have called it a seaside course advisedly, for it is indeed by the sea and the club's boast that you can see the sea from some part of every hole is true, but it is not all links-land by any means; the lower holes along the shore and on shore level are links golf, right enough, but there is a distinct hill which you climb at the fifth and on the upper levels from the fifth green to the ninth tee and then again at the twelfth and seventeenth you are on something more like moorland turf with bracken and heather and thick gorse in the rough.

The course is not by any means abominably long, 6,700 yards off the championship tees and 6,400 off the regular tees, so that several of the par fours are under 400 yards, that is until you get stuck into the second half, when the par fours lengthen out and indeed become bogey fives. Don't be deluded, however. The course is not easy, for on the whole the greens are small and the course is richly bunkered; the greens, moreoever, have some heavy curvatures, steps and slopes, so that when the game needs to be tightened up some pretty difficult pin positions can be selected.

The location of the course is excellent, with a fine view over the Bristol Channel towards Minehead and Exmoor twenty miles or so away, and on down the coast to Ilfracombe. Inland are some attractive hills and across the bay the Gower Peninsula, with Swansea on its flank. Industry does not too much intrude, save for the emission at intervals of some pink smoke from below the sheltering hill to the west, which betrays the presence of the Steel Company of Wales's Port Talbot plant.

The Porthcawl Club started its golf on a different site on a piece of common land to the east, but for nearly seventy years it has been where it now is, occupying a rough triangle of land, as good a shape as any for a golf course, and especially if, as here, there is liable to be plenty of wind. Then the straight-out-and-home course is at its worst and a layout on a triangle far better. The first three holes run out to the west along the shore, the third, indeed, so close that you can drive on to the shingle without any trouble at all. Then you turn back and play inland to a short hole, well bunkered, with its green sitting up for you, none the less, then at number five with its long uphill pull to the green you are on the plateau. Here, as I have said, you are off the links-land, and indeed this part of the course reminded me a great deal of Ganton, but, after all, isn't Ganton a links inland or something very like it? Up here there is a very short hole, only 125 yards, but it is not easy, for it is heavily bunkered, the green is long and narrow and has some big slopes and borrows. The ninth, with a drive across a big dip, is a splendid hole, with a small much beset green and with some good slopes on it, an excellent medium-length par four. My Welsh caddie, whose vast ginger moustache and whiskers, extending from ear to ear, reminded me of Sir Gerald Nabarro, declared that it was the finest hole on the course and I'm not disposed to disagree.

The par fours in the second half really stretch you, holes like the thirteenth, fifteenth and sixteenth, which I couldn't reach on a soft November day, and there are two fine short holes in this half, the eleventh, which is longer than it looks – where I bolted a putt for a two – and the fourteenth, which is shorter, where I missed a much easier putt. Only the two long holes in the back nine seemed to me to be rather below standard, but the eighteenth is a beautiful finishing hole, with a downhill drive off the plateau straight towards the sea; there is a scrubby hollow across the fairway about 270 yards from the regular tee which no doubt bothers some, but keeping short of that was no trouble to me. The green is long and narrow and literally runs on to the shore, so a shot hit 'thin' can well end up on the shingle.

The greens throughout the whole layout are excellent.

From *Famous Fairways* by Sir Peter Allen
(Stanley Paul, London, 1968).

The Very Irish Hazard of Maggie Leonard's Cow

Pat Ward-Thomas

Portmarnock Golf Club in County Dublin is one of my three favourite golf courses this side of the Atlantic and it rates with any of the great British Championship links. Even the 'easier' holes become a challenge when the wind blows off the sea and the 192-yard fifteenth with its two little pothole bunkers flanking the entrance to the green can be a real card-wrecker. It was here in his great year of 1960 that Arnie Palmer smacked a 3-iron across the wind which died within a yard of the hole. Though he failed with the putt, he was round in 69. He and Sam Snead went on to win the World Cup (then called the Canada Cup) by eight clear shots, even though Gary Player for South Africa did a 66, equalling Christy O'Connor's record of the previous year in the Dunlop Masters. Christy, incidentally, played the last twenty-three holes of that Masters in 83 or 9 under par to snatch the title from Joe Carr. He even tamed the testing 466-yard seventeenth, which demands a drive of absolute straightness because of the bunkers. The second shot is often a wood because the wind is rarely helpful. If you pull the ball a fraction or drift it, you will be trapped in bunkers round the green. Yet Christy twice birdied the hole in 3, placing a 4-wood for his second to within feet of the pin, on days when 5s were commonplace. Here Pat Ward-Thomas describes the greatness of Portmarnock.

I.W.

In a land where beauty, poetry, conflict and passionate belief in the individual are constantly intermingled, the Irish have found golf to be a ready expression of their character and flair for games. The enthusiasm of the players, the variety of styles and the quality of courses is remarkable. Ireland is not large, but it has several of the finest tests of golf to be found anywhere in Europe.

Except in the country itself, where local feelings might influence judgement, one would be hard-pressed to find agreement as to which was the greatest course – Portrush, Portmarnock or County Down. These three are not alone, for there are Ballybunion and Rosses Point on the far Atlantic shore; Killarney, serene on its lakeside amid the mountains, and Waterville have elements of majesty.

Of all courses, few are blessed with the natural magnificence of Portmarnock. Within the fine sweep of coastline curving to an end at Howth Hill, the northern guardian of Dublin Bay, there is a long tongue of linksland between the Irish Sea and an inland tidal bay. It is thus almost enclosed by water, a private place where a man is alone with the turf, the sea, the sky and the challenge of the wind. It is brave, splendid golfing country.

Portmarnock's moods can vary from a sternness, that can be savage, to wondrous peace. In summer, with a fresh breeze sparkling the bay and stirring the dune grasses, Ireland's Eye and Lambay rising sharp from the sea, there are few more tempting places for a golfer to be. On such a day, long ago, Sam Snead was at practice, pouring a stream of flawless strokes with a 1-iron into the morning distance. Watching golf could offer little more.

Like its great Irish rivals, Portmarnock often changes direction, somewhat after the fashion of Muirfield, with two distinctive and separate trails finishing by the clubhouse, a graceful white landmark from afar. The spectacular quality and unexpectedness of County Down are absent, but Portmarnock's problems are straightforward, even if considerable and often severe. There are no blind shots to the greens and few from the tees, no sharp changes of level yet no monotonous flatness, either. Several holes follow shallow valleys, but they are never as pronounced as they are at Birkdale. They might suggest, but certainly do not afford, protection from the wind.

The design of the course is natural rather than contrived. The 3rd, along a strath of turf, narrow and slightly convex between sandhills on one side and the marshy fringes of the bay on the other, is an example. So, too, is the one bunker guarding the pin at the 5th. The approaches to the shorter par-fours such as the 2nd and 8th, are beautifully shaped. There are only three short holes – the 7th, into a dell, the 12th, high in the dunes, and the 15th, which can be fearsome with a wind from the sea on the right. To hold the narrow table of green, it may be necessary to swing the shot over the beach – which is out-of-bounds – and back again. Even in still air the green, shelving away on either hand, is difficult to hold. Only a true stroke here will prevail.

The three par-fives can be immense. At times the 6th, along its dimpled fairway and valleys, can be three woods for the strongest, yet the second shot can be as little as a medium iron when the course is running fast. The 13th has a long carry from the tee, behind which the waves pound, and there are bunkers to attract and destroy the second shot. The 16th is of similar shape, down from the sea with the approaches swinging in from the left.

These two noble holes are part of a challenging finish, for the 14th, too, is a great hole although less than 400 yards. According to the wind, the second from a rolling fairway can be anything from a wood to a pitch and must carry huge bunkers in front of a long plateau of green in the dunes. Legend has it that Joe Carr, greatest of Irish amateurs, has driven the green, the ball somehow escaping the bunkers; fact in its turn states that Henry Cotton once took seven strokes here – and lost an Irish Open in the process.

As a strong par-four, the 17th takes a deal of beating. Bunkers flanking the straight fairway are cause for thought on the tee and the second demands a long, accurate shot to a closely guarded green. The 18th, a fine hole, owes less to fortune than it did when the home green was hard by the clubhouse. The hole has been shortened and the green moved to a position offering less of a threat to the constantly peppered building.

Portmarnock has been the setting for many great occasions, played in the wildest extremes of weather. When a tempest assailed the last round of the Irish Open in

1927, George Duncan – one of the greatest of inspirational golfers – was round in 74, the only player to break 80. The weather was such that, even with this historic round, his winning score was 312. Christy O'Connor took 36 strokes fewer when he won the Dunlop Masters at Portmarnock thirty-two years later.

The Dunlop tournament won by O'Connor in 1959 was memorable for the golf of Joe Carr. After three rounds, all under 70, he led a strong field by four strokes and was within sight of being the first amateur to win a major professional tournament in a generation until O'Connor passed him with a final round of 66.

The only time the Amateur championship has been played in Eire, in 1949, it was won by Max McCready. His golf had power, authority and great confidence and it disposed of the two most formidable Americans in the field, Frank Stranahan, the defending champion, in the semi-final, and Willie Turnesa in the final. Thunder prowled the distant hills as the inscrutable Turnesa became one up with four to play, but McCready won the next three holes. Ireland rejoiced that night.

None of this might have happened but for the inspiration in 1893 that impelled two men, J. W. Pickeman and George Ross, to row across the mouth of the estuary from the point where the Sutton clubhouse now stands. By some blessing of the imagination they visualized a golf course on what was then a wilderness of dune and bracken inhabited only by a remote and self-sufficient community of farming and fish folk, yet only ten miles from Dublin.

The first clubhouse was only a shack and the greatest hazard Maggie Leonard's cow, which devoured hundreds of balls. Golfers reached the course by crossing the estuary at low tide in a horse-drawn cart, at other times by boat. There is a road now at the far end of the peninsula and this delightful and very Irish way of reaching the 1st tee has gone the way of Maggie Leonard's cow.

From *The World Atlas of Golf*
(© Mitchell Beazley, London, 1976).

10

SOME MODERN HEROES

Tom Watson

Peter Alliss

For a decade at least from the time of his first British Open win in 1975, Tom Watson was the supreme champion, taking over from Nicklaus as the world's leading player – indeed, he is one of the greatest of all time. I've long admired him. At 5 feet 9 inches he doesn't suffer from being too tall and there is immense power in his arms and legs. On top of that he is the world's best short-putter. Peter Alliss, another long-time admirer of Watson, here gives his shrewd assessment of him as man and golfer.

I.W.

'We're vastly overrated.' That's part of Tom Watson's attitude to the fame and adulation that success brings to golfers (and all other athletes) today. It's always been very apparent to me that Tom is one of those who doesn't relish public attention and the praise of genuine admirers or hangers-on alike. True, he has the ambition to be recognized in golfing history as one of the greatest players but that's a very different matter from enjoying all the razzmatazz that goes hand-in-hand with being in the limelight. As I know only too well, much of that brings little more than occasional embarrassment, frequent boredom and always the feeling of being 'on parade' and having to put on a public face.

Indeed, when Tom is actually on parade as one of our Supreme Champions, in one respect he doesn't quite look the part. I'm sure he has a very lucrative clothing contract yet nothing seems to fit. The trousers are usually a touch too long or too short and the labelled shirts and polo necks too loose or too tight. All very different from, let's say, the casual elegance of Jack Nicklaus or Seve Ballesteros. Yet that same Jack Nicklaus 20 years and more ago, in jockey cap and khaki trousers could himself have been competing for the title of worst-dressed golfer. In Watson's case, such disregard for his attire has never been as openly contemptuous – after all, he belongs to a different era when nearly all conform to what is required of them and may well be fined by their PGAs if they don't!

The clothing contract is just one of several that brings Tom's income to something like $1½ million a year, a sum that dwarfs his tournament money winnings which give him a career total of about $4 million. In business, Watson has been very much his own man. It's a family affair with his wife Linda playing a major role though his manager is Charles Rubin, a lawyer who also happens to be Watson's brother-in-law.

Financially, Tom is obviously set up for life but his motivation remains as strong as ever. On the US Tour he restricts himself to about 20 events a year out of the more than 40 possible. He plays more than Jack Nicklaus and Johnny Miller – but not by that wide a margin. Watson's overseas appearances are limited. Of course, the British Open has absolute priority, Watson's favourite and best event, and he is also to be seen from time to time in Australia and Japan. But that's about it. He has learned to protect 'the property', devising a limited schedule which keeps him keen to play golf and competitively sharp.

Of the great and nearly great players, Watson realized early that the majors are what count and was later to say, 'Charisma is winning major championships'. A waning Johnny Miller may declare that a golfer's record in other tournaments is almost as important but, to be blunt, Miller will be remembered for winning the 1973 US Open and the 1976 British Open Championship far more than for the 22 US Tour events he has won to date or even for those couple of years when he played golf at a standard never seen before or since.

Tom appears to me to be a British Open specialist. Oddly, he had won the championship a couple of times before he really understood what was involved or the armoury needed to combat the difficulties of seaside golf. At Carnoustie in 1975, he made his first appearance in Britain, with only two tournament wins under his belt. Surely he had no thoughts of winning as he went to the 1st tee? Yet there Watson produced a performance that has from time to time been a sort of trademark – keep going and it could be the others who will falter. Watson finished a little ahead of the apparent leading contenders and, lo and behold, they all came back to him – Bobby Cole, Johnny Miller, Jack Nicklaus, Neil Coles, and, of course, Jack Newton.

The play-off between this Australian and Watson swung to and fro. It could have gone either way but it was Watson who got his par on the last hole to win. He was on his way and has never looked back, at times making the British Open Championship and dominance of the US money list seem his by right.

I'm sure that victory took Tom Watson by surprise and he was a far more polished player at Turnberry in 1977, a championship which saw the most sustained man-to-man combat since the championship began in 1860. By this time, Watson was a very different player. If the 1975 championship had almost stolen up on him unawares, in 1977 he had come to believe in himself as the most effective scorer in the game of golf. He also sought perfection and, after the third round, was quick to point out to the Press that his 65 was better fashioned than Jack Nicklaus's had been with more tee-shots on the fairway and superior quality of strike on the irons. He didn't mention the putting and hardly needed to for, I believe, Watson is far and away the greatest short putter among the moderns, while his firm-wristed stroke from long range is also highly effective at keeping the ball on line to the holeside and is allied to unrivalled judgement of pace.

Watson is not the thinking man's perfect player. He certainly hits a long ball but some are rather wild. His very strong 'Popeye' forearms should give him an edge in long- and mid-iron play but, if you'll believe the statistics, he virtually never features in the US Tour figures for getting on the greens in regulation figures. In this department Nicklaus, among many others, earns much higher ratings.

That acute observer, Lee Trevino, claims that Tom hasn't got a soft shot. Everything is played with much the same firm, crisp rhythm. Lee believes that Tom can't pitch in with a high fading pattern of flight, that he has, basically, to bang everything at the flag. Well, they used to say that a certain Gardner Dickinson was more concerned about the shape of a particular shot and would be far more delighted to get a delicate fade or a low-drawn ball to 40 feet than something a little more direct nearer the pin. There are players more intent on the perfection of shot than the result, with Tom Weiskopf a clear example. I pass on the truth of these opinions but I can say that I've never seen anyone, lack of a soft shot or not, more adept at getting it close from around the green and then ramming home the putt, almost as an effort of will. His fellow players tend to think that if, at every hole, everyone missed all the greens, Watson would proceed to win all the tournaments. There may be better putters, chippers and pitchers. But no one else can put it all together as well.

Part of this has to do with practice. So many players go to the practice ground occupied with thoughts of the total golf swing. Will that tip about arching the left wrist just a little bit more work? Should the club be kept low to the ground on the backswing for an extra 6 inches? Well you know it all. Tournament golfers seek the magic solutions just as eagerly as the ordinary club player.

Watson goes through the same drills. But he is not so strong a believer. He'd like to be perfect, like Ben Hogan before him, but is much more a realist. Watson knows that, driving the ball well over 250 yards, many of his tee-shots will finish in the rough. The target areas are narrower at that distance. He'll practise and improvise from that kind of territory as much as others will devote time to watching the flight of, let's say, a 7-iron nudged into a perfect lie. How few golfers do this, yet so many shots are, for example, played when the ball is well down in the grass, from worn and bare turf around a green or when the backswing is impeded by a bush, tree or a wall. Watson spends time practising in all these and many other situations. When he gets into them, he's been there before and knows how to cope. Rather like Walter Hagen before him, Tom expects to hit a few poor shots in a round and then briskly confronts the problem and gets on with it.

This briskness is very obvious in other departments of his play. He may not be quite so fast as Lanny Wadkins but there's very little in it. Watson decides on the kind of shot he'll play as he approaches his ball and then simply looks target, ball, target – and swings. And I can detect hardly any difference if he's 20 strokes behind the leaders in a run-of-the-mill tournament or in hot contention for a major championship.

Two shots at such times in recent major championships will go into golfing history.

For both, Watson was as brisk as ever. Needing to par the tough closing hole at Royal Birkdale to win the Open Championship in 1983 and after hitting a poor drive at the 17th, Watson quickly fired his drive straight down the fairway. He was equally brisk playing a 2-iron, held up against the wind, which finished in the heart of the green, making two putts for victory a formality.

An even more famous shot had occurred a little over a year earlier at Pebble Beach in the US Open Championship. Nicklaus had completed his final round; Watson needed a par, par finish to tie over two difficult holes, a long par-3, followed by a par-5 with an intimidating tee-shot and played right around the cliff tops. Watson then proceeded to stand the situation on its head. For a start, he looked as if he'd lost the championship when his long-iron bounced into quite thick rough just to the left of the green. There seemed little or no chance that he could get his tiny pitch shot to stop near the hole. Instead, in it went for a 2 and Tom needed only par on the last to win. The birdie which followed was not necessary but he had won his first US Open by two.

Two quite different stories have been told since about this legendary pitch-in. The first is that a TV company approached Watson with the request that he attempt to re-enact the shot. Watson refused. Why? Well perhaps he didn't want to tarnish his image by failing. The second is that Tom has since tried to do it again and again for his own personal satisfaction – and failed, seldom getting within several feet. You pays your money and takes your choice.

Perhaps that 1982 US Open assured Tom of golfing immortality but it certainly took many observers of golf a long time to concede him this status. Byron Nelson's opinion is interesting and he knows Tom's game better than anyone. He considers that Watson could prove to be better than both Hogan and Nicklaus, superior from the mid-irons through the pitching clubs and a far better clipper and putter. Although this argues supremacy for Watson in approach play and the short game only there's not much left for Hogan and Nicklaus to be good at is there? Just driving, fairway woods and the long-irons! They are departments of the game where Watson himself is no slouch.

Even so, shot-making was never Tom's main problem but learning to win and to manage both himself and the golf course was. He was introduced to golf at the age of six by his father but he did not have an outstanding amateur career. He won the Missouri State Amateur Championship four times and played for the Stanford University team for three years, finishing as their number one. He had no success at the higher levels of amateur golf, however, and with this record could hardly have been worth a thought as a possible Walker Cup choice.

The accepted route to the US Tour was a Walker Cup place and a proven record in national and regional amateur tournaments which players such as Nicklaus, Wadkins and Crenshaw have enjoyed as part of their golf pedigree. Nevertheless, Watson decided to try his luck on the US Tour and turned professional in 1971. His first season, 1972, was immediately reassuring.

The Bing Crosby National Pro-Am was the second event of the season, played over the testing courses of Pebble Beach, Spyglass Hill and Cyprus Point. Watson finished twentieth, seven strokes behind the play-off between Jack Nicklaus and

Johnny Miller, winning a modest $1,400. It was a start and showed Tom that he could compete with the best. He won money in the next two or three events so in his first month on Tour he had gone a good way towards proving, if only to himself, that he could make a living at the game.

Learning to contend and to win were to take considerably longer. In the rest of the season by far his best result was second place in the Quad Cities Open, his 69 and 66 finishing rounds putting him a stroke behind Deane Beman, now US Tour Commissioner. However, the field wasn't of the highest quality and Tom had yet to face the test of being tournament leader and holding onto it with all the big guns there.

That problem came twice in 1973. In the Hawaiian Open he took a three-stroke lead into the final round but then faltered to end with a 75. Much the same happened in the World Open, a strange and short-lived event dedicated to the idea that eight rounds of golf are a better test than four. In the fifth round, Watson played the splendid Pinehurst Number 2 course in 62, which catapulted him into a six-stroke lead, but he dribbled it away with rounds of 76, 76 and 77. However, by the end of the year he'd moved up from seventy-ninth place in the money list to thirty-fifth.

Watson first became a 'name' in 1974. The event which established him was the US Open at Winged Foot. After three rounds he was the leader by a stroke but on the final day staggered home with a 79. Three failures in a row. Among those in the know, it was openly bandied about that Tom Watson had no iron streak. He was a 'choker', a man who lost his nerve when protecting a lead. This reputation was only partly changed a short time later when Watson won for the first time at the Western Open. This time he had a weak third round but came past the leaders with a 69 on the last day to win by a couple of strokes from J. C. Snead and Tom Weiskopf.

He was by then an established player, and finished the year tenth in the US money list, which made him roughly equivalent to Ryder Cup status. In 1975 Tom Watson became a star but there were still problems along the way. After winning the Byron Nelson Classic in May, he had a second bad experience in the US Open at Medinah. His start of 67 and 68 equalled the championship record for the first 36 holes. Although his finish of 78 and 77 sounds like another total collapse it was a high-scoring event and his total of 290 was only three strokes worse than the winner's. (Lou Graham and John Mahaffey tied and Graham won the play-off.)

Later in the year, after his British Open title, Tom won the World Series and finished seventh on the US money list. Jack Nicklaus commented: 'He knows exactly where he's going. Straight ahead. Nothing distracts him. He has great abilities, super confidence and just enough cockiness. He's not a comer. He has arrived.'

Watson was indeed soon to take over from Jack Nicklaus as the world's leading player though that wasn't to be fully clear for some years yet. His progress was distinguished in the immediate future by being leading money winner four years in a row, 1977–80, with wins in the 1977 and 1981 Masters, but most of all by his extraordinary achievements in the British Open with five championship victories in the space of only nine years. If his victory at Turnberry over Jack Nicklaus remains the most memorable, Muirfield in 1980 saw Watson at another peak. After the first round he was tied for the lead with Lee Trevino and a 64 in the third round took him into a four-stroke lead. Thoughts of whether or not Watson might 'choke' were long gone. We all thought it was inevitable he would win. The final day was indeed rather dull as Tom put together a cast-iron 69 for a four-stroke victory.

By this time, Watson had made another move forward in the major championships. Almost always he was a contender, able to raise his game for the great occasions of golf even when not on his best form. Others may beat him,' as Seve Ballesteros did when he started his final round so strongly in the 1983 Masters. Yet a month or so later, Watson produced form so devastating in the US Open as to leave the Spaniard in his wake. It should have been enough to give Watson his second US Open had that vast putt from 62 feet by Larry Nelson not gone in on the 16th hole.

If Tom has had to learn how to compete and withstand pressure, he has physically always been very well suited to the game. He has almost the perfect golfing body, with magnificent forearms and very strong legs, hands and shoulders and all at what I consider the right height, 5 feet 9 inches. If a player is 6 feet or more the game becomes more difficult. The angles are wrong and many players suffer from a lack of co-ordination. Short men, on the other hand, usually have insufficient power. Watson's physical fitness, like Nicklaus's, has also been vital. I can't remember him having any of the problems with his lower back, wrists and elbows that so many golfers suffer, Trevino and Fuzzy Zoeller, for instance, and whatever has become of those lady stars, Judy Rankin and Sally Little?

As he enters his mid-thirties, it's perhaps the right time to wonder where Watson will go from here. His desire, dedication and determination don't seem to have been diluted by all the success. Unlike so many, he still enjoys playing the game on both the sternly competitive and fun occasions. He was a great success in 1983 on BBC television's Pro-Celebrity series at Gleneagles and aroused great interest with his demonstration of the importance of the constant angle of the left elbow in putting. He could rattle several putts home from a few yards' range without needing to glance at the line again. Watson also enjoys playing with friends and declares he would still make trips to Britain and Ireland even if there were no British Open to play in. He declared Royal Dornoch the most fun he had ever had playing golf and said of the towering duneland of the great Ballybunion course in Western Ireland: 'Golf architects should live and play here before they build courses.'

If Watson keeps that kind of enthusiasm, his tournament and championship successes ought to continue as long as that putting stroke remains firm and decisive. Here he's the early Arnold Palmer, willing to give the hole a chance from long range, confident that he'll be still able to hole those frightening 4- to 6-footers on the way back.

Watson is one of our Supreme Champions who seems to me to have very much benefited from the stability of his family life. It was typical that after his 1982 US Open Championship victory at Pebble Beach he didn't carouse away the night. Instead, he was to be seen on the rocks near the course quietly sharing a bottle of wine with his wife Linda and his two-year-old daughter, Meg. He has also remained in touch with his roots. Although he majored in psychology at Stanford University, he didn't seek the sun of either that state or, another favourite choice, Florida, once success came his way. The golfers who do so aren't necessarily sun-worshippers, of course. It's easier to keep a golf swing in trim during the off-season in warm weather, despite the fact that the golf season is now so long that it's certainly possible to play around the world in a summer climate throughout.

However, Watson has remained faithful to the American Mid-West and his birthplace Kansas City. In fact, he claims actually to enjoy bad weather golf and that has included playing in snow. It's all part of a pattern which has allowed Tom Watson to relish his success but to keep as level-headed as when he's contending for a major championship.

From *Peter Alliss's Supreme Champions of Golf*
(Willow Books, London, 1986).

Super Mex on the British

Lee Trevino

Lee Trevino's is a real rags-to-riches story. A Mexican-American farmboy who started as a caddie at the age of eight, he had a fatherless childhood living rough with his mother and grandfather in a Dallas shack with dirt floors and no plumbing or electricity. He taught himself to play golf well enough to win the US Open with a 275 four-round record in 1968 at Oak Hill and was the first to break 70 in every round. He won the Open again in 1971 in a play-off against Nicklaus and was also victorious in the British Open twice, in 1971 and 1972.

You could call Super Mex (a nickname coined by his agent) a lucky player, especially with that chip that went in and shattered the hapless Tony Jacklin at the seventeenth hole at Muirfield. When Lee is on a high he is brilliant, but not a battler against odds like Player or Nicklaus. His characteristic shot is low and faded, which is why he has never come to terms with the Masters – Augusta demands the opposite. 'Augusta is one type of golf course and I'm another type of golfer. Even on our best days I'd guess you'd say we have our differences,' he admits.

After being struck by lightning in the Western Open in 1976, he recalls, 'I stretched out like a vibrator – your whole life passes before you at that moment. Hey, I never knew I was so bad! I saw a lot of old girlfriends.' His back was affected by a ruptured disc and he had to have surgery. 'I sure as hell wouldn't recommend being struck by lightning, but it turned my life around. It made me appreciate everything I have.' That includes the wise-cracking routine and the chatting between shots which so delights the crowds – though not always his opponents.

In his autobiography Super Mex freely discusses his one-time drink problem, appearing on *The Johnny Carson Show* and falling down drunk, playing tournaments with horrible hangovers, and once winning a championship on the first-hole play-off after staying up till five in the morning. Then in 1974, realizing that this could cut years off his career, he cut down on the hard stuff and limited his beer drinking. He confesses to a love affair with the British and the British courses, as he explains here.

I.W.

Everything went like a dream that week at Royal Birkdale, but that really was no surprise. My experiences with British golf through the years have captured a special place in my heart.

I was introduced to British courses in 1968 and it was love at first sight. My strong showing in championship tournaments just made the romance more glamorous. And after I had played in a dozen British Opens I saw no end to it.

'I'll always play in this tournament,' I said before I teed off in 1981 at Royal St George's. 'I don't care if I shoot eighty-eighty. I'll always play over here. I love this championship. I love the links courses, with the mist and wind sweeping off the sea. I love these people.'

There's nothing quite like playing in the British Isles. Golf is in the air there. You breathe it, like smelling home cooking. It makes you hungry. You want to play.

Now it seems strange that I passed up my first spot in a British Open. I earned that in 1968 when I won the US Open, but I had a commitment to the Milwaukee tournament and didn't think I should break it. I did go to England for a couple of tournaments that fall, then entered my first British Open in 1969 at Royal Lytham and St Anne's. In 1970 we played St Andrews and I led after three rounds, but blew the championship with a final 77. Still, I felt I eventually would win the British Open. Once I got a taste of those seaside courses I knew they were for me.

It doesn't matter if you hit it short. As long as you hit it straight you can run the ball on the greens. And the wind doesn't bother me because I hit a low ball anyway.

As fond as I am of Birkdale, Muirfield, where I won the 1972 championship and finished second to Tom Watson in 1980, is my all-time favorite. I play the courses in Scotland extremely well. I can bump and run the ball better on them than any native. I've told the people there, 'If you believe in reincarnation, I probably was a Scotsman two hundred and fifty years ago.'

I won British championships the last two years they used the small ball. That was one more thing I loved about playing there. The ball was 1.62 inches in diameter as compared to 1.68 for the American ball and that meant less wind resistance, fewer dimples on the ball and less spin. To me, playing with the small ball was like cheating.

While I was always comfortable on the courses, I had some early problems communicating with the people. It took me a while to loosen them up, too. They were pretty damn reserved when I first went over there.

During my first practice round for the Alcan tournament at Birkdale in 1969, my caddie told me, 'You have to be careful here because there's a birn going across the fairway.'

'A what?' I said.

'A birn,' he said.

I hit a drive, then walked down the fairway and found my ball in the water. I looked at him and said, 'Why didn't you tell me there was a creek running through here?'

'I told you, mate. That's a birn.'

The 9th is a blind hole. You go over a hill and down and you can't see the fairway. I stood on the tee for a second, then asked him, 'Where is the fairway going?'

'Hit it straight to the marquee,' he told me.

'Where?' I asked.

'Hit it to the marquee,' he said.

Well, I took my driver and hit my ball into the right rough. 'Damm,' I said, 'I thought the fairway went this way.'

'No,' he said, 'I told you that a straight line off that tee is to the marquee.'

'Let me ask you a question,' I said. 'What the hell is a marquee?'

'That thing over there,' he said, and he pointed at a tent.

I knew right then I had to learn the language.

He wasn't a very good caddie, though, so I got rid of him after nine holes. That's when Willie Aitchison took my bag.

Willie was a Scot who had carried for two British Open winners, first Tony Lema and then Roberto de Vicenzo. Since Roberto wasn't playing in this tournament, I hired Willie and he wound up working for me in Britain and Europe for many years. But first I had to teach Willie how to caddie.

'I've got too many shots and I hit the ball too many different ways,' I told him. 'Look, I want you to go to the drugstore . . .'

'Where?' Willie asked.

'Go to the drugstore,' I said.

'You mean the chemist's,' he said.

'Well, just go there and get a notebook,' I said. 'Bring it out here tomorrow and I'll show you how to diagram each hole and mark down the yardage.'

Willie handled that all right, but there was one problem. He talked more than I do.

'Willie,' I said, 'you've got to be the listener. We can sing together, but we can't talk together.'

He still got involved with talking to too many people. In the Ryder Cup matches at Birkdale in 1969, Miller Barber and I played Tony Jacklin and Peter Townsend and when we came to 18 it was almost dark and we were feeling a lot of pressure. These points were important because the teams were tied and the United States hadn't lost to Great Britain since 1957. When I got to the tee I looked for my bag and Willie wasn't there.

The next thing I knew here comes a guy carrying my bag and I've never seen him before. 'Where's Willie?' I asked.

'He was talking to someone coming up the hill,' this stranger said, 'and he slipped down and broke his ankle.' Now that's got to be a first in the history of golf!

While I was still trying to figure that out, I missed an 8-foot putt to keep us from winning outright and that let Great Britain tie us, 16–16. Hell, the British should have given Willie a team blazer.

When I went to London to play in the Piccadilly World Match Play Invitation in 1968 I didn't know much about the tournament except that it was very exclusive. To play there you have to have won one of the four major titles in the past year, be top money-winner for the previous year or something like that.

Before I got there I played in the Alcan, and the Piccadilly publicity man looked me up. I was wearing slacks, cowboy boots, sports coat and sports shirt with no tie, which is what I liked to wear. He wrinkled his nose.

'My good man,' he said, 'you'll be staying at the Savoy Hotel during the Piccadilly and this is not proper attire.'

I asked him what he meant by that. 'You must wear a solid suit,' he said. I told him I didn't have a solid suit, didn't even have a tie. He gave me a fishy look and walked away.

Well, before I checked into the Savoy, I went to Moss Brothers in London and rented me white tie and tails, top hat, cape and cane – the whole bit. Then I made a big entrance at the hotel and got a whole lot of press.

The publicity man was kind of stunned, but he introduced me to his wife. She told me I must go sightseeing and kept telling me about the Teems. I didn't know what she was talking about.

She pointed out a window of the hotel and said, 'That's the Teems.'

I thought she was pointing at a building, but she told me she was talking about the river that goes through London. I told her, 'Lady, that's a little ol' creek in Texas.' She didn't even know what a creek was.

My British Open victory in 1971 really warmed up the fans, and I think I've had a lot to do with galleries' behavior since then. They've gotten louder, more sociable.

Oh, they were sociable before, but only at the right time and the right place. Galleries were completely different from those in America simply because they have been brought up to believe golf is a very quiet game. You don't talk while anybody is playing, and you sure don't laugh.

Families would come out to watch golf and they might not speak to each other for hours. At my first British Open I was struck immediately by the quietness of the galleries. They were huge, but silent. They were all bundled up in raincoats and boots and they all looked like brothers and sisters. There might be 30,000 people out there, but you never heard a word.

Through the years, because of my strong play in tournaments and the television exposure I've enjoyed with my own show on the BBC, I have gotten the galleries to enjoy themselves more. They have tremendous knowledge of the game. In Scotland once, I hit a beautiful low shot that carried about three or four feet above the ground, right at the flag 190 yards away. The ball hit in the front and just trickled over the green and stopped about four feet off the green but 20 feet from the hole. I got a standing ovation. The guy I was playing with hit a terrible-looking shot that hit the bank and kicked down about four feet from the hole. Nobody made a sound. They knew it wasn't a good shot.

In the United States you'll probably find only 30 percent of the galleries really care about the game. The other 70 percent are just where it's happening, man. It's like a flea market. Look at the Colonial tournament in Fort Worth. It's one of the best in our country, but half the people who go to it never see a golf ball hit. Especially those girls parading around in shorts and halter-tops. They don't give a damn about golf.

When British youngsters come to you for an autograph they never hand you a gum wrapper or a paper bag or a napkin. Every one of those kids has an autograph book. Some of those books go back a hundred years and have been handed down through the generations. I don't mind signing those. They make me a little piece of their family history.

And I've always been fascinated by how the British dress up for golf tournaments. Even the greenskeepers.

All the years I worked on a golf course I always wore the raggediest clothes I could find – old blue jeans, T-shirts, boots. But the guys mowing the fairways and greens there are wearing coats and ties. It's customary. That's why I go to Britain with a coat and tie on and I leave with a coat and tie on.

On a plane I never know if I'll sit next to some chairman of the board who may be looking for someone to endorse his company. If I'm dressed in blue jeans and a

T-shirt and he asks me what I do for a living, he'll look at me and forget it. I'm the last person he wants to endorse anything.

It's none of my business what other athletes wear, but I couldn't believe how John McEnroe was dressed when he flew back to New York from winning Wimbledon. He looked like he'd been working on his car.

Someday these guys are going to realize you don't make nearly as much money in the sport as you can make outside. That's why I carry a three-piece suit and three sports coats with matching ties. A lot of times I have to go to two or three functions in a week and I don't have to wear the same thing. My wardrobe has changed some since I went to that US Open in 1967 and could wash everything for a quarter.

Tradition never changes at the British Open, however. Those people have a tremendous respect for history, rank and honor.

When we played at St George's, I was walking toward the Tented Village, where equipment and clothing companies sell their products, to make an appearance at the John Letters exhibit when I saw an ancient little man totter by wearing a dark blue uniform. Hell, he had a big gold sword buckled around his waist and six or eight rows of huge, fancy medals on his chest.

I thought to myself, 'He better hope there's no lightning around here.'

But if lightning ever did get him, I guess he certainly would want to go in full dress uniform.

Everything is so old there. St Andrews, of course, is the birthplace of golf. It is home of the R&A – the Royal and Ancient Golf Club of St Andrews, which has held the Open since 1860. At Muirfield the Honourable Company of Edinburgh Golfers wrote the Thirteen Articles, the first rules of golf, about thirty years before some of our guys wrote the Declaration of Independence. And St George's, on the English Channel, is only a couple of tee shots from Pegwell Bay, where Julius Caesar first landed in England. There also are a couple of castles in the neighbourhood where Henry VIII hung out.

My locker in that old clubhouse was so small that all I kept in it was a pair of shoes, which I stood on end, and a bottle of whiskey for Seve Ballesteros' father.

'Man,' I told the attendant, 'I can't get my one-iron in this locker!'

But when it's time to play the Open, I don't want to be anywhere else.

The R&A still held the Open championship from Wednesday through Saturday in 1971 and my last day and night there were an unforgettable ending to a wonderful week.

Clyde and I stayed at the Prince of Wales Hotel in Southport that week. Just across the road was the Kingsway Casino, which was owned by George James, a man who treated us wonderfully. We went there every night to have dinner, see a show and then gamble until five in the morning. Then we went back to our room and slept until noon. I'd eat a light lunch and leave for the course around two. I teed off about three-thirty every day so everything worked out. I had some fun, I got some rest and I was always ready to play golf. Then, out of nowhere, Arnold Salinas appeared in the locker room at Birkdale just before I teed off in the second round.

Pete Dominguez, a good friend and a great guy who owns some Mexican restaurants in Dallas and Houston, had made so many bets on me with everyone at the Great Southwest Club that he sent Arnold over to coach me. He bought him a first-class airline ticket and said, 'Go keep Lee company.'

I don't know how Arnold talked his way into the clubhouse because security was extremely tight. But he can get in anywhere. All I know was I was sitting on a bench putting some cleats on my shoe when I heard a voice behind me ask, 'Hey, are there any Mexicans in this tournament?'

I turned around and there was Arnold. 'All right, son!' he said. 'Go get 'em!'

I shot 70 that day, same as Tony Jacklin, and we were tied at 139. I finished strong the next day and my 69 put me one shot up on my old friend from Formosa, Mr Lu, and Jacklin, who was wavering a little. Nicklaus was back some more with 71–71–72.

The weather was beautiful for the final round, just like it was all week. It must have been the best in British Open history: sixty-five or seventy degrees every day. I came out to the first tee in shirt sleeves and Mr Lu, who still had a crewcut, was wearing a straw hat.

We first met in 1959 when I was a Marine stationed on Okinawa and we played a match on Taiwan. Mr Lu beat me, 10 and 8. He was a fine golfer, a great up-and-down player, and a wonderful little man. Those British galleries loved him. He called me Bird, a name he gave me when I was in the Marines because my drives always flew past his.

We shook hands on the first tee and I told him, 'You don't need this trophy. You'd just fill it with flied lice.' He grinned. 'Birrrddd!' he said.

I shot 70 and beat Mr Lu by one shot with a total 278, but the final numbers were deceiving. I had a 5-shot lead with nine holes to play, but I was clowning so much I almost threw it away. It was just one of those times when everything was fun and I figured it was going to work out okay. And it did.

I was so hot on the front nine that I was hitting putts and walking away to the next tee without watching my ball drop in the cup. 'Hey, Bird,' Mr Lu said. 'You want to go through?' I laughed and hit him on the back of the head.

Just before we made the turn I knocked in a long putt and it snaked into the hole. I tossed my putter up, fell to my knees and then face down on the green. That's when the gallery loosened up. They loved it! No one had ever done that on one of their greens.

Well, it was so much fun by then that I almost forgot to finish the tournament. Clyde and Arnold walked along the fairway with me the last three rounds, thanks to the courtesy of an R&A official, so they were right there. On the back nine I would three-putt a hole and think, 'Hell, I've got enough to win.' Then on 17, I hit into a sand dune, knocked it across into the rough, had a hard time getting out of the heather, then stopped a 15-foot uphill putt short and wound up with a double-bogey 7. Suddenly, my lead was down to one!

The last hole at Birkdale is a par-5 of 500-plus yards but my chili was hot and I hit a drive that left me about 200 yards from the pin. Then I smoked a 6-iron to the back edge of the green. Meanwhile, Mr Lu got unlucky. His drive kicked left into a bunker, and when he tried to come out, he hit his ball with the heel of the club and it exploded into the gallery behind him, hitting a woman right between the eyes. She went down like she was shot, bleeding badly. He was sick about it, and I couldn't even bear to look at her. It turned out she was all right but it was terribly unnerving.

His ball bounced back in front of the green, however, and he hit a sensational shot that stopped about six feet from the hole. I had a 40-foot putt but I didn't fear a thing. I knocked it to two and a half feet and I still didn't have any doubts that after Mr Lu sank a birdie putt he forced me to make mine to win. I didn't wait. I just knocked it in and walked away. Clyde and Arnold ran up and hugged me.

'Hey, we did it!' I told Arnold.

'I know you did,' he said.

I won my first British Open championship with a game as good as Jack Nicklaus told me it could be. So in just twenty days I had beaten Jack in our US Open play-off, taken the Canadian Open title and then won in Britain, where Jack was defending champion.

'I wish,' he told a huge crowd at presentations, 'I had kept my damn mouth shut.'

We had a marvelous party at the Kingsway Casino that night. Someone had given us a two-gallon bottle of Bollinger's champagne at the course, so we drank that and then ordered some more. I had some special guests coming – two nuns from the local orphanage.

George James had told me, 'If you win this tournament and give five hundred pounds or fifteen hundred dollars to the orphanage you will really make a hit with them.' Well, my prize money was $13,000 and I told the nuns I would give them $5,000 of it on one condition: they had to come to the casino and drink a glass of champagne with me.

They had never been in a bar in their lives but they did it and had fun. Everybody was raising hell. Mr Lu was there and Jimmy Dean was singing to me. Later that night we raffled off my golf clubs for $1,500. I gave that to the orphanage, too. I wanted to share my joy.

Nicklaus tied for fifth at 283, but he was really fired up when we went to Muirfield for the 1972 British Open. I believe Jack felt if he ever was going to score a Grand Slam of the four major championships he would do it that year because he would play on his favorite courses – Augusta National, Pebble Beach, Muirfield and Oakland Hills, where the PGA was held later that summer.

I had given him a tough battle for the US Open title at Pebble Beach for three rounds but I weakened the last day, which wasn't surprising. I had spent four days in an El Paso hospital with pneumonia before the tournament and got out of bed just in time to fly to California and practise for nine holes. But in the month before I defended my British championship, I trained very hard. I took my family with me to Central Texas, rented a house and trained on Orville Moody's place in Killeeen. I was up at five every morning, running through the hills, and then I played golf. The greens superintendent had a twelve-year-old daughter, a mute who read lips, and she drove the cart with my bag on it. I didn't ride. I ran between shots and I played 36 holes a day. I was determined to be sharp for Muirfield.

Well, I won again at Muirfield with 278 and again I broke out of a 36-hole tie with Tony Jacklin after shooting 71–70. It turned around in the third round. Jacklin had a good edge on the front nine but I sank a 25-footer for a birdie on 14 and that touched me off. I birdied the last five holes and finished with 66 to lead Jacklin by one.

On 16 that day I gave a pretty good example of getting a lemon and making lemonade. I took a 6-iron and just as I got ready to hit my shot the grip unravelled at the bottom. Like a snake, it just tangled up around my hand. It was a funny sight and everyone laughed. I stopped, took a couple of minutes to rewrap it and got my muscles tensed up. When I swung that club it felt like a feather and I hit a bad shot into the bunker, on the back upslope. I had no shot from there so I went with my wedge, hoping to keep it on the green, maybe 30 feet from the flag, and 2-putt for a bogey. I hit the wedge and the ball came out entirely too fast but somehow it hit on the green, took one big hop and went into the cup on the fly. It went in so fast the BBC cameraman missed it.

Coming out of there with a birdie instead of a bogey meant two shots that changed the final outcome because the next day Jack rallied with a 66. But my 71 gave me the championship by one.

That ruined possibly the best shot at a Grand Slam in his career but Jack didn't take that loss as hard as he did losing by one to Tom Watson at Turnberry in 1977. I finished fourth that year, after sharing the 36-hole lead with them, but I was pleased with that because I was working myself back to top form after my back surgery. For me, that was a good tuneup for the Canadian Open, which I won. For Jack, it must have been very tough to play head-to-head with Watson the last 36 holes, shoot 65–66 and see Tom beat him with two 65s. What marvelous golf they played! The whole locker room was out there in the gallery watching them play.

That trip had its special value for me, just as every one to Britain does.

In 1981, for example, I tied for twelfth at St George's and won $10,000, which just about covered expenses for making the trip, but I made deals to play in other tournaments around the world paying a total of $150,000 appearance money.

And there's the pleasure of meeting nice strangers and making new friends I'll always remember.

My golf series on the BBC has gotten me into a lot of homes. I have old women and old men walk up to me on the course every day and say, 'I've never met you and I know nothing about golf but I love your television show. I had to come out and meet you.'

There's so much I like to remember from all those visits. When I played in the 1973 Open at Troon we stayed on a farm where they were harvesting hay. I had no place to practise, so I would go down in the fields and hit balls. The Scot who farmed the place had two sons, about fourteen and eight, and they wanted to play golf, so I got them some cut-down clubs.

The old man looked at them, puffed on his pipe a minute and said, 'I thank you, Mr Trevino, but I don't know when these lads will have a chance to use them. There's w-o-r-r-r-k to be done.'

Those kids worked, all right. The older boy drove the tractor and stored the hay in the barn. The little one fed the cattle and milked the cows. As soon as they got home from school they took off their uniforms, put on their coveralls and worked until dark. And they were up at five in the morning, picking strawberries.

They'll never be kids, just like me. Looking back on my early years, I believe that's why I have such a special relationship with kids and with other people. I'm forty-two years old and I still act like a kid, because I never was one.

There's a kid in me trying to get out. Maybe there always will be.

From *Super Mex – An Autobiography* by Lee Trevino
and Sam Blair (Stanley Paul, London, 1983).

I'm a serious contender this week. How can they beat me? I've been struck by lightning, had two back operations and been divorced twice.

Lee Trevino at Royal Birkdale, 1983.

Seve – the Car Park Champion

Peter Alliss

Seve Ballesteros first made his name in Britain at Royal Birkdale in 1976 when he was just nineteen years old, tying with Nicklaus for second place after Johnny Miller. He is – or was – the boldest, most spectacular player since Arnold Palmer with wildness off the tee accompanied by immense and powerful recovery shots – a technique never better displayed than in the 1979 Open at Royal Lytham St Anne's when he became the first player from the Continent to win in seventy-two years. He was also the youngest winner of the Open since Tom Morris in 1861, and he did it after that sensational visit to the car park. The Americans rather unkindly labelled him 'the car park champion', as if to suggest that he could never do much on a tighter golf course. But he proved them wrong in 1980 at the age of twenty-three when he became the youngest player ever to win the Masters. Here's how Peter Alliss described that remarkable Open win. Today, of course, Seve has a more restrained game, but still knows more about getting down in par from unlikely places than anyone else. There's another major or two left in Seve.

I.W.

Before every Open Championship begins many words are expended by the nation's leading golf correspondents. There are columns to be filled for some four days leading up to the event while golf magazines seem to use well-nigh half an issue. One of the main themes, of course, is: Who is going to win?

For the first time in many, many years Jack Nicklaus was not the favourite in 1979. He had at last been displaced by Tom Watson in the betting. Watson had been again busying himself in America with four tournament victories by the end of May and had tied for the US Masters before Fuzzy Zoeller took the play-off from Watson and Ed Sneed. He was to raise the US Tour money-winning record by almost $100,000 with his eventual total of $462,636 and more, of course, won outside America.

In the betting, Severiano Ballesteros was also well favoured at 12–1, but the pundits, with almost one voice, felt he had little chance of winning. The Spaniard's fairly frequent wild drives were well known and it was thought that a claustrophobic course like Royal Lytham and St Annes would frustrate even his formidable skills in recovery play. Instead a far 'tidier' player, Hale Irwin, recent winner of the US Open, was thought particularly likely to win.

There was also the often expressed thought that no American had won at Royal Lytham. This was not true. A certain Robert Tyre Jones Junior's name can be seen on the trophy for the year of 1926 and he was, incidentally, followed past the post by

Al Watrous, George von Elm and Walter Hagen, all golfers of unimpeachable American nationality. That championship was the first held at Royal Lytham and St Anne's and no American professional has ever won there.

The news story of the first day was the play of Bill Longmuir who had his lowest-ever tournament round. The Open Championship was the right time to find the inspiration. He played the first nine in 29, only the fourth time this had been done for either first or second nines in a British Open. His total of 65 equalled the lowest score for an opening round, set by Neil Coles at St Andrews in 1970 (since beaten by Craig Stadler's 64 at Royal Birkdale in 1983). Longmuir had never made the top 60 on the European Tour but he had won a couple of tournaments overseas, the 1976 Nigerian Open and the Southland Classic in New Zealand the same year. He birdied five holes in a row from the 3rd to 7th, added another at the 9th and moved smoothly into the second nine with more birdies on the 10th and 12th. Thereafter, on the more difficult run-in, he dropped two strokes.

The round gave him a three-stroke lead on the first day over Hale Irwin, who was very keen to become one of those rare birds who have won the championships of both America and Britain in the same year. Rounds under 70 were rare throughout the championship. The only others on the first day came from Irwin and his fellow American Jerry Pate.

The second day largely belonged to Severiano Ballesteros, who notched up a 65 of his own. He reached the turn in 33 and this did not really foreshadow the score that was to come. At Royal Lytham a really good score has to be made on the first nine (three of the four 29s at that time in the Open had been recorded on this nine – by Peter Thomson, Tom Haliburton and, of course, Longmuir).

It was Ballesteros's brilliant finish that brought the 65. Because of the wind direction that day, it was reckoned that the true par for the lst five holes was 4, 5, 4, 5, 4. Ballesteros finished 3, 3, 4, 3, 3 and had 32 for the inward nine.

He had played with Lee Trevino, which may well have helped his cause because the Mexican American, besides speaking his own brand of Spanish, is also a great admirer of Ballesteros's play. If Lee Trevino is not going to win himself, he likes to see Severiano take first place.

After his first-round 73, Ballesteros was now right up near the top:

> 136 Irwin;   138 Ballesteros;   139 Longmuir;   140 Watson;
> 142 Nicklaus;   144 Crenshaw;   145 Aoki.

Ballesteros was later to claim that his attitude to Lytham was very different from that of so much expert opinion. The many bunkers he felt were no real problem because 'I am the best bunker player.' Probably true and even more likely to be true if the player believes it. He did not consider the rough particularly severe and later claimed that he had deliberately driven into it on his practice rounds both to test it out and to see if wide positions to right or left of some of the fairways gave better lines into the green.

Another Spanish speaker had a great influence on Ballesteros. Roberto de Vicenzo had been one of the first to recognize that Ballesteros was a major talent and did indeed recommend him to Ed Barner, the American agent/entrepreneur, who was to manage him until Ballesteros turned to a Spanish friend and former airline-executive, Jorge Ceballos, several years later. De Vicenzo has often been seen with Ballesteros on practice days and an old master–young pupil relationship grew up between them.

De Vicenzo advised him to attack the course, pointing out that Jack Nicklaus's caution may well have cost him several British Opens. Though he felt Nicklaus was the man to beat, de Vicenzo had noticed that his strategy had been cautious on the practice rounds: taking the safest line from the tee rather than the one more likely to set up a birdie chance. He also felt that, with most severe trouble – particularly out of bounds – on the right, Ballesteros should work on the practice ground to shape his shots from right to left. Not much of a problem, as the Spaniard can fade and draw at will, right-handed or left-handed, on one leg or two or, for a lark, on his knees as well. I am sure it was this ability to manoeuvre a ball that so captured Roberto's imagination, for he had so much of the same ability – but not the putting and chipping finesse to anything like the same degree. How many times I have seen Roberto stroll the length of a par-5 bouncing a golf ball on the face of a 9-iron while discussing the merits of the scenery, the standard of food in the locality and the charms of his breakfast waitress. Try it yourself one day. Just hitting a golf ball well is difficult – but that!

Roberto gave Ballesteros one piece of general advice that I find particularly inspirational: '*Tienes las manos. Ahora juega con tu corazon.*' (You have the hands. Now play with your heart.) How about that for a great line? I think most of us would agree that Ballesteros did just that in the 1979 championship.

For the third round, Ballesteros and Hale Irwin were paired, and I dare say it was an experience that was wearing on the American's nerves. Irwin is an exemplary player, one of my favourites to watch, and in the Peter Thomson mould: hit it onto the fairway, then onto the green and don't three-putt. Here he was confronted by a man whose philosophy that year could be summed up as: 'Hit it as far as you can, find it, get it on the green and then try to one-putt. Never mind the bunkers and the rough. You're used to them.'

Both were round in 75 on a blustery day; both still led the field:

211 Irwin;   213 Ballesteros;   214 Nicklaus, James (with his second 69);
215 Crenshaw, Byman, Davis;   216 Aoki, Norman, Longmuir,
Watson;   217 McEvoy, Marsh, D. J. Clark.

With the gap between them only a couple of strokes, Ballesteros struck early, holing a fine putt for a 2 on the 1st to Irwin's par 3. On the 2nd, Ballesteros took the championship lead, parring the hole with a 4 while Irwin took 6 after half-hitting his tee-shot.

The Ballesteros immortalized in this championship was at his most characteristic on the 486-yard 6th hole. With a drawn tee-shot needed to this right-to-left dogleg, he hooked wildly across the 14th fairway. He reckoned he was some 90 yards off-line. From this unaccustomed position, it was no surprise that neither he nor his caddie had much idea which club to use for the second shot. Ballesteros hit about 50 yards through the green. He still got his par and reached the turn in 34.

The 10th, a relatively short par-4, had given Ballesteros trouble in each round. This time he was in rough short of the green in two. He played a weak third and was still not on the green. Rather uncharacteristically he chose to putt and ran it some 3 yards past the hole. A double-bogey threatened, but Seve holed the crucial putt that could have cost him the championship.

The 13th is another short 4 of 339 yards. De Vicenzo advised boldness as the right tactic here. Ballesteros should use his driver and attempt to carry to the green. In the first three rounds, however, he had taken an iron from the tee. On the final day he gave it every ounce. The result can be seen in a well-known photograph by Bert Neale: the momentum of the club was so extreme that there is a kind of recoil from the finish of the follow-through. But what happened to the ball? It hit a mound to the right of the green and ran into a bunker. The carry was a yard or so under 300 yards. From there, the Spaniard's bunker shot was on the fringe, perhaps a dozen yards from the hole. On and on the putt went as he pointed his club, matador-like, at the hole. It dived in; a decisive moment indeed.

There remained the celebrated tee-shot to the 353-yard 16th. Conventionally, the drive should be down the left of the fairway but, because of the flag position well to the left that day, Ballesteros claims he decided to play to the right – and finished in what has often been described as a car park. This gives the impression that Ballesteros must have been about as far off-line as he had been at the 6th, or had carried the clubhouse at the 1st and put it in the road. Yet it was hardly a car park at all, just a reserved area for our BBC vehicles, little more than 30 yards from the edge of the fairway. Nevertheless, it gave certain partisan Americans the opportunity to refer to him as 'the car park champion'. From there, Ballesteros hit a sand wedge 6 or 7 yards from the hole and got the putt. He was poised for almost certain victory.

But what had been happening to the other contenders? Hale Irwin, after his poor start, seemed to lose heart and became almost invisible in contrast to the panache of the Spaniard's play. In the end he staggered in with a 78, not after all to be one of the select band who have won both American and British championships in the same year. His card showed six 5s and two 6s. Seldom can two more contrasting styles have been paired at an Open climax. The Australian Rodger Davis, playing in elegant socks displaying his name in diamonds, was at one time championship leader, having reached the turn in 32. He went in a spell of 6, 5, 6 on the 14th to 16th holes. Crenshaw also played well that last day. When he stood on the 17th tee he was level with Ballesteros, who at that time had five holes to go. But Ben Crenshaw took a 6 – and that was that. Yet another major championship had slipped from his grasp.

Ballesteros's progress was now triumphal, for here was one of the most popular winners of modern times. The British public, of course, want a British winner but Seve was easily the next best thing. He was young, handsome, smiling, a cavalier, with an almost amateurish air about him. On the 17th he was in his last bunker and once again was down in two strokes to save his par. In the championship as a whole, he reckons he was fifteen times in greenside bunkers and just once failed to be down in two, possibly a record.

The diagonal line of bunkers on the 18th fairway has dashed the hopes of many players over the years. Ballesteros, however, was rather more worried by the gorse on the right. Naturally, then, he aimed for the left rough, to avoid both hazards, played a 5-iron to the front of the green and was down in two putts to be champion by a comfortable three-stroke margin.

Said Hale Irwin, shaking his head in disbelief, 'I cannot understand how anyone can drive as badly as that and still win an Open Championship.' There was, indeed, justice in the American's criticism. In his final round, Ballesteros had found the fairway only once with his driver and only eight times in previous rounds. Yet his power and touch from the rough had proved wrong all the pundits who had thought that Lytham would yield only to the man who could keep the ball on the fairway.

Ballesteros had come a long way from his first championship appearance at Carnoustie in 1975. Then he had rounds of 79 and 80, probably confirming his dislike of links courses for, a little earlier, he had scored even higher at Royal St George's in the PGA Championship. Even now that course is no favourite of his, even after winning the 1983 PGA Championship there.

The 1976 Open, however, had brought him to the fore and his Lytham triumph was his 17th in world golf. The Americans who labelled him 'the car park champion' had the smiles taken from their faces by Ballesteros's dominance in the 1980 Masters. His 1983 Masters victory and fine play in the US Open that year were needed before all were prepared to concede that here was a great player.

From *The Open* by Peter Alliss (Collins, London, 1984).

Steady as She Goes – the Way to Win the Open

Nick Faldo

Some major championships have been won by sheer exuberant aggression – like Ballesteros's victory in the 1979 Open at Birkdale where he even played a shot out of the car park. But just one shot that's too aggressive can always lose a championship: just ask Arnie Palmer. The Nicklaus approach has always been one of steadiness and patience, waiting for the right opening to notch a birdie or even an eagle and trying never to drop more than one shot to par at any hole. That was the method that Nick Faldo committed himself to at Muirfield in 1987 and here he explains how it won him a dramatic British victory and his first major championship. His thorough approach and dedication, including the remodelling of his swing to become slightly flatter and more reliable, had finally paid off.

I.W.

The trick with Muirfield is to adhere to a chosen game plan. The premium is placed on driving the ball into the correct position, as the fairways are ingeniously bunkered, and the choice of club – driver, three wood or one iron – is critical off the tee.

It is, of course, easier said than done. Yet I felt that over the first two days of the 116th Open Championship I came as close as one could hope to carrying out my own preconceived plans. My opening 68 provided a sound foundation on which to build, though the Australian Rodger Davis moved smartly into the lead with his 64, but I had more regard for my second round of 69. I was out early in the day and the persistent rain meant that it was all the more important to concentrate on steering a safe passage around the 6,963 yards which make up Muirfield's par-71 Championship examination.

The plan, quite simply, was not to take any gambles. One wayward shot on a course such as Muirfield can, if you are unfortunate, lead to a penalty which is too severe for the 'crime' committed. Coincidentally Arnold Palmer admitted on the Friday at Muirfield to 'taking a gamble and paying for it'. He tried to force something out of the 14th hole after driving into a bunker, and he eventually walked off the green with a *ten* on his card. It had taken him five shots to escape from a greenside bunker. He had, at the age of fifty-seven, turned back the years to be in contention and then, after that 14th hole, he was out of the Championship.

I made mistakes at the 14th and 15th holes in the second round, but on each occasion it cost me only the one shot. Mostly I was happy with the way I swung my way around Muirfield's two splendid loops of nine holes. I hit a seven iron to four feet for a two at the 180 yards-4th. My five iron to three feet for another birdie at the 8th filled me with confidence.

I had brought over David Leadbetter from Florida the previous week in order to fine-tune my swing during the Bell's Scottish Open at Gleneagles. We took a video of the swing and I kept that to turn to for confirmation after David had sorted out a couple of things for me.

Then a 69, for a halfway aggregate of 137, was sufficient at the end of the day to earn me a share of second place alongside the American Payne Stewart, who had an equal best-of-the-day 66, Australia's Gerry Taylor (68) and Davis, who faltered with a 73. The leader now was Paul Azinger, who was seeking to emulate his American compatriots Ben Hogan (1953) and Tony Lema (1964) by winning the Open at the first attempt.

I was to partner Azinger on the third day, when we both scored 71s despite being buffeted by 25-mph gusts. It was a difficult day and Paul continued to defy logic, for he had never seen a links course before setting foot that week on the first tee at Muirfield. It must have seemed so incredibly foreign to him, and yet he played the kind of commonsense golf that suggested he might have been reared on the east coast of Scotland.

So as the final day dawned Azinger was still one shot ahead of David Frost of South Africa and myself. One stroke further adrift was the American trio of Craig Stadler, with whom I was paired, Payne Steward and Tom Watson. All three appeared to me to be threats, but it was Azinger who continued to bowl along in front.

He began the fourth and final round as if it were just a walk in the park. He holed a putt of fully 25 feet for a birdie at the 4th and another of ten feet at the 5th. He was out in 34. I could do nothing but make pars, although I was within inches of birdies at each of the first five holes, but I feel that it was the kind of round, looking back, of which Jack Nicklaus would have been proud. I recall Tom Watson once explaining how early in his career he had partnered Nicklaus in a US Tour event. Nicklaus did nothing spectacular. He simply played conservatively, because he felt that was the order of the day, and when he finished he had won the tournament.

I was pleased at the way I remained composed. On three occasions, in four holes from the 7th, I kept my score intact by getting up and down from bunkers. Andy Prodger, my caddie, thought that the one at the 8th won me the Championship: I exploded out of the sand from 30 yards to three feet. The four-foot putt which I holed at the 11th, after playing an adroit chip round a hillock, was also an important recovery. Azinger had wriggled three shots clear of me but now he dropped a shot at the 10th by being bunkered and another at the next which he three-putted.

I knew now, as the mist began to clear and as I edged closer towards the clubhouse of the Honourable Company of Edinburgh Golfers, that I was within sight of the most elusive prize in the game. I stuck to my game plan when it mattered most, so that without taking a gamble I limited the risk of one destructive shot ruining what could be the most important day in my career. I parred my way through to the end and a 71 gave me a five under par aggregate of 279. It was enough to put Azinger, playing behind me, under pressure.

We have all been in that position before. It can be so important to have your score on the board. Paul Azinger will have his day, of that I am sure, but on this occasion he was to meet his nemesis.

I had been nervous, of course, over the closing holes. I knew that during my last hour on the Muirfield course one mistake could ruin everything. Yet my lasting memory is of my five iron to the last green. I knew as I stood over that shot that it could make all the difference. I didn't want to sit back at the end of my career and accept that I had come close without actually winning the Open Championship. I knew that when that five iron shot – one which I had rehearsed on many occasions – deposited the ball on the green, I had done everything humanly possible to engrave my name alongside the greats of the game on the silver claret jug that is the Open Championship trophy.

From *On Course for the Open* by Nick Faldo with Mitchell Platts (Stanley Paul, London, 1987).

Tony Jacklin looks worried. Is it going to trickle into the rough? (*Peter Dazeley*)

After the agony, the ecstasy. The putt which recorded Tony's last major golfing prize – the 1982 PGA Championship (*Peter Dazeley*)

Greg Norman – at last a Major. Greg celebrates his 1986 Open victory with his wife Laura. (*Peter Dazeley*)

Rivals since schoolboy days in Shropshire. Ian wins a close game against Sandy Lyle in the World Match Play Championship. (*Peter Dazeley*)

Lyle wins the Masters. Oh, the joy and relief after the tension and anxiety of the last few holes when the shots began to dribble away. Then came that brilliant 7 iron bunker shot at the 18th to within 10ft of the hole and a majestic birdie putt to become the first Briton to win the US Masters. (*Associated Press*)

Peter Alliss. If you can't beat the Yips, at least let's have a laugh about them. And come to think of it, Peter hasn't done too badly out of the game, has he? (*Peter Dazeley*)

Ballesteros in killer mood, as he wins the 1984 Open at St Andrews (*Peter Dazeley*)

Nick Faldo . . . steady as she goes. Faldo on the way to winning the 1987 Open with a patient, consistent performance over four rounds. (*Peter Dazeley*)

Gene Sarazen . . . the old maestro makes one of his last tournament appearances at the Masters.
(*Peter Dazeley*)

11

HEROES WITH PROBLEMS

The Yips – and How to Beat Them

George Plimpton

The yips are a terrible thing – that awful nervous affliction on the short putts which results in a convulsive jab and a missed putt. The yips have afflicted the greatest in the game, including Vardon, Snead and Hogan, and some of the greatest strikers of the ball like Peter Alliss. He, poor chap, had a total disaster on his first visit to Augusta in 1966. 'I played one round with Gene Littler and took five putts from 6 feet at the 11th hole,' he recalls. 'Shattering!' It really finished him for the big game. The yips caused Henry Longhurst to throw his clubs into the loft – forever and with no regrets, as he describes in the second piece in this chapter. George Plimpton, the long-handicapper who wrote so amusingly in *The Bogey Man* about 'the world of big-time golf experienced by and reported by the 18-handicap author', investigated the downside of the problem thoroughly.

However, I still insist that where there's the will there's a way, as Bernhard Langer found. From being the worst putter in big-time golf, by sheer dedication – and the reverse grip – he's made himself into one of the best, if not *the* best. He found himself so at home on the super-fast greens at Augusta with their tricky borrows, where four- or five-putting is always possible, that in 1985 when the greens were never faster, and when Watson three-putted four times in one round, Bernhard three-putted just once in four rounds. Not surprisingly, he became the triumphant winner of his first major. He's now so good he's even written a whole book, *Langer on Putting*, from which I take the third and final of these extracts on the yips.

I.W.

One evening in San Francisco I heard for the first time about the 'yips' – a phenomenon talked about rather uneasily by the pros, and with wary respect, as one might talk about a communicable disease ravaging the neighboring township. The yips (a name invented by Tommy Armour, who had them) was the term given the occupational malaise of golf – a nervous affliction that settled in the wrist and hands, finally, after the years of pressure and the money bets and the strain. It was what ultimately drove the pros out of the game to the teaching jobs at the country clubs, setting the balls on the tees for the girls in the Pucci pants who came down for their two free gift lessons of the summer.

The legs don't give out, as in so many other sports, or the wind, or the sense of timing, or the power, but the *nerves*, so that one could see the hands of great golfers beset by the yips tremble visibly on the putting greens, the greatest names in golf completely at the mercy of short putts of 4, 5, 6 feet.

I said I had never heard of such a thing.

Dave Marr told me that he had seen Byron Nelson stand over a 4-foot putt at Florida's Seminole golf course, and, finally, after swaying back and forth several times, he had stabbed at the ball desperately and sent it *40 feet* past the hole.

At that same club, Seminole, Craig Wood had them so badly during an exhibition match, which should have relaxed the pressure, that he hit the first nine greens right on target in regulation strokes, but then putted so badly that his first-9 total was *44*. His dismay was such that he refused to putt out at all during the second nine; when he reached the greens he stooped and picked up the ball and stuffed it in his pocket and walked on to the next tee. The rest of his foursome, sympathetic, allowed him double gimmes, the regulation two putting strokes, and marked him down as such.

There was someone, a curious youngster, unaware of the ravages that the yips are capable of committing, who had gone up to the golfer and had the temerity to ask: 'Why aren't you putting out like the others, Mister Wood? I mean, I don't understand . . .' and then he had stopped in mid-sentence because Wood had such a murderous look on his face.

It seemed to get them all. Leo Diegel had an awful time with nerves. He fussed around with a pendulum stroke with his putter but most people thought he was afflicted with a spastic tic. A great golfer, he never had the right mental equipment and he knew it: 'They keep trying to give the championship to me,' he once said, 'but I won't take it.' In the British Open in 1933 at St Andrews he faced an incredibly short putt, just a foot or so, and he wandered up to it shaking like a leaf and stubbed it past the hole to lose the championship. Vardon, at the end of his career, in 1920, when he was in his fifties, got the yips. They were blamed on two attacks of tuberculosis. He called them the 'jumps' and recommended putting in the dark as effective treatment. Apparently it didn't work. Gene Sarazen (he eventually got them, too) recalls Vardon as the most atrocious putter he had ever seen. 'He didn't 3-putt, he *4*-putted.'

Rod Funseth . . . said that one of the saddest examples of the yips he had seen were those infesting the person of Jon Gustin, who was known for owning one of the prettiest swings on the tour. Funseth went on about him at some length. Apparently, he was a great dresser – he had been a former flag-bearer in the Honor Guards in Washington. Very snappy. 'So you had,' Funseth said, 'the fine combination of a great swing, smooth and pretty as Snead's, and a guy who *looked* great as a golfer, like he stepped out of the advertising pages of *Esquire*, and yet what would happen, because of those yips, was that he would stand over the ball to swing – his irons,

drives, putts, any shot – and his hands would come back, but the *club head wouldn't*.
It would stick there right behind the ball like it was cemented to the ground.'

'Lord Almighty,' I said.

'He had to give up the tour.'

'Worst case I ever saw.'

'No cure, I don't suppose, for the yips.'

'Golfers who have the yips *try* to cure them, God knows,' Funseth said. 'Gene
Sarazen found one – at least one that worked for him. Watch him in the Senior
tournaments. He steps up to the ball and hits it all in one motion – almost like he's
hitting a shot off a polo pony. He doesn't dare stand over the ball, because he knows
he'll freeze. Snead had the idea you could drift into a sort of "pleasant daydream" to
get back to the fundamentals of the practice swing. And then I recall that Bobby
Locke had an idea that the yips could be cured by holding the club very loosely. If the
yips had him bad, why you wouldn't be surprised to see his club just slip out and fall
on the grass. Really no thing to have,' Funseth said. 'There's no sure cure. The yips
can get so bad that you hate the idea of being in the lead in a tournament – where the
pressure can bring on an attack. You begin to crave for a fair round, even a mediocre
one, where the pressure isn't so stiff.'

The great distinction to make was that there was no similarity between the yips and
'choking' – though every once in a while the younger pros, who looked on the yips as
something that couldn't possibly happen to them, would say that yips was just a fancy
word that the older pros thought up to hide the fact that pressure got to them too.

'Who told you that?'

'Oh, one of the younger professionals.'

'That figures. If you want to see choking on a vast scale – I mean, what the caddies
call the Apple Orchard for the big lumps that turn up in the throat – and if you want to
see the eye-staring and those clammy foreheads, then you got to take in the
qualifying tournaments that the rabbits play in. Ludicrous. Or you'll see one of those
kids play in the high 60s for a round or so in the Open, and then what happens to him?
The pressure gets to him. He skies to an 80. He chokes. He's so scared he damn near
closes his eyes when he swings.'

Someone said: 'Pee Wee Reese, the shortstop, used to have a good phrase for the
choke. He'd say, "I know I'm choking when I'm chewing and can't work up a spit".'

'Sometimes a particular hole will cause a choke – a choke hole,' said Marr. 'Like
the 18th at Cypress. It's like walking into a certain room in a big dark house when you
were a kid – you get this fear that hits you.'

Johnny Pott said: 'That's why we spend so much time on the practice tee. You're
down there trying to groove the shot, to tone up the muscle memory, so that when
you get out on the golf course and the pressure's really on – the choke at hand, and
you can sense your eyes popping, and the jaw shaking – the muscles can still perform
in their usual groove and you can get your shot off. You practise to get the muscles
moving almost automatically.'

'Doesn't that work for putting as well?'

'No, because muscle memory doesn't have anything to do with putting. Take Sam
Snead. He's got the most famous swing in golf – you wouldn't find a differential of a

millimeter in the circle of his swing if you took a thousand stop-action films of the guy. Perfectly grooved. Great on long putts, where the demands on muscle and swing are slightly more. But short putts! Give me someone out of kindergarten! His hands come back fine, but then the blade seems to go out of control just at the stroke. Sometimes he hits the top of the ball so that if it drops, it bounces every which way to get in there. Snead has had the yips for years. That's why he took that pro's job at Greenbrier way back in 1937. He thought he was going to have to quit the tour because he had the yips so bad. Or take Hogan, the most tragic case. Best tee-to-green player there ever was. Ever. I mean he put the balls *there* off the tee, then *there*, just where he wants, then *there*, right on the green. You might as well *give* him those shots. But once on the green his troubles begin. He had those two holes to go at Oak Hill – just par-par, that's all he had to do to tie for the 1956 Open, but the yips got him. You know the guy got ten thousand letters from people trying to help him.'

'Ten thousand!' I said.

'That's right.'

I once asked Claude Harmon about those ten thousand letters, and whether he thought I would get an answer if I wrote Ben Hogan and asked him what the most ridiculous of the suggestions received had been – I thought that might be interesting.

'You wouldn't get an answer,' Harmon said, looking at me sharply. 'Because I'll tell you one thing. Hogan would have *tried* every damn one of them – I don't care how "ridiculous" – to rid himself of those things.' He repeated what I had heard so many people say: 'If only Hogan could have putted – Jesus, he'd've made every record in the book look silly.'

Hogan's miseries with the yips reached a climax in the 1954 Masters when, leading the field, he went to pieces on the final holes of the tournament. He 3-putted the 13th, missed a 4-foot putt on the 15th, 3-putted the 17th, and then came to the 18th needing a 6-foot putt to win the tournament. Claude Harmon said that Hogan went off to the side of the green and he made about one hundred practice strokes with his putter, all markedly different – changing his grip, the position of his hands on the club, the stroke itself. Whe Harmon asked him about it later, Hogan said that he had been trying to find a stroke, any stroke at all, in which he felt comfortable – a last-minute desperate search – and after the experimenting at the edge of the big crowd around the green, he had taken one of the styles back out on the putting surface and, perched over the ball, he used it, and not unsurprisingly he missed the putt.

Claude Harmon had an interesting notion that a golfer's control over those shots, putts especially, which were conducive to the yips, was at best fragmentary since the ball traveled over the *ground*, and was at the mercy of irregularities and worm casts and the rubs of the green and beetles sticking up their heads to look round and minuscule pebbles and so forth.

'Even a machine will miss half the time from six feet. It's been tried,' Harmon said. 'Golf is really two games. One is the game in the air. The golfer can lick that part of the game. It sounds like quite a feat – I mean, you've got to get all those parts of your body moving absolutely correctly to send that ball off the tee at over 200 miles an hour. But once the ball is up in the air, there's not much that can happen to it. The air is a medium a golfer can control, as easy as fish in water: he can move the ball in it just where he wants to – fade it, or hook it to his liking, if he's good enough – and he's never going to be surprised unless he makes a mistake himself. Or unless he hits a bird. But the other part of the game is across the ground. It sounds easy. You hardly move a muscle to hit a putt. A child can do it easier than nothing. But the medium controls the ball, that's the difference; the golfer can get the ball moving, that's all. After that, the ball moves and turns and dies by reason of the ground surface. What you can't control gets the best of you after a while – death and taxes, the old song – and that's what the yips are.'

Harmon's story reminded me of Bernard Darwin's anecdote about the famous billiard professional who saw his first game of golf and remarked on it as interesting enough, but wondered why (as he said) 'do golfers on the green first knock the ball up to the hole, and *then* put it in.'

Some golfers felt that any prolonged absence from the game resulted in such a loss of confidence that an infestation of the yips would result. Bobby Cruickshank remembered that when his great rival Bobby Jones returned to competition in 1934 after a four-year layoff, his putting had deteriorated to such an extent that he wandered around the Masters that year asking his fellow golfers if they could spot what was wrong. 'It looked the same,' Cruickshank said. 'I mean you'd see him address the ball, then set the putter in front of the ball, and then at the back of the ball again, and then the stroke – that was the famous procedure he went through. But you could see he had no confidence.'

Claude Harmon told me of a more recent example of the damage a layoff could do – the decision of Mike Souchak to take his family for a month's vacation on the beach after he had a remarkable succession of wins and near-wins on the tour. 'I told him he was crazy. You got to keep at it. When he came back it was gone – it had floated away on him, and what he had was like the yips.'

Occasionally, though, one heard of cures. Roberto de Vicenzo, at one time afflicted with the yips so badly that he had the reputation of handling the spookiest putter on the tour, had been able to do something about it. It had not been easy. In the throes of the disease he had changed putters every week, picking out a new putter every time he went into a pro shop. He looked in a closet at home in Argentina not long ago and found fifty putters standing there, a total not counting many he had given away. No one of the putters seemed better than another. Each seemed utterly unreliable. In 1967 in Australia he blew an eleven-shot lead in the last fourteen holes because of his putting and lost to Alan Murray in a play-off. He talked about an occasion in England when his putters had let him down – his accent heavy, his big hands moving artfully in the air to describe his meaning, his chair squeaking under him, his face expressive under the white baseball-style golf hat he wears to cover his thinning hair.

'In the British Open, in 1965, I think, we are playing the final day, which is thirty-six holes, and in the morning I am leading. I have had one bad green, number 9, which I three-putt in the morning, but I still in very good position. So we come to number nine in the afternoon and I say to myself, "Roberto, you no three-putt this green this afternoon, do you?" I didn't. I make *four* putts. I was so mad I wanted to break all my clubs and quit the game and never play again. I had no confidence. I look at the cup and she look like a little spike mark. I tell myself, "Roberto, you no can put the ball in there." So I lose my confidence and I lose the tournament right there.'

Vicenzo's cure turned out to be a matter of self-application – finding the right type of putter, the correct style of hitting a ball with it, the regaining of confidence, and practice, endless practice. Many golfers go through an equivalent regimen of experiment and practice without finding the answer: Snead had tried a number of putters and such grotesque putting styles – the 'sidewinder' in particular, in which he faces the hole and strokes the ball just off the outer edge of his golf shoe – that only his great grace as an athlete keeps him from looking ludicrous. Vicenzo was lucky. He found his putter two years ago. A mallet putter that he says is appropriate for his big hands. He watched other golfers' putting styles and decided that all the good putters (with the exception of Billy Casper and Doug Ford) use their *arms* primarily in the putting strokes, not the wrists, which had been his style. So he changed his style and found his sense of 'feel' increased immeasurably. His confidence began to return. He practised endlessly – especially to get what he refers to as the 'head in rhythm . . . to work the head and the hands at the same time.' He began to collect some tournament wins – notably the British Open, and then a close run at the Masters which he would have taken to a play-off had he not handed in a mistotaled score card. But he was phlegmatic himself about the future. 'The putt is a funny game. You can't think you got it for always. You can lose it tomorrow. But for the moment,' he said, 'I feel better when I step onto the golf course. I no feel scared to step onto the green. Not any more. Or maybe for the time being, eh?'

Another older player I talked to about the yips was John Farrell, once the great rival of Bobby Jones and now a teaching professional in Florida. He said that if you play in competition long enough you're sure to get the yips. 'Walter Hagen,' he said. 'If you had to vote for the player with the best temperament, well you'd *have* to vote for him. Hell, he had such confidence that there wasn't a shot that held any terror for him: they used to say that when he had a particularly tough shot to make, and he'd stepped up and made a great one of it, why then he'd whisper at his caddy, "Did I make it look hard enough?" and give him a wink, y'see. Well *he* got them. The yips. He got them so bad that he tried strokes and grip styles you could scarcely *believe*: cross-handed putting; or sticking the elbows way out so that the wrist action was throttled down and his whole body moved as stiff as a derrick. He even tried putting in the dark – thought that might cure him. Nothing did. . . .'

I asked the question I had put to the others – if there was any connection between the yips and losing one's nerve.

'It's that you lose *nerves*, not nerve,' Farrell said. 'You can shoot lions in the dark and yet you can quiver like a leaf and fall flat over a two-foot putt.'

'I would think,' I said, 'that years of experience standing over two-foot putts, and gaining all the know-how of reading greens and distance, and the competition – that all of that would be to a golfer's advantage . . . confidence.'

'Oh, I wouldn't want to be so sure as that,' Farrell said. 'I always remember Waite Hoyte, who pitched for the Yankees, you'll recall, and what he used to say about "experience". He said experience *punishes* you. A veteran player *knows* what can happen to him: he comes onto a pitcher's mound and he knows the batter waiting for him can pop the ball right back to the bullpen where he's just come from for a home run. He's gone through it before. So he's something of a fatalist. It's the same in golf. "Experience" punishes you as you continue with the game. That's why in golf we speak of someone being "competitively young" or "competitively old". Craig Wood, you see, he was "competitively young" at forty-three because he started playing serious golf when he was well into his thirties. Then on the other hand Bobby Jones was "competitively old" at twenty-three – he had started at fifteen, you see, which gave him early "experience" but it aged him good and quick as a golfer.

'Experience,' Farrell went on ruefully. 'I won the Open in 1928 at Olympia Fields, and then in 1929 I missed the cut at the Open at Winged Foot. Dropped from the tournament I had *won* the year before! D'you think *that* experience did me any good! Well, I'll tell you. The next year at Interlachen, Minneapolis – in the 1930 Open which Bobby Jones won to fetch himself the Grand Slam – I stepped up on the first tee with the "experience" gained from those bad rounds the year before, and what did I do but get myself an 8 on that first hole. I managed to pull myself together after that and I finished eighth behind Jones, but don't talk to me about *experience*. Snead can't win the Open because of his memories – missing that two-footer in the 1947 Open. Palmer won't win the PGA. He has that block. No; it's the kids, the strong young golfers who have it all. They make great big errors – I mean, a kid like Marty Fleckman coming up with an 80 after leading the Open into the last day in 1967 – but he's at the age when mistakes are easily forgotten; those kids' imaginations aren't jumpy with crucial flubs – y'know, disaster, that's what they don't know about. Not yet. It'll come. They'll get there. Experience will come. Oh yes.'

From *The Bogey Man* by George Plimpton
(André Deutsch, London, 1970).

Pressure is something every golfer feels at one time or another. . . . Sometimes when I putted I looked like a monkey trying to wrestle a football.

Sam Snead, 1970.

How to Give up Golf Without Really Trying

Henry Longhurst

As my travels, writings and broadcasting increased, to say nothing of my age, my golf fell away and it became less and less fun to do progressively more badly something that one had once done reasonably well. I had had every reason to believe that I should turn out in middle age, and even later, to be an accurate and crafty player, always liable to beat an undergraduate, but it was not to be. My swing disintegrated and I became quite pathetically bad. I kept meaning to take myself in hand and go in for a fortnight's serious practice, which I knew was all that was needed, but somehow, with all the travelling about, I never got down to it. If I played on Sunday mornings, I did not enjoy it, and, if I didn't, I had it on my conscience that somehow I ought to be. What settled the problem for me was what we call the twitch and the Americans the 'yips'. This is so ridiculous a disease that non-sufferers can scarcely credit it. It attacks the victim almost always on short putts, though one great professional who might otherwise have beaten the world had it on short pitches. It does not come on all short putts, but you always know in advance when it is coming. You then become totally incapable of moving a piece of ironmongery to and fro without giving at the critical moment a convulsive twitch. Some people simply stab the ground and move the ball a few inches. Others catch it on the twitch and send it shooting past the hole. Bobby Jones has recounted how he was playing with an American professional called Wild Bill Melhorn, who suffered from it, and on one green Melhorn, trying to hole a yard putt, actually putted it off the green and into a bunker. I was reminded only the other day of an occasion I had forgotten when a caddie had said to me, 'I think it would be better if you stroked the ball a bit more, sir,' and I had replied, 'Dammit, you don't think I *mean* to do it like that, do you?' I am, however, in good company. Jones himself got it – he described the sensation as of the ball 'apparently vanishing from sight just as the club was about to strike it'. The great Harry Vardon got it. Sam Snead, still at fifty-seven one of the finest swingers in the game, actually had to take to putting croquet-fashion between the legs. Ben Hogan, the most determined golfer of all time, not excluding Palmer, wanted two par fours for a record fifth US Open and not only missed a yard putt on the 17th but 'yipped' it. 'Once you've had 'em, you've got 'em,' they say, and he was never the same again. The Americans tend rather unkindly to call the affliction 'whiskey fingers', and so it may be with some, but Snead is a lifelong teetotaller and Vardon was a most abstemious man – though I particularly like his reply to the lady who asked him to sign the pledge: 'Moderation is essential in all things, madam, but never in my life have I been beaten by a teetotaller.'

I am afraid that by constantly writing about it I may have served to spread the disease, in which context I am reminded of my friend and neighbour Tubby Ionides, who incidentally won the Grand National Irish Sweep on Sundew. Some people have only to read about that other ridiculous golf shot, the socket, in which the ball shoots off, knee high, almost at right-angles, to start doing it themselves, yet quite unable to do it on purpose. Confessing to be one such, my friend added, 'I am worse. I am a *carrier*.' So perhaps am I with the twitch. After one piece I had written about it an old Austrian doctor wrote to me from London saying that he knew the answer, so I naturally hurried to see him. The answer, he said, lay in the angle of the right elbow, i.e., neither stretched straight nor fully bent, as in putting, and there may be something in this, for if you stretch your right arm out as far and as stiffly as possible, you can make some sort of stroke at a putt even when the curse is upon you.

What really shook me, however, was when he added casually, 'Violinists sometimes get it.' Here we may imagine the twitch in all its full horror. The hushed Albert Hall and the master, as his elbow bends to the fatal angle, giving a sudden and convulsive jerk and nearly sawing the instrument in half, never to play in public again. I was thoughtless enough to tell this to Hogan in Mexico City once and I have an awful fear that it hastened his downfall.

In the end I think they will find it akin to vertigo, or the case of the rabbit and the stoat. The rabbit can do twenty-five miles an hour and the stoat, I suppose, about four, but the rabbit stands paralysed like a man with a four-foot putt. Similarly you could guarantee, drunk or sober, to walk down a road without touching either side, but put the same road, unfenced, over Niagara and you would be on your hands and knees within a few paces. Thus I came one day to the last green in the Medal needing a four for a net 69 and a faint chance of defeating at last one of the most tight-fisted bodies in the world, the handicapping committee of the R. and A. My second got on the green, only to roll back into the Valley of Sin, in which one stands at about eye level with the flag. I pitched up and the ball ran so straight that I had time to think, 'By God, it's in! 68!' It stopped just short, a few inches perhaps – but when I got up onto the green the eye had been deceived from down below and it was a yard short. I was standing idly thinking of nothing while my partner holed out when suddenly it came over me. *I can't do it*. I looked at this hideous thing – just like the one you may have seen poor Doug Sanders missing to win, or rather not to win, the 1970 Open on the same green. I stood over it and remember with the utmost clarity thinking that I would willingly lay down a five-pound note on the green not to have to make this putt. Suddenly I found that the putter had shot to and fro and the ball was as far away the other side. I scuttled round and a moment later it had shot by again and we were back where we started. I doubled back, jerked at it again and this time by sheer good fortune it hit the back of the hole, jumped in the air and went in – but even as it disappeared I knew that my golfing days were numbered.

I forget where it happened but in the middle of a round, which I was regarding with the usual distaste, a small voice within me said, 'You don't *have* to do this,' and I thought, 'No, by God, I don't.' A great wave of relief came over me and on D-Day, 1968, I put the clubs up in the loft with the water tanks, closed the hatch, removed the steps and walked away. Nor have I for one second regretted it. I had travelled a long and happy road since we had cut the holes with our penknives on the Common at Yelverton, but now it was rather like having sucked a very good orange dry and realizing that you were eating the peel. Why not chuck it away and try an apple instead? Which is what I did.

From *My Life and Soft Times* by Henry Longhurst
(Cassell and Co., London, 1971).

I've gotten rid of the yips four times, but they hang in there. You know those two-foot downhill putts with a break? I'd rather see a rattlesnake.

Sam Snead, 1984.

My Cure for the Yips

Bernhard Langer

For the first ten years of my golfing life I played on slow, bumpy greens in Germany. As a youngster I was always a very good putter and by the time I became an assistant professional at Munich I was virtually infallible from 6 feet and closer. Slow, bumpy greens like the ones we had in Germany are in many ways not very demanding. If the ball doesn't go in you always feel you have an excuse because it may not have rolled very well. In many ways it was, therefore, very easy to be confident on these greens. I could blame any miss on the green and not on me. Like many golfers who play on poor greens, I had developed a stroke with a rather long backswing from which I could hit the ball hard. Once I started playing on fast tournament greens as a professional this stroke let me down. I still used to swing the club too far back, but would then have to decelerate to try to keep the putt rolling slowly. It was only when I first played in top professional tournaments in 1976 that I came across fast greens. It took me a considerable length of time to adjust. Many people believe that I only really conquered my putting in 1985 when I won the Masters. In fact I had probably conquered most of my problems by 1983 after beginning to putt cross-handed.

The Cross-handed Cure

My main difficulty in putting was that my right hand used to take over on short putts and jerk the putter head through. This is usually referred to as the 'yips'. Your right hand gets out of control and jerks the putter forward, pushing the ball out off line and often shooting it too far. The faster the green the more frightening this becomes. The difficulty, of course, if you putt badly is that it tends to put pressure on the rest of your game. I used to find myself hitting a good iron shot into the green perhaps 12 feet away, missing my putt for a birdie, and then would be under pressure on the next iron shot feeling that I had to get even closer to make my birdies. Bad putting puts pressure on chipping, pitching and the whole of the long game if you allow it to.

I soon realized that to become one of the best players in the world I had to conquer my putting difficulties. I was producing some good results but they didn't fully satisfy me. If I hadn't putted well as a youngster, and if I wasn't a good chipper and bunker player, I might have doubted that my hand–eye coordination was good enough to putt really well. But I knew that I had it in me, if I could only find the right technique and discover where I was going wrong.

There are two main principles which seem to be common to the technique of most really good putters. *First, they usually keep a firm and consistent angle in the left arm and the left wrist through the whole stroke. Secondly, they manage to combine this with a light, sensitive grip pressure.* I found that with my usual stroke, setting the right hand below the left in the orthodox way, I couldn't keep my left wrist and arm working as a consistent unit *and* stay relaxed with this light grip pressure. If I relaxed, I was always aware of the left side breaking down through impact. As the angle of the wrist and arm altered I felt my club coming off line or the clubface turning. It seemed to allow the right hand to take over. If, on the other hand, I firmed up my left arm and wrist, it seemed to create too much tension.

I therefore decided that I had to find a method which would allow me to keep my left arm and wrist working smoothly as a unit without creating tension. A conventional grip always seemed to force me to bend the left wrist or elbow more than I wanted. I had occasionally seen other good players putting with a cross-handed grip and I decided that it might solve a lot of problems.

I use two quite distinct techniques for short-putting and long-putting. Short-putting to me, and to most tournament professionals, requires a precise stroke which must be absolutely repetitive. Distance is not much of a problem; what I want is an accurate stroke in which the putter moves back and forwards on the right line, returning the clubface absolutely square. Long-putting is very different. With a long putt the skill lies far more in being able to produce feel and sensitivity in your fingertips to get the ball running the right distance and in reading the greens really well. I therefore use a cross-handed method for my short putts, where I am working almost entirely on a repetitive stroke. For my long putts I use a more conventional method which gives me feel in my hands. There is a distance somewhere between 15 and 25 feet at which I may use one method or the other. Sometimes a putt of 20 feet looks very straight and true and then I see a good short-putt stroke without any real difficulty in the line or length. If, on the other hand, the putt seems very fast or there is a big break, I may well decide that my other method is more appropriate to produce good touch. Sometimes with these medium-length putts I may set up one way and then change to the other style if I subsequently see the putt differently. I don't necessarily expect readers to follow my suggestions on cross-handed putting, but even with a conventional grip there must be two distinct approaches to short and long putts.

Short-putting

My aim with a short putt, having read the green and found the line, is to stroke the ball right on the sweet spot of the putter and to set it rolling smoothly on the correct line. From about 15 feet and closer, distance should not be a problem. Obviously one has to get the correct distance, but usually that is secondary and much easier to achieve than getting the right line. With my short putts I want to strike the ball from the correct part of the clubface – the sweet spot – with the clubface perfectly square and the putter head travelling on line. I see good short-putting as being a question of swinging the putter head back and through on a perfectly straight line from ball to target.

On putts of perhaps 5–6 feet or more I am aware of the putter head moving slightly inside this line on the backswing, but my predominant idea for short putts is to obtain a straight swing path.

I know, after hours of research and practice, that the key to my short-putting is to keep my left arm and left wrist as a constant unit. You will see this in nearly all really great putters. I achieve this by letting my left arm hang loosely and freely from the shoulder, and by gripping the club with the left hand very much to the side of the club, with the left thumb straight down the front of the putter. I always use a putter which has a flat-fronted grip. This helps in getting the hands in the right position, with the palms of both hands predominantly to the side of the club and the thumbs down the front. As I look down at my left hand I can see the left *thumb* running straight down the putter shaft, but *not* with the left *hand* on the top as in a conventional long-game grip. My right hand also holds the club with the palm to the side of the grip, never underneath it. Again, the thumb is virtually straight down the front of the grip and the right wrist and elbow are allowed to bend quite naturally. I use a form of reverse overlap grip, with my right index finger overlapping the little finger of my left hand and fitting snugly between the base of the little finger and the third finger. As I set up to the ball I have my eyes directly over the line from the ball to the hole, ensuring that they are never outside this line, with the ball halfway between the centre of my stance and my left instep and my hands very fractionally ahead of the ball. I like to use a fairly wide stance, with my feet about shoulder-width apart, aiming at stability and as little body movement as possible. My feeling is one of having the weight almost evenly distributed between left foot and right foot, but slightly favouring the left, and nicely balanced flat on the feet, neither towards the toes nor the heels.

The set-up has to be absolutely meticulous. It is essential that the clubface is set square to the desired direction.

I feel the left arm and left hand are absolutely dominant, with the right arm, hand and indeed the shoulder in a passive position. I feel as though there is a complete unit, from my left shoulder through my left arm and hand and down into the putter, which controls the whole stroke. By setting up in this cross-handed position I am able to get rid of the unwanted feeling of the right hand being dominant. The whole stroke feels as though it can take place with the left arm perfectly in control.

Long-putting

My long-putting technique is quite orthodox in that I use a fairly conventional grip rather than a cross-handed one. As I have said, there is sometimes a point between about 15 and 25 feet at which I may at first be in two minds as to which method to use. But once I get beyond 25 feet I am invariably working at acquiring a feeling for distance and good judgement, rather than worrying about direction and being precise and accurate with my stroke. I don't wish to sound misleading in suggesting that the stroke is not important, because, of course, it is. But as a rule it is the distance and exact judgement of the strength of the putt that are so crucial. Failure with long putts – by which I mean a putt which isn't left within a foot or so of the hole – is far more a question of a poorly read putt or of badly gauged distance than one in which the line and stroke haven't been good enough.

Having systematically read the putt, I make a practice swing in which I try to visualize the distance involved and rehearse the length of the backswing and throughswing. All too often I see my pro-am partners making practice swings for long putts which bear no resemblance to the swing they make with the ball. This practice swing is important in giving my body the clue to the length of swing and speed of the roll I want with the ball.

When I am putting well my grip seems light and sensitive, and I easily transfer the feeling from my fingers right through to my putter head, feeling the ball coming off the clubface in a very soft and delicate manner. This is something you have to work on to be able to produce the same feel under the pressures of tournament golf. Again, it is essential to stay relaxed to be able to produce a really great touch in tournament golf.

My long-putting is aimed at perfect touch. Sometimes I set up to the ball and seem to have a wonderful feeling of knowing exactly how it is going to roll, easily visualizing it dropping into the right part of the hole. I have a fairly aggressive approach, trying to hole most long putts, except for those which are exceedingly sidehill or downhill, but at the same time being very aware of where I want to leave the ball just in case I should miss – perhaps to leave myself an uphill rather than a downhill putt on the return.

My long-putt technique centres on producing good feel through my fingers and right thumb, reading the greens well and, as with my short putts, adopting and sticking to a rigid routine to create muscle memory for a repetitive stroke.

From Langer on Putting by Bernhard Langer with
Vivien Saunders (Stanley Paul, London, 1987).

How Not to be a Club Thrower

Greg Norman

When I was at school my great ambition was to be a sportsman. Greg Norman was no more keen on his school studies than I was, though as a child of sunny sub-tropical Queensland his mind was always turning to the beach, and as a teenager he says he was in serious danger of turning into a beach bum. He was almost fifteen before he first swung a club – rather unsuccessfully. The ball disappeared up a tree. He then turned his skills to Australian Rules football and got injured in a nasty accident that heavily flattened his nose. Golf still seemed like a quaint activity, but to fill in time he asked his mother, a regular player, if he could caddie for her. He took a few swings, realized the thrill of hitting the ball well – and quite suddenly he was hooked.

He was fifteen and a half in 1970 when he got his first set of golf clubs, and his handicap was 27. Within a little over two years he was down to scratch. Many people, such as the great Australian Peter Thomson, have likened him to Jack Nicklaus, though modestly Greg says the resemblance stops at their fine heads of blond hair. Greg is a fantastic competitor. His driving is so impressive – so long and so straight, which is half the battle. He's bound to have confidence in his irons from where he gets to hit them.

Greg has lost two majors to chip-ins. Larry Mize's 140-foot shot to win the 1987 Masters, coming only a year after Bob Tway's chip-in at the eighteenth hole at Inverness, Toledo, Ohio in the US PGA, might have shattered a lesser man. But Greg is not baby-meat. He said afterwards: 'Hundreds of sympathetic and well-meaning people have told me that Larry would have had no chance of making par and that the tournament would have been mine had he missed that impossible shot from 140 feet. I can't buy that. I am not interested in what might have happened. He holed the damn shot, didn't he? And good luck to him.' You can tell that Greg has had good schooling in the philosophy of the game. It came both from experience and from his father. Here, in this extract from his autobiography, written before he won the Open in 1986, he describes how he had an early lesson from Dad in conquering a fiery temper.

I.W.

When I was very young in golf my father Mervyn once walked off the course in disgust as I displayed my anger in a flurry of club-throwing during a quite unimportant club game at Virginia Golf Club near Brisbane. In my youth I found giving an errant club the good old heave-ho down the fairway a splendidly satisfying method of letting off steam.

The day my father stopped following me at Virginia he left the club without saying a word, but when I arrived home in the evening he sat me down in his study and admonished me in terms that were unmistakable.

As a young man my father was an above-average rugby footballer and played representative football in North Queensland as a second-row forward. He rejected several offers to go south to Brisbane and play, preferring to pursue his career, which has now taken him to a senior executive job with Mt Isa Mines Holdings. He is currently the general manager (engineering services) for the company, and in control of the development of a gigantic new coal-mining enterprise in Queensland involving the building of a town, railway and a port as well as other engineering developments.

There was a wealth of wisdom and experience behind what he had to say.

When my father walked away from me at Virginia on this particular day I had just sent my 7 iron cartwheeling down the fairway with my anger its main propelling force. Club-throwing seemed to me a perfectly natural way to release one's ire.

But I did not stop to think how it looked to outsiders. My father told me, 'If you ever throw a club again I will walk away from you. Son, I do not believe in that sort of thing. No self-respecting golfer or future professional would think of doing what you did today.'

My father's words sank in. I doubt if I have been guilty of throwing a club since, but there is no question that this game of golf can tear at your nerve-ends.

Certainly I have a temper. Sometimes I think I graduated with Straight 'As' in this department, but over the years I have learned to keep it in check. When I look around me there are very few people who play top-level sport who can really bottle up their inner emotions. Take Lee Trevino. He is a nervous type of character, but when things go awry for Lee his comic act is his safety valve. Bjorn Borg did not let a thing upset him, but how different is John McEnroe? Even Jack Nicklaus has those glowering moments when the club is returned to the bag with a force that could send it through the bottom and disgust is written all over his face.

There is a fine line between temper and temperament, and being in control of both these ingredients is an essential prerequisite for success. I am at my angriest on a golf course when I hit a bad shot, because I do not expect to hit bad shots. They upset me. As I am now aware, when I was a kid it got out of control, and I would follow one bad hole with another.

Now I am looking for a birdie, and expect to get it immediately after I have blundered. I can forget my bad shots a lot more quickly.

Sometimes I wonder if golf fans are genuinely aware of the pressures that go hand in hand with golf at international level. I find there is a tendency for them to invade the privacy of the players at the most inopportune times. When I go to the practice fairway before a round of golf I am going to my 'office' where I want to work and concentrate – to sort out any problems that I might have in my swing. That hour or so before the starter calls me to the tee is vitally important, and not the time for answering questions or signing autographs.

To draw a parallel, I can imagine the sort of reception I would get if I walked unannounced into a doctor's surgery and started asking questions, or went uninvited to the cockpit of a Jumbo aircraft and asked the captain for his autograph.

I know other players share my view on this subject.

From *Greg Norman – My Story* by Greg Norman
(Harrap, London, 1983).

It was soon borne in upon me that as a character-builder, or at any rate character-tester, golf left all the virtuous team games standing. Indeed, one could claim without being pompous that this ridiculous game teaches you all the lessons of life in miniature – no sense in losing your temper . . . never give up till the game is lost, and many others – without the disastrous penalties that await failure in higher spheres. For myself, nearing what my friend Leonard Crawley habitually refers to as the 'close of play', I find myself super-tolerant – dust into dust and nothing and nobody really matters, and what business of mine are another man's shortcomings? – but in the early days failure drove me almost out of my mind, so that to this day I sympathize with the silver-tongued, club-throwing golfers of former times so piously frowned upon today. I was in good company, however, for only after similar years of mental anguish did the great Bobby Jones himself become a model of deportment and the best-loved figure in the history of golf. I will not say that I became a model of deportment but I did eventually develop an aptitude for wrapping myself in a sort of cocoon of concentration.

From *My Life and Soft Times* by Henry Longhurst
(Cassell and Co., London, 1971).

The least thing upset him on the links. He missed short putts because of the uproar of butterflies in the adjoining meadows.

P. G. Wodehouse, *The Unexpected Clicking of Cuthbert*.

Why, during those early days on tour Palmer threw them. I have to say he was the very worst club-thrower I have ever seen. He had to learn to play well, he'd never have made it as a thrower.

Tommy 'Thunder' Bolt.

I should throw a provisional if I were you.

John Barratt, captain of Royal Mid Surrey Golf Club,
to a notorious club-thrower whose iron had just
disappeared into thick rough.

12

THE CADDIE

In the early days of the last century, before the term professional was used, a golf club's senior caddie was in effect the pro, green-keeper, club-maker and bag-carrier to the club captain or other important people. The word comes from the French *cadet* (young person) which was imported by Mary, Queen of Scots, who included many *cadets* (or pages) in her entourage when she returned to Scotland after her marriage to the Dauphin. 'Caddie', as the Scots pronounced it, came to refer to people wandering the streets looking for a carrying job.

The normal fee for a caddie before the Second World War was 7s 6d (37.5p) per round plus tip. But when Walter Hagen gave his £75 fee for winning the 1922 Open to his caddie, the pattern was set for much higher fees for professionals' caddies. Lee Trevino once quipped, 'I am going to make so much money this year my caddie will make the top twenty money winners' list'. He added, 'Caddies are a breed of their own. If you shoot 66, they say, "Man, *we* shot 66." But if you shoot 77, they say, "Hell, *he* shot 77." '

Palmer's caddie, Nat 'Ironman' Avery, says, 'We work as a team. I hand him the clubs and he makes the shots.' Sam Snead told his caddie before a tough game, 'When I ask you what kind of club to use, look the other way and don't answer.' Seve Ballesteros grumbled, 'The only time I talk on a golf course is to my caddie – and only then to complain.' My own caddie, Phil Morbey, volunteers information only when I ask him. Sometimes he suggests a different club from the one I have chosen – and more often than not he's right.

The legendary Tommy 'Thunder' Bolt, winner of a US Open in 1958, was known to break irons when he was in a fury. Once, so the story goes, he asked his caddie what iron to take to reach the green. 'An easy 2, Mr Bolt, was the answer. 'Hell, son, I can reach it with a 9, maybe a wedge,' said Tommy. 'There's only the 2 left in the bag, Mr Bolt,' came the reply.

I.W.

My Favourite Caddie

Gene Sarazen

Gene Sarazen, who wrote the following piece, shares with Bobby Jones, Ben Hogan and Tom Watson the distinction of winning both the British and American Open Championships in the same year; 1932 was his big year, but he also won the US Open in 1922 and tied with Lawson Little in 1940, but lost the play-off. Without doubt his most spectacular victory was in the Masters in 1935 when he made up a three-shot deficit at the par 5 fifteenth in the last round with a 'golden eagle' or albatross 2. His drive of 260 yards left him 240 yards from the green. A 4-wood shot cleared the lake in front of the green, bounced twice and rolled into the hole. He did the last three holes in par to tie with Craig Wood, then beat him in the play-off.

In 1960, when he was fifty-eight, Gene returned to St Andrews for the Centenary Open to score a 69 on the Old Course – and he also played in the 1970 Open at St Andrews. He has one of the sagest heads in golf and his philosophy on practice is almost exactly my own. Before a round a player should warm up rather than practise, he believes. Don't practise when you are tired and above all make sure that all your practice is purposive, rather than simply slogging balls. No one has ever put better the bond of loyalty and affection between caddie and player than Gene's moving description of how he won the Open at Sandwich with a then record score of 283 – with the help of the faithful Daniels.

I.W.

After a few days in London, I went down to Prince's to practise. The first person I met, right at the gate, was Daniels. He was overjoyed to see me. While we were exchanging news about each other, I could see that the last four years had taken a severe toll of him. He had become a very old man. His speech was slower. That shaggy mustache of his was much grayer, his limp was much more obvious. And his eyes, they didn't look good.

'Where's you bag, sir?' Daniels asked, hopping as spryly as he could toward the back seat of my auto.

'Dan,' I said – I couldn't put it off any longer though I almost didn't have the heart to say it, 'Dan, this bag is too heavy for you. I know you've been in bad health, and I wouldn't want you to try and go seventy-two holes with it.'

Dan straightened up. 'Righto, sir, if you feel that way about it.' There was great dignity in the way he spoke, but you couldn't miss the threads of emotion in his voice.

'I'm sorry, Dan,' I said, and walked away. I had dreaded the thought of having to turn old Dan down, but I had never imagined that the scene would leave me reproaching myself as the biggest heel in the world. I attempted to justify what I had done by reminding myself that business was business and I couldn't afford to let personal feelings interfere with my determination to win the British Open. It didn't help much.

I was a hot favorite to win. The American golf writers thought that I had a much better chance than Armour, the defending champion, and the veteran Mac Smith, the other name entry from the States. George Trevor of the *New York Sun*, for example, expressed the belief that 'Prince's course, a 7,000-yard colossus, will suit Sarazen to a tee, if you will pardon the pun. It flatters his strong points – powerful driving and long-iron second shots.' The English experts were likewise strong for me until, during the week of practice, they saw my game decline and fall apart. The young caddy from Stoke Poges did not suit me at all. I was training for this championship like a prizefighter, swinging the heavy club, doing roadwork in the morning, practising in weather that drove the other contenders indoors. My nerves were taut and I was in no mood to be condescended to by my caddy. He would never talk a shot over with me, just pull a club out of the bag as if he were above making a mistake. When I'd find myself ten yards short of the green after playing the club he had selected, he'd counter my criticism that he had underclubbed me by declaring dogmatically, 'I don't think you hit that shot well.' I began getting panicky as the tournament drew closer and my slump grew deeper. I stayed on the practice fairway until my hands hurt.

Something was also hurting inside. I saw Daniels in the galleries during the tune-up week. He had refused to caddy for any other golfer. He'd switch his eyes away from mine whenever our glances met, and shuffle off to watch Mac Smith or some other challenger. I continued, for my part, to play with increasing looseness and petulance. The qualifying round was only two days off when Lord Innis-Kerr came to my hotel room in the evening on a surprise visit. 'Sarazen, I have a message for you,' Innis-Kerr said, with a certain nervous formality. 'I was talking with Skip Daniels today. He's heartbroken, you know. It's clear to him, as it's clear to all your friends, that you're not getting along with your caddy. Daniels thinks he can straighten you out before the bell rings.'

I told his Lordship that I'd been thinking along the same lines myself. Daniels could very well be the solution.

'If it's all right with you, Sarazen,' Lord Innis-Kerr said as he walked to the door, 'I'll call Sam the caddymaster and instruct him to have Daniels meet you here at the hotel tomorrow morning. What time do you want him?'

'Have him here at seven o'clock . . . And thanks, very much.'

Dan was on the steps of the hotel waiting for me the next morning. We shook hands and smiled at each other. 'I am so glad we're going to be together,' old Dan said. 'I've been watching you ever since you arrived and I know you've been having a difficult time with that boy.' We walked to the course, a mile away. Sam the caddymaster greeted me heartily and told me how pleased everybody was that I had taken Daniels back. 'We were really worried about him, Mr Sarazen,' Sam said. 'He's been mooning around for days. This morning he looks ten years younger.'

Dan and I went to work. It was miraculous how my game responded to his handling. On our first round I began to hit the ball again, just like that. I broke par as

Dan nursed me through our afternoon round. We spent the hour before dinner practising. 'My, but you've improved a lot since 1928!' Dan told me as he replaced my clubs in the bag. 'You're much straighter, sir. You're always on line now. And I noticed this afternoon that you're much more confident than you used to be recovering from bunkers. You have that shot conquered now.' After dinner I met Dan by the first tee and we went out for some putting practice.

The next day, the final day of preparation, we followed the same pattern of practice. I listened closely to Dan as he showed me how I should play certain holes. 'You see this hole, sir,' he said when we came to the 8th, 'it can be the most tragic hole on the course.' I could understand that. It was only 453 yards long, short as par 5s go, but the fairway sloped downhill out by the 200-yard mark, and eighty yards before the green, rising twenty-five to thirty-five feet high, straddling the fairway and hiding the green, loomed a massive chain of bunkers. 'But you won't have any trouble on this hole,' Dan resumed. 'You won't have to worry about the downhill lie on your second shot. You have shallow-face woods. You'll get the ball up quick with them. I should warn you, however, that those bunkers have been the graveyard of many great players. If we're playing against the wind and you can't carry them, you must play safe. You cannot recover onto the green from those bunkers.' Yes, I thought as Dan spoke, the 8th could be another Suez [the hole at Sandwich which cost Sarazen the 1928 Open when he took a wood from the rough, and then another . . .].

That evening when the gathering darkness forced us off the greens and we strolled back to my hotel, Dan and I held a final powwow. 'We can win this championship, you and I,' I said to Dan, 'if we do just one thing.'

'Oh, there's no doubt we can win it, sir.'

'I know, but there's one thing in particular we must concentrate on. Do you remember that 7 at the Suez Canal?' I asked.

'Do I!' Dan put his hand over his eyes. 'Why, it's haunted me.'

'In this tournament we've got to make sure that if we go over par on a hole, we go no more than one over par. If we can avoid taking another disastrous 7, Dan, I don't see how we can lose. You won't find me going against your advice this time. You'll be calling them and I'll be playing them.'

Mac Smith and Tommy Armour were sitting on the front porch when we arrived at the hotel. 'Hey, Skip,' Armour shouted. 'How's Eugene playing?'

'Mr Sarazen is right on the stick,' Dan answered, 'right on the stick.'

The qualifying field played one round on Royal St George's and one on Prince's. There isn't much to say about my play on the first day at Prince's. I had a 73, one under par. However, I shall never forget the morning of the second qualifying round. A terrific gale was blowing off the North Sea. As I was shaving, I looked out of the window at the Royal St George's links where I'd be playing that day. The wind was whipping the sand out of the bunkers and bending the flags. Then I saw this figure in black crouched over against the wind, pushing his way from green to green. It was Daniels. He was out diagramming the positions of the pins so that I would know exactly how to play my approaches. I qualified among the leaders. You have to play well when you're partnered with a champion.

The night before the Open, the odds on my winning, which had soared 25–1 during my slump, dropped to 6–1, and Bernard Darwin, the critic I respected most, had dispatched the following lines to *The Times*: 'I watched Sarazen play eight or nine holes and he was mightily impressive. To see him in the wind, and there was a good fresh wind blowing, is to realize how strong he is. He just tears that ball through the wind as if it did not exist.'

On the day the championship rounds began, the wind had died down to an agreeable breeze, and Daniels and I attacked from the very first hole. We were out in 35, one under par, with only one 5 on that nine. We played home in 35 against a par of 38, birdieing the 17th and the 18th. My 70 put me a shot in front of Percy Alliss, Mac Smith, and Charlie Whitcombe. On the second day, I tied the course record with a 69. I don't know how much Dan's old eyes could perceive at a distance, but he called the shots flawlessly by instinct. I went one stroke over on the 9th when I missed a curling 5-footer, but that was the only hole on which we took a 'buzzard.' We made the turn in 35, then came sprinting home par, par, birdie, par, par, birdie, birdie, birdie, par. My halfway total, 139, gave me a three-shot margin over the nearest man, Alliss, four over Whitcombe, and five over Compston, who had come back with a 70 after opening with a 74. Armour had played a 70 for 145, but Tommy's tee-shots were giving him a lot of trouble – he had been forced to switch to his brassie – and I didn't figure on too much trouble from him. Mac Smith had started his second round with a 7 and finished it in 76. That was too much ground for even a golfer of Mac's skill and tenacity to make up.

The last day now, and the last rounds. I teed off in the morning at nine o'clock. Three orthodox pars. A grand drive on the 4th, and then my first moment of anguish: I hit my approach on the socket. Daniels did not give me a second to brood. 'I don't think we'll need that club again, sir,' he said matter-of-factly. I was forced to settle for a 5, one over par, but with Daniels holding me down, I made my pars easily on the 5th and the 6th and birdied the 7th.

Now for the 8th, 453 yards of trouble. So far I had handled it well, parring it on both my first and second rounds. Daniels had given me the go-ahead on both my blind second shots over the ridge of bunkers, and each time I had carried the hazard with my brassie. On this third round, I cracked my drive down the middle of the billowy fairway. Daniels handed me my spoon, after he had looked the shot over and tested the wind, and pointed out the direction to the pin hidden behind the bunkers. I hit just the shot we wanted – high over the ridge and onto the green, about thirty feet from the cup. I stroked the putt up to the hole, it caught a corner and dropped. My momentum from that eagle 3 carried me to a birdie 3 on the 9th. Out in 33. Okay. Now to stay in there. After a nice start home, I wobbled on the 411-yard 13th, pulling my long iron to the left of the green and taking a 5. I slipped over par again on the 335-yard 15th, three-putting from 14 feet when I went too boldly for my birdie putt and missed the short one coming back. I atoned for these lapses by birdieing the 16th and the 18th to complete that long second nine in 37, one under par, and the round in 70, four under. With eighteen more to go, the only man who had a chance to catch me was Arthur Havers. Havers, with 74–71–68, stood five strokes behind. Mac Smith, fighting back with a 71, was in third place, but eight shots away. Alliss had taken a 78 and was out of the hunt.

If the pressure and the pace of the tournament was telling on Dan, he didn't show it. I found him at the tee after lunch, raring to get back on the course and wrap up the championship. We got off to an auspicious start on that final round – par, birdie, par, par. On the 5th I went one over, shook it off with a par on the 6th, but when I missed my 4 on the 7th I began to worry about the possible errors I might make. This is the sure sign that a golfer is tiring. The 8th loomed ahead and I was wondering if that penalizing hole would catch up with me this time. I drove well, my ball finishing a few feet short of the spot from which I had played my spoon in the morning. Daniels took his time in weighing the situation, and then drew the spoon from the bag. I rode into the ball compactly and breathed a sigh of relief as I saw it get up quickly and clear the bunkers with yards to spare. 'That's how to play golf, sir,' Daniels said, winking an eye approvingly. 'That's the finest shot you've played on this hole.' He was correct, of course. We found out, after climbing up and over the ridge, that my ball lay only 8 feet from the cup. I holed the putt for my second eagle in a row on the hole, and turned in 35, after a standard par on the 9th.

Only nine more now and I had it. One over on the 10th. Nothing to fret about. Par. Par. Par. A birdie on the 14th. Almost home now. One over on the 15th, three putts. One over on the 16th, a fluffed chip. Daniels slowed me down on the 17th tee. 'We're going to win this championship, sir. I have no worries on that score. But let's make our pars on these last two holes. You always play them well.' A par on the 17th. On the 18th, a good drive into the wind, a brassie right onto the green, down in two for a birdie, 35–39–74, even par. There was no challenge to my total of 283. Mac Smith, the runner-up, was five shots higher, and Havers, who had needed a 76 on his last round, was a stroke behind Mac.

Feeling like a million pounds and a million dollars respectively, Daniels and I sat down on a bank near the first tee and congratulated each other on a job well done. Our score of 283 – 70, 69, 70, 74 – was 13 under par on a truly championship course, and it clipped two strokes off the old record in the British Open, Bob Jones' 285 at St Andrews in 1927. [The record is now 268, achieved by Tom Watson at Turnberry in 1977.] Much as I was thrilled by setting a new record for a tournament that had been my nemesis for a decade, I was even more elated over the method by which I had finally reached my goal. I had led all the way. I had encountered no really rocky passages because I had had the excellent sense to listen to Daniels at every puzzling juncture. Through his brilliant selection of clubs and his understanding of my volatile temperament, I had been able to keep my resolution to go no more than one over par on any hole. The 8th, which I had feared might be a second Suez, had turned out to be my best friend. I had two 3s and two 5s on a hole on which I would not have been unwilling, before the tournament, to settle for four 6s. . . .

After a shower, I changed into my brown gabardine jacket and was going over the acceptance speech I had prepared four years earlier, when the officials told me they were ready to begin their presentation ceremonies on the porch of the clubhouse. I asked them if it would be all right if Daniels came up and stood beside me as I received the trophy, since it had really been a team victory. They regretted to have to turn down a request they could sympathize with, but it was against tradition. I scanned the crowd gathering before the clubhouse, looking for Dan so that I could at least take him down front. I couldn't find him. Then, just as the officials were getting impatient about delaying the ceremony any longer, I spotted Dan coming down the drive on his bicycle, carrying a grandson on each handlebar. On with the show.

After the ceremony the team of Daniels and Sarazen got together for a rather tearful good-bye. I gave Dan my polo coat, and told him I'd be looking for him the next year at St Andrews. I waved to him as he pedaled happily down the drive, the coat flapping in the breeze, and there was a good-sized lump in my throat as I thought of how the old fellow had never flagged for a moment during the arduous grind of the tournament and how, pushing himself all the way, he had made good his vow to win a championship for me before he died.

It was the last time I saw Dan. A few months later some English friends, who kept me posted on Dan, wrote me that he had passed away after a short illness. They said that after the Open he had worn the polo coat continually, even inside the pubs, as he told the golf fans of three generations the story of how 'Sarazen and I did it at Prince's.' When old Dan died the world was the poorer by one champion.

From *Thirty Years of Championship Golf* by Gene Sarazen
(Prentice-Hall, New Jersey, USA, 1950).

A Caddie-ish Trick

Henry Longhurst

At most of the big London golf clubs in the 1930s the regular caddies tended to be brigands in long overcoats, and Walton Heath was no exception. After I had won my single there, my caddie, a man named Wilson, suggested that, as we were evidently so well matched a combination, it would be a good thing if he accompanied me to Rye for the University match, and thus it was arranged. (It was at Walton Heath that there occurred the basis of one of my favourite golfing stories, when Wash Carr hit a drive right up the middle, only to find the ball deep in a divot mark. 'That'd be a nice one to get in the Medal,' he said to his caddie. 'You'd never 'ave 'ad it in the Medal,' said the man darkly.) I mention Wilson because at the critical moment in the singles he put in on my behalf a supreme stroke of gamesmanship. My opponent happened to be an old friend with whom I had often played at Charterhouse, Pat Jackson, and in the morning I was four up at the 16th, well short of the green in three, while Jackson had a five-footer for a four. At this point I holed my chip. I only wish that the Master Gamesman himself, Stephen Potter, had been there to admire the timing by which, not a moment too soon nor a moment too late, Wilson, on picking the ball out of the hole, remarked to the world in general, 'Yuss. I thought we should 'ave one of *them* before long.' Jackson stood staring for a moment and then, having said simply, 'You little worm!' missed the putt. One of the many charms of golf and its infinite variety is that you accumulate over the years a whole host of personal memories – *this* happened here and *that* happened there – and thus in all the times I have played at Rye since, I have never passed the 16th green without thinking, 'It was exactly from *there* that I holed that chip.'

From *My Life and Soft Times* by Henry Longhurst
(Cassell and Co., London, 1971).

The Caddie who Out-earned the Open Champion

Sam Snead

The purse of $600 [for winning the 1946 British Open] was such a joke that I decided then and there not to defend the title. My travelling expenses alone were over $1,000, and nobody but me picked up that tab. On top of that, all my hitting muscles 'froze' in the icy wind at St Andrews. For days I ached in every joint.

Then there was my caddie friend, 'Scotty,' who got himself sprung from jail and begged me to give him the winning ball. 'Maun,' he promised, tearfully, 'I'll treasure it all my days.'

That ball was worth some cash, and Scotty proved it. An hour later he sold it for fifty quid. So he made more off the Open than I did.

For years afterward, British and American writers panned me for passing up the British Open, but like I've always said – as far as I'm concerned, any time you leave the USA you're just camping out.

From *The Education of a Golfer* by Sam Snead
(Cassell and Co., London, 1962).

Caddie Backchat

Vardon (playing badly) to Caddie: What on earth should I take now?
Caddie: Well, sir, I'd recommend the 4.05 train.

I think it's slightly straight, Mr Faulkner . . .

> Mad Mac, the dirty-raincoated eccentric caddie who 'read' the green through opera glasses without lenses, advising Max Faulkner (British Open Champion 1951) on a putt.

I've been caddying for him for ten years and he's never had a bad lie yet . . .

> Skeets, caddie for Bob Hope.

He told me just to keep the ball low . . .

> A caddie's putting advice to Chi Chi Rodriguez, the former shoeshine boy from Puerto Rica who spent many years in the US top sixty. Only 5 feet 7 inches tall, he could drive 300 yards. Known as 'the Clown Prince of the Tour' and 'the Four-stroke Penalty', he was asked by both Palmer and Nicklaus to cut down on the wise-cracking while playing.

13

GOLFING INTELLIGENCE

It *Does* Take Brains to Play Golf – or Does it?

Gene Sarazen

It takes some intelligence to play good golf. An ambitious player must think clearly about his practice habits and his equipment. On the course he must know his limitations and not expect to hit eighteen perfect tee-shots. Middlecoff and Mangrum don't. He mustn't destroy his concentration before a shot by wondering if thirty-three anatomical parts are going to perform their appointed functions. If he falls into an error which he does not understand, that's what qualified professionals are for. He must remember that a good grip is the foundation of a good golf swing. If your foundation is right, your house will stand firmly down through the years. If the foundation is faulty, it doesn't matter how well you have decorated the rooms, the house will collapse anyway. I am sincerely convinced that if the average player approaches the game sensibly, he will soon discover that he is well above average.

From *Thirty Years of Championship Golf* by Gene Sarazen
(Prentice-Hall, New Jersey, USA, 1950).

Give me a man with big hands, big feet and no brains and I will make a golfer out of him.

Walter Hagen.

Question: What do you think of when you play a shot?
George Duncan (winner of the 1920 British Open and Ryder Cup captain, 1929): Nothing. Nothing at all.

It is impossible to outplay an opponent you can't out-think.

Lawson Little, US Open Champion, 1940.

THERMAL ANALYSIS

VOLUME 2

Inorganic Materials and Physical Chemistry

Proceedings of the Second International Conference on
Thermal Analysis
Held at Holy Cross College
Worcester, Massachusetts
August 18-23, 1968

THERMAL ANALYSIS

VOLUME 2

Inorganic Materials and Physical Chemistry

Edited by

Robert F. Schwenker, Jr.

Personal Products Company
Division of Johnson & Johnson
Milltown, New Jersey

and

Paul D. Garn

Department of Chemistry
University of Akron
Akron, Ohio

Academic Press · New York · London · 1969

ACADEMIC PRESS, INC.
111 Fifth Avenue, New York, New York 10003

United Kingdom Edition published by
ACADEMIC PRESS, INC. (LONDON) LTD.
Berkeley Square House, London W.1

LIBRARY OF CONGRESS CATALOG CARD NUMBER: 69-12287

PRINTED IN THE UNITED STATES OF AMERICA

CONTENTS OF VOLUME 2

Section 3. Inorganic Materials and Metallurgy

CONTENTS

Section 4. Physical Chemistry

CONTENTS

Section 5. Minerals

CONTENTS

Section 6. Applied Sciences

CONTENTS

CONTENTS OF VOLUME 1

Section 1. Advances in Instrumentation

CONTENTS

CONTENTS

Section 2. Organic Materials, Including Polymers

CONTENTS

CONTRIBUTORS

Pages 1-706 refer to Volume 1, 707-1512 refer to Volume 2

FOREWORD

Thermal analysis is a method of physicochemical analysis which is employed in the study of substances and the processes taking place in a substance during heating or cooling. The development of thermal analysis and its application to various branches of science and technology have in recent years required the establishment of firm contacts among the scientists working in this interesting field, with the help of the organization of international conferences.

The period between the First International Conference (1965) and the Second (1968) was characterized by the elaboration of the problems of unification and standardization in thermal analysis as well as a further broadening of the spheres of its application. We can mention here such methods of analysis as thermogravimetry, thermogasvolumometry, linear and volume dilatometry, and viscosity. In addition there are the measurements of electrical conductivity, as well as of magnetic, dielectric, photoelectric, thermodynamic, and thermophysical properties.

One of the main reasons for the growth of the popularity of thermal analysis in the investigation of various materials is its constant progress. Unfortunately, thermal characteristics of materials appear to differ with different investigators because of the use of different experimental conditions. It would be desirable to have detailed descriptions of the conditions published as proof of the data.

The Proceedings of the Second International Conference on Thermal Analysis reflect the various methods and spheres of thermal analysis at present and the distribution of various aspects of thermal analysis in different countries. We hope that in the future these methods will find even wider application in science and technology.

L. Berg
President, ICTA
1965–1968

University, Kazan, USSR

PREFACE

Dynamic methods of thermal analysis readily have fulfilled their earlier promise for the study of diverse basic and applied research problems. The "art" of thermal analysis is becoming a more exact science and the greatest progress has been made in elucidating the fundamental behavior and structure of materials. That this has been achieved was clearly demonstrated at the Second International Conference on Thermal Analysis held at Holy Cross College, Worcester, Massachusetts, during August 18–23, 1968. The Proceedings of that Conference are contained in this and a companion volume. The papers embrace a wide range of applications from fundamental thermodynamics and kinetics to industrial process development. The interest and involvement of the scientific community in thermal analysis are reflected in the work presented by 163 scientists from 20 countries.

The exigencies of time and the unknowns that always face a pioneering venture limited the Proceedings of the First International Conference to essentially long abstracts of the papers presented. As a consequence, many worthy papers and much valuable data were never published. In the planning of the Second Conference the decision was made to publish Conference papers in full to provide, hopefully, a lasting document that would be of maximum use to scientists of today and of the future.

We, the editors, wish to thank the many authors represented for their contributions, for their cooperation, and for their efforts in the preparation of these Proceedings. We are grateful to Dr. C. B. Murphy, General Chairman and organizer of the Conference, for his guidance and encouragement. One of us (RFS) wishes to express his gratitude to his secretary, Miss Linda Slagada, for invaluable assistance in the preparation of manuscripts and other material. Finally, it is a pleasure to acknowledge the helpfulness and patience of the Academic Press staff in the production of these volumes.

Robert F. Schwenker, Jr.
Paul D. Garn

Milltown, New Jersey
May, 1969

SECTION 3

INORGANIC MATERIALS AND METALLURGY

Chairmen:

G. Berggren
T. Sudo
F. Freund

DIFFERENTIAL THERMAL ANALYSIS OF
BORIC ACID, BORIC OXIDE AND POTASSIUM FLUOBORATE*

R. T. Marano and E. R. Shuster

Nuclear Materials and Equipment Corporation
Lewiston, New York

The manufacture of isotopically enriched elemental boron-10 from the boron-10 trifluoride product removed from the isotope separation system utilizes either potassium fluoborate or boric acid as an intermediate product depending on the reduction process to be employed. In either case the chemical reaction involves precipitation from aqueous solution, filtering and drying steps.

The purposes of this investigation were to aid in determining the thermal characteristics of these plant materials in order to optimize the conditions under which these materials are dried, to compare these materials to their commercial counterparts of natural enrichments, and to develop a suitable analytical tool to define product quality, if possible.

The study was performed using a standard commercial thermal analyzer manufactured by Fisher Scientific Company including the Fisher Model 360 Linear Temperature Programmer and the Model 260 furnace. The thermograms were recorded on a Texas Instruments two pen strip chart recorder with 1 mv full scale response. The sample holder was an Inconel cylinder with eight symetrically arranged round holes. The sample was placed in either a quartz or graphite crucible which in turn was placed in a sample holder. The thermocouples were then inserted into the sample and the holder, crucibles, thermocouples and sample were then placed in the furnace. The lead cable from the programmer was connected to the sample holder and the outputs of the temperature and differential thermocouples were connected through the programmer to the recorder. The sample atmosphere was introduced into the furnace

* Work supported by the U.S. Atomic Energy Commission under Contract AT-(40-1)-3292

through the handle of the sample holder and dispersed at
four points just above the top of the sample crucible.
The atmosphere filled the furnace and then vented at the
furnace top. All data was collected using chromel-alumel
thermocouples and alumina as reference material and diluent as noted. A flowing argon atmosphere of 2 SCF/H
was used except for runs E-H which were made in a static
ambient environment.

Samples of material from commercially available
sources were used to optimize analytical parameters.
Boric acid was reagent grade purchased from Fisher Scientific, boric oxide was technical grade purchased from B&A
Division of Allied Chemical, potassium tetrofluoborate
was 99%+ pure purchased from ALFA Inorganics and technical
grade purchased from B&A Division of Allied Chemical. The
remainder of the samples were either manufactured at our
plant or obtained from non-commercial sources.

The graphite crucibles were manufactured to our design by Poco Graphite Inc. from Spectro AZ grade graphite,
which has high purity, strength, and electrical resistivity, and low thermal conductivity. These graphite crucibles were required due to the reaction of the boric acid
and potassium tetrafluoborate with the standard quartz
crucibles designed for the Fisher system. A drawing of
the graphite crucible is shown in Fig. 1.

The first compound investigated was boric acid.
Table 1 is a summary of the DTA analysis performed on this
material. All of the thermograms for boric acid were obtained using graphite crucibles. Preliminary experiments
yielded an optimum heating rate of 5°C per minute, which
was used for all subsequent runs. The major peak which
appears at a temperature of 150°-159° has been attributed
to the first dehydration of boric acid. The second peak
at 175°-190° has been attributed to the second dehydration and subsequent boiling of the sample. Peaks above
the range of 175°-190° are the bubbling of the sample. On
two of the thermograms, one of Fisher boric acid and the
other of Argonne II boric acid, an endothermic peak was
noted on the first dehydration peak at a temperature of
148°-150°. This endothermic peak was not noted on any of
the other boric acid samples. On one sample of NUMEC production run H_3BO_3 a peak was noted at 100°. This peak has
been attributed to excess water contained in the boric
acid. Figure 2 shows thermograms of boric acid.

710

The second compound of interest to us was boric oxide. Table 2 is a summary of DTA analysis of this compound. The thermograms for the boric oxide were run using the quartz crucibles and in all but the first run the sample was diluted 1:4 with the Al_2O_3 reference material. The thermograms of boric oxide were characterized by the absence of any major peaks, with the exception of one at a temperature of 690°-700°. This peak was well above any reported melting point[1] for B_2O_3 and the thermograms lacked a peak at the reported melting point. The major peak is believed to be either a reaction of the boric oxide with the alumina or quartz or a phenomenon of the liquid state of boric oxide. This peak was found at a temperature above the limit for the graphite crucibles which began to react with the oxides at a temperature of 450°-500°. Figures 3-5 are thermograms of boric oxide.

The third compound to be investigated was potassium tetrafluoborate. Table 3 is a summary of the DTA analysis of this material. This investigation was also carried out using graphite crucibles. The graphite was chosen for this investigation because of the fluoride salt attack on the quartz in a preliminary study. The sharp major peak which appears at a temperature of 270°-280° is a crystal lattice rearrangement from the rhombic to the cubic form. The rearrangement has been reported to take place at a temperature of 273°-280°[2,3]. This investigation has confirmed the rearrangement taking place at a temperature of 270°-280°. On two of the thermograms the temperature was recorded on an expanded scale permitting a measurement of the rearrangement temperature as being 278°-280°. Figures 6 and 7 are thermograms of potassium tetrafluoborate.

The sharpness and repeatability of this peak and its reversibility on cooling have permitted its use by this laboratory in subsequent work as a temperature reference standard.

In conclusion, we have found that differential thermal analysis is a very useful tool in assuring uniformity of batch-to-batch quality in the production of these boron-10 enriched compounds.

References

1. Handbook of Chemistry and Physics, 47th Ed. B 160, The Chemical Rubber Co. (1966-1967)

2. H.S. Booth and D.R. Martin, Boron Trifluoride and Its Derivatives, 102, John Wiley & Sons, Inc. (1949)

3. M. Stacey, J.C. Tatlor, and A.G. Sharpe, Advances in Fluorine Chemistry, 1, 81, Butterworths Scientific Publications (1960)

4. W.W. Wendlandt, Thermal Methods of Analysis, Interscience Publishers (1964)

5. H.G. McAdie, Anal. Chem., 39, 543 (1967)

TABLE 1

Differential Thermal Analysis of Boric Acid

Curve	Source	Weight Mg	Major Peak °C	Minor Peak °C
A	Fisher	295	159	150,190
B	Argonne II	270	153	148,180
C	NBL	170	156	175
D	NUMEC	160	150	100,175

TABLE 2

Differential Thermal Analysis of Boric Oxide

Curve	Source	Weight Mg	Major Peak °C	Minor Peak °C
E	B&A	210		RT,690,750
F	B&A	130*	710	
G	B&A	230*	690	100,150
H	NUMEC	250*	700	100,125,200
I	NUMEC	200*	690	RT,175,425
J	B&A	200*	700	470

*Diluted 1:4 w/al 203

TABLE 3

Differential Thermal Analysis of
Potassium Tetrafluoborate

Curve	Source	Weight Mg	Major Peak °C	Minor Peak °C
K	Alfa	300	270	470-480
L	Alfa	280	278	400-490
M	Alfa	250	280	510
N	B&A	325	280	480,510
O	NUMEC	180	278	470,525
P	Alfa	290	280	
Q	Alfa	290	278	

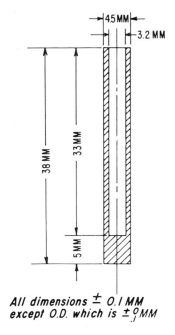

*All dimensions ± 0.1 MM
except O.D. which is ± .9MM*

Fig. 1 Drawing of Graphite Crucible

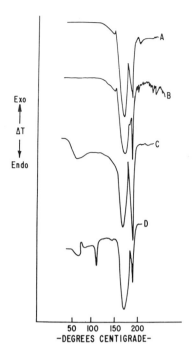

Fig. 2   DTA Curves of Boric Acid Heating Rate 5°C/min.

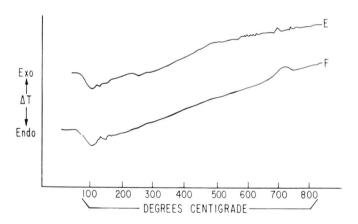

Fig. 3   DTA Curves of Boric Oxide Heating Rate 10°C/min.

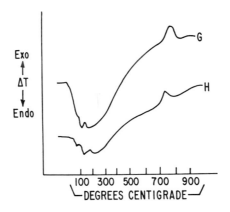

Fig. 4   DTA Curves of Boric Oxide Heating Rate 25°C/min.

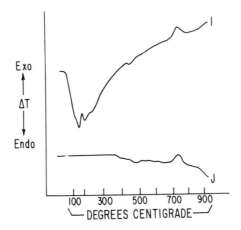

Fig. 5   DTA Curves of Boric Oxide Heating Rate 20°C/min.

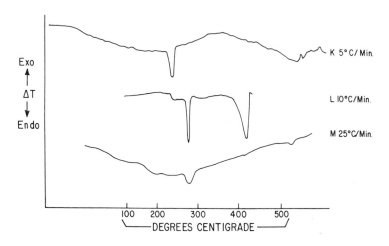

Fig. 6   DTA Curves of Potassium Tetrafluoborate

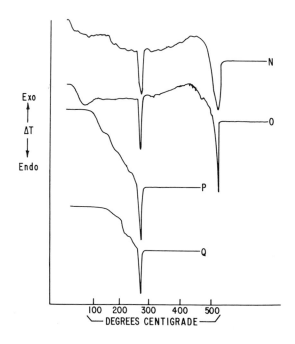

Fig. 7   DTA Curves of Potassium Tetrafluoborate Heating
Rate 10°C/min.

THE PYROSYNTHESIS OF ALKALINE EARTH ZINCATES

H. G. McAdie

Ontario Research Foundation
Sheridan Park
Ontario, Canada

Abstract

Earlier studies on the pyrosynthesis of strontium zincate, employing a combination of DTA, simultaneous DTA-TG, and x-ray diffraction, have been extended to other alkaline earth systems.

No evidence was obtained for the formation of magnesium or calcium zincate. Barium zincate was produced from barium carbonate and zinc oxide in an oxygen atmosphere, however in CO_2 formation of the eutectic $BaO.2BaCO_3$ appeared to be favoured. Formation of barium zincate was accompanied by sintering and its reported melting point may be somewhat high.

Introduction

Earlier studies of the pyrosynthesis of strontium zincate (1) by a combination of DTA, simultaneous DTA-TG, and x-ray diffraction, revealed that this material may be produced by crystallization from a fused mixture of strontium and zinc oxides, independently of whether a carbon dioxide or oxygen atmosphere prevails over the sample. Reversible thermal effects corresponding to fusion and recrystallization were observed, having a temperature hysteresis of about 60°C., and the final room-temperature product gave a diffraction pattern corresponding to that for $SrZnO_2$ (2).

Similar studies have now been carried out on the pyrosynthesis of the zincates of other alkaline earths, the results of which form the subject of this paper.

717

Experimental

Equimolar mixtures of MgO, $CaCO_3$ and $BaCO_3$ with ZnO were prepared by weighing the appropriate quantities of reagent-grade materials into the sample holders employed. Ethanol was added, the mixture slurried in the sample container, and dried at low temperature prior to beginning the programmed studies.

Simultaneous DTA-TG experiments were carried out using the Mettler Vacuum Thermoanalyzer equipped with the MP-21 sample holder using conical platinum crucibles of total volume ca. 0.1 cm.^{3} Heating and cooling rates were 10°C. min.$^{-1}$ under gas atmospheres flowing over the samples at 5 l.hr.$^{-1}$ DTA, DTG, TG and traces were obtained on each sample at the sensitivities indicated on the figures.

Additional DTA studies were made using the R.L. Stone Model SH13BP2-PTW sample holder with cylindrical platinum cups. Heating and cooling rates were again 10°C.min.$^{-1}$ under an atmosphere flow of ca. 1 l.hr.$^{-1}$

Debye-Scherrer diffraction patterns were obtained on samples cooled to room temperature using conventional techniques.

Results

MgO + ZnO in O_2

On heating an equimolar mixture of these two oxides a very slow loss in weight was observed up to 1200°C., above which the rate of weight loss increased slightly. This was attributed to decomposition of the zinc oxide. When cooled from 1500° weight loss ceased about 1400° and a slight regain was noted. No further mass change was observed on cooling, nor were any thermal effects detected during either heating or cooling.

$CaCO_3$ + ZnO in CO_2 and in O_2

With the exception of differences in the thermal records attributable to the decomposition of $CaCO_3$ under these two different atmospheres, no evidence for the interaction of CaO and ZnO was found to 1500°C. On cooling from this temperature in CO_2 some recarbonation of the CaO was detected, the final product showing a diffraction pattern attributable to CaO + ZnO with traces of $CaCO_3$. Under oxygen, only CaO and ZnO were found in the cooled product.

Barium Zincate

Barium zincate was first prepared by Scholder and Weber (3) from solution. High-temperature formation was described by Hoppe (4) and by Schnering and co-workers (5) who detailed the synthesis from a mixture of barium and zinc acetates, and from mixtures of barium hydroxide, oxide or peroxide with zinc oxide. The crystal structure was suggested to involve Zn^{++} and $O^=$ arranged in a distorted β-quartz structure with Ba^{++} occupying the widened holes between oxygen tetrahedra (6), or as an arrangement of $ZnO_2^=$ similar to that of α-quartz with Ba^{++} located in the interstitial holes (5). Somewhat different preparative conditions were employed in these two reports, and it is possible that two modifications of barium zincate may exist, analogous to the case of strontium zincate (2), having slightly different cell dimensions and dependent upon the rate of cooling from high temperatures.

Hulbert & Klawitter (8) have studied the kinetics of the reaction between $BaCO_3$ and ZnO in air, using isothermal TG in the region 1050-1125°C. to follow loss of CO_2. The kinetics were described by the nuclei growth equation and the activation energy found to be 54.6 kcal.mole^{-1}, however these authors appear to have been unaware of barium zincate being one of the products.

$BaCO_3$ + ZnO in CO_2 (Fig. 1)

On heating from room temperature constant weight was maintained through the $BaCO_3$ phase transitions at 825° and 988°C. to a procedural decomposition temperature (p.d.t.) of 1235°C. The primary TG trace, as well as the DTG and DTA records, indicated a two-step weight-loss process complicated by the onset of a third process associated with decomposition of zinc oxide between 1300° and 1400°C. Thus, it was difficult to define accurately the temperature at which $BaCO_3$ decomposition was concluded and the extent

719

to which the weight loss agreed with that expected.

On cooling from 1500° three weight gain processes were observed, the most rapid commencing at 1176° accompanied by an exothermal effect and ascribed to recarbonation of the barium oxide. This latter process ceased rather abruptly at 1066°, accompanied by a further exothermal effect, which would be consistent with freezing of the eutectic BaO.2BaCO₃ reported at 1060° under equilibrium conditions (7). Further cooling produced only a minor gain in weight, while the presence of exotherms at 970° and 775° showed a portion of barium carbonate was free to undergo the cubic → hexagonal and hexagonal → orthorhombic transitions at the respective temperatures. The cubic → hexagonal transition was less affected by supercooling than the higher enthalpy hexagonal → orthorhombic transition. Such supercooling in solid state phase transitions is frequently encountered (9) and has been observed in pure samples of barium carbonate (10). The hexagonal → orthorhombic transition also appeared to involve two stages, as indicated by a second smaller exotherm below the main effect. This has also been noted in pure samples of barium carbonate under nitrogen at slower cooling rates (10).

When reheated from 700° the endothermal phase transitions in barium carbonate were observed at 815° and 980°, approximately 10° below the temperatures observed during the first heating cycle possibly due to thermal annealing. A relatively sharp endothermal process at 1122° was consistent with melting of the BaO.2BaCO₃ eutectic.

A p.d.t. of 1270° for barium carbonate was observed during the second heating cycle, the weight loss beginning more sharply but being less than during the first heating cycle due to the limited recarbonation of the barium oxide. The weight loss-regain pattern about the 1500° cycling temperature was similar to that found during the first cycle, except for a reduced recarbonation of the barium oxide indicative of reduced surface area through sintering. Some increase in the area of the eutectic crystallization exotherm, together with reduction in the areas of the barium carbonate phase transitions suggested a gradual ordering of the sample into the eutectic, the extent of which could depend upon the residence time at temperatures above the eutectic melting point.

The x-ray diffraction pattern of the sample cooled to room temperature after two heating-cooling cycles corresponded mainly to $BaCO_3$ and ZnO, with minor amounts of BaO. No clear evidence was found for the presence of barium zincate.

$BaCO_3$ + ZnO in O_2 (Fig. 2)

On heating initially from room temperature the barium carbonate phase transitions were observed at 829° and 990°C. Loss of CO_2 commenced at 916°C., considerably lower than reported elsewhere (7), and showed three distinct steps in the ranges 916-1150°, 1150-1300° and 1300-1350°C. Above 1350° a further weight loss was observed to 1500° which reversed on cooling from this temperature.

A distinct weight loss was found consistently in the region 1350-1500° throughout a series of systems involving zinc oxide, and was considered initially to be due to sublimation. However, the weight regain on cooling in oxygen suggested the process was one of decomposition on heating followed by recombination during the cooling cycle.

Weight loss processes were accompanied by endothermal effects having peak temperatures at 1138°, 1203° and 1302°C. These effects were reproducible over a series of experiments but their origin was not established.

On cooling from 1500°C., constant weight was achieved by 1150°, corresponding to the sample weight plateau between 1275° and 1300°C. found on heating. The DTG record indicated two steps in the weight regain process accompanied by exothermal effects at 1342° and 1298°. No further mass change was observed to 700°.

At 1070° a violent exothermal process was found. The absence of subsequent thermal activity to 700° indicated the absence of significant amounts of barium carbonate and suggested that the exothermal process was an interaction between barium and zinc oxides. The sharpness of the exotherm is indicative of a crystallization process, occurring about 100° below the reported melting point of barium zincate (5).

When reheated from 700° a strong endothermal process was observed at 1150° with no accompanying weight change, suggesting a fusion process. This was succeeded by a further small endotherm at 1175° which may be due to inhomogeneity in the fused sample rather than to a unique process.

Weight loss was observed again at 1300°, accompanied by a small endothermal effect. Reversal of the temperature programme at 1500° arrested this loss, with regain beginning at 1385° and showing two stages accompanied by small exotherms at 1343° and 1294°. On this cycle, however, regain amounted to only 50% of the weight loss in the 1300-1500° range.

Further cooling again resulted in the violent exotherm at 1075°, in the absence of any weight change, and no further thermal activity was observed to 700°.

The x-ray diffraction pattern of the sample cooled to room temperature was complex in that many of the strongest diffraction lines for the principal species tend to overlap. Barium zincate was identified as the major constituent, and the presence of some splitting of the major diffraction lines suggested that two forms of this material were present differing only in degree of order within the overall lattice. Minor amounts of BaO, ZnO and, possibly, $BaCO_3$ were also identified within the limitations of the powder pattern method.

Comment

There is no evidence from present work that magnesium or calcium zincates are produced by interaction of the corresponding oxides below 1500°C. Possibly the smaller ionic radii of magnesium (0.66 Å) and calcium (0.99 Å) with respect to strontium (1.12 Å), all in the divalent state, are inadequate for the formation of a thermodynamically stable structure analogous to strontium zincate.

In carbon dioxide, barium oxide and zinc oxide did not interact appreciably in the time of the programmed experiments, the formation of barium carbonate on cooling from

1500°C. leading to preferential formation of the eutectic $BaO \cdot 2BaCO_3$. However, under oxygen barium zincate crystallizes from the mixed oxides over a narrow temperature range. The process is reversible, with a melting point of about 1150°C., so that considerable supercooling appears to accompany the crystallization process. This would be expected if the nuclei growth mechanism proposed by Hulbert and Klawitter (8) applies.

Acknowledgements

The author gratefully acknowledges the kind cooperation of Mettler Instrumente, A.G., Zurich, Switzerland and, particularly, of Mr. H. G. Wiedemann who performed the simultaneous DTA-TG work described in this paper and assisted in other aspects of the study. The project was sponsored by a research grant to the Ontario Research Foundation from the Province of Ontario received through the Department of Trade and Development.

References

1. H. G. McAdie, J. Inorg. and Nuclear Chem. <u>28</u>, 2801 (1966).
2. H. G. von Schnering and R. Hoppe, Z. anorg. allgem. Chem. <u>312</u>, 87 (1961).
3. R. Schnolder and H. Weber, Z. anorg. allgem. Chem. <u>215</u>, 355 (1933).
4. R. Hoppe, Z. anorg. allgem. Chem. <u>294</u>, 135 (1958).
5. H. G. von Schnering, R. Hoppe and J. Zemann, Z. anorg. allgem. Chem. <u>305</u>, 241 (1960).
6. U. Spitsbergen, Acta Cryst. <u>13</u>, 197 (1960).
7. National Bureau of Standards, Circular 500 (1952).
8. S. F. Hulbert and J. J. Klawitter, J. Am. Ceram. Soc. <u>50</u>, 484 (1967).
9. K. J. Rao and C. N. R. Rao, J. Materials Sci. <u>1</u>, 238 (1966).
10. H. G. McAdie, Unpublished results.

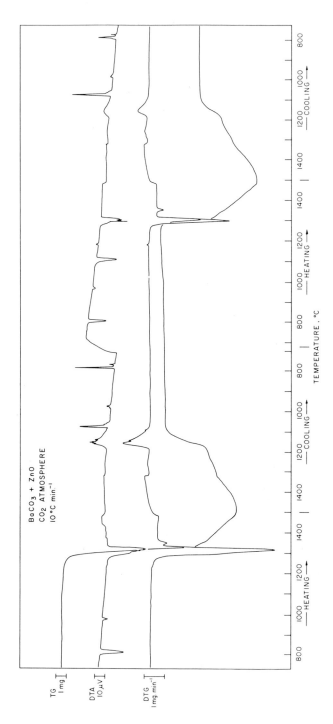

Fig. 1.

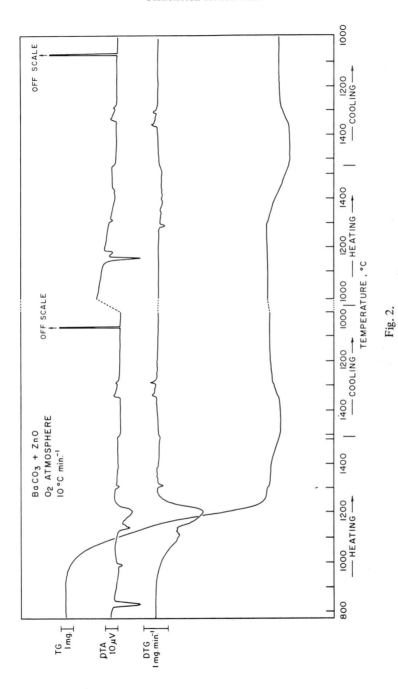

Fig. 2.

725

THERMAL ANALYSIS OF PROMETHIUM OXALATE[a]

C. E. McNeilly and F. P. Roberts

Battelle Memorial Institute
Pacific Northwest Laboratory
Richland, Washington

Abstract

Differential thermal analysis (DTA) and thermogravi-metric analysis (TGA) have been used to study the decomposition of promethium oxalate. TGA results were quite similar to those for samarium oxalate, as expected; however, the DTA results were almost entirely different, with respect to both types and temperatures of reaction.

The starting material was shown by TGA to correspond to the formula $Pm_2(C_2O_4)_3 \cdot 3 H_2O$. Differential thermal analysis, performed over a one-month period, showed a marked change taking place in the material, presumably due to radiolytic decay of ^{147}Pm to $^{147}Sm + \beta$. Radiation damage due to the beta particles results in the formation of a material with the apparent formula $Pm_2O_2CO_3 \cdot 3 H_2O$ as determined by TGA.

Introduction

Although most people now generally realize that the so-called rare earth elements are really not so rare, it is probably not appreciated just how rare some of them are. Promethium does not occur at all in nature and is strictly a by-product of nuclear fission occurring in plutonium production and power reactors. Promethium-147 has a half-life of 2.62 years and decays by beta emission to samarium-147.

---

[a]Work performed under United States Atomic Energy Commission Contract AT(45-1)-1830.

It has recently become apparent that [147]Pm has certain characteristics which make it desirable for use in isotopic heat sources (Fig. 1). As with most rare earth metals, the sesquioxide is the most chemically and physically stable compound and hence most suitable form of the element for heat source applications.

Since these oxides undergo at least one and sometimes two or three polymorphic phase changes on heating, it is important for encapsulation purposes to know the temperature and nature of these changes. Differential thermal analysis is, of course, an ideal method for studying these transitions. However, since the promethium is chemically separated from other fission and decay products and precipitated as a hydrated oxalate, it is necessary to calcine it to the oxide. DTA and TGA were also used in studying this calcination and it is these results which are presented here.

Apparatus

Because of the biological hazard from the β emitting promethium, all analyses were performed with equipment located in totally enclosed glove boxes. The DTA apparatus was constructed locally from our own design. Its major features are those which are necessary to facilitiate operation and, probably more important, maintenance in the glove box. The furnace has all Pt/Pt-10 Rh thermocouples and has a Pt-40 Rh winding. We also use a Pt liner in the furnace tube and DC power to reduce electrical "noise" in the differential signal. This allows us to operate with a differential signal sensitivity of 2 μV/in on the recorder although 10 μV/in is more commonly used.

The TGA includes a standard Ainsworth semi-micro automatic balance (10 mg full scale sensitivity) and a Pt-40 Rh wound furnace.

Atmosphere control is available on both DTA and TGA although most of this work was performed in air. Sample sizes were standardized at 17 ± 1 mg for both DTA and TGA and all heating rates were 10°C/minute.

Results and Discussion

It was anticipated that since Pm and Sm are so

chemically similar that the oxalates would also decompose similarly. That this is not the case is shown in Fig. 2, which shows the DTA patterns to be not at all similar. The Pm oxalate apparently loses all its water of hydration at the same time (and at a lower temperature) compared to three distinct stages for the Sm oxalate. Most unexpected, however, was the absence of any indication of oxalate decomposition, which shows up so predominantly with Sm and most other rare earth oxalates.(1,2)

The Pm oxalate analyzed here, however, had been prepared several weeks earlier and it appeared that perhaps we were seeing an effect of radiolytic damage due to the beta decay, particularly when TGA analysis showed only about a 32 wt% loss instead of the theoretical 44 wt% from $Pm_2(C_2O_3)_3 \cdot 3 H_2O$. (The tri-hydrate was determined by TGA analysis and confirmed independently on different samples with different apparatus by both authors.)

Some newly prepared Pm oxalate was obtained and DTA and TGA were performed regularly over a period of several weeks. True $Pm_2(C_2O_4)_3 \cdot 3 H_2O$ exists only for a few hours after gentle drying of the precipitate. Fig. 3 shows DTA and TGA results for material which was dried at about 50°C to constant weight (about two hours) in the apparatus. Analysis of the TGA results show, by calculating back from the Pm_2O_3 which is obtained at about 660°C, that the starting material was very nearly $Pm_2(C_2O_4)_3 \cdot 3 H_2O$ and that $Pm_2(C_2O_4)_3$ and $Pm_2O_2CO_3$ are intermediate decomposition products.

The DTA for this material also shows the expected oxalate exothermic reaction, although it is at a higher temperature than expected from the results on samarium oxalate.

Fig. 4 shows the results on this same material four days later. This material, however, had been dried at 50°C for about 48 hours. It is difficult to tell how much of the change is due to excessive drying and how much to radiolytic damage. Since the DTA and TGA runs during the next few days did not show extensive change it can probably be assumed that the effect was primarily due to the drying treatment.

The longer term effect of the radiolytic damage is shown in the DTA results in Fig. 5. The endotherm due to water remains approximately the same at about 120°C while the oxalate exotherm at about 580°C decreases in magnitude. An additional endotherm appears in the vicinity of 655°C which appears to be due to the decomposition of the $Pm_2O_2CO_3$. This is supported by results shown in Figs. 6 and 7. From Fig. 6 it is readily apparent that a carbonate decomposition which occurs at about 815°C in a CO_2 atmosphere is probably the same as that which occurs at 655°C in air. The calculations performed on the data shown in Fig. 7 indicate that the compound $Pm_2O_2CO_3$ is quite stable in CO_2 up to 815°C where it decomposes readily to Pm_2O_3 + CO_2.

It should be pointed out that this material had been held in a vacuum dessicator for about 18 hours before the DTA and TGA were performed. This treatment is sufficient to remove all water, including the chemically combined water. The fact that the chemically combined water normally comes off at about 120°C would seem to indicate that this water is not very tightly bound in the lattice.

Fig. 8 shows a series of TGA results obtained over a period of 978 hours (approximately 41 days) starting with freshly precipitated promethium oxalate. The first curve is for one-day old material which had been air dried only and so contained excess water. The formula for this material calculates out to be $Pm_2(C_2O_4)_3 \cdot 10 H_2O$. The results obtained at 120 and 264 hours were for material dried at 50°C for 48 hours and show the more usual 3 moles of water. They also illustrate the fact that the sample is no longer pure oxalate and that $Pm_2O_2CO_3$ appears to be an intermediate product. The sample analyzed at 978 hours had been air dried only since precipitation and in addition to the 3 moles of water indicates the presence of stable $Pm_2O_2CO_3$.

In some cases, calculating back from the Pm_2O_3 indicates that the starting weight is not sufficient to be $Pm_2(C_2O_4)_3 \cdot 3 H_2O$ or even just $Pm_2(C_2O_4)_3$. This shows that the starting material must have had a lower average molecular weight than the oxalate. For example, for the 978-hour run, if the starting material had been $Pm_2(C_2O_4)_3 \cdot 3 H_2O$, we should have had a sample weight of 23.62 mg (to give 13.2 mg of Pm_2O_3) instead of 20.25 mg. For 20.25 mg to result in 13.2 mg of Pm_2O_3 the average molecular weight must have been 525 instead of 612. This would indicate a mixture of 62 wt% $Pm_2(C_2O_4)_3 \cdot 3 H_2O$ and 38 wt% $Pm_2O_2CO_3$.

That such a conversion can take place is evidenced to some extent by the information shown in Fig. 9. This material was analyzed about 600 hours after precipitation and drying; however, it appears to be nearly $Pm_2(C_2O_4)_3 \cdot 3 H_2O$. It had been kept in a sealed container since drying, while the material analyzed for Fig. 8 had been periodically opened to remove a sample. The conversion of the oxalate to an oxy-carbonate follows the reaction

$$Pm_2(C_2O_4)_3 + \frac{3}{2} O_2 \xrightarrow{\beta} Pm_2O_2CO_3 + 5 CO_2 \uparrow$$

As the partial pressure of CO_2 in the container increases it follows that the reaction is going to be retarded and hence very little of the oxalate will be converted.

Summary

1. The normal hydrated oxalate of promethium has the formula $Pm_2(C_2O_4)_3 \cdot 3 H_2O$ although up to 10 H_2O may be present in undried material.

2. The oxalate decomposes at about 520°C as shown by TGA although the exothermic reaction does not show up until about 585°C by DTA.

3. $Pm_2O_2CO_3$ is a stable intermediate compound which decomposes endothermically at about 660°C.

4. Radiolytic decay of ^{147}Pm to ^{147}Sm causes partial decomposition of the promethium oxalate to an oxy-carbonate ($Pm_2O_2CO_3$). This effect is much more pronounced in a dry sample than a wet one.

References

1. W. W. Wendlandt, et. al., J. Inorg. Nucl. Chem., 273, 280 (1961).

2. S. L. Blum and E. A. Maquire, Amer. Cer. Soc. Bull., 39, 310 (1960).

HALF LIFE	**2.6 YEARS**
WATTS/GM	**0.33**
COMPOUND FORM	Pm_2O_3
WATTS/GM-COMPOUND	**0.27**
DENSITY	**6.6 GM/CC**
POWER DENSITY-COMPOUND	**1.8 W/CC**
TYPE OF RADIATION	β
SHIELDING	**MINOR-1" LEAD FOR 1Kw SOURCE**

Fig. 1   Radioisotopic characteristics of promethium-147.

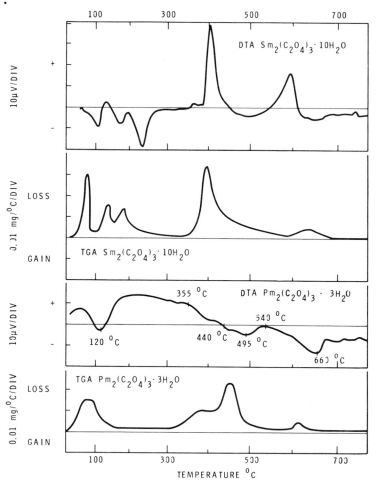

Fig. 2   DTA and TGA of samarium and promethium oxalates.

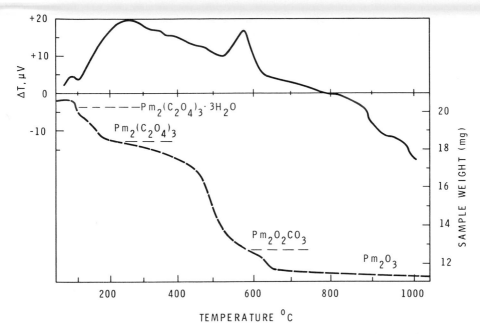

Fig. 3   DTA and TGA of freshly precipitated and dried
$Pm_2(C_2O_4)_3 \cdot 3 H_2O$.

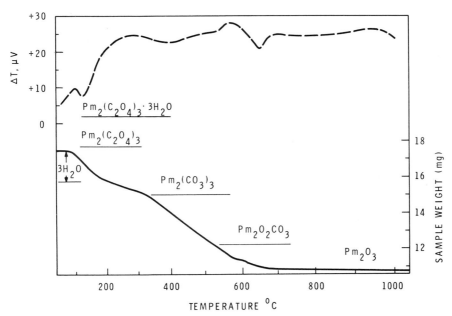

Fig. 4   DTA and TGA of promethium oxalate four days
after preparation.

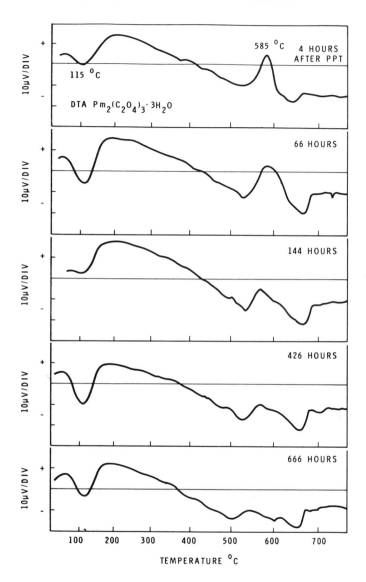

Fig. 5   Effect of time on promethium oxalate as shown by DTA.

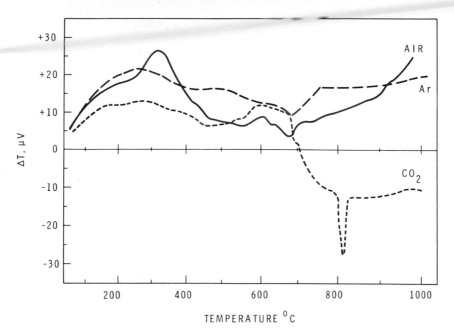

Fig. 6   Effect of atmosphere on DTA of vacuum dried
promethium oxalate 500 hours after preparation.

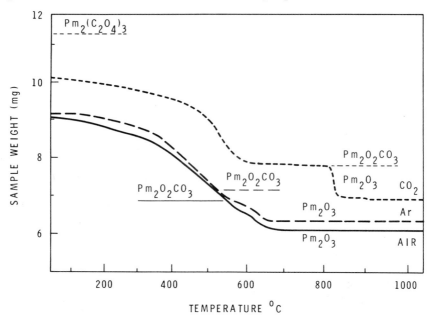

Fig. 7   Effect of atmosphere on TGA of vacuum dried
promethium oxalate 500 hours after preparation.

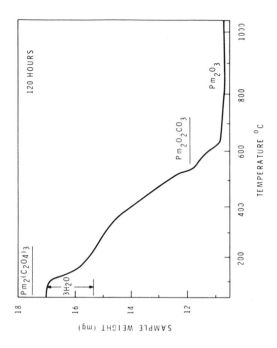

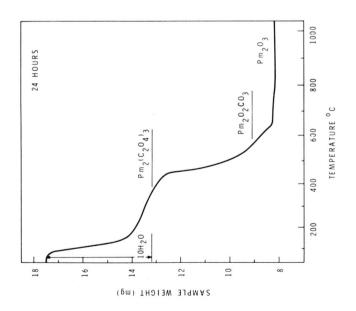

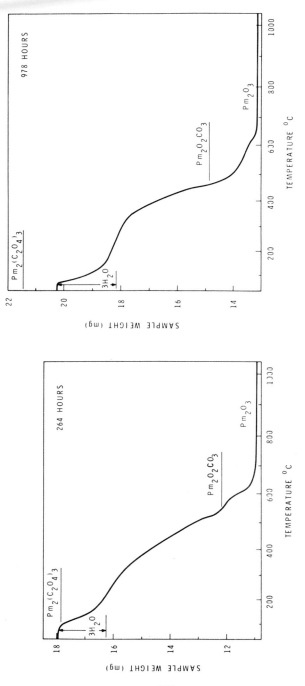

Fig. 8   Effect of time on promethium oxalate as shown by TGA.

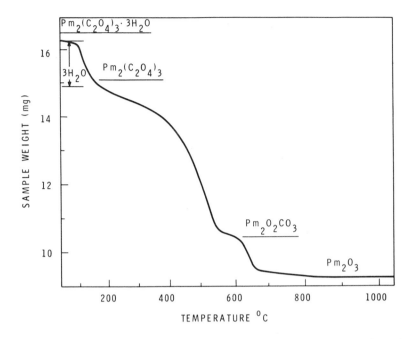

Fig. 9   TGA of promethium oxalate stored in air-tight container for 600 hours.

THE THERMAL DECOMPOSITION OF POTASSIUM OXALATO COMPLEXES OF NICKEL, COBALT AND COPPER

D. Broadbent, D. Dollimore and J. Dollimore

Department of Chemistry and Applied Chemistry

and

Department of Pure and Applied Physics

University of Salford, Salford 5, Lancashire, England.

Abstract

Details are given of the preparation of the potassium oxalato complexes of nickel, cobalt and copper. The nickel and cobalt salts had the general formula $K_2M(C_2O_4)_2 6H_2O$ whilst the copper salt was $K_2Cu(C_2O_4)_2 2H_2O$. The nickel complex lost water in both air and nitrogen over the range $60°-200°$, the anhydrous salt being stable up to $320°$. The complex breaks down above $320°$, and a stable residue is formed about $400°$. This residue is K_2CO_3 and NiO in air, and K_2CO_3 and Ni in nitrogen. At about $800°$ the potassium carbonate begins to decompose to K_2O, but the carbonate is still present at $1000°$. The decomposition of the cobalt complex is similar but there is some evidence that the breakdown of the anhydrous complex is a two-stage process. Dehydration of the potassium copper oxalate takes place in the region $120°-180°$ in a single stage. The anhydrous material is stable up to $300°$. Decomposition in air gives a weight loss to just beyond the level expected for the formation of a $CuO + K_2CO_3$ mixture, but a slight gain in weight just after decomposition gives a total weight change about 1% below the theoretical figure. At $1000°$ the residue is a K_2O-CuO mixture. In nitrogen, the complex breaks down at about $250°$ to give a mixture $K_2C_2O_4$ and elemental copper.

Introduction

The studies reported in this paper form part of a general investigation into the thermal decomposition of complex oxalates. The thermal decomposition of the oxalate complexes of iron, and of aluminium and titanyl are reported elsewhere (1,2). A comprehensive review of the chemistry of the metal oxalato complexes if given by Krishnamurty and Harris (3). Attention has been given in some studies to the trivalent cobalt oxalato complexes which reveal a change in the valency state of the cobalt during decomposition (4,5). The simple oxalates of nickel, cobalt, and copper have been extensively studied, and their thermal decomposition reported (6,7). These studies showed the importance of the gaseous environment in affecting the course of the decomposition. Some oxalates which gave endothermic decomposition reactions in nitrogen gave exothermic decomposition in air or oxygen. The reason for this was twofold, firstly some decomposition products in nitrogen were immediately oxidised in air, e.g. nickel metal to the oxide, or MnO to Mn_2O_3; secondly, oxide products served as catalyst surfaces for the exothermic reactions,

$$CO + O_2 \rightarrow CO_2 \text{ or } C + O_2 \rightarrow CO_2$$

The complex oxalates studied in this investigation are of the general formula

$K_2M(C_2O_4)_2 xH_2O$, where M is Ni, Co or Cu and x is 6 for Ni and Co and 2 for Cu.

The study is characterised by the special attention which is given to the effect of the surrounding gaseous environment upon the decomposition.

Experimental

Thermogravimetric Analysis (TG)

The TG results were obtained on a modified Stanton thermobalance type H.4. In each experiment 0.5 g. of sample was used in a platinum crucible. Results were corrected for buoyancy. The temperature rise was $4^{\circ}C/Min.$ although in some cases this was reduced to $2^{\circ}C/Min.$ The flow of gas was downwards at a nominal rate of 50 ml/min. The gases used were air, nitrogen and carbon dioxide, all previously dried. The last traces of oxygen were removed from the nitrogen and carbon dioxide. A thermocouple was used positioned immediately above the sample to measure the temperature.

Differential Thermal Analysis (DTA)

The apparatus used was a Netzsch differential thermal analyser modified to give results on a potentiometric recorder. The sample consisted of 0.8 g. of a 10% w/w mixture of the oxysalt in alumina that had been heat treated at 1250°C, the reference being 0.8 g. of the same alumina. A heating rate of 5°C/Min. was used. The samples were decomposed in flowing atmospheres of air, nitrogen and carbon dioxide, treated as described for the TG apparatus and at the same flow rate.

X-Ray Powder Diffraction

The preparation of residues for x-ray or chemical analysis was undertaken on the Stanton thermobalance since the exact weight loss from the material was known. Under an atmosphere of nitrogen the procedure involved cooling the sample to room temperature while still under the nitrogen atmosphere. X-ray analysis of all the residues was carried out with either a Newton-Victor generator and a Unicam 9 cm. powder camera or a Phillips generator and a 11.48 cm. camera. In the case of the cobalt salts, the evacuated unicam camera was used with a cobalt target, in the other salts the target was copper. The constituent compounds of a particular residue were identified either by direct comparison with a photograph of a standard material or by comparing the data with that from the A.S.T.M. powder data file.

Chemical Analysis

The oxalate content of the original complexes and of the residues was determined in all cases. This combined with the TG data was sufficient to assess the purity of the original materials and to characterise the residues. Additional carbonate and alkali content determinations were carried out on residues when deemed necessary.

Preparation and Characterisation

The potassium complexes of nickel and cobalt were prepared by adding the single oxalate slowly to a hot concentrated solution of potassium oxalate until no more would dissolve. The excess was filtered off and the filtrate cooled overnight. The nickel complex crystall-ised from solution as dark turquoise crystals, and the cobalt complex as deep magenta crystals. Both these products soon became coated with a thin opaque layer on drying, due to surface dehydration.

The potassium copper oxalate was prepared according

741

to the method suggested by Bailar and Jones (8), in which 12.5 g. of copper sulphate pentahydrate dissolved in 25 ml. of water at 90° was added rapidly with vigorous stirring to a solution of 36.8 g. of potassium oxalate monohydrate in 100 ml. water also at 90°. The resulting solution was cooled to 10°, the precipitate filtered off and rapidly washed with 25 ml. of cold water. This precipitate was then dried at 50° for 12 hours. The complex is formed as dark blue crystals, which decomposed to copper oxalate in warm water.

The thermal analysis of potassium nickel and potassium cobalt oxalates indicated that these complexes contained six molecules of water of crystallization per molecule giving 24.5% weight loss for the nickel salt (theor. 25.66%) and 25.6% for the cobalt salt (theor. 25.60%), corresponding to the known formulae for these salts of $K_2M(C_2O_4)_2.6H_2O$, where M = Ni or Co. Chemical analysis for oxalate content gave 42.81% (theor. 41.82%) for the nickel salt and 41.67% (theor. 41.79%) for the cobalt salt. Potassium copper oxalate was found to contain 10.2% water (theor. 10.18%), and 48.55% oxalate content (theor. 49.75%) corresponding to the formula $K_2Cu(C_2O_4)_2.2H_2O$. X-Ray powder diffraction patterns were obtained for each complex, and this served to identify these materials when present in residues from thermal decomposition. In the original hydrated complex samples no diffraction lines could be detected for free potassium oxalate or the respective single oxalates.

The x-ray diffraction data for the three complexes, are given in Table 1.

RESULTS

Thermogravimetric Analysis and X-Ray Powder
Diffraction Data.

The thermogravimetric analysis of potassium nickel oxalate in air and in nitrogen is given in Figures 1 and 2. The complex begins to lose water at 60° in both air or nitrogen, and water is continuously evolved up to 200°, the anhydrous salt being stable up to 320°. Above this temperature breakdown of the complex begins and a stable residue is formed at 400°. The weight loss data in air shows this residue is a mixture of potassium carbonate with nickel oxide, whilst in nitrogen it consists of potassium carbonate and nickel, and this was confirmed by x-ray powder photographs. About 800° the potassium carbonate began to decompose but the theoretical figure for the formation of K_2O and NiO in air or K_2O and Ni in nitrogen was not attained. X-ray powder photographs of samples obtained at 1000° still indicates the presence of potassium carbonate as well as the metal or its oxide.

The thermogravimetric analysis of potassium cobalt oxalate hydrate in air and nitrogen are shown in figures 3 and 4. The decomposition is similar to the nickel complex. Water is lost above 60° and the anhydrous material is stable up to 280° in air. In nitrogen an inflexion occurs in the dehydration curve at a weight loss of 21.5% corresponding to a loss of five molecules of water of crystallization, and the anhydrous material is stable up to 340°. At 280° in air the anhydrous complex breaks down and a stable residue is formed above 430°. The decomposition curve shows an inflexion at about 360° indicating that the complex breaks down by at least a two stage process. This two stage process is again evident when decomposition occurs in nitrogen, in this case a stable residue is formed at 480°.

Further decomposition set in above 650° with continued weight loss up to 1000°, this probably being potassium carbonate decomposition. Five samples of the residue from thermal decomposition were prepared, the results are summarized in Table 2, and each residue contained a mixture of compounds, each component was clearly resolved. This shows good agreement with the TG data.

The TG plots for potassium copper oxalate dihydrate in air and in nitrogen are given in Figures 5 and 6. In air single stage dehydration takes place between 120°-180° and the anhydrous material is stable up to 300°. The complex then breaks down and decomposition proceeds to just beyond the level expected for the formation of a copper oxide-potassium carbonate mixture. However, the material gains weight slightly soon after the completion of the decomposition (at about 350°) and the net weight change is about 1% below the expected level. The potassium carbonate formed starts to decompose slowly at 800° and continues up to 1000° the final weight lost corresponding to the formation of a K_2O-CuO mixture. In a nitrogen atmosphere the

743

anhydrous complex breaks down at 250° giving an inclined plateau corresponding to the formation of a mixture of potassium oxalate and elemental copper.   This mixture loses weight rapidly at 350° and a stable residue is formed at 41.2% weight loss corresponding to a mixture of potassium carbonate and copper.   The carbonate starts to decompose at 750°, but the theoretical weight loss for the formation of K_2O and copper is not attained.   The TG in carbon dioxide was determined since slight differences occurred between the DTA curve in nitrogen and CO_2.   The only difference in the latter atmosphere was that final decomposition of the potassium carbonate did not start until the temperature was almost 1000°.

The x-ray results from selected samples confirmed the TG findings.   A sample prepared at 600° in air gave a diffraction pattern corresponding to a mixture of cupric oxide and potassium carbonate.   Samples prepared at 300° and 600° in nitrogen corresponded respectively to a mixture of copper and potassium oxalate, plus a trace of carbonate, and to a mixture of copper and potassium carbonate.   All the samples prepared were well crystallised and the components easily identified by direct comparison of the x-ray films with the standard patterns.

Differential Thermal Analysis

The DTA data for all these complex salts in nitrogen and air, and for the copper salt additionally in carbon dioxide is given in Figures 7, 8 and 9.   DTA data (Differential Thermal Analysis) is also given as the results show how the peaks in the DTA closely correspond to the weight changes observed on the TG apparatus.

The results show that the endothermic dehydration of the copper salt is a single stage process with a ΔT_{min} at 120° but the nickel and cobalt complexes dehydrate in a number of stages.   The broad endothermic peak in the case of the nickel complex shows for minima in air at 85°, 100°, 120° and 140°.   A similar trace is obtained for the cobalt complex dehydration peak.   This has three ΔT_{min} at 75°, 110° and 150°.   The main oxalate decomposition reaction of the nickel salt gives a large exothermic peak with ΔT_{max} at 350° in air and as two smaller endothermic peaks with ΔT_{min} at 350° and 380° in nitrogen.   For the cobalt salt

744

the decomposition reaction produces two exothermic peaks in air with ΔT_{max} at 310° and 370°, while in nitrogen a broad endothermic peak occurs of two overlapping peaks with ΔT_{min} at 365° and 385°. These results show that the main oxalate decomposition consists of at least a two stage process.

The decomposition of anhydrous potassium copper oxalate in air produces a single exothermic peak with ΔT_{max} at 290°C. In nitrogen a broad endothermic peak with ΔT_{min} at 380° appears, followed at 448° by a small exothermic peak. A comparison of the DTA and the DTG graphs shows that the initial decomposition reaction with a maximum rate at 270° produces no peak of any kind on the DTA graph at or about this temperature. Dollimore and Griffiths (7) have shown that the corresponding DTA trace for copper oxalate is exothermic in nitrogen, this is not observed for any other single oxalate with the exception of the oxalates of mercury and silver. It is possible, then, that when potassium copper oxalate breaks down, copper oxalate may be an intermediate product which breaks down immediately to copper — the two stages (endothermic for the first and exothermic for the second) being thermally balanced. The DTA in CO_2 show only small deviations from that under nitrogen. Two endothermic peaks are observed with ΔT_{min} at 370° and 415° instead of the broad single peak at 380°. In nearly all the DTA traces an endothermic hump appears about 900°, this being either the melting of potassium carbonate, its decomposition, or both.

DISCUSSION

The Dehydration and Configuration of Complex Oxalates

In the case of the complex oxalates considered here, there are three possible ways in which the water of crystallization can be held. It can be bonded to the metal ion, attached to the oxalate ion or it may be held as lattice or crystal water. Thermal analysis data can indicate the possible manner in which the water is held, for if the water is bonded to the metal, then dehydration might be accompanied by decomposition of the oxalate ion. The DTA data of the complex oxalates investigated in this paper together with similar data in the single oxalates previously reported (7) are summarized in Table 3. It is noticeable that the DTA shows dehydration is an endothermic reaction occurring in a series of stages not apparent by an inspection of the TG curves.

The data in Table 3 indicates that in the complex oxalates the water is less firmly held than in the corresponding single oxalate. In most single oxalates the water is usually evolved in a single well defined stage. In their investigation of nickel oxalate dihydrate Jacobs and Kureishy (9) consider that the water utilises Ni^{2+} orbitals (presumably the vacant 4S orbitals) for bonding. These orbitals are required to receive electrons from the oxalate ions in the thermal decomposition of the anhydrous oxalate. Hence dehydration must precede decomposition even though the water is bonded to the metal ion. It should be pointed out that when the dehydration of the divalent metal oxalate complexes occurs at a relatively high temperature (as is the case in Co, N, and possibly Cu studied here), then the complex is known to possess some partial ionic character. It is possible that in these cases the water is attached by a coordinate bond to the central metal ion and this is removed before the oxalate (held by ionic bonding) decomposes. Their behaviour in this respect is similar to the single oxalates.

The complexes of nickel and cobalt each crystallise with six molecules of water and reference to their x-ray diffraction data (Table I) shows that many of the x-ray "d" values for the two salts are similar, thus suggesting isomorphism. Both salts dehydrate in a number of stages though these are not resolved by thermogravimetry except in the case of the last molecule of water in the cobalt complex Both the nickel and the cobalt oxalato hydrates are paramagnetic, the nickel being blue green in colour and the cobalt deep pink or magenta, suggesting an octahedral configuration for both complexes. In this case two water molecules would be placed one below the plane containing the metal atom and the two chelated oxalates. The rest of the water would be taken up as lattice water, although each of these would be in different structural environments requiring different thermal dissociation energies. In the cobalt complex, dehydration would probably be followed by a change from octahedral (pink) to tetrahedral (blue) configuration since the square planar arrangement is unlikely in cobalt (II) complexes with three unpaired electrons, (10,11). This is supported by the deep blue-violet colour of the anhydrous salt. The retention of only one water molecule

746

is, however, difficult to explain on these lines. The
nickel complex on the other hand shows no colour change on
dehydration, and a mechanism at first seems possible whereby the water is lost from the coordination sphere leaving
the planar 4-coordinating anhydrous complex which only in
the case of a strong ligand field will be diamagnetic and
of a different colour (yellow-red) (12). However, it is
probable that molecular association could result in the
planar structure becoming effectively octahedral.

The complex oxalate of copper (II) contains two molecules of water of crystallization which are lost in a single
stage indicating that both molecules are equally bound.
Cotton and Wilkinson (13) suggest that the copper salt has
the two water molecules situated above and below the plane
containing the copper ion and the two oxalate ions as in
the case of the nickel salt. Graddon (14) also supports
the view that the salt is essentially an inner complex
with $3d4s4p^2$ hybridisation. It should also be noted that
the dehydration of the oxalate complex of cobalt (II) and
nickel (II) causes no significant change in their infrared absorption spectrum (14).

Thermal Decomposition of the Anhydrous Oxalato Complexes

TG data indicates that all three oxalato complexes
studied in this paper existed as stable anhydrous complexes.
Table 4 summarizes the DTA data on the decomposition of
these anhydrous complexes and the corresponding simple
oxalates. It is appreciated that these temperatures do
not represent the true thermodynamic decomposition
temperatures, but they are adequate for the purposes of
comparison. Reference to Table 4 shows that the formation of a complex oxalato compound does not affect the
thermal stability of the oxalate radical. There is, in
fact, a slight decrease in stability. The decomposition
temperatures quoted for the complex oxalates follow the
same trend as those for the simple oxalates, in this case,
Co^{2+}, Ni^{2+} and then Cu^{2+} in order of decreasing stability.
From this it could be postulated that the factors which
affect the stability of simple oxalates also play a large
part in the stabilities of the complex materials. The
differences in decomposition temperatures could be due to
the differences in the ionic character of the metal
oxalate bond brought about by complx formation. There is

no evidence from this investigation to suggest that differences arise due to differences in configuration of the anhydrous complex.

The anhydrous complexes considered decompose as if they were mixtures of the simple metal oxalate and potassium oxalate, the initial products of decomposition containing some free potassium oxalate. This supports the view that pure covalent bonds between the metal and oxalate groups are not always formed, since then, thermal decomposition would involve a breakdown of the oxalate group to carbon dioxide and carbon monoxide (or just to carbon dioxide) without the formation of the oxalate ion.

The factors which decide whether the free metal or its oxide is formed apply equally to the decomposition of simple and complex oxalates. Dollimore, Griffiths and Nicholson (6) consider the decomposition of simple oxalates from thermodynamic considerations, and point out that it is possible to decide whether in an inert atmosphere at a particular temperature, an oxalate will decompose to the metal or to an oxide. This will depend on the relative values of the free energies of formation of the metal oxides and of the free energy of formation of carbon dioxide from the oxidation of carbon monoxide at the temperature of the decomposition. Thus they have demonstrated that the oxalates of copper, nickel, lead, cobalt and cadmium will yield metal on thermal decomposition, whereas zinc, chromium, manganese and aluminium will always form oxides. Dollimore et al also point out that in the oxalates of the divalent metals, the extent to which the M-O bond is covalent depends on the electronegativity of the metal. Decomposition will occur when a temperature is reached at which rupture of the M-O link is possible, or at which rupture of the C-O bond nearest the metal occurs. Fujita and co-workers (15) from infra-red studies on the complexes of Cu (II), Co (II) and Ni (II) suggested that as the M-O bond comes stronger the adjacent, C-O bond becomes longer and exhibits a lower stretching frequency, and this has been correlated by them with the observed stability order. This however refers to the stability in solution and not the thermal stability in the solid state.

Ephraim (16,17) has reported an extensive series of studies of the decomposition temperatures of polyhalides and of ammine complexes of the transition elements. His interpretations arising from these studies led to several generalizations concerning thermal stabilities of complexes. For example, he states that if a metal ion of an ammine complex may exist in more than one oxidation state, the higher state corresponds to the more stable complex. Clearly this does not apply in the case of the oxalato complexes of iron and cobalt since in both cases the lower (II) valency state is formed when these solid complexes decompose. Ephraim also states that the divalent metal complexes of small ionic volume are more stable than those of larger ionic volume. The hexammines of divalent manganese, cobalt, nickel and iron follow the relationship $(VT)^{1/3} = $ constant where V is the ionic volume and T the absolute temperature for the decomposition; such a relationship does not hold for the corresponding oxalato complexes.

There are indications (18,19) that the mechanisms of thermal decomposition of some complex oxalates in the solid state and in solution are similar to the mechanisms of photodecomposition in solution. The irradiation, for example, of solutions of the ions $Cu(C_2O_4)_2^{2-}$ with ultraviolet light results in the production of metallic copper (20).

It has been demonstrated by Dollimore and Griffiths (7) that the decomposition of the simple oxalates of nickel and cobalt are endothermic in nitrogen. Copper (II) oxalate in common with the oxalates of mercury and silver decomposes with an exothermic reaction and it is possible that this is associated with the auto-catalytic nature of their decomposition. The complex oxalates of nickel and cobalt also show an endothermic reaction, and as mentioned earlier the simplest explanation for the non-appearance of such a peak in the decomposition of the copper complex is to postulate the production of simple oxalate of copper as an intermediate. It is then possible that the exothermic breakdown of the copper oxalate, masks the endothermic decomposition of the copper complex. The exothermic nature of the decompositions in air in both the simple and complex oxalates is the result of the oxidation of the metal produced as the result of the decomposition by the oxygen in the air. It should be noted that in air, in all cases oxides NiO, Co_3O_4 and CuO are formed and there is no indication of complex oxide formation with potassium under the conditions of the experiments reported in this study.

References

1. D. Broadbent, D. Dollimore and J. Dollimore, J. Chem. Soc. A., 451, (1967).

2. D. Broadbent, D. Dollimore and J. Dollimore, The Analyst, in the press.

3. K.V. Krishnamurty and G.M. Harris, Chem. Revs., 61, 213, (1961).

4. W.W. Wendlandt, T.D. George and K.V. Krishnamurty, J. Inorg. Nucl. Chem., 21, 69, (1961).

5. W.W. Wendlandt and E.L. Simmons, J. Inorg. Nucl. Chem., 27, 2317, (1965).

6. D. Dollimore, D.L. Griffiths and D. Nicholson, J. Chem Soc., 2617, (1963).

7. D. Dollimore and D.L. Griffiths, Proc. of 1st Int. Congress of Thermal Analysis, Aberdeen, 126, (1965).

8. J.C. Bailar and E.M. Jones, Inorganic Synthesis, (ed. H.S. Booth), 1, 37, (1939) McGraw-Hill Book Co. Inc., N.Y.

9. P.W.M. Jacobs and A.R.T. Kureishy, Trans. Farad. Soc., 58, 551, (1962).

10. B.N. Figgis and R.S. Nyholm, J. Chem. Soc., 12, (1954).

11. R.S. Nyholm, Quart Rev., 7, 377, (1953).

12. R.H. Holm, J. Amer. Chem. Soc., 82, 5632, (1960).

13. F.A. Cotton and G. Wilkinson, Advanced Inorganic Chemistry, 758, (1962), Interscience Publishers.

14. D.P. Graddon, J. Inorg. Nucl. Chem., 3, 308, (1956).

15. J. Fujit, K. Nakamoto and M. Kobayashi, J. Phys. Chem. 61, 1014, (1957).

16. F. Ephraim, Ber., 36, 117, 1815, 1912, (1903), J. Phys Chem., 18, 513, (1912).

17. F. Ephraim and Wagner, Ber., 50, 1088, (1917).

18. A.W. Adamson, H. Ogata, J. Grossman and R. Newbury, J. Inorg. Nucl. Chem., 6, 319, (1958).

19. T.B. Copestake and N. Puri, Proc. Roy. Soc., A228, 252, (1955).

20. N.A. Bisikalova, Ukrain. Khim. Zhur., 17, 807, (1951).

TABLE 1

X-Ray Diffraction Data on Oxalato Complexes
of Nickel, Cobalt and Copper

$K_2Ni(C_2O_4)_2 6H_2O$		$K_2Co(C_2O_4)_2 6H_2O$		$K_2Cu(C_2O_4)_2 2H_2O$	
dÅ		dÅ		dÅ	
5.93	VS	5.96	VS	8.12	VS
5.14	VS	5.23	VS	6.85	VS
4.29	W	4.67	W	4.96	VS
3.569	W	4.31	W	4.84	VS
3.441	W	3.593	M	4.61	W
2.907	M	3.197	M	4.37	W
2.793	VS	2.939	S	4.17	W
2.620	W	2.789	S	4.06	W
2.553	VS	2.639	M	3.951	W
2.454	W	2.577	VS	3.801	W
2.377	W	2.471	W	3.591	W
2.243	W	2.380	W	3.467	W
2.212	W	2.247	W	3.329	W
2.140	W	2.156	W	3.284	W
2.061	M	2.075	M	3.194	M
1.965	W	1.888	W	2.954	M
1.927	W	1.800	W	2.894	VS
1.890	W	1.735	W	2.780	W
1.867	W			2.702	W
1.794	M			2.667	W
1.762	W			2.501	M
1.744	W			2.389	M
1.723	W			2.368	M
				1.973	M
				1.902	M

VS - Very strong
M - Medium
S - Strong
W - Weak

TABLE 2

Potassium Cobalt Oxalate: X-Ray Examination of Residues

Conditions		% Wt. Loss	X-Ray Findings
230°	Air	25.6	Anhydrous complex only
335°	Air	32.2	Anhydrous complex only
540°	Air	48.5	Co_3O_4 + K_2CO_3
400°	N_2	49.0	Co + $K_2C_2O_4$
600°	N_2	52.5	Co + K_2CO_3

TABLE 3

Dehydration Data and Structure of Oxalato Complexes

Containing Co, Ni and Cu

Complex	ΔT_{min} in Endothermic Dehydration Peak °C		Colour of Complex		Probable Configuration	
	Complex Oxalate	Single Oxalate	Hydrate	Anhydrous	Hydrate	Anhydrous
$K_2Co(C_2O_4)_2 6H_2O$	75,110,150 (50)	195	Deep Pink	Deep Blue	Dist. oct.	Tetrahedral
$K_2Ni(C_2O_4)_2 6H_2O$	85,100,120,140 (60)	250	Green	Green	Dist. oct.	Dist planar
$K_2Cu(C_2O_4)_2 2H_2O$	120 (90)	-	Blue	Blue	Dist. oct.	Planar

N.B. (1), The figures in brackets are the temperatures at which dehydration could just be detected from weight loss curves.

(2) The data for the single oxalates is taken from Dollimore and Griffiths[7].

TABLE 4

Thermal Decomposition of Complex Oxalates of Co, N and Cu

Complex	Atomic No.	No. of 3d Electrons Total	Unpaired	Probable Configuration	Decomposition Temperatures in Nitrogen		Products of Initial Decomposition in N_2
					Complex	Simple	
Co^{2+}	27	7	3	Tetrahedral	365	375	Co, $K_2C_2O_4$
Ni^{2+}	28	8	2	Dist.Octahedral or planar	350	355	Ni, K_2CO_3
Cu^{2+}	29	9	1	planar	270	280	Cu, $K_2C_2O_4$

Data for single oxalates taken from Dollimore and Griffiths[7].

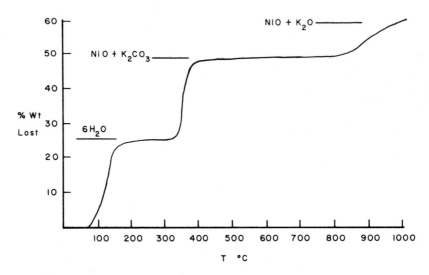

Fig. 1. Thermogravimetric Analysis of Potassium
Nickel Oxalate Hexahydrate in Air

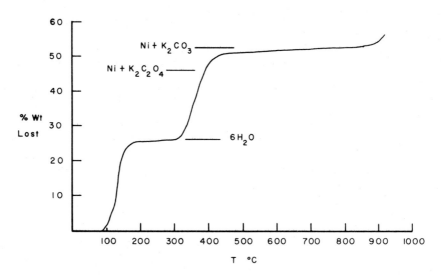

Fig. 2. Thermogravimetric Analysis of Potassium
Nickel Oxalate Hexahydrate in Nitrogen

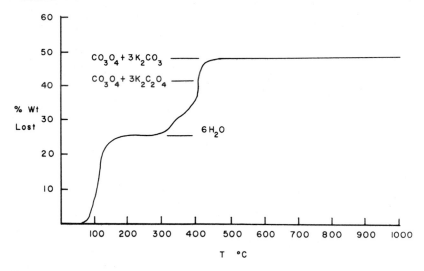

Fig. 3.　Thermogravimetric Analysis of Potassium
Cobalt Oxalate Hexahydrate in Air

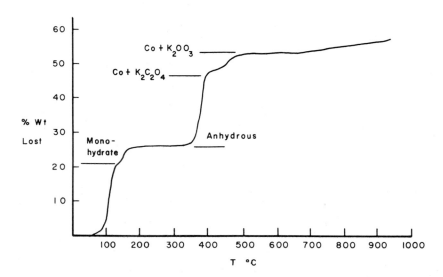

Fig. 4.　Thermogravimetric Analysis of Potassium
Cobalt Oxalate Hexahydrate in Nitrogen

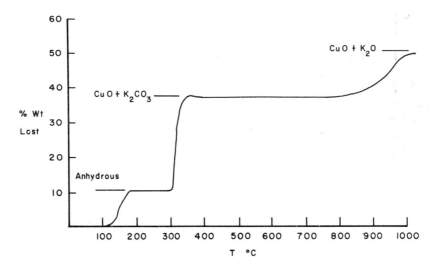

Fig. 5. Thermogravimetric Analysis of Potassium
Copper Oxalate Dihydrate in Air

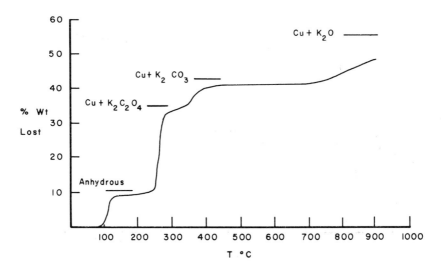

Fig. 6. Thermogravimetric Analysis of Potassium
Copper Oxalate Dihydrate in Nitrogen

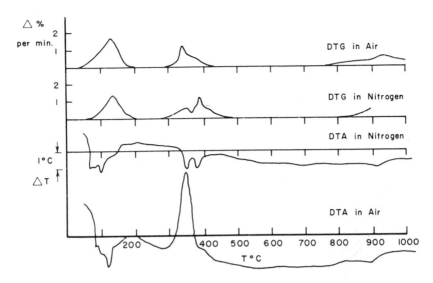

Fig. 7.   DTA and DTG for the Thermal Decomposition
          of Potassium Nickel Oxalate Hexahydrate.

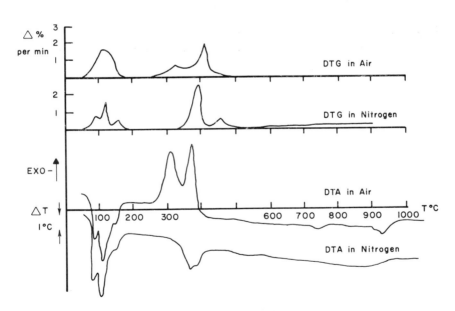

Fig. 8.   DTA and DTG for the Thermal Decomposition
          of Potassium Cobalt Oxalate Hexahydrate

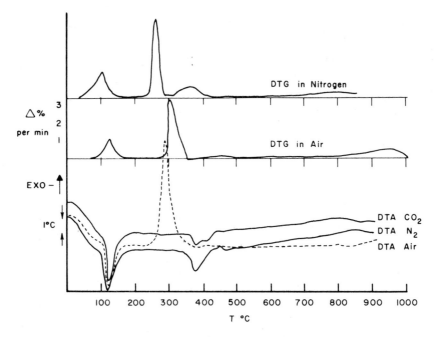

Fig. 9.   DTA and DTG for the Thermal Decomposition
of Potassium Copper Oxalate Dihydrate

DTA AND X-RAY ANALYSIS OF
"RARE EARTH - CHALCOGEN" SYSTEMS

E. I. Yarembash

The N. S. Kurnakov Institute of the USSR
Academy of Sciences (Moscow)

RE-chalcogenides of new types Me_4X_7, (Me_4X_9), Me_3X_7, Me_4Te_{11} (Me=La, Ce, Pr, Nd, Sm; X=Se, Te) have been synthesized. Some data about the structure of phase-diagrams "RE-X" systems were indicated. The possibilities of DTA method has been discussed.

Introduction

Progress of scientific knowledges and concepts about RE-chalcogenides is due to the work of scientists of many countries: W. Klemm, H. Vogel (Germany) (1); J. Flahaut, M. P. Pardo, L. Domange, M. Patrie, M. Picon, (France) (2); A. Jandelli (Italy) (3); H. Steinfink, J. Miller, Bro. F. Reid, S. Kurnick, M. Cutler, M. Houston, R. Vickery, H. Muir (USA) (4); G. V. Samsonov, W. P. Juze, N. C. Abrikosov, N. P. Lujnaja, W. G. Kusnetsov, A. A. Eliseev, W. A. Obolonchik, W. I. Marchenko, G. W. Lashekarev (USSR) (5) and others.

Papers of these scientists have been published and now are well known. They contain many interesting data about stoichiometry, crystal structures and some physical properties of RE chalcogenides. However, the descriptions of phase-diagrams of "RE - X" systems were until now absent. It hinders or makes practically impossible a consistent interpretation of the

results, obtained by measuring of physical properties because the real phase composition of
samples remained in many cases unknown. Unfortunately, until the present, most studies concerned RE chalcogenides of the types MeX, Me_3X_4
and Me_2X_3 only. But the total amount of
individual compounds in "RE-X" systems reaches
from 6 to 9. It should not be overlooked, that
16 RE elements in connection with 4 chalcogens
makes 64 binary systems. Thus the number of RE-
chalcogenides comes probably up to 300-400.

General Considerations

The main point of the work was the physical-
chemical study the binary systems "RE-chalcogen"
(R.E = La, Ce, Pr, Nd; X = Se, Te) with the purpose to establish the conditions of formation of
the chemical compounds and the solid solutions as
well as to investigate some physical properties
of them. The work was carrying out in the laboratory of semiconductors of N. S. Kurnakov
Institute. It have been used the following main
methods: Differential Thermal analysis, X-Ray
phase shift method, Microscopic and Chemical
analysis. The electro conductivity, thermal emf,
Hall effect, magnetic susceptibility etc. on the
compacted powder samples, alloys and single crystals of some compound obtained by transfer reactions have been measured. All samples were synthesized directly from elements of a purity 99.5-
99.8% (RE) and ~ 99.99% (Se and Te). In the most
cases the data of experiments were well reproducible. The measuring errors were in full
accordance with common practice.

The basic types of chemical compounds detected in "RE-S", "RE-SE" and "RE-Te" systems are
shown in Table 1. The total number of basic
types of compounds increases from the systems
"RE-S" to the "RE-Te". It reaches in "RE-Te"
systems in total 9-10. This fact suggests that
in Te-systems besides pure ionic chemical bonds
should manifest the covalence bonds. It can be
supposed the formation of them is due of acceptor

capacity of practically empty f- and d-orbitals
of light RE atoms. The organization of covalence
bonds results also from the value of effective
charges on RE atoms. It is apparent, that the
trend to establishment of reverse donor-acceptor
bonds "Me←X decreases with rise of ordinal numbers of RE elements. Likewise should be
decreased the number of the stable chemical compounds. Figures 1 and 2 give the phase diagrams
of Pr-Se and Pr-Te systems. The structures of
the phase diagrams of La-Se, Ce-Se, Pr-Se, Nd-Se
systems are similar. That can be pointed out in
the case of series. La-Te, Ce-Te, Pr-Te, Nd-Te.
But it should be emphasized, that in spite of the
common resemblance of Me-Se and Me-Te phase diagram systems, some structure's details of several
domaines (f.i. 50-67 at. X) are different. This
circumstance correlates with feature of crystal
structures of RE selenides and tellurides which
exist in the above pointed interval of concentrations. Considering the results of investigation
we concluded that the systems "RE-Se" and "RE-Te"
with light RE atoms could be classified in three
principal types (Fig. 3).

In series of the similar types of chalcogenides of light RE element (from La to Eu) the
domaines of homogeneity decrease owing to deficit
of chalcogen atoms. The individual character of
compounds Me X becomes clearer in series from La
to Eu. Compounds of Me X and Me X types form
continuose solid solutions. But in the case of
Nd-X and Sm-X systems the domaines of homogeneity
of solid solution $Me_{3-y} X_4$ is not extended up to
Me_2X_3 (that is: $y < 0.33$). The whole amount of
crystal modification of Me X compounds decreases
(for the same RE metal) in series S, Se, Te, but
increases (in case of the same chalcogen) in
series from La to Eu Re-elements.

Polytellurides of RE elements have the com-
mon formula: Me_4X_7, MeX_2, (Me_4X_9), Me_3X_7, Me_2X_5,
Me_4X_{11} and MeX_3. They are crystallized in layer

structures and can be regarded as a kind of
"polytypes". However this case of polymorphism
is caused not only by periodic disturbance of
packing arrangements of layers, but it is also
due to the insignificant change of composition of
matter. It is interesting to note that RE iones
in RE polychalcogenides possess the valency
"3+". Chalcogenides of Sm and Eu can be considered as an exception. This conclusion was
drawn on the basis of the results of magnetic
susceptibility measurements (in collaboration
with V. I. Chechernikov) and the data obtained by
the study of L_{III} - X-Ray absorption spectra
(with E. E. Vaĭnstein) Some data about crystal
structures and physical properties of chalcogenides Me X and Me X (Me = La, Ce, Pr, Nd) are
shown in table 2. On account of these data and
the results obtained by study of temperature
dependence of electroconductivity can be concluded that Me_3X_4 are semi-metals, all Me_2X_3 are
semi-conductors. Chalcogenides of La X type are
superconductors (f-i, for $La_3Se_4T_c \approx 7.9$ °K).
The examination of crystal structures data and
physical properties permits to note that the
majority of RE chalcogenides exists in form of
phases of variable composition. DTA method is of
a great importance for establishment the ranges
of concentration of this nonstoichiometric compounds. It is well known that DTA-method permits
to estimate the values of calorific effects
caused by phase transitions. DTA method is a
great importance for quick-finding the optimal
conditions of synthesis of RE chalcogenides
directly from elements. Fig. 4 shown the heating
curves of stoichiometric mixture "Pr+Te"; it can
be noted the different stages of Pr_2Te_3
synthesis. The curve "d" corresponds to equilibrium sample. In this work DTA method was used
also to study gas-transfer-reactions utilized
for RE chalcogenides crystal growing. Fig. 5
shows single crystals of certain selenides and
tellurides of RE elements. They can be produced
by using of different kinds of transfer matters
(I_2, Br_2, NH_4 Cl....). The chemical reactions

occuring between the parent compound and transfer
matter are very complicated. For instance, in
system of "$Pr_2 Se_3 + I_2$" takes place a multistage
reaction; there are many secondary and side
reactions:

$Pr_2Se_3 + 3I_2 \rightleftarrows OrU_3 + 3/2\ I_2$

$Pr_2Se_3 + I_2 \rightleftarrows PrSeI + \frac{1}{2}Se_2$

$PrI_3 + Se_2 \rightleftarrows PrSe_2 + 3/2I_2$

$PrI + Se_2 \qquad PrSe_2 + \frac{1}{2}I_2$

$Pr_2Se_3 \qquad \rightleftarrows PrSe + PrSe_2$

$PrI_3 \qquad \rightleftarrows PrI + I_2\ (or:\ PrI_3 \rightleftarrows PrI_2 + \frac{1}{2}I_2)$

$2Pr_2Se_3 \qquad \rightleftarrows Pr_3Se_4 + PrSe_2$ etc.

It is clear, that the use of mass-spectrometrical
and optical methods for study the quality of gas-
phase requests usually a lot of time. The
measurements of gas-phase pressure is also connected with difficulties. But the use of DTA-
method, in complex with X-Ray "Microscope" technique and Chemical analysis can help to get
express-information about the nature of different
phases and the possibility of existence of a
reversible reaction. In that way it can be found
the optimal conditions for transfer-reaction.
The small dimensions of obtained crystals do not
prevent its study by DTA-method. Fig. 6 shows
the heating curve of $PrSe_{1.9}$ single crystal
(weight about 20 mg). It can be suggested, that
the use of DTA method for study of single crystals
gives some new information about some properties
of substances.

In conclusion it must be pointed out that at
present there are two tendencies in use of DTA.
The first one - DTA equipment bears resemblance
with the equipment for calorimetry, it gives in
many cases just the same precision. The second
one is the aspiration to use DTA as an express-
method to establish of phase transitions (an
indicator of the change of physical state).

The both tendencies in development of DTA method probably are equal. That becomes especially clear by regarding DTA - designs and records, constructed in different corporations: Bureau of unique designs of USSR, Perkin-Elmer Corporation, Mettler, Xerox Corp., VEB Electro Bad Frank and others. It is to be underlined that the application of assembly of different methods for measuring some physical properties in step with DTA-method will extend its possibilities.

TABLE I

Types of Chemical Compounds in "RE-Chalcogen" Systems

M - S	M - Se	M - Te
MS	MSe	MTe
M_3S_4	M_3Se_4	M_3Te_4
(M_5S_7)	-	
Me_2S_3	M_2Se_3	M_2Te_3
-	M_4Se_7	M_4Te_7
MeS_2	MSe_2	MTe_2
-	-	(M_4Te_9)
-	Me_3Se_7	M_3Te_7
-	-	M_2Te_5
-	-	M_4Te_{11}
-	-	MTe_3

TABLE II

Some Physical Properties of La, Cl, Pr, Nd
Chalcogenides of Me_3X_4 and Me_2X_3 Types

	a Å (1)	Melt Point °C	om^{-1} cm^{-1}	mcV.deg^{-1}	10^2 Watt· cm^{-1}d^{-1}	10^6 CGSM
La$_3$S$_4$(2)	8,730	2100	4,16	207;354	0.67	$7,1 \cdot 10^{-1}$
La$_3$Se$_4$	9,048	1850	3.10^1	10 – 40	0.57	$-6,9 \cdot 10^{-1}$
La$_3$Te$_4$	9,621	1525	10^{-1}	20 – 30	–	$-0,68 \cdot 10^{-1}$
Cl$_3$S$_4$(2)	8,623	2100	10^2-10^3	–	–	–
Cl$_3$Se$_4$(2)	8,973	1800	–	–	–	2310
Cl$_3$Te$_4$	9,542	1645	66	40	8.5	2150
Pr$_3$S$_4$(2)	8,611	2100	–	–	–	–
Pr$_3$Se$_4$	8,881	1800	$0.7 \cdot 10^3$	30	2.4	5370
Pr$_3$Te$_4$	9,482	1700	$0,3 \cdot 10^3$	20 – 40	1.1	5150
Nd$_3$S$_4$(2)	8,524	2040	–	–	–	–
Nd$_3$Se$_4$	8,879	1750	–	–	–	5800
Nd$_3$Te$_4$	9,430	1650	$0,1 \cdot 10^3$	40	8.6	5600

(1) Structure Type Th$_3$P$_4$ (2) Other Authors

(3) Incongruent Melting

TABLE II
(Continued)

	a Å	Melt Point °C	om⁻¹ cm⁻¹	McV.d⁻¹	10^2 Watt. cm⁻¹ d⁻¹	E eV
La$_2$S$_3$(2)	8,723	1915	$2 \cdot 10^{-6}$	11,68	0,57	2.26
La$_2$Se$_3$	9,045	1650(3)	10^{-1}	–	–	1.5
La$_2$Te$_3$	9,619	1450	$2 \cdot 10^{-1}$	80–100	0,7	0.67
Ce$_2$S$_3$(2)	8,635	2060	10^{-10}	–	–	2.24
Ce$_2$Se$_3$	8,973	1750	10^{-6}	–	–	–
Ce$_2$Te$_3$	9,530	1560(3)	$7 \cdot 10^{-2}$	320	3,8	0.57
Pr$_2$S$_3$(2)	8,611	1795	–	–	–	2.20
Pr$_2$Se$_3$	8,895	1570	$9 \cdot 10^{-7}$	300	0,3	2.0–2.4
Pr$_2$Te$_3$	9,482	1500(3)	$10^1 - 10^2$	40–100	0,7	0.7
Nd$_2$S$_3$(2)	8,527	2010	–	–	–	2.12
Nd$_2$Se$_3$	8,871	1650	10^{-6}	–	0,9	2.2–2.4
Nd$_2$Te$_3$	9,421	1550(3)	$0.5 \cdot 10^{-2}$	140	7,7	0.6

(1) Structure Type Th$_3$P$_4$ (2) Other Authors

(3) Incongruent Melting

References

1. W. Klemm, K. Meisel, H. Vogel. ZS. an. allg. Chem., _190_, 123 (1930)
2. I. Flahaut, L. Domange, M. Patrie. Bull. Soc. Chim. France, pp. 159, 2048 (1952)
M. P. Pardo, I. Flahaut, L. Domange, Compt. Rend., _256_, 953, 1793 (1963)
M. Guittard, J. Flahaut, L. Domange. Compt. rend., _256_, 427 (1963)
M. P. Pardo Theses de Doct. Paris 1963
3. A. Iandelli. Gazz. Chim. Ital. _85_, 881 (1959)
A. Iandelli. Rare Earth Research. Ed. by E. V. Kleber. M. Milan Comp. 1961
4. W. L. Cox, H. Steinfink, W. F. Bradled. Inorg. Chemistry. _5_, 318 (1966)
F. L. Carter, R. C. Miller, F. M. Ryan. Advanced Energy Conversion _1_, 165, 175 (1961)
S. W. Kurnick, M. R. Merriam, R. L. Fitzpatrick, ibid. (p. 157)
R. C. Vickery, H. M. Muir. Nature _190_, 4773, 336-7 (1961)
J. F. Miller, F. J. Reid, R. C. Himes. J. Electrochem. Soc., _106_, 1043 (1959)
W. Lin, H. Steinfink, E. J. Weiss. Inorg. Chemistry, _4_, 9, 1462 (1965)
T. H. Ramsey, H. Steinfink, E. J. Weiss. Inorg. Chemistry, _4_, 8, 1154 (1965)
M. D. Houston, Rare Earth Research. Ed. by Kleber E. V. MacMillan Co. N.Y. 1961
P. Bro. J. Electrochem. Soc., _109_, N 8, 750, 1110 (1962)
5. B. V. Samsonov and S. V. Radzikovskaya, Advances in Chemistry _30_, No. 1, 60 (1961)
S. V. Radzikovskaya and V. I. Narchenko, "Sulfides, Rare Earth Metals, and Actinides", Abstracts of the USSR Academy of Learning, Kiev 1966.

V. A. Obolonchik and G. V. Lasinkaryov,
"Selenuim and Tellurite Rare Earth Metals
and Actinides", Ibid.

V. P. Zhuze, A. V. Golubkov, E. Y., Goncharova,
and V. M. Sergeyeva, Abstracts, 257, Ibid.
1964

G. V. Lashkarev and U. B. Paderno, Inorganic
Materials, 1462 (1965)

E. I. Yarembash, E. S. Vigileva, A. A.
Yeliseyev and V. I. Kalitin, Abstracts AN
USSR, Sulfur Physics 28, 1306 (1964)

E. I. Yarembash, A. A. Yeliseyev, K. A.
Zinchenko, AN USSR, Inorganic Materials 60
(1965)

E. I. Yarembash, E. S. Vigilyeva, A. A.
Yeliseyev, A. A. Reshchikova, Abstracts AN
USSR, Inorganic Materials 330 (1965)

A. A. Yeliseyev, E. I. Yarembash, V. G.
Kuznetzov et al, Abstracts AN USSR, Inorganic
Materials 2, 1027 (1965)

E. I. Yarembash, Chemistry Congress, UPAC,
Thesis D-60, 1965

V. I. Kalitin, E. I. Yarembash, Abstracts AN
USSR, Inorganic Materials, 2165 (1965)

N. P. Luzhnaya, E. I. Yarembash, Z. S.
Medvedyeva, Herald AN USSR No. 10 (1965)

E. I. Yarembash, A. A. Yeliseyev, V. I.
Kalitin, L. I. Antonova, Abstracts AN USSR,
Inorganic Materials 2, 95A (1966)

V. I. Kalitin, E. I. Yarembash, N. P. Luzhnaya, Abstracts AN USSR, Inorganic Materials, 2, 1930 (1966)

K. A. Zinchenko, N. P. Luzhnaya, E. I. Yarembash, A. A. Yediseyev, Abstracts AN USSR, Inorganic Materials, 2, 1747 (1966)

K. A. Zinchenko, E. I. Yarembash, A. A. Yeliseyev, N. P. Lyzhnaya, L. D. Chernayev, Abstracts AN USSR, Inorganic Materials 3, 29 (1967)

I. C. Lisker, B. E. Malkovich, V. I. Kalitin, Abstracts AN USSR, Inorganic Materials 3, 753 (1967)

V. I. Chukalin, E. I. Yarembash, A. I. Vilenski, Abstracts AN USSR, Inorganic Materials 3, 1538 (1967)

E. I. Yarembash, A. A. Yeliseyeb, E. S. Vigilyeva, L. I. Antonova, Abstracts AN USSR, Inorganic Materials 2184 (1967)

E. E. Vonstain, M. N. Brill, I. V. Starri, E. I. Yarembash, Abstracts AN USSR, Inorganic Materials 3, 1685 (1967)

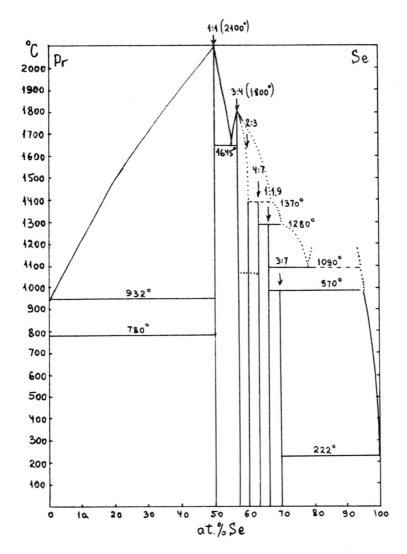

Fig. 1. Phase Diagram of Pr-Se System

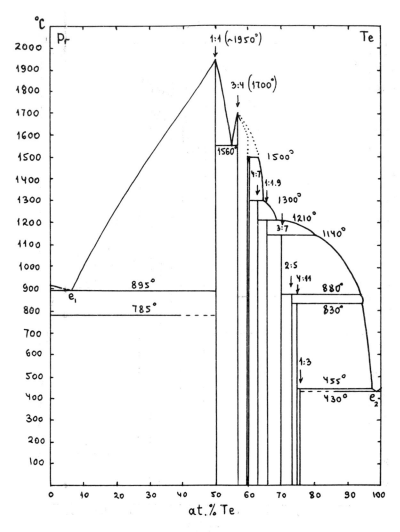

Fig. 2. Phase Diagram of Pr-Te System

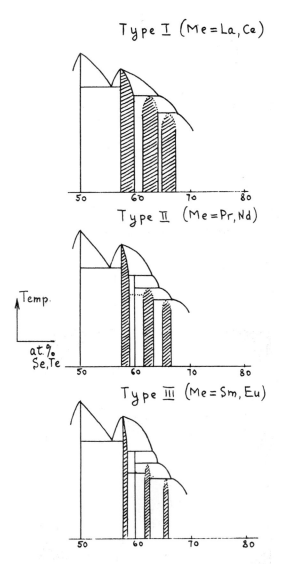

Fig. 3.   Types of "RE-Chalc." Systems

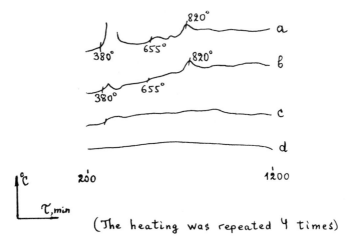

(The heating was repeated 4 times)

Fig. 4. DTA of Pr + Te (2:3) Mixture

Fig. 5. $LaTe_2 \cdot La_4Te_7$ Single Crystals
(Magnification - 18X)

776

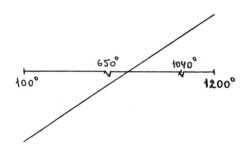

Fig. 6.   DTA of PrSe$_{1,9}$ Single Crystal (20 mg)

THERMOGRAPHIC STUDY OF THE STRUCTURES OF SOME SIMPLE , MIXED AND BINUCLEAR CHELATES OF EDTA

A.V.Nikolaev, V.A.Logvinenko, L.I.Myachina

Institute of Inorganic Chemistry, Siberian Department of Academy of Sciences of the USSR, Novosibirsk-90, USSR

In our studies it has been shown, that the dissolution of some oxalates and carbonates in aqueous solutions of polyamino-polycarboxylic acids (complexones) is accompanied by the production of mixed complexes. The metal cation in these complexes co-ordinates both the ligand of complexone and the carbonate-(or oxalate-)group. The mixed carbonate-ethylenedinitrilotetraacetates of magnesium, calcium and lanthanum and the corresponding simple chelates have been synthesized, all of them as sodium salts:

$$Na_4MgTCO_3 \cdot 4H_2O , Na_4CaTCO_3 \cdot 3,5H_2O ,$$

$$Na_3LaTCO_3 \cdot 4H_2O , Na_2MgT \cdot 4H_2O , Na_2CaT \cdot 3,5H_2O ,$$

$NaLaT \cdot 3H_2O$ (where T^{-4} is an anion of ethylenedinitrilotetraacetic acid, EDTA).

Formerly the mixed chelates of EDTA were studied only in solution, the description of the syntheses for such compounds are not numerous. No investigations of the structure of the co-ordination sphere and the "chelation number" of ligands[x] were almost carried out.

The simple chelates of magnesium, calcium and lanthanum were synthesized by the well-known procedures (1-2). The mixed carbonate-chelates were isolated by the crystallization of the com-

[x] A quadridentate ligand has a chelation number of four, etc.

pounds while evaporating the water from the solutions, containing equimolecular quantities of
the simple chelates and sodium carbonate. The
carbonate-group in mixed chelates is monodenta-
te according to the infra-red spectra. The remainder details of the structure (a nature of
the water binding and a chelation number of complexone) were determined in terms of thermal
properties of the compounds.

The water in crystalline hydrates may be
considered either as the crystal, or as co-ordination that. The strength of binding of these
molecules in the crystal lattice is different,
that results in various dehydration temperatures. The structure of the first co-ordination
sphere of chelates can be judged by the light-
ness of the water elimination. So as to obtain
some generalisations we have dealt with the results of the certain studies on the dehydration
of the chelates having known crystal structure
(under non-isothermal conditions at a speed from
6 to $9^{\circ}C$ per minute). The elimination of crystal
water proceeds at temperatures from $60^{\circ}C$ to
$170^{\circ}C$ (cobaltic chelate), the elimination of co-
ordinatively linked water – at $200^{\circ}C$ (cupric che
late), at $300^{\circ}C$ (nickelous chelate) and from
$100^{\circ}C$ to $210^{\circ}C$ (lanthanum chelate) (2-5).

Thus, the water loss at temperature $200^{\circ}C$ and
above is certain to point to its co-ordination
by the metal atom. The water, eliminating at
$150^{\circ}C$ and below can be considered as the crystal
that. But the water, eliminating at intermediate
temperatures, evidently can be co-ordinatively
linked water as well as the crystal one. The
strength of binding of the latter can rise by
the occurrence of evolved hydrogen bonds.

In co-ordination of the additional ligand
(carbonate-group) the chelation number of complexone can decrease. There are following possibilities for its determination in an independent way. In the work by T.R.Bhat on the thermal analysis of chelates the specific regula-
rity in their decomposition has been found. The
decomposition of the unhydrous chelate to the

780

metal carbonates in two steps acknowledges the complexone to be quadridentate (namely, two carboxylate groups are not co-ordinated). If the transition to the carbonates takes place with one weight loss stage, the ligand will be sexidentate or quinquedentate (4).

From our data the simple chelates of magnesium and calcium are completely dehydrated from $100^\circ C$ to $130^\circ C$, the unhydrous chelates are stable up to $350^\circ C$ and are decomposed through one weight loss stage to carbonates /fig.1/. The dehydration of the calcium-chelate is succeeded by melting in the crystal water and transition to the poly-chelate.

The carbonate-chelate of magnesium, Na_4MgTCO_3. $4H_2O$, is dehydrated stepwise, losing one molecule of water at $90-140^\circ C$, two molecules of water at $140-200^\circ C$ and the last molecule at $200-250^\circ C$ /fig.2/. The endothermal effects at $140^\circ C$, $160^\circ C$ and $250^\circ C$ conform with this dehydration. The anhydrous compound is stable up to $338^\circ C$. The loss of weight at $595^\circ C$ agrees with the transition to magnesium and sodium carbonates, the decomposition to carbonates occuring by two stages ($338-507^\circ C$ and $507-595^\circ C$). The further loss of weight is related to the dissociation of the magnesium carbonate.

The mixed calcium chelate, $Na_4CaTCO_3 \cdot 3,5H_2O$, loses one molecule and a half of water at $100-190^\circ C$ and two molecules of water - at $190-295^\circ C$ (endothermal effects at $147^\circ C$ and $260^\circ C$). The uhhydrous complex is stable up to $320^\circ C$, the decomposition to the calcium and sodium carbonates proceeds through two weight loss stages ($320-510^\circ C$ and $510-830^\circ C$, - fig.3).

According to the regularities of the dehydration and thermal decomposition, being discussed above, the studied complexes must be assigned the following structure: The ligand is sexidentate and all the water is crystal in simple chelates. The EDTA is quadridentate, two co-ordination position are occupied by one molecule of

781

water and carbonate-group in mixed magnesium chelate. In mixed calcium chelate the EDTA is quadridentate, two molecules of water and one carbonate-group occupy three co-ordination position. The co-ordination number seven is possible for calcium.J.L.Hoard, in particular, has found the polyhedron of calcium with seven apexes in calcium salt of cyclohexylenedinitrilotetraacetato-ferrate (6).

Just the same consideration of the data on the thermal decomposition of lanthanum chelate doesn't give unumbiguous results. Three molecules of water of the simple lanthanum chelate are eliminating within 120–250°C /fig.4/. The unhydrous complex is stable up to 350°C, within the interval 350–520°C the decomposition to La_2O_3.CO and Na_2CO_3 takes place at once (as calculated from the loss of weight). The transition to lanthanum oxide takes place at 750°C. As far as the simple lanthanum chelate is decomposed through one weight loss stage, the ligand is sexidentate According to the structure of the lanthanum chelates octahydrates, described by J.L.Hoard (7), the lanthanum is considered to co-ordinate three molecules of water and to have the co-ordination number being equal to nine. But not very high eliminating temperature of the three water molecules (120–250°C) leads one to turn to the additional confirmation of their co-ordinative nature in trihydrate. There is such a confirmation. The dehydrated lanthanum chelate is x-ray-amorphous, small non-isotropic table-form particles (with refractive index N=1,570±0,005) are observed in microscope. The preparation of the x-ray-amorphous product explains the non-zeolite character of water binding, its co-ordination by the lanthanum atoms. In such a case the dehydrated ionic net is unstable and re-groups to form the amorphous substance.

In accordance with the results of the conformation analysis (8–9) the ligand of EDTA is known to be unable to give undistorted octahed-

ron of the donor atoms around the lanthanide cation because of the unsufficient flexibility of
the hydrocarbonic chain. Six donor atoms of ligand in the lanthanum chelate octahydrate occu-
pies not more than a half of the co-ordination
sphere around the lanthanum atom (7). There is
no information about the change of the co-ordination polyhedron during the dehydration. The
x-ray-structural investigation of the structure
of the unhydrous amorphous lanthanum chelate has
been carried out by us together with G.S.Jur'ev.
The intensity curve is taken in x-ray diffractometer with Cu-radiation. The effect of the divergence of the x-ray beam and Kompton dispersion are taken into account in calculations, the
corrections for polarization and the standardization are made. The radial distribution curve
of the atoms is estimated on a computer. There
was made the comparison of the areas under the
maxima of the radial distribution curve, measured and calculated in terms of the supposed model, as to settle the question of the structure.
The general conclusion is so that the amorphous
lanthanum chelate consists of dimeric molecules,
and the length of the bond La - O is somewhat
decreased in comparison with that in the crystalline hydrate. After dehydration two ligands
seems to be bound simultaneously with two central atoms. Such a transformation in the structure of the complex may be accounted for significant structural role of water in the initial
crystalline hydrate.

The lanthanum carbonate-chelate, Na_3LaTCO_3.

$4H_2O$, begins to dehydrate at $60^{\circ}C$, the decomposition of the organic part occuring at once after the dehydration. The change in the rate of
the weight loss on this boundary is noticeable
in DTG-curve. The slow decomposition step is
succeeded by the fast one ($145-355^{\circ}C$ and $355-$
$-515^{\circ}C$). There is the noticeable field of the
existence of the lanthanum carbonate on the
weight loss curve ($515-540^{\circ}C$). The next decomposition steps are the transition to oxy-carbonate

and lanthanum oxide /fig.5/. The peculiar property for all the three mixed chelates of lanthanum, investigated by us - oxalate-ethylene-
dinitrilotetraacetate, oxalate-cyclohexylene-
dinitrilotetraacetate and concerned carbonate-
chelate,- is the formation of the lanthanum carbonate during the thermal decomposition. The
simple chelate decomposes at once to oxy-carbonate, $La_2O_3.CO$. Such a change of the nature of
the decomposition clearly indicates of the ente-
ry of the oxalate- and carbonate-groups into the
inner sphere of the complexes. The decomposition
of the lanthanum carbonate-chelate to the sodium
and lanthanum carbonates through two steps seems
to be in connection with the occurence of the
tetradentate ligand. This conclusion is borne
out by the great joining of proton of the complex in solution. The carbonate-group is mono-
dentate according to the data of the infra-red
spectroscopy. We have failed in examination of
the quantity of water, being co-ordinated by the
central atom.

The investigations of binuclear chelates of
EDTA are described in literature mainly by the
works of twenty years prescription. In those
works such compounds are described as simple
salts with non-co-ordinate structure. We have
synthesized two series of chelates, $Me_2T.nH_2O$
and $MgMeT.nH_2O$:

$Ba_2T.2,5H_2O$, $Sr_2T.5H_2O$, $Mg_2T.9H_2O$, $Ca_2T.7H_2O$,
$Mn_2T.9H_2O$, $Co_2T.7H_2O$, Zn_2T , $Cd_2T.4H_2O$,
$Pb_2T.H_2O$, $Cu_2T.5H_2O$;
$Mg_2T.9H_2O$, $MgCaT.9H_2O$, $MgMnT.9H_2O$,
$MgCoT.6H_2O$, $MgZnT.6H_2O$, $MgCdT.9H_2O$,
$MgPbT.9H_2O$, $MgCuT.6H_2O$.

The structures of complexes in solutions is
appreciated upon the relationship of the solubility in water from stability constants. The donor groups of the ligand seems to be uniformly

distributed between two cations in bimetallic chelates of zinc, lead, cadmium and copper. In remainder homogeneous chelates the ligand is binded with one cation much stronger than with another (by the greater number of donor atoms).

In general one should not expect the same analogies in the structure of the crystalline hydrates, so far as the change of the co-ordination sphere is possible in the crystallization. The infra-red spectra of compounds are very individual and not allow themselves to be divided by groups. But the significant spectrum-line splitting, associated to carboxylic group and to the bond $C - N$, indicates the distinct strength of the carboxylic groups binding in binuclear chelates, in comparison with Na-salts of chelates. We appreciate this as an evidence on the participation of the both cations in the co-ordination of the groups of a ligand. The tentative structural data for the series of binuclear chelates have got by N.N.Neronova together with us; all of them have a number of formula units in elementary cell being equal to four. The magnesium chelates have nearly the same cell parameters, the part of these chelates are isostructural.

The properties of all the synthesized chelates have been investigated. Only a part of all results is discussed here. Having such a series of the compounds we consider to try to appreciate the strength of binding of water molecules not only by the temperature intervals, but also by estimating the value of activation energy of the dehydration from kinetic data. The calculation have been made on the assumption, that the relationship of rate constant of the reaction from the temperature is described by the Arrenius equation under non-isothermal conditions. The resulting activation energy may be, naturally, the complex function of the activation energies of some individual stages of heterogeneous reactions. But this estimation is held to be true for this series of chelates. The method of calculation, proposed by H.H.Horowitz, G.Metzger,

T.V.Mesheryakova and N.D.Topor (10-11), has been
used. The temperature of the maximum rate of reaction have been determined upon the DTG-curve,
then the order of the reaction and the activation energy have been calculated.

All magnesium chelates lose the whole of water simultaneously, at the interval to $290^{\circ}C$.
In such a case it should be regarded that both
the crystal water and the water of co-ordination
sphere are lost simultaneously and bound with
the same strength. If the part of the water is
at the primary co-ordination sphere, it will be
eliminated together with the crystal water
/fig.6/. The activation energy of the dehydration of the crystal water and the water, co-ordinated by magnesium, lies within the limits of
11 - 20 kcal/mol in all series of the crystalline hydrates of magnesium chelates.

The magnesium-lead chelate differs in crys-
tall cell parameters from the other chelates and
seems to be non-isostructural to them. It is dehydrated stepwise. Three last molecules of water
are lost within $215-280^{\circ}C$, that pointed to their
co-ordination in the primary co-ordination sphere by the lead atom /fig.7/. The activation
energy of dehydration of these three water molecules is 30 kcal/mol.

The lead cation have very great radius($1,20\overset{o}{A}$),
 the incomplete co-ordination of groups of EDTA
is assumed to be in the Na-salt of lead chelate
because of the unsufficient flexibility of the
hydrocarbonic chain. In magnesium-lead chelate,
where the competition between two cations for
the donor groups takes place, more uniform distribution of the donor groups may be more advantageous in geometrical respect, than in the
other magnesium chelates.

We have determined the activation energy of
dehydration of differently bound water molecules in carbonate-chelates, mentioned above.
While losing the crystal water, the activation
energy lies within the limits of 15 - 20kcal/mol
The activation energy is 32 - 38 kcal/mol while
losing the water, which is believed to be co-

ordinately bounded. These values of the activation energy seem to be possible for the consideration of the nature of the water binding in distinct chelates - polynitrilo-polyacetates.

References

1. D.T.Sawyer, P.J.Paulsen, J. Amer. Chem.Soc.
   80, 1597, (1958).
2. G.Brunisholz, E.Vescovi, M.Loretan,
   Helv. Chim. Acta , 38, 1186 (1955).
3. M.L.Morris, J. Inorg. Nucl. Chem.
   20, 274 (1961).
4. T.R.Bhat, R.K.Jyer, J. Inorg. Nucl. Chem.
   29, 179 (1967).
5. R.G.Charles, J. Inorg. Nucl. Chem.
   28, 407 (1966).
6. G.H.Cohen, J.L.Hoard, J. Amer. Chem. Soc.
   88, 3228 (1966).
7. J.L.Hoard, B.Lee, M.D.Lind, J. Amer. Chem.
   Soc. 87, 1612 (1965).
8. T.Moeller, F.Moss, R.H.Marschall,
   J. Amer. Chem. Soc. 77, 3182 (1955).
9. D.Busch, J.Beilar. J. Amer. Chem. Soc.
   75, 4574 (1953).
10. H.H.Horowitz, G.Metzger, Analyt. Chem.
    1963, N 10, 1464 .
11. T.V.Mesheryakova, N.D.Topor, Vestnik
    MGU, Seriya Him. 1967, N 3 , 73.

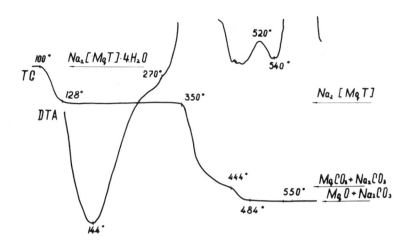

Fig.1: Thermograms for the decomposition of
$Na_2[MgT].4H_2O$ in air; the weight of the
sample — 1000 mg., a heating rate 6°C/min.

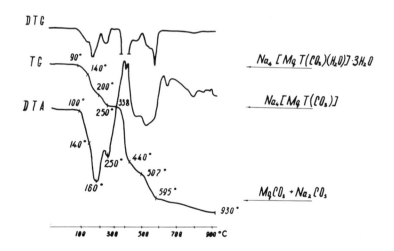

Fig.2: Thermograms for the decomposition of
$Na_4[MgT(CO_3)(H_2O)].3H_2O$ in air; the
weight of the sample — 733 mg., a heating
rate 6°/min.

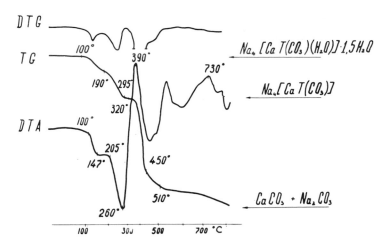

Fig.3: Thermograms for the decomposition of
$Na_4[CaT(CO_3)(H_2O)_2]\cdot 1,5H_2O$ in air; the
weight of the sample – 733 mg., a heating
rate 6°/min.

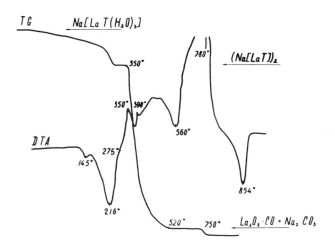

Fig.4: Thermograms for the decomposition of
$Na[LaT(H_2O)_3]$ in air; the weight of the
sample – 1000 mg., a heating rate $6^{\circ}C$/min.

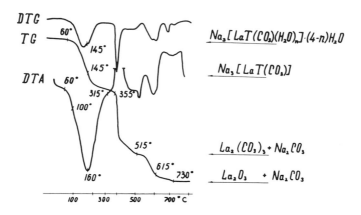

Fig.5: Thermograms for the decomposition of $Na_3[LaT(CO_3)(H_2O)_n].(4-n)H_2O$ in air; the weight of the sample - 733 mg., a heating rate $6°C/min$.

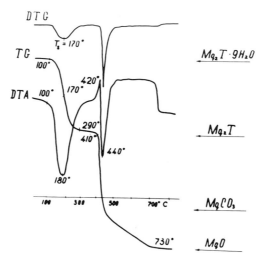

Fig.6: Thermograms for the decomposition of $Mg_2T.9H_2O$ in air; the weight of the sample - 600 mg., a heating rate $6°C/min$.

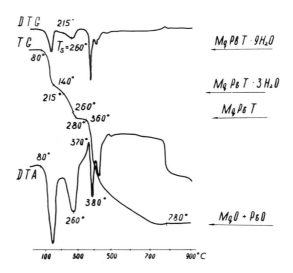

Fig.7: Thermograms for the decomposition of MgPbT.9H$_2$O in air; the weight of the sample – 700 mg., a heating rate 6°C/min.

THERMOGRAPHY AS A METHOD OF INORGANIC SYNTHESIS

A.V.Nikolaev, A.A.Opalovsky, V.E.Fedorov

Institute of Inorganic Chemistry
Siberian Division
USSR Academy of Sciences

The widespread use of thermography for solving a great variety of inorganic chemistry problems is well known,its efficacy and efficiency is now established and obviously needs no further confirmation or proof.We think that thermography holds especial promise in formulation of conditions necessary for synthesis of inorganic compounds, either previously known or new.The basic conditions in these cases frequently are the quantitative ratios of parent ingredients and the temperatures required to effect a certain reaction.

A thermographical investigation of the corresponding processes provides the most reliable and quickest way to determine these conditions.Yet this method is far from being frequently employed by chemists engaged in synthesis.In a number of cases this results in unwarranted complications inadequate and sometimes even plainly erroneous specifications for synthesis.

This paper summarizes experimental data on thermography obtained by the authors while developing methods to synthesize some simple and complex inorganic compounds.

A simple,widely employed and rather accurate method for synthesis of binary compounds envolves direct interaction of the elements.For example, most intermetallic compounds are obtained in this way.Thoroughly mixed elements are heated either in an evacuated sealed vessel or in an inert atmosphere until the desired reaction is fully completed.This stage is often followed by a prolonged thermal treatment to homogenize the compound thus obtained (sometimes the mixture is repeatedly fired after a second grinding).

Simple as these reactions are, a critical analysis of data on conditions of synthesis of the intermetallide phases brings us to the conclusion that heat treatment techniques, cited in literature on the subject, are often completely unjustified. The best optimal conditions for synthesis may be obtained by a thermographical study of these reactions.

Table I presents data on conditions of synthesis of chalcogenides of molybdenum, tungsten and rhenium, as given by several authors. One is at once striken by the arbitrary choice of the thermal regimes. Synthesis of several different compounds is alleged to be effected under a single "typical" regime, though it is clear that there must be certain optimal conditions for production of each compound.

It seems to us that at least two parameters determine the heat regime for a synthesis: temperature of interaction of the elements on one side and temperature of decomposition of the compound being synthesized on the other side.

One can see from Table I that ditellurides of molybdenum, tungsten and rhenium are fiered at temperatures that are unreasonably high (1000-1200°), since, according to our investigations, $MoTe_2$, WTe_2 and $ReTe_2$ are thermally stable only up to 600°.

As an example which illustrates efficiency of the thermographic methods in similiar cases we will give an account of results obtained by the authors in the course of research on interaction processes between some transient metals and chalcogenes.

Thermographic data show considerable difference in interaction of pulverized molybdenum, tungsten and rhenium with sulfur, selenium and tellurium (Figs. 1 to 3). While reactions of the three metals with sulfur and selenium proceed very rapidly, tungsten and rhenium are oxidized by the molten tellurium rather slowly and only at high

794

temperatures, as testified by thermal effects, which are insignificant and greatly stretched out in time.

The following points from the results of thermal research on character of interaction between molybdenum, tungsten, or rhenium and chalcogenes seem to be of most interest. Firstly, it is evident that high temperatures at which interaction of metals with sulfur begins (570° for molybdenum, 400° for tungsten and 540° for rhenium) and great exothermic effect of these reactions creates a great pressure in sulfur vapours within the closed reaction volume. Secondly, the character of thermographic curves indicates that reactions between tungsten and rhenium and the molten tellurium, even at elevated temperatures (640° and 670°, respectively) proceed with considerable difficulty.

These conclusions, drawn from thermographical investigations of the above reactions, were fully confirmed by experiments made to synthetize these chalcogenides. It was found that synthesis of sulfides of molybdenum, tungsten and rhenium from pure elements could be successfully effected only with small quantities of these elements and only under a strictly-defined thermal regime. Synthesis of ditellurides of tungsten and rhenium takes place with such difficulty that even prolonged annealing of the W+2Te and Re+2Te mixtures, repeated grinding of the reacting mixture and repeated firings fail to bring the reaction to entire completion. This is disclosed by results of chemical and X-ray analysis, as well as by effects of the melting tellurium. The latter diminish, though do not disappear completely, and are recorded when the reaction products are subjected to a thermographical analysis (Fig.4).

This example also demonstrates efficiency of thermography when it is employed to check completeness of a reaction and to determine the time required for a synthesis. A thermographical investigation may also produce a definite conclusion on lack of efficiency of a given method of synthesis and the necessity to develop new means for production of a substance (or a group of substances) under study (as may be seen from example with WTe_2 and $ReTe_2$).

Among the methods for production of the lower states of oxidation (such as halides, oxides, chalcogenides) reactions of reduction or decomposition of the corresponding compounds in higher states of oxidation are used more frequently than others. In a rather limited selection of reducing agents hydrogen is the one used most widely, as action of the other reducers in majority of cases was not studied adequately. However, when hydrogen is used as a reducing agent, experimenter meets serious difficulties, because operating conditions must be maintained with very great accuracy. Even slight elevation of the temperature (coupled with prolonged action of hydrogen) or an increase in duration of the experiment results in reduction of the parent compound to metal or to a compound which belongs to a lower stage of oxidation than the one required. These remarks are equally true also for thermal decomposition of compounds, if their thermal stabilities do not differ substantially. All these factors make it very difficult to obtain final products in a pure form.

If parent substances or the products obtained are volatile at the reaction temperature, additional difficulties complicate the synthesis. Furthermore a great loss of materials occurs in such processes.

It seems to us, that the most effective and convenient method to obtain many halides and chalcogenides at the lower states of oxidation from viewpoints of purity of the product obtained and their yield is interaction of compounds of this metal at higher oxidation states with the proper metal in a closed reactor. Of course, when the compounds at lower states of oxidation are to be produced in this manner, a reaction may be conducted successfully in the desired direction only if their thermodynamical characteristics noticeably differ from those of the parent substance.

As it is necessary in all cases to maintain strictly the temperature regime, a prior thermographic investigation of these reactions assumes special importance.

A good illustration to this statement is the problem of synthesis of the lower halides of molybdenum.At present the most practicable method for synthesis of sufficiently pure molybdenum dichloride is believed to be the method of thermal decomposition of molybdenum trichloride in an inert atmosphere or in vacuum (12):

$$2 \text{ MoCl}_3 \text{ (solid)} = \text{MoCl}_2 \text{ (solid)} + \text{MoCl}_4 \text{ (gas)}$$

Data of a DTA have shown that in sustained vacuum of the order of 10^{-4} mm Hg MoCl$_3$ begins to disproportionate intensively at about 550°(Fig.5a). Molybdenum dichloride thus produced is thermally unstable and if heated further (640°,Fig.5a) quickly decomposes according to reaction:

$$2 \text{ MoCl}_2 \text{ (solid)} = \text{Mo (solid)} + \text{MoCl}_4 \text{ (gas)}$$

MoCl$_2$ thus obtained is usually somewhat contaminated by metallic molybdenum,because at temperatures at which MoCl$_3$ decomposition rate is adequate,the second reaction's rate also reaches a considerable magnitude.

Molybdenum trichloride is synthesized in most cases simply by interaction of molybdenum pentachloride with hydrogen.However,as we have noted above,this reduction process when conducted in hydrogen does not produce pure MoCl$_3$ and requires subsequent purification of the synthesized product.Obviously methods of synthesis that require subsequent operations (which are sometime rather coplicated,protracted and labour-consuming) to purify the resulting substance suffer a loss in attraction,even if they are simple,practicable, etc.

Besides,in the course of reactions of decomposition and reduction unavoidable heavy losses of parent materials occur,resulting in a very low yield.

In the light of the reasons stated above it is more convenient and safe to synthesize MoCl$_3$ and MoCl$_2$ by reactions:

$$3 \text{ MoCl}_5 + 2 \text{ Mo} = 5 \text{ MoCl}_3$$

$$2 \text{ MoCl}_5 + 3 \text{ Mo} = 5 \text{ MoCl}_2$$
$$2 \text{ MoCl}_3 + \text{ Mo} = 3 \text{ MoCl}_2$$

Interaction between molybdenum pentachloride and metallic molybdenum proceeds by stages (Fig.5,b,c).Firstly trichloride is obtained (exothermic effect at 220°),which then reacts with excess metal,forming molybdenum dichloride (exothermic effect at 680°).The synthesis of MoCl_3 and MoCl_2 is effected by heating a mixture of calculated quantities of the initial components (a slight excess of initial chloride is employed) in sealed quartz ampules at temperatures 30 to 50° above the point (as determined by thermography) at which these reactions begin.Upon completion of process the reaction product are subjected to thermal distillation in vacuum.The result is pure substances with yield of the final product at theoretical level and with practically 100% utilization of the parent materials(Table II).

We have studied interaction between molybdenum trichloride and molten chalcogenes.Reaction between MoCl_3 and sulfur or selenium at temperature about 400° results in formation of chlorchalcogenides of molybdenum,whose composition is $\text{Mo}_3\text{Cl}_4\text{X}_7$,where X=S or Se (Table III,1,4).If temperature of synthesis was above 550°,the final products are the corresponding dichalcogenides MoS_2 and MoSe_2 (Table III,2,5) because molybdenum chlorchalcogenides decompose when heated – $\text{Mo}_3\text{Cl}_4\text{S}_7$ at 530°, $\text{Mo}_3\text{Cl}_4\text{Se}_7$ at 450° (Fig.6,Ia,IIa) apparently according to scheme:

$$2 \text{ Mo}_3\text{Cl}_4\text{X}_7 = 6 \text{ MoX}_2 + \text{X}_2\text{Cl}_2 + 3 \text{ Cl}_2$$

The reduction process of these compounds by hydrogen is easily observed by thermography.This process proceeds in steps,with products of an indefinite nature and poor in chlorine forming first.On thermographs this process corresponds to endothermic effects at temperatures of 285° and 265° for $\text{Mo}_3\text{Cl}_4\text{S}_7$ and $\text{Mo}_3\text{Cl}_4\text{Se}_7$ respectively (Fig.6,Ib, IIb).A further drop in temperature

798

brings reduction to dichalcogenides,which correspond to exothermic effects at 330° and 290° for
chlorsulfide and chlorselenide respectively
(Fig.6,Ib, IIb; Table III,3,6).

One of the most intricate directions in synthetic chemistry is the development of methods for
obtaining compounds either simple or complex,
which under usual conditions are unstable substances easily decomposing in the air.Many halides belong to this class of substances,with fluorides
and fluorcomplexes of the transition elements.

Halogene complexes of transition metals are
often obtained by interaction of halides of these
metels with corresponding salts in a suitable solvent,sometimes with simultaneous reduction or oxidation in the solution itself.Another widely employed method for obtaining halide complexes is a
direct reaction of a corresponding halides with
salts in absence of a solvent.As a rule,such processes are effected by heating in closed reactors.
Thermographical investigations of such reactions,
for selection of the optimal regime for synthesis,
is indispensable because mere mixing of the reacting ingredients,in accordance with the exact
stoichiometric relatoinship,gives no assurance
that the product thus obtained is actually an individual compound,not a mixture of different pha-
ses.The experiment is much simplified when one of
the reacting substances – the one taken in excess-
may be easily removed after reaction (i.e. when
this substance is volatile or can be dissolved
off in a solvent which is neutral to the product
being obtained).

For example,a thermographical study of the interaction between $MoOF_4$ and MoO_3 (Fig.7,b) resulted in development of a new method for synthe-
sizing pure molybdenum dioxidifluoride MoO_2F_2 ,
which is easily produced by heating the ingredients to 180 – 200°.

Thermographic study of mixture of molybdenum
pentafluoride,hexafluoride and oxytetrafluoride
with fluorides of the alkali metals showed great
tendency of MoF_5, MoF_6 and $MoOF_4$ to form comp-

lexes.In this case fluor- and oxyfluor complexes of molybdenum are produced,which belong to type $MMoF_6$, $MMoF_7$ and $MMoOF_5$,where M= K,Rb,Cs.

All syntheses of fluor- and oxyfluor complexes of molybdenum are accomplished in evacuated and sealed ampules with volatile component being in slight excess,which is distilled off under vacuum when the reaction is completed.

However,interaction between substances cannot always be distinctly recognized from the heating curve alone.For example,reaction between MoF_4 and $MoOF_4$ because of a very slight thermal effect is but faintly recorded in the heating curve(Fig.8,a). Only repeated thermographic study of the reaction products provides an account of changes that occured in this system (Fig.8,b).Interaction between molybdenum tetrafluoride and molybdenum oxytetrafluoride may be described by equation:

$$MoF_4 + MoOF_4 = MoF_5 + MoOF_3$$

We confirmed it not only by chemical analysis and thermography /endothermal effect at 48° on the differential curve "b" (Fig.8) is due to melting of MoF_5/ but also by the EPR method.The latter showed that at temperatures above 170° spectral lines of Mo^V (which is absent in the parent mixture) appear in the spectrogram (Fig.9) due to occurence of the indicated reaction.

The obtained data made it possible to effect synthesis of a new molybdenum oxytrifluoride $MoOF_3$ in a sealed ampule,with temperature at about 200° for a period of 8 to 10 hours.

It is appropriate to mention here that a chemist may successfully employ thermography for solving a number of problems in inorganic synthesis: to control completeness of a reaction,identify the synthesized products,to determine purity of the substances obtained, etc.An advantage of such determinations (besides their objectivity,high sensitivity and speed) is due to the fact that they may be successfully conducted within a wide range of temperatures,either low (-150° and up) or extremely high,because no direct visual observation of the substance is required here. In certain cases these advantages make the thermographic method the only method available for a study of the heterogeneous processes.

Of course, comprehensive information in interaction of substances may be obtained only by a complete physical and chemical analysis of the corresponding systems. We have studied, using the thermal analysis method, the meltability diagram for system $MoF_5 - MoCl_5$ (Fig.10). Formation of four congruently melting new compounds, answering to MoF_4Cl, MoF_3Cl_2, MoF_2Cl_3, $MoFCl_4$ was established.

To conclude, it should be noted that the authors intentionally did not dwell extensively on chemical and physico-chemical identification of the substances being synthesized, because their first purpose was to emphasize the main factor - the role and importance of thermography in inorganic synthesis. Recognizing the exceptionally great role of the thermal analysis for inorganic synthesis, the authors, however, fully understand that this method, if used alone, is not sufficient to solve successfully the various experimental tasks that stand before a synthetics chemist. Only a harmonious combination of the different physico-chemical methods produces the maximum effect and brings a researcher to the goal along a certain and shortest route. Yet, the thermal analysis method should be the primary and basic method to be employed for synthesis of a number of inorganic compounds.

Acknowledgements

The authors would like to thank K.A.Khaldojanidy for the contribution of fluoride samples and the participation in the experimental work.

References

1. Ju.M.Ukrainskiy, A.V.Novoselova, Doklady Akad. Nauk SSSR, 139,1136 (1961)
2. L.H.Brixner, J.Inorg.Nucl.Chem. 24, 257(1962)

3.D.Puotinen, R.E.Newnham, Acta Cryst.14,691(1961)
4.O.Knop, D.Donald, Canad.J.Chem. 39,897(1961)
5.H.Guennoc, U.S.Dept.Com.,Office Tech.Serv.
          AD 265,121(1961)
6.W.T.Hick, J.Electrochem.Soc. 3,1058(1964)
7.I.A.Champion, Brit.Appl.Phys. 16,1035(1965)
8.R.Kershaw, Inorg.Chem. 6,1599(1957)
9.O.Knop, H.Haraldsen, Canad.J.Chem.34,1142(1956)
10.N.W.Alcock, A.Kjekshus, Acta Chem.Scand.
                19,79(1965)
11.S.Furuseth, A.Kjekshus, Acta Chem.Scand.
                20,245(1966)
12.T.T.Campbell, J.Electrochem.Soc.106,119(1959)

Table I

Conditions for synthesis of dichalcogenides
of molybdenum, tungsten and rhenium

Compound	Conditions for primary heat treatment		Conditions for homogenizing roasting		Literature
	$t, °C$	τ, hours	$t, °C$	τ, hours	
$MoSe_2$	700	100	–	–	1
	600–700	10–15	1100–1200	10–15	2
$MoTe_2$	600–700	10–15	1100–1200	10–15	2
	1100	5–10	–	–	3
	460	16	600	48	4
	600	2 days	–	–	5
WSe_2	600–700	10–15	1100–1200	10–15	2
	550	15	1000	–	6
	600–700	several days	–	–	7
	600	4 days	800	4 days	8
WTe_2	700–800	several hours	500	several days	9
	600–700	10–15	1100–1200	10–15	2
	600–700	several days	–	–	7
$ReSe_2$	700	100	–	–	1
	1000	2 days	700	20 days	10
$ReTe_2$	700	20 days	500–1100	–	11

Table II

The Lower Molybdenum Chlorides

Compound	Equation for reaction of synthesis	Conditions for synthesis		Chemical composition, % weight	
		t,°C	τ,hours	Mo	Cl
$MoCl_3$	$3MoCl_5 + 2Mo$	250–300	10–12	47,42	52,58
$MoCl_2$	$2MoCl_3 + Mo$	720	20–30	57,50	42,45
$MoCl_2$	$2MoCl_5 + 3Mo$	I firing 250–300 5 II firing 720 20–30		57,45	42,60

Calc.: $MoCl_3$ — Mo=47,42;   Cl=52,58

$MoCl_2$ — Mo=57,50;   Cl=42,50

Table III

Chemical Composition of Molybdenum Chlorchalcogenides and Products of Their Decomposition

		Chemical composition, % weight:					
		Calc.			Found		
No	Compound	Mo	Cl	S,Se	Mo	Cl	S,Se
1.	$Mo_3Cl_4S_7$	44,0	21,7	34,3	43,8	21,8	34,1
2.	MoS_2 (600°)	60,0	–	40,0	59,5	traces	39,6
3.	MoS_2 (H_2, 400°)	60,0	–	40,0	59,8	traces	40,2
4.	$Mo_3Cl_4Se_7$	29,3	14,4	56,3	29,5	14,2	56,0
5.	$MoSe_2$ (600°)	37,8	–	62,2	37,5	traces	62,0
6.	$MoSe_2$ (H_2, 400°)	37,8	–	62,2	37,4	traces	62,3

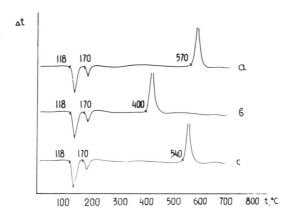

**Fig.1 DTA-curves of mixtures: a- Mo + 2S;
b - W + 2S;   c - Re + 2S**

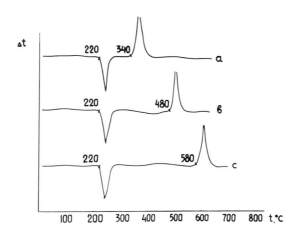

**Fig.2 DTA-curves of mixtures: a- Mo + 2Se;
b - W + 2Se;   c - Re + 2Se**

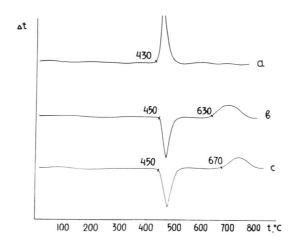

Fig.3   DTA-curves of mixtures: a- Mo + 2Te;
b - W + 2Te;   c - Re + 2Te

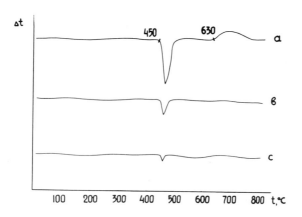

Fig.4   DTA-curves of the mixture W + 2Te:
a - the parent mixture,   b - the mixture
after roasting for a period 20 hours at
700°,   c - the mixture after roasting for
a period 50 hours at 700°

807

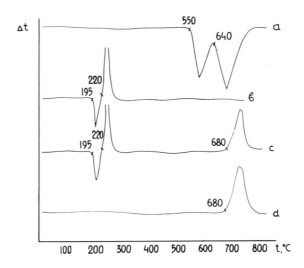

Fig.5 DTA-curves: a–the composition of $MoCl_3$ in sustained vacuum; b–the interaction $2Mo+3MoCl_5=5MoCl_3$; c–the interaction $3Mo+2MoCl_5=5MoCl_2$; d–the interaction $Mo+2MoCl_3$

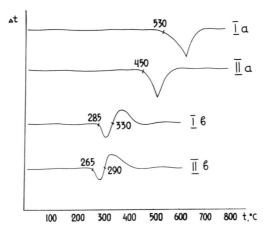

Fig.6 DTA-curves $Mo_3Cl_4S_7(I)$ and $Mo_3Cl_4Se_7(II)$:
a – the heating in a vacuum,
b – the heating in hydrogenium

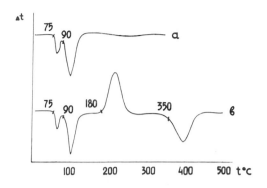

Fig.7 DTA–curves: a–MoOF$_4$,   b–MoOF$_4$ + MoO$_3$

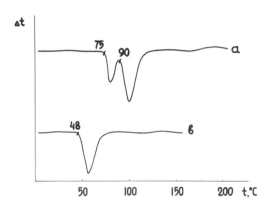

Fig.8 DTA–curves of the mixture   MoF$_4$ + MoOF$_4$:
a – the parent mixture,
b – the mixture after the reaction takes
place

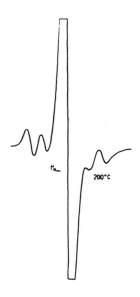

Fig.9 EPR–spectrum Mo^V in (MoF$_5$ + MoOF$_3$)

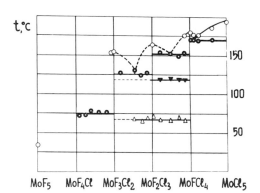

Fig.10 The system MoF$_5$ – MoCl$_5$

A THERMOANALYTICAL STUDY OF THE EFFECTS OF VARIOUS FLUORIDES ON THE REACTION BETWEEN POTASSIUM CHLORATE AND MAGNESIUM

Clement Campbell and Francis R. Taylor

Picatinny Arsenal
Dover, N. J.

Abstract

Thermoanalytical techniques have been utilized to investigate the mechanism by which certain inorganic fluorides can cause normally unreactive magnesium–potassium chlorate mixtures to ignite propagatively. Preliminary results indicate that the effective fluorides produce an effect both on the thermal decomposition of potassium chlorate and the reactivity of atomized magnesium in molten chlorate.

Introduction

Standard military pyrotechnic compositions generally consist of mixtures of inorganic oxidants and powdered metal fuels. The ignition and burning characteristics of these mixtures can be altered by the inclusion of various additives in the compositions. An interesting example is the dramatic effect of the addition of small amounts of certain inorganic fluorides on the ignitibility of the pyrotechnic system potassium chlorate-magnesium. This paper describes the application of thermogravimetry and differential thermal analysis to an investigation of the mechanism of this reaction.

Experimental Procedure

Reagents: The reagents used were as follows: $KClO_3$ Mallinckrodt Analytical Reagent; atomized magnesium powder Golwynne Chemical Co. (99.1% metallic Mg, 325/400 screen fraction, 49 microns average particle diameter); NaF, KF, CaF_2, KCl and KI Fisher Certified Reagent; LiF J. T. Baker Analyzed Reagent; RbF Fairmount Chemical Co. Purified; CsF City Chemical Corp. 99.9+%; MgF_2 and BaF_2 Baker and Adamson Purified; SrF_2 Variacoid Chemical Co. Chemically Pure; and KBr Merck Reagent Grade.

Apparatus: Thermogravimetric analyses were performed with a Chevenard Thermobalance converted to electronic recording (1). These experiments were conducted in dynamic atmospheres of argon or oxygen using a flow rate of 300 cc/min. Coors #0000 porcelain crucibles were used to hold the samples. The bead of the chromel-alumel thermocouple used as the sample temperature sensor was held in contact with the outside bottom of the sample container. A linear heating rate of $10^{o}C$/min. was used and the curves were recorded as a function of sample temperature on a Honeywell Model 320 X-Y recorder. Differential thermal analyses were conducted with a DuPont Model 900 Differential Thermal Analyzer using the intermediate temperature heating cell. The sample and inert reference (Al_2O_3) were contained in 4mm diameter Pyrex tubes and the experiments were conducted in a dynamic atmosphere of Argon using a flow rate of 300 cc/min and a heating rate of $10^{o}C$/min. X-ray diffraction analyses were performed using a Siemens Crystalloflex II x-ray diffraction unit.

Results and Discussion

A thermogravimetric curve describing the thermal decomposition of $KClO_3$ is shown in Figure 1. This curve was obtained by heating a 200 mg sample of $KClO_3$ in an argon atmosphere at $10^{o}C$./min. It is seen that the $KClO_3$ begins to lose weight about $475^{o}C$. and decomposes with continual evolution of oxygen until the decomposition is complete about 640°C. Using a 200 mg sample of $KClO_3$, a weight loss of 78 mg occurs which corresponds to the conversion of $KClO_3$ into KCl according to the reaction

$$2KClO_3 \longrightarrow 2KCl + 3O_2 \qquad (1)$$

When a loose unconfined mixture of 200 mg $KClO_3$ and 119 mg magnesium powder (stoichiometric according to the reaction $KClO_3 + 3\ Mg \longrightarrow KCl + 3MgO$) was heated under the same conditions the curve shown in Figure 1 was obtained. The $KClO_3$ begins to decompose just after its melting point, 356°C., and rapidly generates oxygen until 540°C. The loss of oxygen from the $KClO_3$ amounts to 72 mg, the remaining 6 mg of oxygen reacting with the magnesium non-propagatively to form MgO as verified by x-ray diffraction analysis of the residue. When 20 mg of sodium fluoride is added to the stoichiometric mixture of 200 mg $KClO_3$ and 119 mg magnesium, however, an interesting phenomenon occurs (see Figure 1). The $KClO_3$ does not begin to lose its oxygen until about 490°C and after about 25% of the oxygen has been lost, ignition and propagative combustion of the mixture occurs. A mixture of 200 mg $KClO_3$ with 20 mg NaF was then heated to determine what effect NaF has on the decomposition of $KClO_3$. Figure 1 shows that the $KClO_3$ begins to decompose at the same temperature as pure $KClO_3$ but proceeds at a somewhat faster rate, completing its weight loss about 15°C. lower than the pure chlorate. A final weight loss of 78 mg occurs, corresponding to complete loss of oxygen from the system. X-ray diffraction analysis of the residue shows only the presence of KCl and NaF in the residue.

The systems presented in Figure 1 were then examined by means of differential thermal analysis. The DTA curves obtained are presented in Figure 2. Like the previously discussed TGA studies these experiments were conducted at a heating rate of 10°C./min. in a dynamic argon atmosphere, however, using sample sizes 1/10 those used in the thermogravimetric analyses, viz, 20 mg $KClO_3$, 11.9 mg Mg, and 2 mg NaF. The DTA curve for $KClO_3$ in Figure 2 first shows an endotherm corresponding to its melting at 356°C., then exothermal behavior beginning above 500°C. where weight loss was first noticed on the thermogravimetric curve. This exothermal behavior is exemplified by two distinct peaks occurring at approximately 560 and 600°C. Markowitz and co-workers (2) have reported that the first exotherm is associated with the decomposition of $KClO_3$ by the following two competitive reactions:

$$KClO_3 \longrightarrow KCl + 3/2\ O_2 \tag{2}$$

$$KClO_3 \longrightarrow 3/4\ KClO_4 + 1/4\ KCl \tag{3}$$

By chemical analysis these workers showed that 12.1% of the $KClO_3$ decomposes according to equation (2) and 87.0% of the $KClO_3$ decomposes to form $KClO_4$ by equation (3). Finally they stated that the second exotherm occurring at about 600°C. is due to the decomposition of $KClO_4$ according to the following reaction:

$$KClO_4 \longrightarrow KCl + 2\ O_2 \tag{4}$$

The final endotherm seen in the DTA curve for the $KClO_3$ decomposition is the melting of the KCl residue.

In the curve for the $KClO_3$ - NaF mixture (see Figure 2) the exotherm corresponding to the thermal decomposition of $KClO_3$ is minimized while the second exotherm which is probably due to the decomposition of $KClO_4$ is reinforced. This indicates that the presence of NaF enhances the formation of the more stable $KClO_4$ during the decomposition of $KClO_3$.

DTA curves of mixtures of $KClO_3$ and Mg, an example of which is shown in Figure 2, exhibit just one broad exothermal peak occurring immediately following the fusion endotherm for $KClO_3$. This exotherm although large does not lead to propagative ignition. This curve also shows that two small endotherms occur at 650°C and 750°C. corresponding to the fusion of unreacted Mg and KCl, respectively.

Finally the DTA curve for the $KClO_3$-Mg-NaF ternary
(see Figure 2) exhibits a small intensity exothermal reaction
which occurs shortly after melting of the $KClO_3$. Another
exothermal reaction commences about $500^{\circ}C$. which, after an
initial exothermal peak, culminates in propagative ignition.
From the thermogravimetric and DTA experiments it appears
that the presence of NaF in the $KClO_3$-Mg system inhibits the
catalytic effect of magnesium on the decomposition of $KClO_3$ and
enables oxygen to be retained in the system until it reaches a
high enough temperature for propagative reaction to occur
between $KClO_3$ and magnesium.

Experiments were conducted to determine the effects of
varying the NaF concentration on the ignitibility of Mg-$KClO_3$
compositions. Figure 3 presents thermogravimetric curves for
stoichiometric mixtures of 200 mg $KClO_3$ and 119 mg. Mg with 4,
10, and 20 mg. of NaF. These thermograms show the interesting
result that as the concentration of NaF is decreased below 20 mg.
the ignition temperature of the ternary composition increases and
the amount of oxygen lost prior to ignition increases. For
example, adding 20, 10 and 4 mg. of NaF causes ignition to occur
at $530^{\circ}C$. after a 24% weight loss, $559^{\circ}C$. after a 55% weight
loss, and $597^{\circ}C$. after a 82% weight loss, respectively. Thus
these experiments demonstrate that the addition of a small
quantity of NaF, e.g. less than 4 mg., negates the catalytic
effect of magnesium on the thermal decomposition of $KClO_3$.
Further additions of NaF produce a return of the decomposition
temperature towards the value for the $KClO_3$-Mg binary, and at
the same time produces a continuous reduction in ignition temperature. At concentrations of NaF above 20 mg, the ignition
temperature increases again probably due to excessive dilution.

Before proceeding with investigations involving other
fluorides, a study was made of the high temperature behavior of
NaF, Mg, and NaF-Mg compositions. Figure 4 presents
thermogravimetric curves obtained in these interesting experiments. Heating NaF in an inert atmosphere shows that no
weight change occurs until about $750^{\circ}C$. where a gradual weight

loss begins, probably due to sublimation of some of the sample. Similarly magnesium showed considerable thermal stability exhibiting no appreciable weight change until vaporization of the liquid begins about 750°C. When a binary mixture of NaF and magnesium is heated in an inert atmosphere, no significant weight changes occur until 585°C. where the sample begins to lose weight rapidly in a stepwise manner. X-ray diffraction analysis of the residue showed that it consisted largely of MgF$_2$. The presence of MgF$_2$ can be explained by the following reaction:

$$2NaF + Mg \longrightarrow MgF_2 + 2Na \qquad (5)$$

Under these conditions the sodium would be formed as a vapor accounting for the observed weight loss. Upon heating a similar binary mixture in oxygen ignition occurs at 585°C., the point at which weight loss initially occurs. This ignition can be attributed to the following highly exothermal pre-ignition reaction

$$4Na + O_2 \longrightarrow 2Na_2O \qquad (6)$$

which triggers the propagative oxidation of the magnesium. To eliminate the possibility that the reaction of magnesium with oxygen was responsible for this ignition at 585°C., a thermogravimetric curve was obtained for the binary mixture of MgF$_2$ and Mg in oxygen. Figure 4 shows that this composition containing magnesium diluted with MgF$_2$ does not ignite but merely begins to gain weight above 600°C due to the formation of MgO.

The other alkali metal fluorides were investigated to find out if they have the same effect as NaF on the ignitibility of KClO$_3$-Mg compositions. Figure 5 presents thermogravimetric curves for mixtures containing 20 mg. of each of these fluorides with 200 mg of KClO$_3$ and 119 mg of magnesium. All of these fluorides induce ignition. The KClO$_3$-Mg system with LiF ignites at 578°C. after 40% (31 mg.) of the oxygen has been lost from the KClO$_3$. The mixture containing KF, however, ignites at 410°C., with only a 2.5% (2 mg.) loss of oxygen prior to ignition. Compositions containing RbF and CsF ignite at 414 and 524°C. with respective weight losses prior to ignition of 1.2%

(1 mg.) and 57% (45 mg.). Differential thermal analyses of these compositions are shown in Figure 6. The DTA curves for the LiF and NaF bearing compositions were similar, producing ignition at approximately 570°C. It must be noted that the latter ignition temperatures are somewhat higher than those previously determined from the TGA curves for the similar mixtures. With the present instrumentation, the DTA ignition temperatures are more exact since the sensing thermocouple is located directly in interior of the sample. Whereas with the TGA equipment, the thermocouple is in contact with the outside bottom of the sample crucible. In mixtures containing KF, RbF, and CsF (DTA not shown) a solid-state exotherm begins before fusion of the $KClO_3$ which is interrupted by the melting endotherm. After this interruption, the exothermal reaction continues culminating in propagative ignition.

Mixtures of $KClO_3$ and magnesium with the various alkaline earth metal fluorides were likewise studied to determine if these compounds had a similar effect on the ignitibility of this system. Figure 7 presents thermograms for thermogravimetric analyses of these compositions. The fluorides of all the alkali metals with the exception of beryllium were utilized. All of these fluorides affected the decomposition pattern of the $KClO_3$ but none of these mixtures ignited. Magnesium fluoride produced the most profound effect on the decomposition of $KClO_3$, causing a continuous loss of oxygen beginning immediately after the $KClO_3$ fusion.

DTA curves obtained for $KClO_3$-Mg compositions containing the aforementioned alkaline earth fluorides are presented in Figure 8. All of these curves are very similar in structure exhibiting the dual exotherms attributable to the previously discussed decompositions of $KClO_3$ and $KClO_4$. These latter exotherms are well resolved for the composition containing MgF_2. This resolution apparently results from gradual decomposition of oxidant as contrasted with the rapid decompositions exhibited by the other fluoride systems. Mixtures of these alkaline earth metal fluorides with magnesium undergo no reaction when they are heated to 900°C.

817

A series of thermogravimetric analyses were conducted to determine if the halide anion plays any role in inducing ignition of KClO3-Mg mixtures. The results of this study are illustrated in Figure 9. It is seen that when 20 mg. of KI, KBr, KCl and KF are added to KClO3-Mg samples, the only halide producing ignition is the fluoride, giving an ignition temperature of 410°C. Two other significant facts are evident from Figure 9. First, the KF produces ignition with negligible loss of oxygen. Secondly, although the various other halides do not induce ignition they have a significant effect on the decomposition of the chlorate.

Several fluorides of metals from other groups of the periodic table were available and were examined to determine their effect on the KClO3-Mg system. These include AgF (Group IB), ZnF2 (IIB) and PbF2 (IVA). Thermogravimetric and DTA curves show that all of these compounds induce propagative ignition. For example, AgF produces ignition at 374°C. after a 1.3% loss of oxygen from the KClO3, ZnF2 gives ignition at 334°C. after 4.5% loss of oxygen, and PbF2 yields ignition at 374°C. with a 7% loss of oxygen. Figure 10 presents the DTA curves obtained in these studies. In each of these thermograms it is seen that exothermal reactions begin prior to the melting of the KClO3 which rapidly culminate in ignition. This phenomenon is noteworthy since pyrotechnic compositions rarely ignite at slow heating rates until a phase change occurs in one of the ingredients, for example, a crystalline transition or fusion.

Conclusions

The study of the effects of fluorides on the ignitibility of KClO3-Mg compositions has dealt primarily with NaF. This fluoride is the only one capable of being incorporated in normal pyrotechnic systems since it is the only one which is non-hygroscopic. The evidence which has been accumulated concerning the effects of NaF is as follows:

1. When binary mixtures of KClO3 and magnesium are heated at slow rates, the magnesium catalyzes the decomposition

of $KClO_3$ lowering the decomposition temperature 75-100°C. The oxygen is evolved below the temperature required for propagative oxidation of magnesium (3, 4).

2. The addition of a very small quantity of NaF, e.g., 4 mg, almost nullifies the catalytic effect of the Mg on the thermal decomposition of $KClO_3$.

3. It was experimentally observed that NaF dissolves in molten $KClO_3$ prior to its decomposition.

4. The presence of NaF enhances the formation of $KClO_4$ during the decomposition of $KClO_4$.

5. Magnesium reacts with NaF about 585°C to produce MgF_2 and Na.

From these experimental observations a possible mechanism for the effect of NaF on the ignition of $KClO_3$-Mg mixtures is suggested. Mobile NaF dissolved in molten $KClO_3$ diffuses through the porous oxide coating on the magnesium to alter the surface characteristics of the magnesium. This alteration may consist of a conversion of the oxide coating to a fluoride coating. This resulting change in the surface of the magnesium minimizes the catalytic effect of the magnesium or MgO on the decomposition of $KClO_3$ allowing it to retain its oxygen until the system reaches a higher temperature. When the Mg-$KClO_3$-NaF mixture reaches a temperature somewhat above 500°C. the NaF may react with the magnesium producing sodium vapor which reacts exothermally with oxygen from the decomposing $KClO_3$ or $KClO_4$ thus triggering the propagative reaction of magnesium with the oxygen from $KClO_3$ or $KClO_4$.

This proposed mechanism probably applies to all alkali metal fluorides but certainly not to systems involving AgF, ZnF_2 and PbF_2 which induce ignition in $KClO_3$-Mg mixtures prior to the fusion of $KClO_3$.

References

1. S. Gordon and C. Campbell, Anal. Chem. <u>28</u>, 124 (1956).

2. M. Markowitz, D. Boryta, and H. Stewart, Jr., J. Phys. Chem. <u>68</u>, 2282 (1964).

3. M. Markowitz and D. Boryta, Anal. Chem. <u>33</u>, 949 (1961).

4. E. Freeman and C. Campbell, Trans. Faraday Soc. <u>59</u>, 165 (1963).

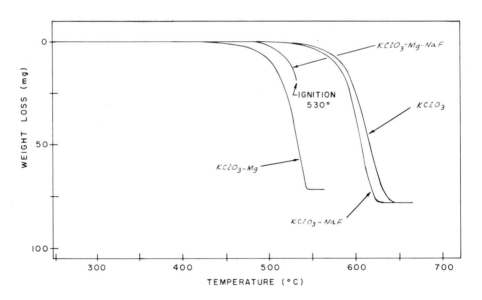

Fig. 1   TGA curves showing the effects of Mg and/or NaF on the thermal decomposition of KClO₃   (KClO3 200 mg, Mg 119 mg, NaF 20 mg).

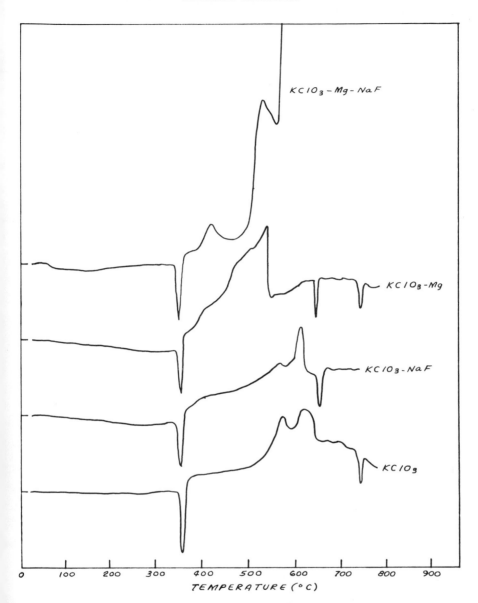

Fig. 2 DTA curves showing the effects of Mg and/or NaF on the thermal decomposition of KClO3 (KClO3 20 mg, Mg 11.9 mg, NaF 2 mg).

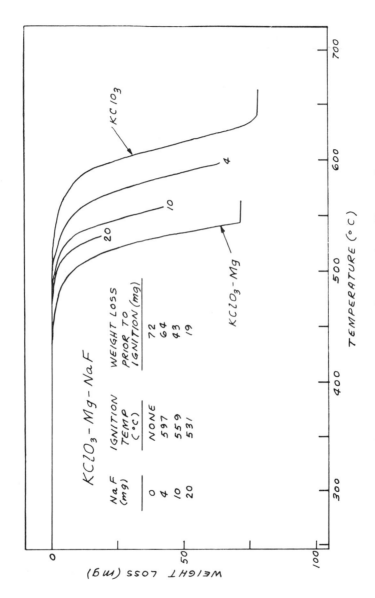

Fig. 3 TGA curves showing the effects of NaF concentration on the $KClO_3$-Mg-NaF reaction ($KClO_3$ 200 mg, Mg 119 mg).

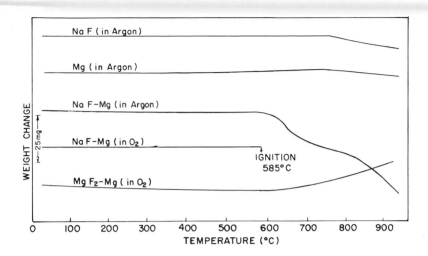

Fig. 4   TGA curves showing the high temperature behavior of NaF, Mg, and Mg–NaF mixtures. The latter mixtures contained 22.4% by weight of Mg and 88.6% NaF.

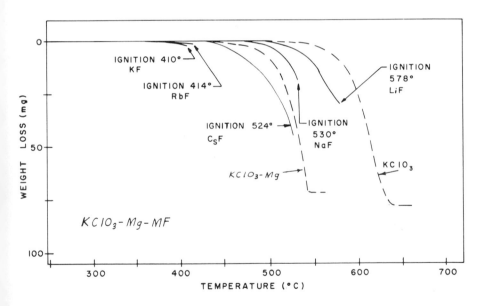

Fig. 5   TGA curves showing the effects of alkali metal fluorides on the KClO₃–Mg system   (KClO₃ 200 mg, Mg 119 mg, MF 20 mg).

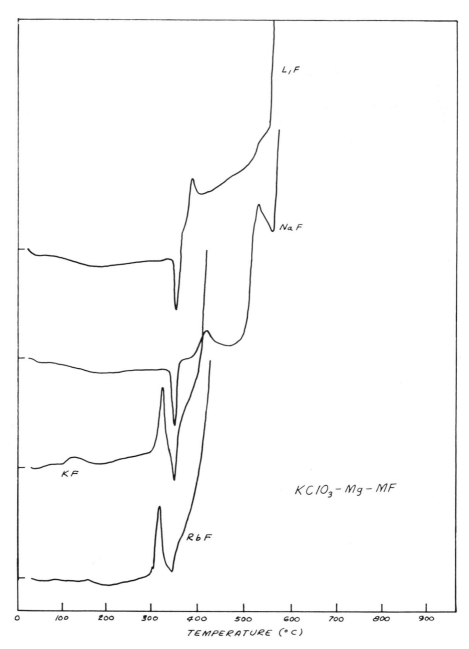

Fig. 6 DTA curves showing the effects of alkali
metal fluorides on the KClO3-Mg system (KClO3
20 mg, Mg 11.9 mg, MF 2 mg).

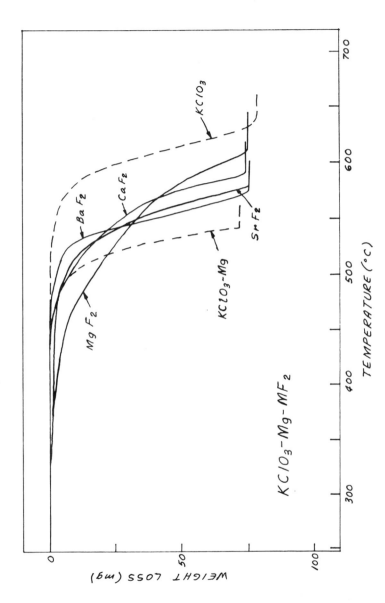

Fig. 7 TGA curves showing the effects of alkaline
earth metal fluorides on the KClO₃–Mg system
(KClO₃ 200 mg, Mg 119 mg, MF₂ 20 mg).

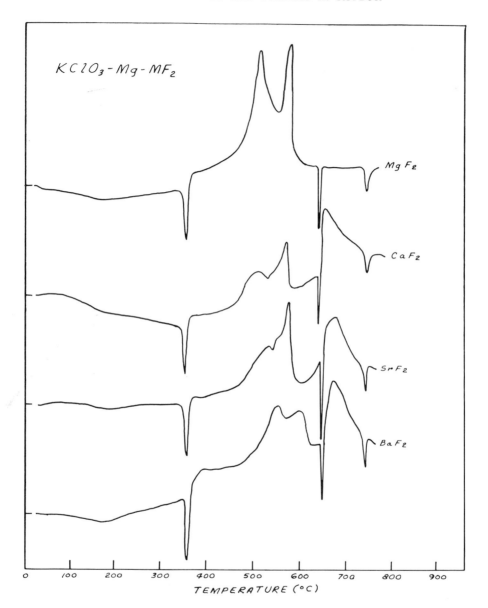

Fig. 8   DTA curves showing the effects of alkaline earth metal fluorides on the $KClO_3$–Mg system ($KClO_3$ 20 mg, Mg 11.9 mg, MF_2 2 mg).

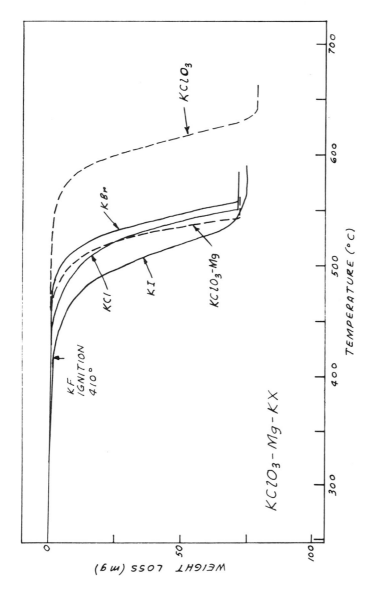

Fig. 9 TGA curves showing the effects of potassium halides on the KClO₃-Mg system (KClO₃ 200 mg, Mg 119 mg, KX 20 mg).

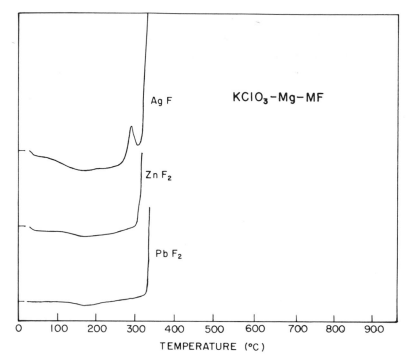

Fig. 10   DTA curves showing the effects of heavy metal fluorides on the $KClO_3$-Mg system ($KClO_3$ 20 mg, Mg 11.9 mg, MF 2 mg).

APPLICATION OF DIFFERENTIAL THERMAL ANALYSIS TO THE STUDY OF PHASE EQUILIBRIA IN METAL SYSTEMS

Don E. Etter, Philip A. Tucker
and L. J. Wittenberg

Monsanto Research Corporation
Mound Laboratory*
Miamisburg, Ohio

Abstract

Differential thermal analysis has been used extensively in the study of phase equilibria of condensed systems because of its ability to detect very small thermal effects. An apparatus employing chromel-alumel thermocouples for use from ambient temperature to 1000°C is described. Detailed interpretations of thermograms are presented for selected compositions of a hypothetical binary phase diagram including congruently and incongruently melting compounds and solid solution, eutectic and liquidus reactions. The Pu-Cu system is presented as an example of a phase diagram determined by DTA. The stoichiometry of the congruently melting compounds $PuCu_2$ and Pu_4Cu_{17} and the incongruently melting compounds $PuCu_4$ and Pu_2Cu_{11} was established completely by DTA. Eutectic reactions and liquidus temperatures were clearly defined; however, unusual thermal effects were observed because of the "S" shaped liquidus curve.

---

*Operated for the U. S. Atomic Energy Commission under Contract No. AT-33-1-GEN-53.

829

Differential thermal analysis is particularly useful for the rapid determination of the purity of certain metals, since small quantities of impurities influence the melting point and may cause subsolidus reactions. The addition of as little as 0.1 at.% (0.024 wt %) Fe, Co, or Ni to Pu depressed the melting point approximately 15°C and caused additional phase transformations between 407 and 412°C.

Introduction

During recent years a broad program of phase equilibria investigations in metal systems has been conducted at Mound Laboratory. Differential thermal analysis (DTA) has been used extensively in this work as a primary experimental technique complemented by other techniques such as metallography, x-ray diffraction, and electron microprobe x-ray analysis. The development and application of DTA for these studies are described in this report.

The use of thermal analysis has been emphasized in the past as a technique for studying metallic materials.[1,2,3] However, the DTA technique was developed and employed in this work because of its higher inherent sensitivity. DTA permitted the use of smaller samples and at the same time provided greater resolution in the interpretation of data. The sensitivity and accuracy of the DTA thermograms were found to be influenced by many factors such as sample size, heating rate, sample geometry, thermal conductivity of sample container, and method of measurement of sample temperature. These variables were adjusted to optimize the desired characteristics of the DTA apparatus. The ability to detect small thermal

effects and to define isothermal reactions were
essential characteristics.

Apparatus

A schematic diagram of the apparatus employed for
studies up to 1000°C is shown in Fig. 1. The
heating and cooling rates of the resistance
furnace are controlled by a program controller.
A sealed capsule containing the alloy and a
similar reference capsule containing alumina are
held in oversized holes of a cylindrical Inconel
block. Each capsule is centered and insulated
electrically from the block by an aluminum
silicate ring at the top of the capsule and by a
thermocouple insulator below the thermowell. The
capsule rests on the thermocouple in such a manner
that the thermocouple bead maintains intimate
contact with the top of the thermowell.

The block assembly is enclosed in a stainless
steel vacuum chamber fitted at the top with a
water-cooled flange and an O-ring seal. The
apparatus is evacuated and backfilled with helium
before each determination. Helium provides a
very desirable heat transfer medium and prevents
oxidation of the capsules.

A disassembled block assembly and chamber are
shown in Fig. 2. Chromel-alumel thermocouples
are mounted in porcelain insulators and the leads
are extended out from both capsules. The
differential emf is amplified 20 times by a DC
amplifier and then recorded on an X-Y recorder.
A pen-positioning control voltage is applied in
series with the differential voltage to position
the base line of the heating and cooling traces.

Initially the chromel-alumel thermocouples were
calibrated by determination of the melting points
of pure aluminum and lead (obtained from the
National Bureau of Standards) as well as high
purity inorganic salts. It was found that the
thermocouples were always reproducible within
1°C. The accuracy of the determinations was
limited by the accuracy (±2°C) with which the
transitions could be read from the recording
paper. Some designs of DTA apparatus employ a
third thermocouple to record temperature, while
others use the reference thermocouple. As a
result, during an exothermic or endothermic
reaction, the sample temperature will be greater
or less, respectively, than the measured temperature. To circumvent this problem, the
temperature is read directly from the sample
thermocouple in this apparatus.

Heating rates of 1 to 3 °/min were the most
desirable. Because of the dynamic nature which
yields the differential temperature (ΔT), it is
desirable to heat rapidly. Slow heating reduces
sensitivity while fast heating increases sensitivity. An excessive heating rate results in
an incorrect sample temperature indication
because of heat leakage to the sample thermocouple from the hotter environment surrounding
the sample, thus precluding the demonstration of
an isothermal reaction. The heating rate is not
excessive if the beginning of melting and the
peak of melting of a high purity metal can be
observed at essentially the same temperature.
This capability of the DTA apparatus to demonstrate isothermal melting is a necessity to
support the correct interpretation of thermograms.

Sample containers were usually small tantalum
capsules provided with thermowells and sealed by

TIG welding. Both a completed capsule and a sectioned sample capsule, showing details, appear in Fig. 3. Sealed sample capsules were found to be desirable for ease of sample handling, homogenization, protection against oxidation, and prevention of composition change for alloys involving high vapor pressure metals.

Interpretation of Results

The correlation of DTA data with the features of phase diagrams requires a knowledge of both the characteristics of the apparatus and the thermal effects which are typical of the various inter-metallic reactions. The hypothetical binary phase diagram shown in Fig. 4 is presented to illustrate the interpretation of results in simple cases. This system includes incongruently and congruently melting compounds and solid solution, eutectic and liquidus reactions. The thermograms of seven selected compositions are depicted. These thermograms are heating traces which are preferred to cooling traces because of their freedom from supercooling.

The thermogram for composition "A" shows only the α solid solution starting to melt and continuing until the liquidus temperature is reached. The sharp reversal of the trace above the peak is indicative of the liquidus.

Composition "B", located on the composition of the incongruently melting compound β, exhibits a trace that has a sharp thermal arrest. At this temperature (the peritectic temperature) the sample undergoes an isothermal decomposition. Above this temperature melting continues to occur at an increasing rate until the liquidus is reached. Nonequilibrium conditions usually occur

in peritectic reactions because of the nature of
the reaction and will influence the DTA thermograms. For instance, during cooling of composition "B", the α phase and liquid are present just
above the peritectic isotherm, and as the temperature is lowered, the β phase forms at the
interface between the α and the liquid establishing a barrier which prevents the reaction from
going to completion. In a subsequent DTA heating
trace the composition would show a eutectic
reaction due to the nonequilibrium conditions.
Equilibrium conditions (illustrated by thermogram
"B") can be demonstrated by DTA after holding the
sample at a temperature just below the incongruent
melting temperature long enough for the reaction
to go to completion.

Composition "C" is located on the eutectic side
of the incongruent compound. Here, the first
reaction occurs when the β and γ phases simultaneously melt at the eutectic isotherm. As the
temperature is increased the β phase dissolves in
the liquid until a second thermal arrest is
reached. At this temperature the remaining β
phase decomposes into α plus liquid, and melting
then continues until the liquidus is reached.

Composition "D" shows only a single isothermal
reaction as it is located exactly on the eutectic
composition. The eutectic arrest will be the
largest at this composition.

The thermogram for composition "E", located
directly on the congruently melting compound γ,
shows only one sharp arrest which is its melting
point.

Composition "F" is located on the right side of
the compound γ between the compound and a

eutectic.   Two arrests are apparent depicting the
eutectic isotherm and continued melting until the
liquidus is reached.

The final composition "G", to the right of the
eutectic, exhibits two arrests which are definitive of the eutectic isotherm and the liquidus
reaction.

By re-examination of the compilation of traces
described above, one can start to construct the
binary phase diagram. A dashed line has been
drawn through the liquidus points defining the
liquidus curve of the system. An isotherm is
suggested at T_1 in traces "C" and "D" because of
the sharpness of the transformations as well as
their occurrence at the same temperature. Other
isotherms are indicated at T_2 and T_3 from traces
"F" and "G" and "B" and "C" respectively for the
same reasons. Trace "C" has two isotherms
indicated. Close examination of the relationship
between the liquidus temperatures and the
isotherm temperatures, along with their relative
sizes, suggests the presence of both a peritectic
and a eutectic reaction. In a relatively simple
binary system such as this, a few more strate-
gically located compositions would completely
define the system.

Fig. 5 shows an equilibrium thermogram for an
alloy in a binary system which exhibits complete
solid solubility. Solid solutions are subject to
extensive coring which must be removed by
annealing prior to DTA analysis. The vertical
portion of the thermogram between the start and
completion of melting indicates a uniform rate of
conversion of solid to liquid with increasing
temperature. This rate is a function of the
lever arm relationships[4] of the system.

From the preceding illustrations it might appear
that interpretation is relatively simple;
however, this is not always the case. Fig. 6 is
the Pu-Cu binary system which was originally
determined by DTA[5] and later confirmed by
metallographic and x-ray diffraction analyses.
The liquidus curve between the eutectic (~6 at.%
Cu) and 60 at.% Cu was found to be S-shaped.
Compositions in the 30 to 60 at.% Cu region
yielded unusual traces in that double thermal
arrests were present above the 626°C eutectic.
Typical examples of these results are evident in
Fig. 7 and 8. The lower of the two arrests
occurred at the same temperature for all compositions while the temperature of the upper thermal
arrest rose indicating the liquidus. Since the
peak of the lower themal arrest occurred at
constant temperature, it first appeared to be a
peritectic reaction indicating the presence of
an incongruent compound. Additional investigation did not, however, support the presence of
such a compound. The explanation was obtained by
further interpretation of the liquidus curve.
Between 6 and 10 at.% the liquidus curve was
quite steep, and between 10 and 30 at.% the
liquidus curve was relatively flat. When
compositions containing greater than 30 at.% Cu
were heated through the corresponding temperature
range, liquid formed and changed in composition
across the entire region. As the liquid
composition varied from 6 to 10 at.% Cu, very
little solid melted per unit of temperature rise.
However, when the composition of the liquid
exceeded 10 at.% Cu, a sudden increase occurred in
the amount of solid which melted per unit of temperature rise. The sudden change in the melting
rate produced a thermal arrest which did not
represent a phase transformation.

The remainder of the phase diagram, including the compositions of compounds, was constructed from DTA data alone. Fig. 9 shows a thermogram of a composition just 1 at.% to the left of the incongruently melting compound $PuCu_4$. Three thermal arrests are present, including two isothermal arrests which were identified as eutectic and peritectic reactions. The third arrest was assigned as the liquidus.

The determination made on an 80 at.% Cu alloy was indicative of an incongruent compound at that location ($PuCu_4$) because the thermal arrest at the peritectic isotherm temperature (905°C) was greater than for any other composition and because of the absence of the 849°C eutectic. The composition at 80.9 at.% was further evidence, since no thermal arrest was apparent for the peritectic isotherm. The appearance of the thermogram further suggested the existence of a congruently melting compound at that composition (Pu_4Cu_{17}) since only one large transformation was present at 954°C. The 83.33 at.% Cu alloy was investigated with a resulting sharp thermal arrest at 926°C and a liquidus at 948°C giving additional support to the identity of the congruently melting composition.

Further investigation of compositions in this area showed an incongruently melting compound to be present at a composition slightly less than the $PuCu_6$ composition based on the size of the peritectic reaction and the absence of a eutectic reaction. The assignment of Pu_2Cu_{11} was based on the formula with the smallest whole numbers at this composition. More recent work by single crystal x-ray techniques at Mound Laboratory[6] has confirmed that the compound is indeed Pu_2Cu_{11}

and not $PuCu_6$. A eutectic at 881°C was also detected between this compound and pure Cu.

The Pu-U binary system[7] was reinvestigated by DTA. This system is rather complex as it contains a number of solid solution phases. Fig. 10 shows the binary phase diagram and a thermogram for the 50 at.% U alloy. The first arrest occurs from 495 to 540°C which covers the solid state two-phase region of η plus ζ. No further arrest is apparent on continued heating until the two-phase region of η plus ε is reached giving rise to the transformation from 660 to 685°C. The first indication of liquid appears at 740°C, and melting continues until the liquidus is reached at 820°C.

The thermogram for the 70 at.% U alloy, shown in Fig. 11, crosses two peritectoid isotherms prior to the liquidus reaction. Two sharp thermal arrests are displayed at 580 and 695°C. A noticeable change of slope is present near the peak of the second isotherm indicating an additional reaction. The change of slope is caused by the two-phase region of ι plus ε which is quite small, but detectable. It is obvious from these traces that considerable information is present if proper interpretation is applied. In this system solid-state equilibrium conditions were achieved under dynamic conditions. In many instances, however, this cannot be done. In such cases the alloys must be adequately annealed prior to analysis to assure reliable data.

DTA has also been useful in the detection of small quantities of impurities in certain metals.[8] Examples of this phenomenon are shown in Fig. 12, 13, 14, and 15. The first thermogram, Fig. 12, illustrates high purity Pu

metal which contains 260 ppm total impurities as
determined by spectro-chemical analysis. The
melting range is approximately 1°C. Fig. 13 is
a thermogram of the same material with 240 ppm
(0.1 at.%) of Fe added. A 15°C melting range is
evident and two small additional reactions at 407
and 412°C are present that did not occur in the
original Pu. The 407°C thermal arrest is most
likely the eutectic reaction of the Pu-Fe binary
system. The arrest at 412°C was attributed to
the conversion of the δ phase plus liquid to
solid ε phase, since an inverse peritectic
reaction (retrograde melting) was encountered in
this system.[9]

A thermogram for the high purity Pu with 240 ppm
Ni added is shown in Fig. 14. An additional
reaction is apparent at 410°C, probably due to
the eutectoid isotherm in the Pu-Ni binary system
where δ Pu plus PuNi transform to ε Pu. Melting
begins at 630°C, 10°C below the mp of high purity
Pu. Fig. 15 shows a thermogram for the Pu metal
with additions of 120 ppm each of Fe and Ni. The
small thermal arrests that were noted for the
independent additions of Fe and Ni are absent;
however, a reaction at 390°C is evident for this
ternary alloy, and the composition melts from
622 to 634°C.

It must be emphasized that the ability of DTA to
detect small concentrations of impurities is not
applicable to all cases since it is completely
dependent on the phase relationship of the
components involved.

Summary

The DTA technique has been successfully applied to the study of phase equilibria of metallic systems. It was first necessary to develop an apparatus with suitable characteristics and to demonstrate those characteristics with known materials as a basis for interpretation of experimental materials. The ability to detect small thermal effects and to define isothermal reactions are essential characteristics. The correlation of DTA data with the features of phase diagrams requires a knowledge of the typical thermal effects exhibited by the various intermetallic reactions as well as a knowledge of the nonequilibrium difficulties which can influence the reactions. Specific reactions can often be recognized by the shape and magnitude of thermal arrests.

Acknowledgment

The authors gratefully acknowledge the contribution of Dr. T. B. Rhinehammer who developed the original DTA apparatus at Mound Laboratory and applied it to the study of phase diagrams.

References

1. W. Hume-Rothery, J. W. Christian, and W. B. Pearson, _Metallurgical Equilibrium Diagrams_, The Institute of Physics, London (1952), pp. 97-108.

2. F. N. Rhines, _Phase Diagrams in Metallurgy_, McGraw-Hill Book Co., Inc., New York (1956), pp. 290-311.

3. G. V. Raynor, "Phase Diagrams and Their
    Determination," in Physical Metallurgy
    (R. W. Cahn, ed.) North-Holland Publishing
    Co., Amsterdam (1965), pp. 318-327.

4. F. N. Rhines, op. cit., pp. 22-23.

5. T. B. Rhinehammer, D. E. Etter, and
    L. V. Jones, in Plutonium 1960 (E. Grison,
    W. B. H. Lord, and R. D. Fowler, eds.),
    Cleaver-Hume Press, London (1961), p. 289.

6. D. B. Sullenger, Mound Laboratory, private
    communication.

7. F. W. Schonfeld, "Plutonium Phase Diagrams
    Studied at Los Alamos", in The Metal
    Plutonium (A. S. Coffinberry and W. N. Miner,
    eds.) University of Chicago Press (1961),
    p. 247.

8. D. E. Etter and L. J. Wittenberg,
    Differential Thermal Analysis Study of
    Impurities in Plutonium, USAEC Document
    MLM-1172 (1963).

9. F. W. Schonfeld, op. cit., p. 243.

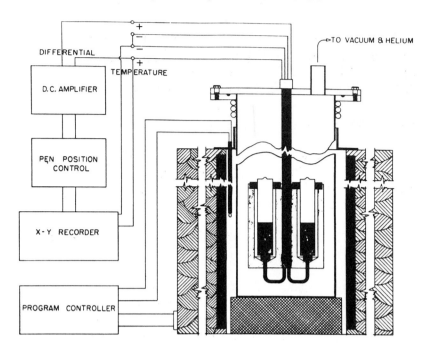

Fig. 1.   DTA apparatus.

Fig. 2.   Disassembled block assembly and vacuum chamber.

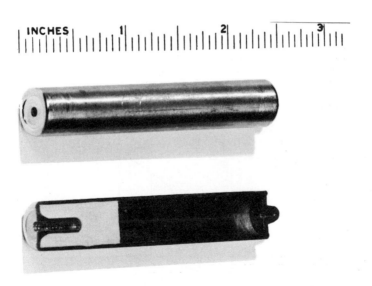

Fig. 3.   Tantalum differential thermal analysis capsules.

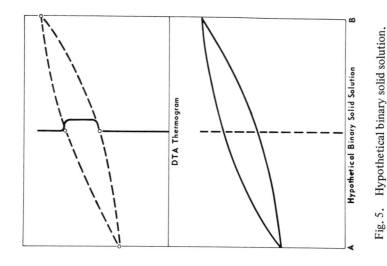

Fig. 5. Hypothetical binary solid solution.

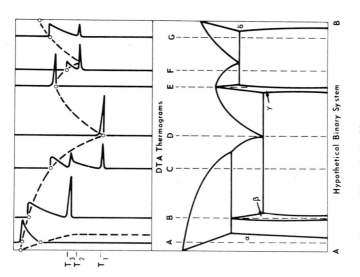

Fig. 4. Hypothetical binary system.

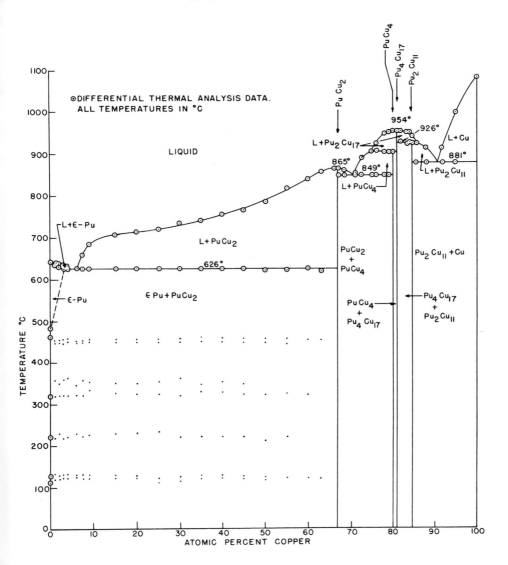

Fig. 6. The Pu–Cu binary phase diagram.

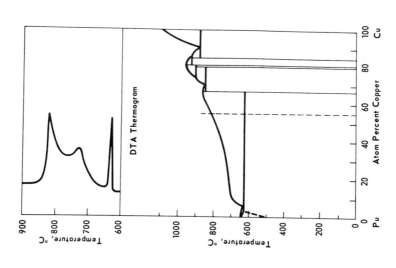

Fig. 8. Pu–Cu binary phase diagram and associated DTA thermogram for 55 at.% Cu composition.

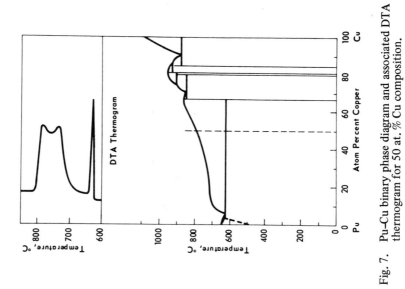

Fig. 7. Pu–Cu binary phase diagram and associated DTA thermogram for 50 at.% Cu composition.

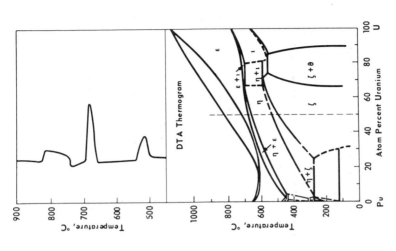

Fig. 10. Pu–U binary phase diagram and associated DTA thermogram for 50 at. % Pu composition.

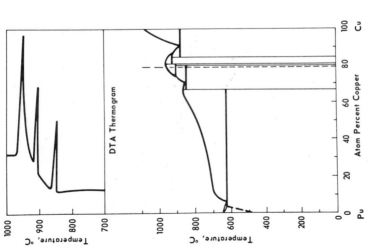

Fig. 9. Pu–Cu binary phase diagram and associated DTA thermogram for 79 at. % Cu composition.

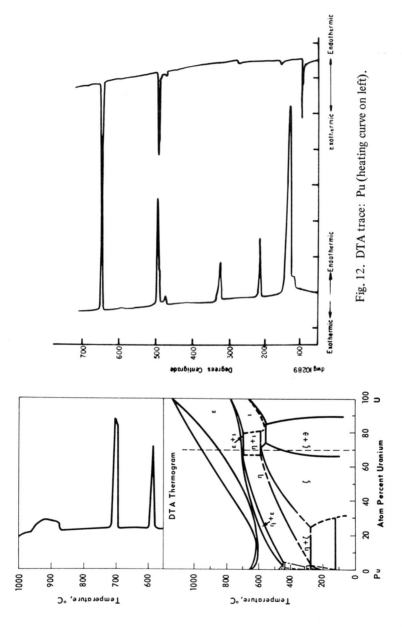

Fig. 12. DTA trace: Pu (heating curve on left).

Fig. 11. Pu–U binary phase diagram and associated DTA thermogram for 70 at.% Pu composition.

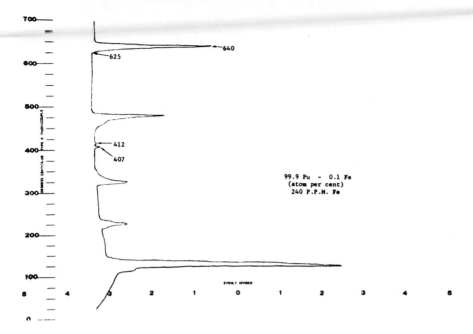

Fig. 13. DTA trace: 99.9 Pu – 0.1 at. % (0.0234 wt %) Fe.

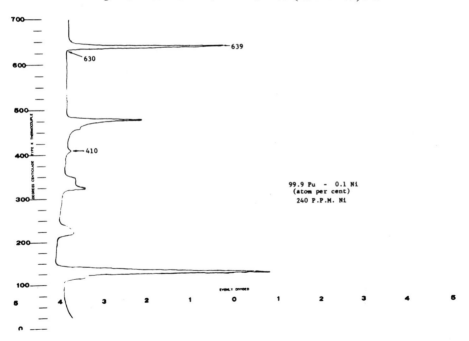

Fig. 14. DTA trace: 99.9 Pu – 0.1 at. % (0.0246 wt %) Ni.

849

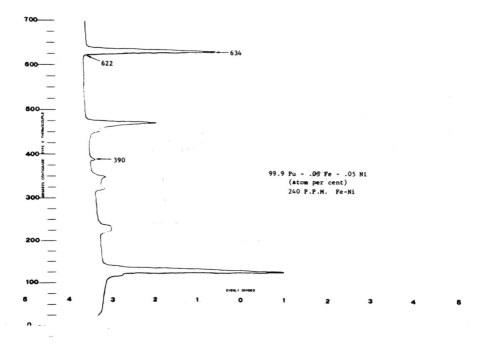

Fig. 15. DTA trace: 99.9 Pu – 0.05 Fe – 0.05 at. % Ni.

USE OF DTA FOR THE DETERMINATION OF THE MONOCLINIC-TETRAGONAL TRANSFORMATION IN ZIRCONIA AND ZIRCONIA-BASED SYSTEMS

Robert Ruh and Harold J. Garrett

Air Force Materials Laboratory
Wright-Patterson Air Force Base, Ohio 45433

Abstract

The martensitic monoclinic-tetragonal transformation in zirconia was studied as a function of heating rate using differential thermal analysis. From an understanding of the characteristics of martensitic transformations supplemented by high temperature XRD data on ZrO_2, the DTA results proved meaningful. They revealed basic information about the transformation as well as the general suitability and optimum conditions for its determination by DTA. Having demonstrated its suitability, DTA was then used to determine the transformation in zirconia-based binary systems.

Introduction

Differential thermal analysis seemed potentially well suited for the determination of the martensitic monoclinic-tetragonal transformation in zirconia and zirconia-based systems. Since these materials were important in the laboratory research program, an investigation was initiated to determine the merits of this method. In the first phase of this project, equipment was designed and built to make high resolution measurements at temperatures to 1700°C, thus adequately covering the

851

temperature range of interest. This equipment has been described.[1] In the second phase of this program, the monoclinic-tetragonal transformation in pure ZrO_2 was investigated in detail by DTA and parallel work was done using high temperature XRD. (The relative merits of these methods have been presented previously.[2]) Pure ZrO_2 was used because the transformation had been determined most accurately in this material. In the current work, the transformation was investigated as a function of heating rate. From an understanding of the characteristics of this martensitic transformation, the DTA curves at low heating rates are significant and reveal basic data about the transformation. From a practical point of view, the determination of the trans-formation by DTA is best done at a heating rate of 3°C/ min. or greater. Hafnia has been found to be the best standard material and has been used exclusively. The suitability of HfO_2 is understandable because of its extreme similarity to ZrO_2. The third phase of the pro-gram was the employment of DTA to determine the monoclinic-tetragonal transformation as a function of composition in zirconia-based binary systems. Current-ly, the systems which have been investigated are ZrO_2-HfO_2, ZrO_2-Sc_2O_3 and ZrO_2-Y_2O_3.

Evaluation of the DTA Technique

Before a discussion of the characteristics of the DTA data of the ZrO_2 monoclinic-tetragonal transfor-mation is presented, there is a need to identify certain important phenomena related to the transformation mechanism. This is particularly true of this transfor-mation because the evidence strongly indicated that it is a martensitic type, an equilibrium thermodynamic mis-fit. This problem may be the result of changing criteria used to identify it as a type, the unfortunate choice of names, or the failure of the experimentalist to criti-cally observe all the pertinent factors. The cause of the last problem is probably the requirement for the use of a number of technical disciplines for the characterization of each phenomena.

Martensitic transformations have only one uniquely definitive characteristic, change of shape. Shear-like shape changes exist between the transformed and untransformed specimen shape. The often observed characteristics of transformation temperature-coldwork dependence, athermal determination of the phase ratio, progression of the transformation interface in geometric shaped steps, acoustic step velocities, etc., are not all characteristic of each material exhibiting this type of transformation. Some nucleation-and-growth transformations exhibit one or more of these general characteristics, but not the single unique feature - change of shape. The definitive characteristic is often not easily observed. However, with ZrO_2 the unique and many of the general martensitic phase transformation characteristics are observed.

Hot stage microscopy studies [3] show crystallographically related surface deformation, the shape change characteristic, during the heating portion of the transformation cycle. The inability to polish the sample surface at temperatures above the cooling transformation prevents observation of the shape change in this direction. Evidence supporting the occurrence of shape change on cooling was obtained through the use of a Sc_2O_3 modified ZrO_2 sample in which the transformation temperature was sensitive to the state of oxidation. By controlling the oxidation parameter, it was possible to observe the change of shape of a polished surface which had undergone the tetragonal-monoclinic transformation.

High temperature XRD studies of the transformation provide particularly helpful quantitative data on

the phase ratio and transformation temperature relationship and the factors influencing this relationship.
Figure 1 graphically presents some of the more important results of these studies. Consider first the lower
portion of this graph where the percent monoclinic or
tetragonal versus temperature is plotted. It has been
determined that a well annealed sample of high purity
material will transform according to the solid curve,
i. e. , the tetragonal phase will begin forming at 1150°C
and the sample will be all tetragonal at 1190°C. On
cooling, the monoclinic phase will begin forming at
1020°C and the sample will be all monoclinic at 925°C.
If the sample is cycled through the transformation loop
several times, the phase ratio-temperature relationships will change to that shown by the dashed curves.
The phase ratio-temperature relationships could be
returned to the original solid curves by high temperature
annealing of the tetragonal phase. This observation is
interpreted as evidence for coldwork by transformation
cycling. For undetermined heat treatments or states of
structural equilibrium, something in between is often
seen as shown by the dot-dash lines. The most important fact is that reproducibility can be obtained, since
an anneal after each cycle will produce the curve shown
by the solid lines. Another important point is that the
temperature-phase ratio relationships are independent
of heating rate, within the response time of the equipment. This includes heating rates of up to 120°C/sec.
The curves plotted above the phase ratio curves are
obtained from the product of the slope of the phase ratio-
temperature data and the rate of temperature change.
Having observed the high speed at which the unique
phase ratio is established and the independence of rate
of change of temperature on the phase ratio, the
derived variations in amplitude indicate the comparative response to experiment controlled rate of temperature change, hence the resulting rate of phase change.
This effect of controlled rate of transformation and its
depicted nonlinear character is a major factor that

ultimately determines the response behavior of a DTA
experiment.

Transmission electron microscopy studies of this
transformation [4] have shown that in the monoclinic-
tetragonal direction, the ductility of the transformed
tetragonal phase is great enough to allow deformation by
mobile dislocations. In the cooling direction, the transformed monoclinic phase is deformed by twinning and
stacking fault formation. Mechanical testing has also
shown a sharp change in properties at the transformation temperature that results in superplasticity. [5]

The mechanisms of mechanical deformation are
intimately related to the transformation phenomena that
produce the shape changes. The coordinated movement
of a large array of atoms occurs at high velocities.
Shear-like relationships exist between the transformed
and untransformed phases. At the interfaces of these
large, rapidly produced, crystallographically related
regions, large intergrated strain concentrations
develop. The self deformation mechanisms noted are
the material's internal devices for controlling this
strain.

Stating an energy description of the transformation
relative to terms which influence the DTA response,
the following is proposed.

$$E = \Delta H + \Delta Q_s + \Delta Q_d$$

where E is the resulting heat effect, ΔH is the change in
configurational energy, ΔQ_s is the work required for the
coordinated transfer of large numbers of atoms and
ΔQ_d is the work of deformation of the transformed
phase. The signs of ΔQ_s and ΔQ_d are negative and
independent of the direction of the transformation, ΔH
on the other hand is negative for the monoclinic to

tetragonal transformation and positive in the opposite
direction. The ΔH and ΔQ_s terms have the same time
relationship as the transformation rate. The ΔQ_d term
is diffusion controlled in the heating direction (mobile
dislocations) and can proceed with acoustic velocities in
the cooling direction (stacking faults and twinning). The
rate at which energy is used or released in the sequence
of events related to the transformation determines the
DTA response to the phenomena. The heat flow mechanisms that tend to produce thermal equilibrium are
controlled by temperature gradients and time. Therefore the total energy contribution of a transformation
phenomena is not as important as changes in the sample
temperature produced by a fast acting phenomena. The
accumulative effects of reduced range of temperature
and additive energy terms results in a larger DTA
response in the heating direction than in the cooling
direction except for those instances in which the size
and rate of the work of deformation produce unusual
effects. Looking further at possible interactions of the
transformation and the DTA experiment, it is noted that
all the identified energy terms oppose the continuous
rate of temperature change in the heating direction. In
the cooling direction both opposition and support for
lowering the sample temperature is indicated.

The DTA data of Fig. 2 support this analysis of
the transformation and the predicted observations. In
the experiment, temperature change rates of 0.5, 1.0,
1.5, 2.0, and 3.0°C/min. were used. The 3°C/min.
results were not plotted in this figure because the
larger size required greater crossing of data lines.
They added no more than the extension of the evidence
for the increased sensitivity of the heat effect for
sustained transformations. On the right of the figure,
the DTA data for the monoclinic-tetragonal transformation at decreasing heating rates of 1.5, 1.0, and
0.5°C/min. increasingly show the self-arresting
effects caused by use of heat by the sample without

increasing its temperature. It also shows that arresting
the sample temperature eventually results in a thermal
gradient sufficiently large to increase the rate of heat
flow and sustain the transformation. This is the result
of a fixed rate of temperature change for the heat source.

In the tetragonal-monoclinic transformation the self-
arresting effects are also observed but not until the
slowest heating rate of 0.5°C/min. is reached. This
condition would be expected from a consideration of the
work terms of the transformation, which help to decrease the temperature. The DTA data for the 0.5°C/
min. rate of cooling clearly demonstrate the effects of
sample influenced temperature change. In the trace in
Fig. 2 the transformation is seen to begin at approximately 1030° and then stop at approximately 1020°C.
The transformation is stopped because the sample temperature does not continue to decrease as a result of
the slow heat flow established by the 0.5°C/min. cooling
rate. With time, the continuously cooling system
increases the thermal gradient, the rate of heat
removal is then increased, and again the sample temperature is lowered. The data indicate that this arrest
occurred for a time duration of about 15 minutes in
which the furnace cooled 7-1/2°. The only basis for
assuming fixed or reversal of temperature at transformation arrest points is the fact that many high temperature XRD investigations demonstrate a continuous
temperature-phase ratio relationship through the
transformation range. After the first arrest in this
0.5° cooling data series, a very fast rate of transformation for a time duration of five minutes is indicated
followed by a second transformation arrest. This
second arrest continues for a time period of more than
twenty minutes, and a system temperature decrease of
over 10° suggests the need to consider an increased role
for the deformation work factor of the transformation.
It is probable that the transformed phase, resulting

from the indicated high transformation rate, has an unusually high dislocation density and thermal diffusion
of pinning dislocations must occur before twinning takes
place. This delayed use of energy for deformation
could allow observations of both positive and negative
heat effects. The DTA record of the transformation is
not completed until the sample exhibits a third and
fourth thermal arrest. The observed shifts in temperature of the maximum DTA response points for the
different heating and cooling curves may be interpreted
as resulting from sample produced variations in the rate
of temperature change and sample history.

In summary and review of the transformation
phenomena that influence the amplitude, shape, and
temperature relationships of DTA data for the ZrO_2
transformation, the following are relevant to experimental apparatus and techniques used in this work. The
quantity of the phase transformed is not dependent on
time; it is totally dependent on the temperature and prior
history of the sample. The athermal rate is limited
only by the rate at which energy is supplied or removed
from the sample. In heating, the energy is used for the
configurational factor, acoustic coordinated transport
of large array of atoms, and the slower work of deformation of the transformed phase by dislocation diffusion.
All oppose the temperature increase of the sample,
serving as a self limiting control of the quantity of the
transformed phase at a given instant. To observe a
continuous, accumulative heat effect by DTA for this
transformation, the heat flow to the sample must be
large enough to supply the transformation energy
requirements and to continuously increase its temperature. This condition is satisfied at a heating rate of
$3°C/min$. The transformation in the cooling direction
presents an entirely different thermal problem. In the
experimental situation where the heat flow is large
enough to continuously reduce the sample temperature,
the sum of the exothermic change in configuration

energy and energy using work terms results in a decrease in the DTA heat effect. The opposite signs of the configurational and work terms help to support the continuation of the temperature decrease and the progress of the transformation. The difference in the rate at which the energy is used in the work of crystal deformation also contributes to the response of the DTA apparatus. The relative rate difference for each direction of the transformation and the mechanism of deformation for each favors instrumental response to this term on cooling.

From the previous data and discussion on the effect of heating rate on the monoclinic-tetragonal transformation in ZrO_2, it is apparent that a slow heating rate is not practical for the routine determination of this transformation. Considering the nature of the transformation as well as the equipment characteristics, a heating rate of 3°C/min. was found most suitable for determining this transformation. A representative trace at 3°C/min. for the forward and reverse transformation is seen in Fig. 3 where the heat effect versus temperature is plotted. In interpreting these curves, the start of the transformation is reported as the first deflection of the trace from the base line, and the completion as the point at which the curve returned to the base line. In Fig. 3 the forward transformation began at approximately 1172°C, the maximum deflection occurred at 1198°C and the transformation was completed at 1250°C. The reverse transformation began at approximately 1040°C, the maximum deflection occurred at 1021°C and the transformation was completed at 981°C. It is seen that the monoclinic-tetragonal transformation has a greater heat effect than the tetragonal-monoclinic transformation as would be expected from the earlier discussion.

Application to Specific Binary Systems

(1) The ZrO_2-HfO_2 System

The monoclinic-tetragonal transformation was determined in the ZrO_2-HfO_2 system as part of a program to determine the phase relationships of this system.[2] Differential thermal analysis was used and results correlated with high temperature XRD data. The DTA data are illustrated in Fig. 4 where temperature versus composition is plotted. The start and finish of the monoclinic-tetragonal transformation is represented by an inverted "V" enclosed by a circle and the start and finish of the tetragonal-monoclinic transformation is represented by a "V" enclosed by a circle. It is seen that there is a continuous increase in the transformation temperature as the composition moves from ZrO_2 to HfO_2. Also the size of the hysteresis associated with the transformation is decreased as the composition moves toward HfO_2. In general, the martensitic characteristics of the transformation were observed at all compositions. A detailed discussion of this data as well as the high temperature XRD data is given in the above reference.

(2) The ZrO_2-Sc_2O_3 System

The monoclinic-tetragonal transformation was investigated in the ZrO_2-Sc_2O_3 system using DTA as part of a program to determine the phase relationships of this system.[6] Results of this work are presented in Fig. 5 where temperature versus composition is plotted. Data points are identified in the same manner as Fig. 4. As Sc_2O_3 is added to ZrO_2, the transformation temperature is lowered sharply as seen in the figure. Data for the 0.75 and 1.50% Sc_2O_3 compositions are most significant since these compositions lie in the monoclinic phase field at room temperature. It is seen that the temperature range over which the transformation occurs is increased both on heating and cooling. Also the hysteresis is decreased. The 2.5 and 3.75% Sc_2O_3 compositions lie in the two phase mono- clinic plus tetragonal region at room temperature so that the completion of the monoclinic-tetragonal trans- formation is the only significant data point. Results of DTA on the 5.0% Sc_2O_3 composition indicated that no inversion occurred as would be expected, since this composition is tetragonal at room temperature.

The heat effect observed in the transformation in the ZrO_2-Sc_2O_3 system is presented in Fig. 6. Here the height of the DTA peak versus the Sc_2O_3 content is plotted. The peak height is the maximum difference in temperature between the inert material and the sample which is undergoing the transformation. The upper curve is the heat effect of the monoclinic-tetragonal transformation and the lower curve is the heat effect of the tetragonal-monoclinic transformation. The expla- nation for the greater heat effect for the monoclinic- tetragonal transformation has been given in an earlier section. Also, as the transformation temperature decreases, its range increases, thus decreasing the observed heat effect maximum. This also accounts for the tetragonal-monoclinic transformation being un- observed in the 3.75% Sc_2O_3 sample while the monoclinic-tetragonal transformation is clearly seen. These data are only relative but they do illustrate the sharp decrease in the heat effect of the transformation as scandia goes into solid solution. At the solubility limit of the monoclinic phase at 2% Sc_2O_3, the heat effect is approximately 25% that of pure ZrO_2.

(3) The ZrO_2-Y_2O_3 System

The monoclinic-tetragonal transformation was investigated in the ZrO_2-Y_2O_3 system in an investi- gation similar to one previously described. Results of this work are presented in Fig. 7 where temperature versus composition is plotted. As with Sc_2O_3, the addition of Y_2O_3 lowers the transformation sharply. Data for the 0.2, 0.7 and 1.0% compositions are most significant since these compositions lie in the monoclinic phase field at room temperature. It is seen that the temperature range over which the transformation occurs is increased both on heating and cooling, and that the amount of hysteresis is decreased. The 1.5 and 2.0% Y_2O_3 compositions lie in the two phase monoclinic plus tetragonal region at room temperature so that the completion of the transformation is the only significant data point for these compositions. The 3.5% Y_2O_3 composition is tetragonal at room temperature and no transformation is observed.

The heat effect observed in the transformation in the ZrO_2-Y_2O_3 system is given in Fig. 8. This is a plot similar to the heat effect data for the ZrO_2-Sc_2O_3 system shown previously. Here again the heat effect of the heating transformation is less than that of the cooling transformation. At the solubility limit of the monoclinic phase at 1.5% Y_2O_3 the heat effect is about 20% that observed in pure ZrO_2. As the composition is increased beyond 1.5% Y_2O_3, the heat effect decreases and is unobserved at 2.5% Y_2O_3 for the cooling transformation and unobserved at 3.5% Y_2O_3 for the heating transformation. The latter point is the start of the one phase tetragonal region.

Conclusions

An investigation was made of the monoclinic-tetragonal transformation in ZrO_2 by DTA with a two-fold purpose; first, to learn basic information about the transformation and second, to evaluate DTA as a tool for determining this transformation in zirconia-based binary systems. The transformation was determined as a function of heating rate and results revealed that the progress could be arrested at very low heating or cooling rates. This was found to occur at 1.5°C/min. for the transformation on heating and 0.5°C/min. for the transformation on cooling. This is reasonable when the energy terms are considered. These studies further reveal that the transformation is best determined by DTA when the heat flow is large enough to supply the transformation energy requirements and continuously increase or decrease the temperature, whatever the case may be. This condition is satisfied at a heating rate of 3°C/min. for the equipment used in this work. Having determined the suitability of this technique, it was employed to determine the transformation in the ZrO_2-HfO_2, ZrO_2-Sc_2O_3 and ZrO_2-Y_2O_3 systems.

References

1. R. Ruh, E. D. Wysong and N. M. Tallan, Ceramic Age 83, 44 (1967).
2. Robert Ruh, H. J. Garrett, R. F. Domagala, and N. M. Tallan, Jour. Am. Ceram. Soc. 51, 23 (1968).
3. L. L. Fehrenbacher and L. A. Jacobson, Jour. Am. Ceram. Soc. 51, 157 (1965).
4. J. E. Bailey, Proc. Roy. Soc. (London) 279A, 395 (1964).
5. J. L. Hart and A. C. D. Chaklader, Mat. Res. Bull. 2, 521 (1967).
6. R. F. Domagala, Robert Ruh and H. J. Garrett, Presented at the Sixty-Ninth Annual Meeting, The American Ceramic Society, New York, May 3, 1967.
7. Robert Ruh, K. S. Mazdiyasni and H. O. Bielstein, Presented at the Seventieth Annual Meeting, The American Ceramic Society, Chicago, Illinois, April 24, 1968.

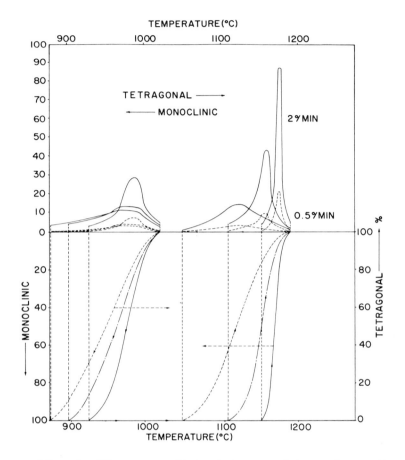

Fig. 1 The monoclinic-tetragonal transformation in ZrO_2 by high temperature XRD as a function of heating rate.

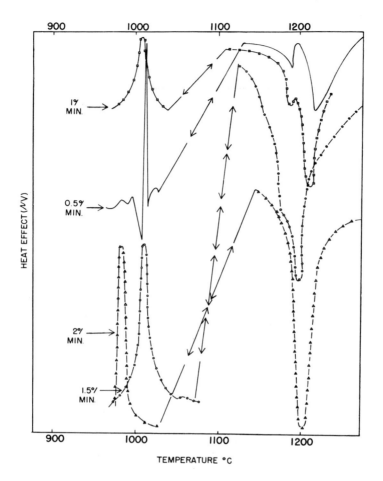

Fig. 2 The monoclinic-tetragonal transformation
in ZrO$_2$ by DTA as a function of heating rate.

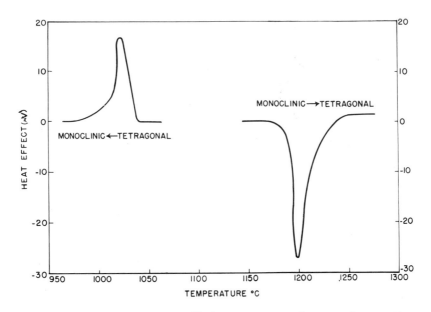

Fig. 3 The monoclinic-tetragonal transformation in ZrO_2 by DTA at a heating rate of 3°C/min.

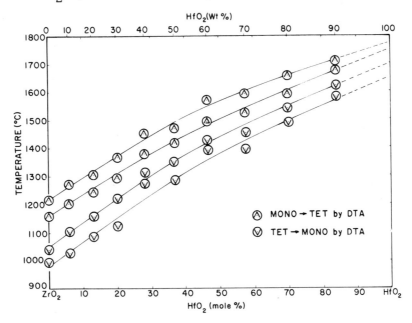

Fig. 4 The monoclinic-tetragonal transformation in the ZrO_2-HfO_2 system by DTA (After Ruh, Garrett, Domagala and Tallan).

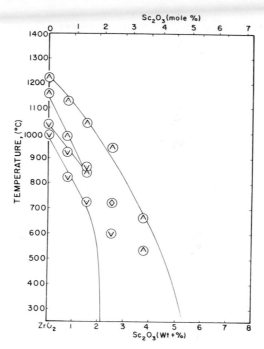

Fig. 5   The monoclinic-tetragonal transformation
in the ZrO_2-Sc_2O_3 system by DTA (After Garrett, Ruh
and Domagala).

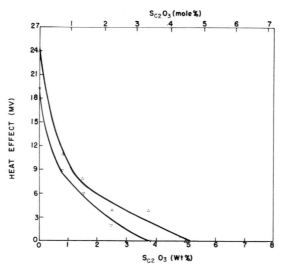

Fig. 6   Heat effect versus Sc_2O_3 content for the
monoclinic-tetragonal transformation in the ZrO_2-Sc_2O_3
system.

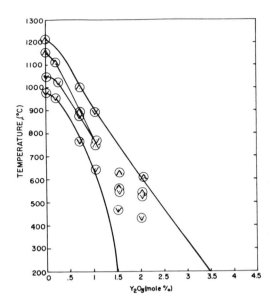

Fig. 7 The monoclinic-tetragonal transformation in the ZrO_2-Y_2O_3 system by DTA (After Ruh, Mazdi-yasni and Bielstein).

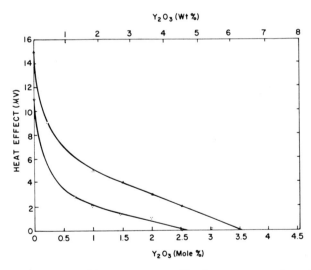

Fig. 8 Heat effect versus Y_2O_3 content for the monoclinic-tetragonal transformation in the ZrO_2-Y_2O_3 system.

STUDIES ON THERMAL ANALYSIS OF THE VANADATES OF TIN AND SILVER AND CHEMISORPTION OF OXYGEN AND HYDROGEN ON THESE VANADATES AS CATALYSTS

S.K. Bhattacharyya and (Miss) Jayasree Ghose

Department of Chemistry, Indian Institute of Technology
Kharagpur, India.

Abstract

The thermal characteristics of tin vanadate and silver vanadate have been studied by Differential Thermal Analysis (DTA), Derivative Thermogravimetric (DTG) and Thermogravimetric (TG) analyses. DTA thermograms show that tin vanadate undergoes two endothermal changes (the first between room temperature and 270° C and the second between 300° C - 370° C respectively), followed by an exothermal change between 390° - 440° C. DTG and TG curves show that the endothermal changes are accompanied by weight loss. During the second endothermal change tin vanadate decomposes into V_2O_5 and SnO_2. The decomposition products have been confirmed by X-ray and I.R. studies of decomposed tin vanadate. DTA, DTG and TG curves of silver vanadate show that it does not undergo any change upto 450° C. However, an endothermic peak appears above 450° C which is not accompanied by any weight change. Silver vanadate is stable upto 350° C which is indicated by X-ray and I.R. studies of the silver vanadate sample preheated to 350° C. A study of the chemisorptions of oxygen and hydrogen has been made on the thermally treated vanadates to explain the role of these vanadates as catalysts. These results confirm the formation of the decomposition products, as identified by X-ray and I.R.

Symbols

q = volume adsorbed
t = time
a and α = constants
t_o = $1/a\,\alpha$

1. Introduction

The thermal characteristics of the vanadates have not been studied thoroughly. The literature on this subject is extremely meagre. The only references that could be traced are related to the studies of ammonium metavanadate (1) by Differential Thermal Analysis(DTA), Thermogravimetry (TG), X-ray etc., of copper orthovanadate (2) by TG and of cobalt vanadate (3) by DTA. In view of the great importance of some of these vanadates as catalysts in oxidation reactions, the thermal characteristics of tin vanadate and silver vanadate have been thoroughly studied by Differential Thermal Analysis and Thermogravimetry and the products of thermal decomposition have been identified by X-ray analysis and I.R. spectra studies.

2. Experimental

2.1 Preparation and analysis of the samples.

All the chemicals used were of A.R. quality.

TIN VANADATE : Blood red precipitate of tin vanadate was obtained by the addition of a little excess of a cold solution of anhydrous stannic chloride (specific gravity 1.075) to a hot saturated solution of ammonium metavanadate. The precipitate was filtered and washed on a buchner funnel with hot water, untill it was free from chloride ions. The oven dried precipitate (sample 1) was analysed as follows -
About 1 gm. of tin vanadate was heated in a crucible at 500° C untill the weight was constant. To this a small amount of ammonium iodide was added and kept at 425° - 475° C for half an hour, cooled and weighed. This process of addition of ammonium iodide, heating, cooling and weighing was continued untill the weight became constant. The total loss in weight gave the amount of tin present in tin vanadate; Vanadium was analysed by titrating the tin vanadate solution in sulphuric acid with standard ferrous sulphate solution using diphenylamine-phosphoric acid indicator;
The total amount of ammonia present in tin vanadate was determined by digesting the tin vanadate in alkali, absorbing the issuing gases in standard sulphuric acid and then titrating it with standard alkali.
From the analyses, sample 1 was found to have the composition -
$SnV_2O_7 \cdot 2\frac{1}{2} H_2O \cdot \frac{1}{2}NH_3$ (Sn = 29.5%; V = 24.44%; NH_3 = 2%; H_2O = 9%)
Sample 2 of tin vanadate was prepared by heating sample 1 in a current of air at 450° C.

SILVER VANADATE : A dilute solution of silver nitrate was added to a hot saturated solution of ammonium metavanadate with constant stirring untill a little excess of the former was present in the solution. The orange precipitate was filtered and washed on a buchner untill it was free from nitrate ions. The oven dried sample of silver vanadate (sample 1) was analysed as follows -

The amount of silver in silver vanadate was determined by titration of the nitric acid solution with standard ammonium thiocyanate solution, using ferrous ammonium sulphate as indicator;

Vanadium and ammonia were determined by the same methods used in the analysis of tin vanadate.

From the analyses results the composition of sample 1 was found to be $AgVO_3$ ($Ag = 51.2\%$; $V = 24.67\%$; $NH_3 = 0$: $H_2O = 0$). Sample 2 of silver vanadate was prepared by heating sample 1 in a current of air at 350° C.

2.2 Differential thermal analyses and Thermogravimetric analyses of tin vanadate and silver vanadate were carried out in a B.U. MOM Derivatograph, model no. 874373. Differential thermal analyses were also carried out separately in air as well as in nitrogen atmosphere using a manually operated DTA apparatus (4).

2.3 The X-ray diffraction patterns of both samples of tin vanadate and silver vanadate (samples 1 and 2) were determined by the standard Debye - Scherrer method.

2.4 The Infrared absorption spectra of tin vanadate preheated to 450° C and silver vanadate preheated to 350° C were studied using a Perkin Elmer spectrophotometer in 1% KBr pellets.

2.5 Oxygen and hydrogen chemisorption measurements were made in a volumetric adsorption apparatus. The amounts adsorbed were directly represented by the drop in pressure (ΔP) in a constant volume system, without converting it to volume.

3. Results

3.1 The thermal characteristics of tin vanadate (sample 1), as revealed by DTA, DTG and TG curves are represented in Fig. 1. DTA thermo-gram shows that tin vanadate undergoes two endothermal changes, followed by an exothermal change on heating it upto 450° C. The first endothermic peak is at 130° C, the second at 360° C and the exothermic peak is at 420° C. The DTG curve showed similar peaks and an additional peak at 390° C. The TG curve indicates that the two endothermal changes are accompanied by loss of weight, - 7.5% after the first endothermal change and 6.5% after the second endothermal change. There is no loss of weight corresponding to the exothermic peak. The DTA curves shown in Fig. 2, obtained by separate DTA apparatus, show that the exothermic peak is considerably suppressed in nitrogen atmosphere.

The thermal characteristics of silver vanadate (sample 1) are represented by the DTA, DTG and TG thermograms as shown in Fig. 5. DTA curve shows that silver vanadate does not undergo any thermal change on heating upto 450° C; above this temperature, it undergoes an endothermal change which may be due to decomposition after fusion. However, this change is not accompanied by any weight change, as indicated by the straight line DTG and TG curves.

3.2 In the X-ray diffraction patterns of the two samples of tin vanadate, sample 1 (oven dried) did not show up any line. Sample 2 (preheated to 450° C) gave sharp peaks which were similar to those due to V_2O_5. The lines were quite sharp, indicating the well crystalline character of the V_2O_5 phase present in the sample. Four or five bands, superimposed on the pattern at positions approximating those due to tin oxide, SnO_2 (cassiterite) indicated the presence of SnO_2 of small crystallite size - of the order of 50 - 100A$^\circ$.

X-ray diffraction patterns of the two silver vanadate samples, showed a large number of sharp peaks attributable to well crystalline compounds. But the peaks could not be identified with those of any of the standard patterns given in the A.S.T.M. cards for standard substances. The diffractometer traces, however showed that the two vanadate samples, oven dried and preheated to 350°C, were identical in structure, both registering all the lines exactly at the same positions, except a few lines which were enhanced in the pattern of the preheated silver vanadate sample. All other lines were more or less of similar intensity in both the patterns and both the samples were well crystalline, particle size of the crystallites being of the order of 1500A$^\circ$.

3.3 The I.R. spectra of tin vanadate (sample 2) is shown in Fig. 3. The spectra exhibit a sharp absorption band at 1025 cm^{-1} similar to V_2O_5, as shown by Frederickson and Hausen (5).

I.R. spectra of silver vanadate (sample 2) is shown in Fig. 6. The spectra exhibit characteristic V-O stretching frequencies in the regions $800 - 1000 \text{ cm}^{-1}$. It is the same frequency as is obtained for V-O stretching in most of the metavanadates.

3.4 The chemisorptions of oxygen and hydrogen were studied at different temperatures and the kinetics of adsorption followed the Elovich equation,

$$dq/dt = ae^{-\alpha q} \quad ,$$

$$\text{or} \quad , \quad q = 2.3/\alpha \, \log(t+t_0) - 2.3/\alpha \, \log t_0$$

The chemisorption kinetics of oxygen on V_2O_5(6) at different temperature also followed the Elovich equation. The kinetic plots, $\Delta P \rightarrow \log(t+t_0)$ of oxygen chemisorption on V_2O_5 and on preheated tin vanadate samples at $450°$ C, are given in Fig.4.

Studies on the chemisorption of oxygen on silver vanadate show that there is very little chemisorption, and studies on hydrogen chemisorption show that it reduces silver vanadate very readily at low temperatures.

4. Discussion

TIN VANADATE : From Fig.1 it is evident that tin vanadate undergoes thermal changes on heating it upto $500°$ C. The first endothermic peak below $200°$ C in the DTA curve may be due to the loss of water from the compound. Thermogravimetric studies show that the weightloss below $200°$ C is 7.5% which corresponds to the loss of one and a half molecules of water. The second endothermic peak below $370°$ C is accompanied by 6.5% weightloss. The gases coming out during the second endothermal change are ammonia and water. Analysis of the compound showed that it contains 2% ammonia which corresponds to half a molecule of ammonia in one molecule of tin vanadate. Thus the weightloss during the second endothermal change may be due to loss of one molecule of water and half a molecule of ammonia. Ammonia is liberated only at high temperatures, which indicates that it remains strongly bound in the compound, or it may form a complex compound with tin vanadate, which decomposes only at high temperatures with the liberation of ammonia. The possibility that ammonium metavanadate may remain as such in the tin vanadate precipitate, cannot be ruled out completely. However, in whatever form ammonia is present, it could not be removed from the precipitate at room temperature, even after washing it several times with hot water.

873

Together with the liberation of ammonia and water, the second endothermic peak represents the decomposition of tin vanadate. From X-ray analyses studies it is found that tin vanadate decomposes into SnO_2 and V_2O_5 when it is heated upto $450°$ C. Sachtler and coworkers (7) have also studied the X-ray analysis of tin vanadate preheated to $500°$ C. They found that it yielded the diffraction pattern of V_2O_5 and lines which could be attributed to SnO_2, although the lattice constant was found to be 2% smaller than in crystalline SnO_2. No lines in their sample indicated a chemical compound "tin vanadate". They suggested that the SnO_2 lattice is capable of dissolving tetravalent vanadium on tin sites which may be the cause for the contraction of SnO_2 lattice. I.R. spectra of tin vanadate (sample 2), also indicate the fromation of V_2O_5 by thermal decomposition.

The course of the decomposition may be represented as follows, which is in accord with the loss in weight at different temperatures -

$$SnV_2O_7 \cdot 2\tfrac{1}{2}H_2O \cdot \tfrac{1}{2}NH_3 \xrightarrow{-1\tfrac{1}{2}H_2O} SnV_2O_7 \cdot H_2O \cdot \tfrac{1}{2}NH_3$$

$$SnO_2 + V_2O_5 \xleftarrow{\phantom{-\tfrac{1}{2}NH_3 \quad -H_2O}} SnV_2O_7 \quad \Big\downarrow \substack{-\tfrac{1}{2}NH_3 \\ -H_2O}$$

The exothermic peak after the decomposition may be either due to oxidation or a phase change. Since the exothermic peak is considerably suppressed when the DTA is done in nitrogen atmosphere, it appears that the exothermic peak is due to an oxidation process, following the decomposition of tin vanadate.

In case of ammonium metavanadate it has been found that the ammonia liberated, during the course of decomposition, degrades on the surface of the decomposed product , V_2O_5, which again oxidises in air to give V_2O_5. This oxidation is represented by the exothermic peak following the decomposition of ammonium metavanadate.

Similarly, in the thermal decomposition of tin vanadate, the ammonia liberated may degrade on the surface of V_2O_5 formed and the reoxida -tion of the latter in air may be represented by the exothermic peak. In nitrogen atmosphere, the reoxidation process is hindered whereby a suppressed exothermic peak is found. Moreover, the product formed by heating tin vanadate in nitrogen atmosphere is black, the same colour as that of lower valent oxides of vanadium. On heating this black compound in air, yellow V_2O_5 is formed. The additional small peak at

390°C, shown in the DTG curve, may be due to the process of ammonia degradation on $V_2 O_5$.

From Fig. 4 it is apparent that oxygen chemisorption on $V_2 O_5$ and preheated tin vanadate follow the same kinetics and give straight line $\Delta P \longrightarrow \log(t + t_o)$ curves. However, the straight line due to tin vanadate is steeper than due to $V_2 O_5$ which indicates that the rate of oxygen chemisorption on tin vanadate is comparatively greater and this may be due to the promoter action of SnO_2 on $V_2 O_5$, in tin vanadate. Hydrogen chemisorption on tin vanadate takes place at a much lower temperature than on $V_2 O_5$ and the former is reduced more readily.

SILVER VANADATE : DTA and DTG curves shown in Fig. 5, indicate that silver metavanadate does not undergo any thermal change when heated upto 450° C. However, the DTA curve shows that above 450° C it undergoes an endothermal change which is not accompanied by any weightchange, as indicated by the straight line DTG and TG curves. Deschauvres and Raveau (8) have reported that silver metavanadate does not undergo any decomposition before fusion. Hence the endothermic peak at 470°C may be due to the fusion of silver metavanadate, which is found to melt only above 400° C. X-ray diffraction and I. R. spectra studies also indicate that silver metavanadate undergoes no thermal change before, fusion. However, X-ray analyses studies reveal that there may be minute traces of silver, silver oxide and $V_2 O_5$ in the silver metavanadate when it is heated, as some enhanced sharp lines are obtained with the sample heated at 350° C, over the oven dried one.

The very small oxygen chemisorption on silver metavanadate preheated to 350° C, may be due to the minute traces of $V_2 O_5$ present in it.

Acknowledgements

Thanks are due to Prof. S. K. Sidhanta, Head of the Department of Chemistry, Burdwan University, for helping us in using the Derivato-graph and Mr. D.P. Dutta, Central Fuel Research Institute, Dhanbad, for helping us in taking the X-ray diffraction patterns of the vanadates.

References

1. Taniguchi, M., and Ingraham, T.R., Can. J. Chem. 42 , 2467(1964).
2. Strupler, N., Compt. Rend. 255, 527-9 (1962).
3. Joubert, J.C. and Durif, A., Bull. Soc. France, Mineral. Crist. 87(1), 47-9 (1964).

875

4. Bhattacharyya, S.K. and Ramchandran, V.S., Bull. Nat. Inst. Sci., India, 12, 23(1959) (Proc. of the Symposium on Contact Catalysis, 1956, Calcutta).

5. Frederickson, Leo D., Jr. and Hausen, D.M., Anal. Chem. 35 (7), 818-827 (1963).

6. Bhattacharyya, S.K. and Mahanti, P., Proceedings of the Fourth International Congress on Catalysis, Moscow, 1968.

7. Sachtler, W.M.H., Dorgelo, G.J.H., Fahrenfort, J. and Voorhoeve, R. J. H., Proceedings of the Fourth International Congress on Catalysis, Moscow, 1968.

8. Deschauvres, A. and Raveau, B., Compt. Rend., 259 (20), 3553-4 (1964).

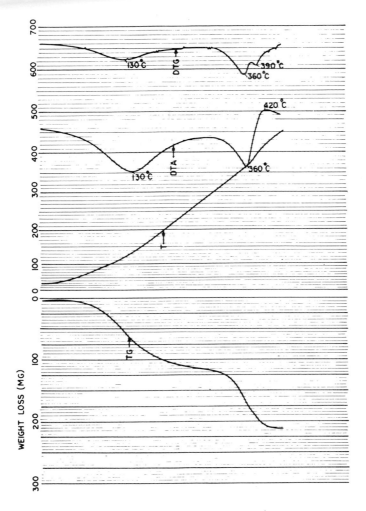

<u>Fig. 1</u> - Differential Thermal Analysis and
         Thermogravimetric Analysis of Tin
         Vanadate

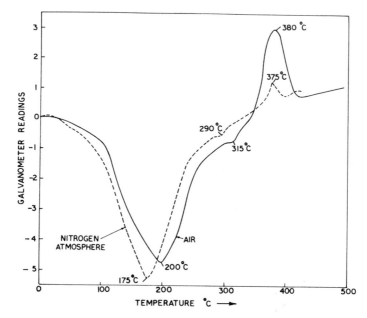

Fig. 2 - Differential Thermal Analysis of Tin
         Vanadate in Air and Nitrogen Atmosphere

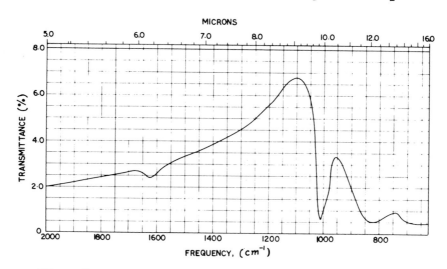

Fig. 3 - Infra Red Spectra of Tin Vanadate
         Sample 2 (Preheated to 450°C)

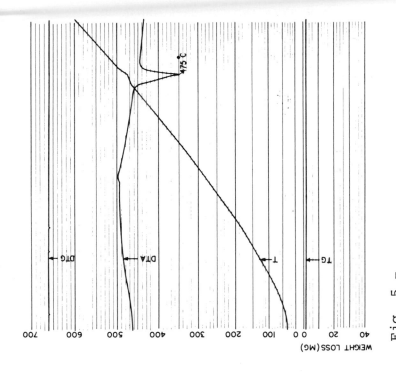

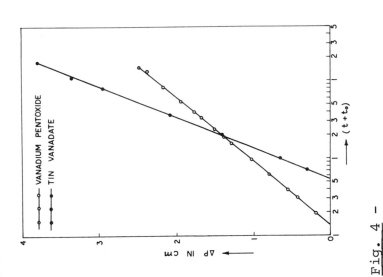

Fig. 5 -

Differential Thermal and Thermogravimetric Analysis of Silver Vanadate

Fig. 4 -

Elovitch Plots for Kinetics of Oxygen
Chemisorption at 350°C on Vanadium
Pentoxide and Tin Vanadate

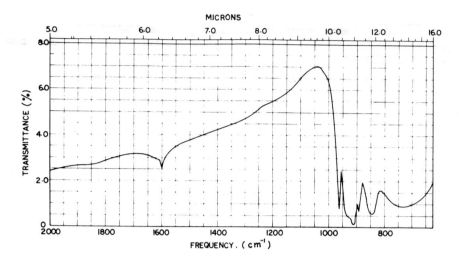

Fig. 6 — Infra Red Spectra of Silver Vanadate
Sample 2 (preheated to 350°C)

THE INFLUENCE OF OXIDE ADDITIONS ON THE REDUCTION OF UO_3 AND U_3O_8 AS MEASURED BY DTA AND TG

G. Berggren and A. Brown
AB Atomenergi, Studsvik, Sweden

Abstract

U_3O_8 and UO_3 powders mixed with various amounts of CeO_2 and PuO_2 have been examined by means of DTA, X-ray diffraction and TG in order to study the reduction kinetics. A novel DTA device for use in reducing atmospheres with W/Re thermocouples is described.

Simple methods for calculating kinetic parameters from DTA curves have been reviewed and applied. The activation energy for UO_3 and U_3O_8 reduction is not influenced by the oxide additives within the experimental errors ($\pm$ 15 %).

X-ray diffraction was used to identify intermediate and final products. Comparison with TG was satisfactory.

Introduction

Amorphous UO_3 and various ammonium complexes comprise the products of the precipitation and drying of ammonium-uranates. In order to produce nuclear grade UO_2 additional heating and reduction steps must be used. The literature dealing with these problems is very extensive.

With the introduction of mixed PuO_2-UO_2 as potential thermal and/or fast reactor fuels, interest has been focussed on physical mixing of the binary oxide compounds. Subsequent heat treatment is assumed to afford homogeneous or solid solution products of stoichiometric composition.

It seems reasonable to expect that solid solution formation will be facilitated by phase changes and by oxygen

881

mobility during heat treatment in a suitable atmosphere.

Fast reactor fuels have been prepared by mixing, milling and sintering a mixture of UO_3, U_3O_8 and PuO_2 [1]. This implies certain technological advantages.

Our aim is to investigate the stepwise reduction of production route UO_3 and the effect on reduction mechanism of CeO_2 (and PuO_2) additions. CeO_2 has been used in most of the experimental work because of its similarity to PuO_2 [2]. The work reported here is a part of an experimental programme still in progress.

The present investigation is based on a combination of DTA, TG and X-ray diffraction techniques. Similar practice has been used by Bergstein et al. [3]. A combination of the above mentioned techniques has been used in a simultaneous analysis of UO_3 disintegration by Besonov et al. [4].

Experimental

DTA and TG measurements were carried out in devices manufactured by Netzsch (Germany). Similar devices are used for radioactive substances [5] and are shown in Fig. 1. DTA sample holders were made of nickel or alumina. The latter type was used in reducing atmospheres at temperatures above 1000 °C together with 3 % W/Re - 25 % W/Re thermocouples. In all other cases Pt - 10 % Rh/Pt thermocouples were employed.

The W/Re alloy can be used in vacuum, in inert gases and reducing atmospheres. Oxidising or carbon containing atmospheres destroy the thermocouple. There is no need for cold-junction correction between 0 °C and 25 °C. The thermoelectric power is given in Table 1.

Table 1.   3 % W/Re - 25 % W/Re thermocouple

Temperature (°C)	mV	mV/°C
400	6.128	0.019
600	10.093	0.020
1000	18.251	0.020
1400	25.912	0.018
2200	38.339	0.012

The hot junction tends to become brittle after 10 to 15 heating-cooling cycles, which also results in variation of the output.

The commercial TG device was modified in order to allow measurements in various atmospheres. Temperature was measured outside the reaction chamber. Sample temperature was plotted from experimentally determined correction curves. Alumina sample holders were used.

X-ray diffraction patterns of samples quenched to room temperature were recorded in a Guinier-Hägg camera. The radiation used was strictly monochromatized $CuK\alpha_1$ which affords the best conditions for line resolution.

Powder properties

The starting materials were checked by X-ray diffraction, chemical analysis and specific surface area measurement.

The UO_3 samples (designated "UO_3") were taken from the production route. The separate steps of the decomposition are of considerable complexity [6] and stable UO_3 is seldom obtained. The resulting UO_2 powder is, however, extremely pure. Powder properties are given in Table 2.

Table 2. Powder properties

Composition	Structure	BET-area m^2/g	Source
"UO_3"	amorphous	4.3 4.6 (milled)	AE
U_3O_8	orthorhombic	3.6	AE
PuO_2	cubic, fluorite type	3.8	CEA
CeO_2	cubic, fluorite type	1.3	Fluka

The "UO_3" powder contains ammonium and nitrate ions and carbamide to a total of 4.4 %. The uranium content and O/U ratio as determined by chemical analysis were 78.7 ± 0.3 w/o and 2.99 ± 0.01, respectively. The mixtures contained 5, 15 and 30 a/o cerium and 10 a/o plutonium. The physical mixing

was performed in a Spex Mixer-Mill by co-milling for 20 minutes. A number of pellets were prepared by pressing the powder at 2 ton/cm^2. Some of the pellets were used for DTA
measurements.

Experimental procedure

The heating rates used were 10 $^\circ$C/min for DTA and 5
$^\circ$C/min for TG, respectively. The recorder strip chart feed
was 120 mm/h. The gases comprised a 6 % H_2-94 % N_2 mixture
and compressed air (max 100 ppm H_2O). Control by means of a
solid state electrolyte cell showed an oxygen pressure of
10^{-20} atm at 1000 $^\circ$C for the hydrogen-nitrogen mixture.

Gas flow was maintained at 15 l/h during all measurements. The type of gas flow achieved in the reaction space
of the thermobalance renders buoyancy corrections unnecessary.

The steps were as follows: a) heating in H_2-N_2 to 800
$^\circ$C and cooling, b) renewed heating in air to 800 $^\circ$C and
cooling, c) heating in H_2-N_2 to 800 $^\circ$C.

In several cases the temperature in steps a) and b) was
increased to 1550 $^\circ$C.

Samples for X-ray powder diffraction were taken at different stages of the process.

Experimental results

Fig. 1 represents DTA curves of "UO_3" as reduced in air
or in a reducing atmosphere. Diffraction patterns were recorded for samples at points A, B and C. The phase conditions of B and C are difficult to identify and have a resemblance to the orthorhombic β-UO_3 phase. Ammonium, nitrates
as well as carbon from organic residues are difficult to remove without decomposing the trioxide. Thus the two exothermic peaks in reducing atmosphere do not represent the stepwise reduction of UO_3, but correspond to the complex decomposition of our "UO_3" to UO_2.

The DTA curve in air shows the decomposition at a lower
temperature (400 $^\circ$C) and a definite phase change to U_3O_8.

The composition at A has an O/U ratio of 2.71 and could be interpreted as a separate phase [7].

DTA curves for various mixtures as well as for U_3O_8 in reducing atmospheres are given in Fig. 2. The general appearance of the curves is not altered by the addition of CeO_2. The steps for U_3O_8 reduction [8] shown by three exothermic peaks have been slightly distorted by the addition of CeO_2. It must be noticed, that reduction of "UO_3" is completed at lower temperature than the reduction of U_3O_8.

TG measurements are shown in Fig. 4. They confirm the DTA results, whereas the latter give a more detailed picture of the reactions.

Experiments extended to higher temperatures are given in Fig. 5. Similar DTA curves for PuO_2 addition have been reported before [5]. The resolution when using alumina sample holders is not satisfactory and the results cannot be used for the calculation of kinetic data.

Reduction of pure CeO_2 or PuO_2 is dependent on the powder characteristics [5]. Complementary TG measurements show that reduction begins at approximately 700 °C and O/M = 1.90 is reached during a TG experiment even in oxide mixtures.

The degree of crystallinity was relatively poor after the reduction of "UO_3" as seen by diffraction line broadening. The material became more crystalline after a subsequent oxidation-reduction cycle.

Powders or compacts submitted to heat treatment in reducing atmosphere at 1700 °C for 4 h showed several phases, namely UO_2, CeO_2 and solid solution. Similar results are found for PuO_2 addition.

Evaluation of results

A DTA curve represents the dependence of a reaction on time and temperature and can thus be used for the evaluation of reaction kinetics [9-11]. Certain assumptions that the greatest reaction rate has been reached at DTA peak temperature may depend rather on sample holder configuration. To obtain the activation energy we have therefore used the method of Piloyan et al. [11].

The rate and temperature dependence of a reaction may be expressed by the equation

$$\frac{d\alpha}{dt} = A\ f(\alpha)\ \exp(-E/RT)$$

where A = constant, $f(\alpha)$ = function of the extent of the reaction. It was shown that the deviation from the baseline in the initial stages of the reaction is described by the expression

$$\Delta T = S\ \frac{d\alpha}{dt}$$

where S = area of thermal effect.

The change in temperature during a DTA measurement is said to have a greater effect on ΔT than the change in α (valid for α = 0.05 to 0.8) which justifies the use of the equation

$$\ln \Delta T = C - E/RT$$

This equation is said to be also suitable for diffusion kinetics.

ΔT values are taken directly from the DTA curve (in mm) and used for the calculation of activation energies by straight line fitting.

The method has been used to investigate the dissociation of solid compounds [12], for which errors of the order of ± 15 % were obtained. This method appears to be suitable for digital plotting and numerical computing. The data represented in Table 3 are the results of studies still in progress.

The calculation of the order of reaction was made by means of the graphic method presented by Kissinger [9]

$$n = 1,26\ \sqrt{a/b}$$

The graphic methods are shown in Fig. 6.

Calculation of activation energies from TG traces has

been made by the method described by Šesták et al, [13]. The
results are given in Table 3.

Table 3. Activation energies (kcal/mole)

Reaction	As calculated from DTA	TG
"UO_3"$\rightarrow UO_{2.71}$ (n=0.8)	49.8	(80.1)
$UO_{2.71} \rightarrow UO_{2.67}$ "	89.8	(85.2)
$U_3O_8 \rightarrow U_3O_{8-x}$	28.9	(31)
	26.4 (30 % Ce)	
$U_3O_{8-x} \rightarrow U_4O_9$ (n=0.4)	34.5	
	33.7 (30 % Ce)	
$U_4O_9 \rightarrow UO_2$	21.8	
"UO_3"$\rightarrow UO_{2.9}$ (n=0.9)	42.3	(35.6)
	43.6 (5 % Ce)	
	41.2 (15 % Ce)	
$UO_{2.9} \rightarrow UO_2$ (n=0.9)	24.6	(22.9)
	24.4 (5 % Ce)	
	25.2 (15 % Ce)	

Discussion of results

The experiments do not show any significant influence
of CeO_2 (or PuO_2) addition to the reduction mechanism of
uranium oxides. The activation energy calculated for the
reaction $UO_{2.9} \rightarrow UO_2$, approximately 25 kcal/mole, as well as
for $U_3O_8 \rightarrow UO_2$ from DTA curves is in accordance with literature values.

The mechanism of U_3O_8 reduction is however different
from "UO_3". The reduction is completed at higher temperatures, even if low activation energies are encountered for
the final step of reduction [14]. Also the reaction order
for U_3O_8 reduction, n $\sim$ 0.4 indicates a combination of heterogeneous adsorption and diffusion.

DTA curves may be more difficult to interpret than TG.
DTA gives on the other hand evidence of several thermal
changes than is indicated by TG. Comparison with TG afford

however acceptable agreement by and large. The development of strictly quantitative DTA devices [15] may remove some of the shortcomings.

The diffusion rate of oxygen in fluorite-type oxides is especially high for overstoichiometric compounds. Ternary oxides show, however, a lower mobility at high temperatures. From a technological point of view this implies certain difficulties. Metastable states may be the result of various heat treatments and one can find evidence that even previous co-precipitation does not facilitate solid solution formation. This is especially the case when various shapes of solids are being formed by pressing and subsequent high temperature sintering in unsuitable atmospheres.

It seems reasonable to expect that when reduction of ternary oxides is shifted to temperatures above 1000 °C by a slightly oxidising atmosphere, solid solution formation could be facilitated. DTA may prove a useful tool for investigating reduction kinetics.

Acknowledgements

The authors would like to acknowledge the assistance of Dr. J. Šesták in the experimental set up of thermal analysis and in fruitful discussions. We would also like to thank following persons for their assistance in experimental work: Mr. A. Kronberg, TG measurements, Mr. L. Jacobsson, X-ray diffraction and Mr. T. Karlsson, BET-area measurements and pellet preparation.

References

1. Dean, G., Pelou, C. and Beugnies, D., in Report CEA-R 2737 (1965); Claudson, T.T., Peterson, R.E. and Hanson, J.E., in Report BNWL-569, 86 (1967)
2. Blank, H., Report EUR 3563 e (1967)
3. Bergstein, A., Šesták, J., Holba, P., Kleinert, P. and Funke, A., Czech. J. Phys. B17, 686 (1967)
4. Besonov, A.F., Shalaginov, V.N., Vlasov, V.G. and Taksis, G.A., Zh. Prikl. Khim., 40, 1128 (1967), (in Russian)
5. Berggren, G. and Forsyth, R., in Plutonium 1965, eds. Kay, A.E. and Waldron, M.B. (Chapman & Hall, London 1967)

6. Peterson, A., EAES Symp. Fundamental Aspects Prep. Uranium Oxides, Arnhem 1962
7. Holmberg, B., Stockholm University, privat communication
8. Sato, R. and Doi, H., J. Nucl. Mat. 15, 146 (1965)
9. Kissinger, H.E., Anal. Chem. 29, 1702 (1957)
10. McMillan, J.A., American Physical Soc. Autumn Meeting, Chicago, 1965, AED Conf. 1965 312-15
11. Piloyan, F.O., Ryabchikov, I.D. and Novikova, O.S., Nature No 5067, 1229 (1966)
12. Berggren, G., to be published (AE-RKP-80)
13. Šesták, J., Šatava, V. and Řihák, V., Silikáty 11, 315 (1967) (in Czechish)
14. Volpe, M. and Mihailovich, S., Report ANL-6475 (1962)
15. Speros, D.M., this conference

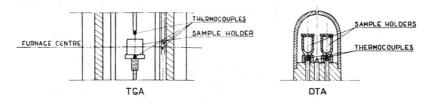

Fig. 1. Thermal techniques

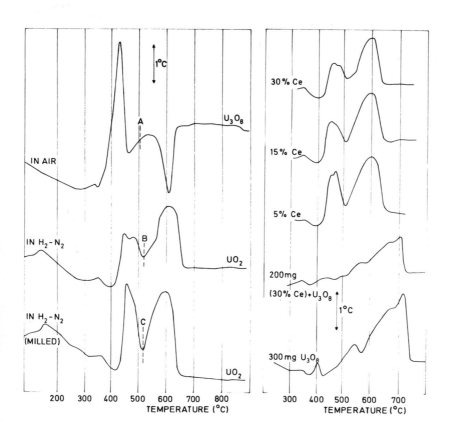

Fig. 2. DTA curves of "UO₃" powders. Sample weight 200 mg, U₃O₈ or UO₂ as reference material

Fig. 3. DTA curves of the reductions "UO₃" → UO₂, and U₃O₈ → UO₂

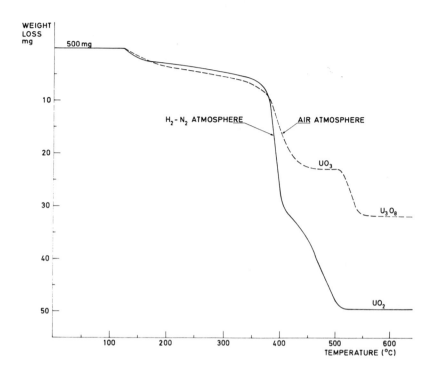

Fig. 4. TG curves for "UO_3" reduction

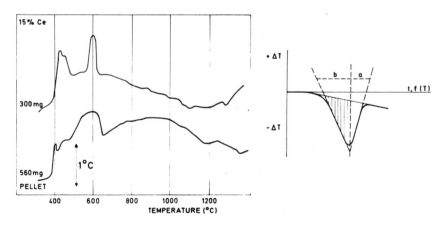

Fig. 5. DTA curves using alumina sample holders

Fig. 6. Graphic eval-
uation of a DTA curve

891

THERMAL OXIDATION OF NICKEL SILICON ALLOY

F. Saegusa

Advanced Research Laboratory
Watervliet Arsenal
Watervliet, New York

Abstract

Thermogravimetric techniques have been used to study oxidation of nickel alloys containing 0.1 to 3.2 wt % silicon at temperatures up to 1300°C. Due to the appearance of internal oxidation the effect of silicon addition on the oxidation process was complex. The thermograms showed a simple curve for lower silicon content, but two consecutive curves for higher content. The oxidation mechanism was interpreted in terms of isothermal kinetics and the corresponding structural changes.

Introduction

It is generally known that the thermal oxidation kinetics of nickel is described by a parabolic rate law over a wide range of temperature with a formation of a single phase oxide, NiO, indicating the reaction is diffusion controlled. Silicon oxidation was recently re-examined (1-2) and a relationship of mixed parabolic rate was derived based on a model relative to the reactions taking place at the two boundaries of the oxide layer and the diffusion process involved.

Silicon is often used to improve the oxidation resistance of many metals at high temperatures. However, little work has been reported on the oxidation behavior of nickel silicon alloys. In an earlier work, Horn (3) made a qualitative statement indicating that the effect of an addition of a second element on nickel oxidation is greater, the larger the difference in atomic radius. At 900°C the addition of silicon up to 0.5 atm % increases the oxidation rate but further addition up to 4 % reduces the oxidation rate. Gil'dengorn and Rogelberg (4) studied the oxidation of nickel alloys containing 0.9 - 6.4 wt % silicon in air. It was found that the silicon addition increases the oxidation resistance of nickel at 1000 - 1200°C, and in most cases the oxidation kinetics follow an approximately parabolic rate law particularly at 1100 and 1200°C.

In the present work, a thermogravimetric method was used to study the oxidation of homogeneous nickel silicon alloys in the temperature range 300 - 1300°C. Thermograms were interpreted in terms of kinetics involving external and internal oxidation. Analyses of structural change were made relative to the corresponding kinetics.

Experimental

Materials: The alloys were prepared from high-purity materials in an arc-melter. Zone-refined nickel with the following analysis: Ag < 0.02; Al 0.3; Fe 12; Si 0.2 ppm and 6/9s silicon were used. The bars were cold worked to 1/8 inch thickness and annealed in vacuum. Analysis of the alloys for silicon gave the following composition in weight %: 0.08, 0.50, 1.00, 2.98, and 3.21. One-quarter inch square coupon specimens weighing approximately 1 gram were cut from the sheets. The surfaces were polished through 100 grit emery paper and degreased prior to use. Chemically pure oxygen supplied from a cylinder was further improved by successive passage through a purifier and dryer train. The oxygen flow rate was maintained at 100 cm^3/min throughout the runs.

Apparatus: Mettler's thermoanalyzer was used for gravimetric measurements. The specimen was supported in a fine platinum wire basket positioned over the top of a thermocouple tip to minimize the difference in temperature reading. Weight changes were continuously recorded as the specimen was heated at a linear heating rate or at a constant temperature in a steady flow of oxygen. For the linearly-programmed-temperature experiments, the heating rate was 4°C/min, while the temperature was controlled

894

within ± 0.5°C. The weight recording sensitivity was
0.1 mg.

After oxidation, the oxide products were identified
using electron and x-ray diffraction and the polished cross
sections of oxidized alloys were subjected to metallographic
and electron microprobe examination.

Results

Oxidation at Linear Heating Rate

Thermograms were obtained for each alloy composition.
In Fig. 1 the specific weight gain is plotted against
temperature over the range 300 - 1300°C. The plot shows
that increasing additions of silicon generally tend to
reduce oxidation of nickel. In some cases, however, such as
at lower temperatures with silicon additions up to 1%, an
increased oxidation is shown. The oxidation behavior
becomes complex in the neighborhood of 900°C at or above 3%
silicon addition.

For pure nickel, the oxidation curve consists of two
parabolic segments joined with a short straight portion
around 900 - 1000°C. This suggests two oxidation mechanisms
for the temperature ranges below and above 900°C, and coincides with the finding by Berry (5) and Van der Broek (6)
who showed a pronounced kink at about 950°C in Arrhenius
plots. The oxidation rate of nickel is dependent on the
concentration gradient of cation vacancies in the oxide and,
over a limited temperature range, only one charge state for
the vacancy is likely to predominate. Berry's data satisfactorily followed the singly ionized nickel vacancy-mech-
anism at 800 - 900°C and the doubly ionized vacancy mechanism at 1000°C or above. Van der Broek attributed the
kink to a change in the number of oxide layers from a
single layer at lower temperatures to a double layer at
higher temperatures.

For dilute alloys containing up to 1% silicon,
oxidation is represented by a single smooth parabolic curve.
When the silicon content exceeds 3%, the oxidation is
described by two consecutive curves with a break around
900°C and an appreciable reduction in oxidation is observed

in the higher temperature region.

Isothermal Oxidation

Oxidation was carried out at three temperatures for 16 hrs. The logarithmic plot of weight gain vs oxidation time is shown in Fig. 2. Most of the data are represented by one or two straight lines indicating the power-law dependence, $(\Delta m)^n = kt$, with n ranging from 1 to 3. In most cases the plots consist of two straight line portions. For the 0.5 and 1% silicon alloys the plots indicate an initial linear oxidation rate followed by a parabolic rate except for the 1% alloy at 800°C, which is closer to a cubic rate. For the 3% alloy the initial rate changes from cubic (800°C) to parabolic (1000°C) followed by a much higher power rate at longer times. For the 3.2% alloy at 800° and 1000°C the rate changes from the initial parabolic behavior to cubic. At 1200°C both 3 and 3.2% alloys obey almost a single rate between parabolic and linear.

Oxide

The oxide formed was analyzed by electron and x-ray diffraction techniques. Since the electrons penetrate a few hundred angstroms, this technique identifies the oxide present at the outer surface only. All the diffraction patterns showed that the oxide consisted of a single oxide, NiO. X-ray diffraction analyses were performed in a diffractometer using Cu radiation with a nickel filter at 35KV and 15 milliamperes. The x-ray diffraction analyzes all of the oxide layer and the base metal. With the exception of the thick layers which absorb x-rays from the matrix all the patterns matched those of NiO and Ni. Oxide scale peeled off from the matrix was analyzed using a powder camera and was identified as NiO plus a small amount of Ni_2SiO_4. The above findings are listed in Table 1 with those of surface appearance.

Metallographic inspection of the polished cross section of the oxidized alloys revealed a subscale formation of precipitated particles. The outer scale consisted of a mono- or double-layer depending on alloy composition and oxidation temperature. Precipitation of oxide particles followed the general pattern of internal oxidation. Typical

TABLE 1

Oxidation Product, Appearance & Analysis

% Si	Temperature, °C					
	800		1000		1200	
0.5	gray	NiO (e) NiO+Ni(x)	gray-green	NiO (e) NiO+Ni(x)	met. gray	NiO (e) NiO (x)
1	gray	NiO+tr. SiO_2(e) NiO+Ni(x)	br. gray	NiO (e) NiO+Ni(x)	dark gray	NiO (e) NiO (x)
3	gray	NiO (e) NiO+Ni(x)	gray-green	NiO (e) NiO+Ni(x)	green-d.gray	NiO (e) NiO (x)
3.2	gray-brown	NiO (e) NiO+Ni(x)	gray	NiO (e) NiO+ Ni_2SiO_4(p)	dark gray	NiO+ Ni_2SiO_4(p)

(e) electron diffraction, (x) x-ray diffraction and
(p) powder method

photomicrographs are shown in Figs. 3-5. At low temperature
precipitation takes place mainly along grain boundaries and
with increasing temperature precipitation develops throughout the grain (Fig. 3). With increasing silicon content
higher temperatures of oxidation are required for uniformly
dispersed precipitate. The 3% silicon alloy showed a little
precipitation at lower temperatures, but an evenly dispersed
precipitate was observed at 1200°C. (Fig. 4). No appreciable precipitation was observed in the 3.2% alloy (Fig. 5).

To support the above observation, electron microprobe
analysis was made for each element while the specimen was
traversed at right angles to the original surface for a
distance of approximately 200 microns into the metal matrix.
The path of the beam is indicated by arrows in the metallographs. The corresponding traces, shown in Figs. 6-9,
indicate the relative distribution of each element. For

comparison the representative x-ray images for Ni and Si are shown together with the metallographs in Figs. 3-5. It is readily seen that for 1 and 3% alloys no silicon increase is observed in the outer scale. The former shows a broad granular zone adjacent to the scale/metal interface containing a spotty concentration of silicon particularly along grain boundaries. The latter shows small silicon precipitates within a similar area. The 3.2% alloy shows a sharp increase in Si content in the outer layer adjacent to the scale/metal interface and no change in Si within the matrix indicating formation of Ni_2SiO_4 and the absence of internal oxidation.

Discussion

Since thermograms obtained with a linear-heating rate are smooth in the temperature range above $900^\circ C$, an activation energy of oxidation can be estimated using Kofstad (7) method.

The general rate law may be expressed by

$$(\Delta m)^{n-1} \frac{d (\Delta m)}{dt} = A \exp \left(\frac{- Q}{RT} \right) \qquad (1)$$

Temperature increase at a linear rate with time is given by

$$T = a t + b \qquad (2)$$

Substituting (2) and $A/a = B$ in (1),

$$(n-1)\ln (\Delta m) + \ln \frac{d (\Delta m)}{dT} = \ln B - \frac{Q}{RT} \qquad (3)$$

The slope of the straight line obtained by a plot of the left side of (5) against $1/T$ gives an activation energy, Q. Values obtained in this work (n=2) are listed in Table 2. Although this method gives an approximate value, the data indicate a marked difference from that of nickel metal. The values obtained in this work for nickel were in agreement with those of Berry and Van der Broek, who gave 24 and 20 kcal/mole for the temperature range below $950^\circ C$, and 57 and 50 kcal/mole above 950°C, respectively.

TABLE 2

Activation Energy, Q (Kcal/mole)

Ni		Ni - Si alloys (% Si)			
500–800°C	950–1300°C	0.1%	0.5%	1%	3.0%
20.8	46.5	60.2	59.7	61.3	65.0

Since NiO is a metal deficit, p-type semiconductor the oxidation of nickel is controlled by diffusion of nickel ions through cation vacancies and electron holes. Recently Mrovec (8) explained the double layer formation mechanism by outward diffusion of cation in two stages: (1) a compact monolayer scale is formed until the consumption of metal is compensated by the plastic flow of the scale, and (2) at a certain critical thickness the scale begins to lose its contact with metal by crack development. Consequent reduction in the rate of metal transport leads to secondary formation of a porous layer followed by gradual dissociation of the outer layer. The morphological structure depends on the plastic deformation of the reaction product, surface geometry, and reaction time and temperature.

In Ni-Si alloys the base metal oxide, NiO, is formed principally by the outward diffusion of nickel ions through the scale whereas internal oxidation takes place by the inward transport of oxygen to form SiO_2 precipitates in the matrix. The internally formed SiO_2 can further react with NiO at the scale/metal interface to form a silicate. The total reaction is written as follows with free energy changes at 1000°C:

$$Ni(s) + 1/2\ O_2(g) = NiO(s): \quad \Delta G_4^{o} = -35{,}900\ cal \qquad (4)\ ^{9)}$$

$$Si(s) + O_2(g) = SiO_2(s): \quad \Delta G_5^{o} = -166{,}800\ cal \qquad (5)\ ^{9)}$$

$$2NiO + SiO_2 = Ni_2SiO_4(s): \quad \Delta G_6^{o} = -7{,}340\ cal \qquad (6)\ ^{10)}$$

It was observed that a small addition of Si increased the oxidation of nickel in some cases. The introduction of Si^{+4} to the NiO lattice requires dissolution of internally oxidized SiO_2 at the NiO/Ni interface. The amount of Si in equilibrium at the interface in solid solution in Ni can be calculated by the following equilibrium constant:

$$SiO_2(s) \longrightarrow \underline{Si} \text{ (alloy)} + O_2(g) \tag{7}$$

$$RT \ln K_7 = RT \ln a_{si} \, Po_2 = \Delta G_5^o \tag{8}$$

Using values for ΔG_5^o and $Po_2 = 5.0 \times 10^{-11}$ atm (NiO/Ni) at $1000^{\circ}C$, (8) yields $a_{si} = 2.0 \times 10^{-16}$ ($1000^{\circ}C$). It can also be seen that a very slight amount of silicon is needed to initiate internal oxidation.

When a small amount of Si is added to nickel, the oxide precipitation taking place at the scale/metal inter-face in the initial stage of reaction gives rise to break down of full contact between scale and metal. Thus the stage (2) described in the case of pure nickel takes place immediately at the interface resulting in formation of a porous inner layer and loss of compactness of the outer layer, which is growing by outward diffusion of nickel ion. If the anisotropic dissociation of the outer layer or the transport of oxygen in the crack is the slow process, the formation of the inner porous layer follows a linear rate law. With increasing thickness of the porous inner layer, diffusion becomes a rate-determining step. The oxidation kinetics, therefore, are characterized by a shift from linear to parabolic at a certain thickness of the porous layer as shown in 0.5 and 1.0 alloys (Fig. 2, a b).

Generally plastic flow of the scale is not observed in the binary alloys, and the inward transport of oxygen mole-cules is carried out through perpendicular discontinuities in the scale while the outer layer is formed by outward lattice diffusion of metal. In the 3% alloy oxidation kinetics are controlled by parabolic diffusion until the internal oxide precipitate becomes a mechanical obstacle to the diffusion process (Fig. 2, c). In the 3.2% alloy, where no internal oxidation is observed, the initial reaction kinetics are parabolic diffusion controlled (Fig. 2, d).

The quasi-cubic rate observed at 800°C for the 1 and 3% alloys appears to be caused by a superposition of two parabolic steps, whereby the rate constant of gas consumption becomes smaller as time increases (11). At higher temperatures where the scale loses its adherence to the metal, the parabolic rate tends to deviate towards a linear rate.

The secondary solid-solid reaction between the oxides are observed only at the 3.2% alloy. To calculate the silicon content at which an alloy is in thermodynamic equilibrium with a mixture of Ni_2SiO_4 and SiO_2, the following equation is written

$$Ni_2SiO_4(s) + Si \text{ (alloy)} = 2\ SiO_2(s) + 2\ Ni \text{ (alloy)} \quad (9)$$

The equilibrium constant is

$$RT \ln K_9 = RT \ln a_{Ni}^2/a_{si} = -\Delta G_9^o$$

where

$$\Delta G_9^o = \Delta G_5^o - 2\ \Delta G_4^o - \Delta G_6^o = -87,660 \text{ cal } (1000^\circ C)$$

Thus for $a_{Ni} = 1.$, $a_{Si} = 1.1 \times 10^{-15}$. It appears that SiO_2 is more stable at the scale/metal interface, if the silicon content does not fall below this value. The formation of Ni_2SiO_4 phase, however, has no effect on the weight change measurements.

Recently a mathematical treatment on the growth rate of subscale depth on simultaneous external and internal oxidation was developed by Maak (12) extending Wagner's equation. However, further information on precipitation dispersion is awaited for application of this treatment to thermogravimetry.

Acknowledgement

The author wishes to thank J. F. Cox for his critical

review of the manuscript and R. Peterson and R. Lazzaro for their assistance with the experimental work.

References

1. B. E. Deal and A. S. Grove, J. Appl. Phys. 36, 3770, (1965).
2. A. G. Revesz, K. H. Zaininger and R. J. Evans, Appl. Phys. Letters 8, 57 (1966).
3. L. Horn, Z. Metallk. 40, 73 (1949).
4. I. S. Gil'dengorn and I. L. Rogel'berg, Fiz. Metal. Metalloved. 17, 527 (1964).
5. L. Berry and J. Paidassi, Compt. Rend. 262C, 1353 (1966).
6. J. J. Van den Broek and J. L. Meijering, Acta Met. 16, 375 (1968).
7. P. Kofstad, Nature Lond. 179, 1362 (1957).
8. S. Mrowec, Corros. Sci. 7, 563 (1967).
9. J. F. Elliott and M. Gleiser, "Thermochemistry for Steelmaking", Vol. 1 (1960).
10. N. A. Toropov and V. P. Bazakovskii, "High-Temperature Chemistry of Silicates and Other Oxide Systems", Transl., Consultant Bur., New York (1966).
11. K. Hauffe, "Oxidation of Metals", Plenum Press, N. Y. (1965).
12. F. Maak, Z. Metallk. 52, 545 (1961).

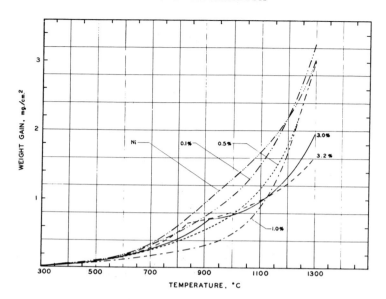

Fig. 1 Oxidation of Ni–Si alloys at a linear-heating rate in 1 atm. oxygen.

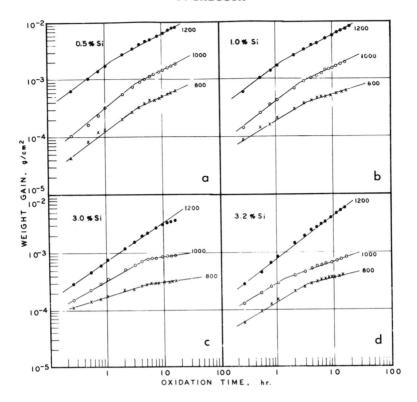

Fig. 2 Isothermal oxidation of Ni alloys containing
a) 0.5% Si, b) 1.0% Si, c) 3.0% Si and d) 3.2% Si.

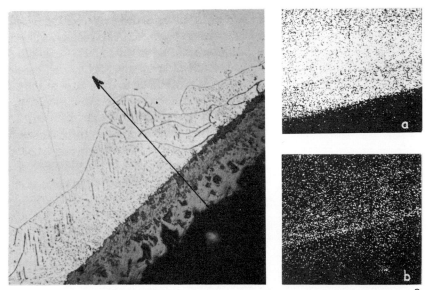

Fig. 3 Cross-section of Ni-1.0% Si oxidized at 1200°C for 16 hr, unetched, 250X. a) X-ray image for Ni and b) for Si in the corresponding area.

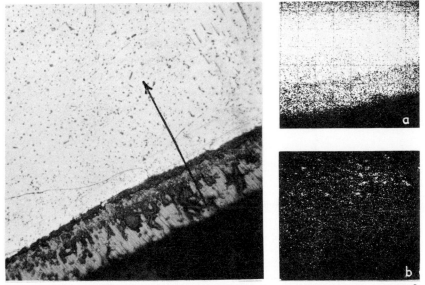

Fig. 4 Cross-section of Ni-3.0% Si oxidized at 1200°C for 16 hr, unetched, 250X. a) X-ray image for Ni and b) for Si in the corresponding area.

Fig. 5 Cross-section of Ni-3.2% Si oxidized at 1200°C for 16 hr, unetched, 250X. a) X-ray image for Ni and b) for Si in the corresponding area.

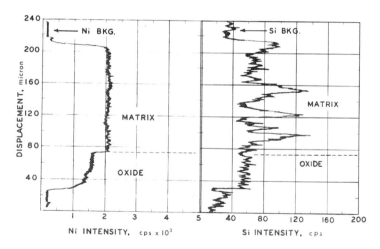

Fig. 6 Electron microprobe trace of a) Ni and b) Si on the oxidized Ni-1.0% Si cross-section along an arrow in Fig. 3.

906

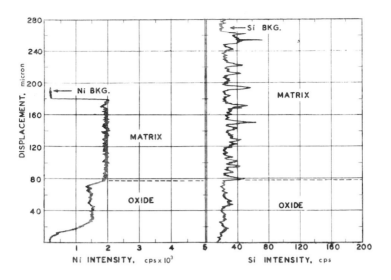

Fig. 7 Electron microprobe trace of a) Ni and b) Si on
the oxidized Ni-3.0% Si cross-section along an arrow in
Fig. 4.

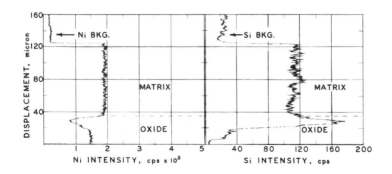

Fig. 8 Electron microprobe trace of a) Ni and b) Si on
the oxidized Ni-3.2% Si cross-section along an arrow in
Fig. 5.

STUDIES ON THERMAL ANALYSIS OF THE VANADATES OF COPPER, LEAD AND COBALT

S.K. Bhattacharyya, G.S. De* and N.C. Datta

Department of Chemistry, Indian Institute of Technology,
Kharagpur, India

Abstract

Thermal characteristics of the vanadates of copper, lead, and cobalt have been studied by Differential Thermal Analysis (DTA), Thermogravimetric Analysis (TG) and Derivative Thermogravimetric Analysis (DTG) under ordinary air atmosphere. Chemical analyses indicate the following compositions of these vanadates : 1) $Cu_3(VO_4)_2 \cdot 3H_2O$, 2) $Pb_4V_6O_{19} \cdot H_2O$ and 3) $2Co(VO_3)_2 \cdot 5H_2O$.

The DTA curve of the derivatogram of $Cu_3(VO_4)_2 \cdot 3H_2O$ shows one endothermic peak at 320°C and the DTG and the TG curves indicate the dehydration of $Cu_3(VO_4)_2 \cdot 3H_2O$ to $Cu_3(VO_4)_2$ at 320°C. The DTA thermograph of $Cu_3(VO_4)_2 \cdot 3H_2O$ taken in air by the DTA apparatus shows two endothermic peaks at 175°C and 360°C respectively and a pronounced exothermic peak at 485°C. This exothermic peak is considerably suppressed in nitrogen atmosphere. X-ray diffraction patterns of the various samples heated at different temperatures have also been taken.

In the derivatogram of $Pb_4V_6O_{19} \cdot H_2O$ the DTA curve shows one flat endothermic peak at 110 - 265°C followed by two successive exothermic peaks at 275°C and 350°C respectively after which two endothermic peaks at 460°C and 500°C occur. The TG curve indicates about 1.25% weight-loss within the temperature range 110 - 265° C. From X-ray analysis, it has been found that the two exothermic peaks at 275°C and 350°C are due to transitions of the compound from a more disordered to ordered state. Moreover, the endothermic peak at 460°C is most probably due to sintering and the endothermic peak at 500°C is due to simultaneous fusion and reversion of the compound from ordered to original

---
* Department of Chemistry, University of Burdwan, India.

disordered state.

In the DTA curve of the derivatogram of 2 $Co(VO_3)_2 \cdot 5H_2O$ endo-thermic peaks appear in the temperature ranges : 110-200° C, 250-280° C and 290-375° C. These are due to step-wise dehydration of $2Co(VO_3)_2 \cdot 5H_2O$ to $Co(VO_3)_2$. X-ray analysis of this cobalt vanadate heated at different temperatures indicates a change in the crystal structure during the course of dehydration.

1. Introduction

The techniques of Differential Thermal Analysis (DTA), Thermo-gravimetric (TG) and Derivative Thermogravimetric (DTG) Analyses have not been much widely used in the structural studies of inorganic and organic compounds. In recent years, Bhattacharyya and coworkers have successfully introduced the technique of DTA in the study of structural properties of solid catalysts (1-8). The vanadates of different metals are reported to have catalytic activity for various oxidation reactions, but nothing is known practically about their physico-chemical properties and their role in catalytic reactions. No systematic and exhaustive thermal analysis of the vanadates have been reported so far. Only a few references could be traced (9,10). Recently, Bhattacharyya and Ghosh (11) have studied the thermal analysis of the vanadates of tin and silver followed by X-ray diffraction studies.

In the present paper the results of an exhaustive study of the DTA, TG and DTG analyses of the vanadates of copper, lead and cobalt have been presented. As a supplement of this work the X-ray diffraction studies of these vanadates subjected to different thermal treatment have been made.

2. Experimental

2.1 **Preparation of the vanadates** : All the reagents employed were of Anala R quality.

A. Copper vanadate : 1.5 litres of ammonium metavanadate solution saturated at room temperature (about 3 gms./litre) were added with stirring (150 ml. at a time) to about 0.3 (M) solution of copper nitrate (10 gms. per 150 ml. water).

B. Lead vanadate : Warm (40-50°C) 0.1(M) solution of sodium metavanadate (12 gms./litre). acidified with nitric acid to pH 3-3.5, was added to 1(M) lead nitrate solution (33 gms/100 ml.) at 80-90 °C and pH 3(12).

C. Cobalt vanadate : It was prepared by adding hot 0.25(M) ammonium metavanadate solution (20 gms./750 ml.) at 80-90°C to warm 0.5(M) solution of cobalt nitrate (20 gms./100 ml.) (40-50°C) with stirring followed by digestion for 45 mins.

All the substances were allowed to settle, filtered in a Buchner funnel, washed repeatedly with hot water, then dried in an air-oven at 110°C.

2.2 Chemical Analysis of the vanadates :

A. Vanadium : Vanadium in all cases was determined by red-ox titration with Mohr's salt in sulphuric acid medium using diphenylamine - phosphoric acid indicator. Prior separation of metal ions was done in all cases except in the case of cobalt vanadate.

B. Metal ions : Copper was determined gravimetrically by precipita - tion of copper $\propto$- benzoin oximate from ammoniacal solution. Lead was estimated as lead sulphate; cobalt was weighed as cobalt sulphate via precipitation of cobalt from slightly acidic solution with $\propto$- nitroso β - naphthol.

C. Miscellaneous : Ammonia was estimated by digestion of a known weight of the sample in alkali and by back-titration of the excess standard acid left after the absorption of liberated ammonia. Water was determined by absorption of water in magnesium perchlorate.

When lead vanadate was subjected to usual test of sodium by zinc uranyl acetate, the response was negative.

2.3. Instrumentation and procedure : MOM Derivatograph (Model No. 874373) was used for the recording of DTA, TG and DTG curves of all these vanadates. The sensitivity ranges were : T 800°C, DTA 1/20, DTG 1/10, TG 200 mg (for copper vanadate and lead vanadate) and 500 mg (for cobalt vanadate). The amount of substances taken for the Derivatographic studies was : 430 mg. copper vanadate, 560 mg lead vanadate and 1520 mg. cobalt vanadate. Exactly equal amount of cal- cined alumina (A.R.) was taken as inert reference substance in each

911

case. Both the drum gear box and the heating gear box were maintained at 100' so that the rate of heating in case of copper vanadate and lead vanadate was 6 °C/min. and in case of cobalt vanadate was 4.5 °C/min. The furnace atmosphere in all cases was air. In all experiments parti- cles of an average size between 90 to 110 microns were studied.

2.4 X-ray diffraction studies : The substances were heated to the following temperatures and kept at these temperatures for half an hour in each case :

Copper vanadate : 110°C, 350°C, 750°C (fused at this temperature)
Lead vanadate : 110°C, 270°C, 360°C, 470°C, 550° C (substance fused at this temperature)
Cobalt vanadate : 110°C, 140°C, 200 °C, 290°C, 330°C, 650°C (substance fused at this temperature)

Photographs of all the substances were taken in a Guinier camera using CuK_{∞} radiation and an exposure for six hours.

4. Results and Discussions

The compositions and the results of thermal analysis are shown in Table 1.

4.1 Copper vanadate : Derivatogram of this compound is presented in Fig. 1. The DTA curve of Fig.1 shows one endothermic peak at 320 °C (range 150 - 350°C). The DTG thermograph is identical with the DTA thermograph except a very small peak appearing in the former at 305 °C. The TG curve represents a gradual weight-loss starting from 120 °C and ending at 330°C. Total weight-loss was calculated and found to be 11.63% which corresponds to the removal of three molecules of water from one molecule of $Cu_3(VO_4)_2 . 3H_2O$. Thus it is clear that the endo- thermic peak at 320°C. is due to the reaction

$$Cu_3(VO_4)_2 . 3H_2O \longrightarrow Cu_3(VO_4)_2 + 3H_2O.$$

The DTG and the TG curves do not give any clear indication about the formation of any intermediate stage in the process of dehydration, though the small peak of the DTG curve at 305 °C corresponds to the elimination of two molecules of water at this temperature. The dehydra- tion probably takes place in two stages :

1) $Cu_3(VO_4)_2 . 3H_2O \longrightarrow Cu_3(VO_4)_2 . H_2O + 2H_2O$ (upto 305 °C)

2) $Cu_3(VO_4)_2 \cdot H_2O \longrightarrow Cu_3(VO_4)_2 + H_2O$ (at 305-330 $^\circ$C)

These two reactions occur so successively that these have not been observed by Strupler (9) in their study of thermogravimetric analysis of $Cu_3(VO_4)_2 \cdot 3H_2O$.

X-ray analysis of this compound heated at 350 $^\circ$C did not indicate any change in the crystal structure of the original compound after dehydration. Normally crystals of salt hydrates undergo structural changes after dehydration. It is therefore difficult to explain identical structures of the anhydrous and the hydrated samples of copper vanadate.

Decomposition of copper orthovanadate to the component oxides could not be detected by X-ray analysis of the compound heated even upto 750 $^\circ$C. The fused compound exhibited a completely different X-ray pattern from that of the original compound but neither CuO nor V_2O_5 could be detected. The fused compound at 750 $^\circ$C is most likely a non-stoichiometric compound, $3CuO \cdot V_2O_4$, as reported by Strupler (loc. cit.).

But when the DTA of copper orthovanadate trihydrate was studied in a separate DTA apparatus described earlier by Bhattacharyya and Ramchandran (6) under controlled atmospheres of air and nitrogen at a heating rate of $11 \pm 1 ^\circ$C, the results were slightly different. The DTA thermogram obtained in this case is shown in Fig. 2. In air the small endothermic peak at 175 $^\circ$C is most probably due to elimination of free water and that at 360 $^\circ$C is due to the removal of bound water. The usual dehydration reaction $Cu_3(VO_4)_2 \cdot 3H_2O \longrightarrow Cu_3(VO_4)_2 + 3H_2O$, as is observed from Fig. 2, is complete at 360 $^\circ$C in both air and nitrogen; larger heating rate is obviously responsible for such displacement of the peak temperature. But in addition to these two endothermic peaks, which can be easily accounted for, one pronounced exothermic peak appears at 485 $^\circ$C (range 425-525 $^\circ$C) in air atmosphere. In the DTA curve of the derivatogram (Fig. 1) there is no evidence of this exothermic peak except a little downward drift of the base line at that temperature. But this peak has been considerably suppressed in nitrogen. It is difficult to explain this exothermic change. It may be possible, $Cu_3(VO_4)_2$ passes exothermally to some other phase at 485 C.

4.2 Lead vanadate : As already stated in section 2.1, lead vanadate was prepared by a method which was earlier described by Timofeeva et al (12) for the preparation of lead metavanadate. But on chemical analysis of this compound Pb : V ratio was found to be 2 : 3 instead of 1 : 2. The composition was established as $Pb_4V_6O_{19} \cdot H_2O$. This

913

discrepancy may be accounted for by the fact that the ultimate composition of a metal vanadate depends upon several factors, namely, temperature and concentration of the reactants, pH of the medium and digestion period, and any variation in any one of the conditions will substantially alter the final composition of the precitate.

The derivatogram of $Pb_4 V_6 O_{19} . H_2 O$ is shown in Fig.3. There is a slow downward base-line drift in the DTA curve of lead vanadate within the temperature range 110-265°C. At 275°C (range 265 - 300°C) a sharp exothermic peak appears followed by another exothermic peak of smaller magnitude at 350°C (335 - 380°C). Then two successive endothermic peaks are seen at 460°C and 500°C. The peak at 500°C has a much larger magnitude than that at 460°C. In DTG thermograph nothing is clear. In TG thermograph about 1.25% weight-loss is observed within 110-265°C. The DTA thermogram of the vanadate obtained by the DTA apparatus was found to be identical with that shown in Fig.3.

This weight-loss (1.25%) corresponds to the elimination of one molecule of water from one molecule of $Pb_4 V_6 O_{19} . H_2 O$. Therefore the flat peak at 110-265°C is due to this dehydration reaction $Pb_4 V_6 O_{19} .$ $H_2 O \longrightarrow Pb_4 V_6 O_{19} + H_2 O$. X-ray diffraction pattern of the substance heated at 270°C did not indicate any change in the crystal structure of the original compound. Moreover, from the structures of complex polyvanadates it can be suggested that the vacancies in the large rigid framework of $Pb_4 V_6 O_{19}$ can easily accommodate one water molecule so that its removal does not involve any change in the crystal structure of the original polyvanadate.

X-ray analysis of the substances heated at 360°C and 470°C gave identical diffraction pattern which was completely different from that of the original substance. Original substance showed only seven very faint lines and one strong line at d = 3.44 A°, whereas the vanadate heated at 360°C and 470°C showed at least thirty five lines; some of them were of medium intensities and the strongest line was at d=3.01A°. This suggests that the original compound has a more disordered structure which is very near to amorphous state. But on heating reversion to ordered lattice takes place with evolution of thermal energy. The endothermic peak at 460°C is most probably due to sintering.

At 500°C the substance melts, but all the lines of the X-ray diffraction pattern of the substance heated at 550°C were entirely identical with those obtained from the original substance. This indicates that at high temperature reversion of the ordered lattice to original disorder takes place again. So the thermal changes in lead vanadate may be summed up as follows :

$$Pb_4V_6O_{19} \cdot H_2O \xrightarrow[-H_2O]{110-265\,^\circ C} Pb_4V_6O_{19} \xrightarrow{275-360\,^\circ C} Pb_4V_6O_{19}$$

(Disordered form)   (Disordered form)   (Ordered form)

$\downarrow 460\,^\circ C$

$$\text{Melting} + \text{Reversion} \xleftarrow{500\,^\circ C} \text{Sintering}$$
to the original
disordered form

4.e Cobalt vanadate : The derivatogram of this vanadate is presented in Fig.4. The DTA curve of Fig.4 indicates one broad endothermic peak at 110 - 200 °C followed by two well-defined endothermic peaks at 270° C (250-280 °C) and 315 °C (290-375 °C). The TG thermograph indicates a total weight-loss of about 15.13% corresponding to the loss of 5 molecules of water per molecule of $2Co(VO_3)_2 \cdot 5H_2O$. It also has two less well-defined plateaus in the TG curve suggesting two or more intermediate stages occuring in the course of dehydration. The DTG curve is completely identical with the DTA curve suggesting that 1) complete dehydration occurs in steps, 2) each endothermic DTA peak is responsible for one step of dehydration, 3) there occurs no crystalline transitions of first order or second order. From the projection of the peaks of the DTG curve on the TG curve, stoichiometry of each step was calculated :

1)   Upto 200° C 1.5 molecules of water are removed from $2Co(VO_3)_2 \cdot 5H_2O$ giving rise to $2Co(VO_3)_2 \cdot 3.5H_2O$ and accounting about 4.4% weight-loss.
2)   At about 270 °C $2Co(VO_3)_2 \cdot 2.5H_2O$ is formed by removal of one water molecule (about 3.1% weight-loss).
3)   At about 315 °C rapid dehydration of $2Co(VO_3)_2 \cdot 2.5H_2O$ to $Co(VO_3)_2$ occurs by removal of 2.5 molecules of water (about 8% weight-loss).

X-ray diffraction patterns of the substances heated at 110° C, 140 °C and 200 °C were identical (strongest line at $d = 4.00$ A°), whereas the substance heated at 290 °C showed a different crystalline

structure (strongest line at $d = 3.25A^°$) and this structure was retained
even upto the fused state ($650^°$ C). The above results indicate that the
original crystal structure changes in course of dehydration after $270^°$ C
and the completely dehydrated sample is less crystalline than the original compound. The X-ray results did not indicate at any stage the decomposition of this cobalt vanadate to component oxides.

Acknowledgement

The authors are thankful to Dr. B.K. Banerjee, Head of the Physical
Wing, and to Dr. A.K. Guha, Research Physicist, of P & D Division,
Fertilizer Corporation of India Ltd, Sindri, for helping in taking the
X-ray diffraction patterns of the samples. They are also grateful to the
authorities of this Institute for awarding a Research-fellowship to one
of them (N.C.D.).

References

1. Bhattacharyya, S.K., Proc. First Int. Cong. Thermal Analysis,
   Aberdeen, p. 239, (1965).
2. Bhattacharyya, S.K. and Ganguly, N.D., Proc. Nat. Inst. Sci.,
   India, 27A, 538 (1961).
3. Bhattacharyya, S.K., Presidential Address, Section Chemistry,
   Proc. 55th Ind. Sci. Cong., Part II (1968).
4. Bhattacharyya, S.K., Srinivasan, G. and Ganguly, N.D., Jour.
   Indian Chem. Soc., 41, 233, (1964).
5. Bhattacharyya, S.K. et al. "Advances in Catalysis", Academic
   Press, New York, IX, 114 (1957).
6. Bhattacharyya, S.K., and Ramchandran, V.S., Bull. Nat. Inst. Sci.,
   India, No.12, 23 (1959).
7. Bhattacharyya, S.K. and Kameswari, S., J. Chim. Phys., 56, 823
   (1959).
8. Bhattacharyya et al., Z. Physikal. Chem., 214, 191 (1960).
9. Strupler, N., Compt. Rend., 255, 527-9 (1962).
10. Taniguchi, M. and Ingraham, T.R., Can. J. Chem., 42, 2467 (1964).
11. Bhattacharyya, S.K. and Ghosh, (Miss) J., Proc. 2nd Int. Cong.
    Thermal Analysis, Worcester, U.S.A., p.   1968. (Ph.D. Thesis
    submitted at I.I.T., Kharagpur, 1967 by Miss. J. Ghosh).
12. Timofeeva. E.G., Kalinichenko, I.I., Nikitin, V. D. and Purtov,
    A.I., Zhur. Neorg. Khim. 5, 1168 - 70 (1960).

T A B L E - 1

Results of Thermal Analysis

Substance	Composition	Formula	Fig.	Endothermic peak temp. °C	Range of temp. °C	% wt. loss.	Endothermic peak temp. °C	Range of temp. °C
Copper vanadate	Cu - 39.73 % V - 21.43 % H_2O - 11.21 %	$Cu_3(VO_4)_2$. $3 H_2O$	1	320	150 - 350	11.63	-	-
Copper vanadate (in a DTA apparatus)	do	do	2	AIR 175 360 NITROGEN 140 360	190 - 210 210 - 380 115 - 175 200 - 400	-	485	425 - 525
Lead vanadate	Pb - 56.35 % V - 19.09 % H_2O - 1.2 %	$Pb_4 V_6 O_{19}$. H_2O	3	- 460 500	110 - 265 415 - 470 480 - 520	1.25 -	275 350	265 - 300 335 - 380
Cobalt vanadate	Co - 19.2 % V - 33.53% H_2O - 15.2 %	$2Co(VO_3)_2$. $5H_2O$	4	- 270 315	110 - 200 250 - 280 290 - 375	4.4 3.1 8.0	-	-

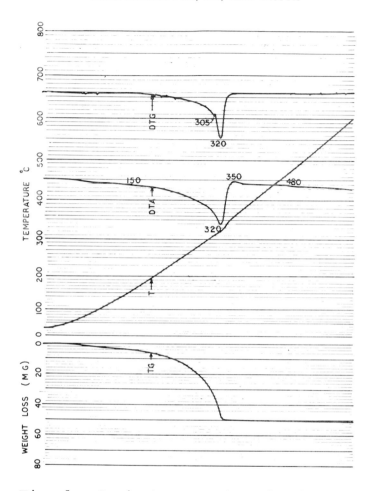

Fig. 1 - Derivatogram of $Cu_3(VO_4)_2 \cdot 3H_2O$

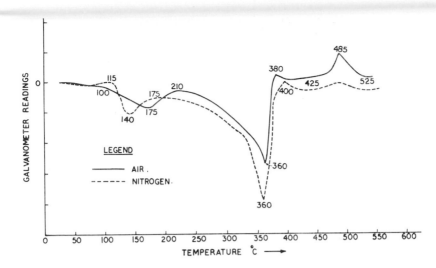

Fig. 2 - DTA Thermograph of Copper Vanadate in a
DTA Apparatus

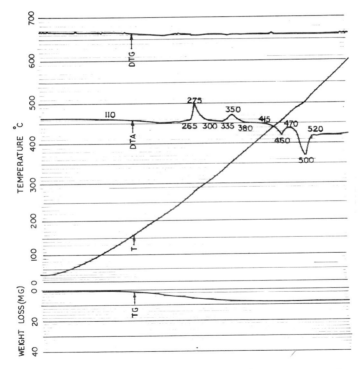

Fig. 3 - Derivatogram of $Pb_4V_6O_{19} \cdot H_2O$

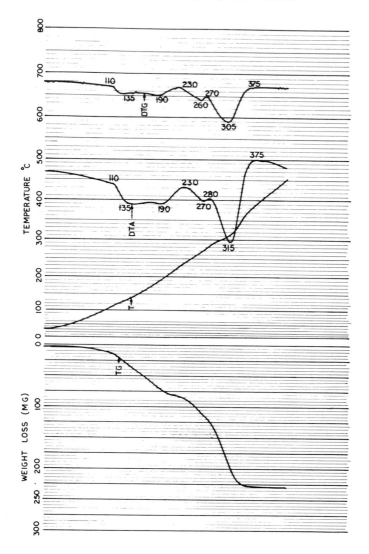

<u>Fig. 4</u> – Derivatogram of $2Co(VO_3)_2 \cdot 5H_2O$

Relative Thermal Stabilities of Copper (II)
Sulfate Pentahydrate and Barium Chloride
Dihydrate Compared to Their Deuterium Oxide
Analogs

Paul D. Garn, Ph.D.,
Professor of Chemistry
The University of Akron
Akron, Ohio, USA

Study of the extant literature on
hydrated salts and on the effect of
isotopic substitution led to a hypothesis that crystalline hydrates would
have thermal stabilities different from
their deuterium oxide analogs, and that
the hydrates might be either more or
less stable than their heavy-water
counterparts. Although the general
isotope effect and heat of solution
data would suggest that the heavy-water
solvate should be more stable, the two
cases tested did not behave in this
manner. Barium chloride dihydrate and
copper sulfate pentahydrate are more
stable, thermally, than their deuterium
oxide analogs.

From time to time an active experimenter
notes an anomaly either in his own data or in the
literature and after wondering about it for a
while he draws a hypothesis and proceeds to test
it. Even though definitive proof or disproof may
not be obtainable from a small set of measurements, successful prediction of a behavior is
strong evidence.

Some years ago McGrath and Silvidi (1)
measured the internuclear distances for hydrogens
in several crystalline hydrates and found the

separation to range from 1.57 to 1.61 Angstrom
units. Examination of the paper led to the conclusion that the differences were real, rather
than falling within experimental error. Bending
or stretching a molecule away from its normal
shape obviously requires energy; this energy is
necessarily supplied by the environment, that is,
the neighboring ions or atoms. It must also be
very dependent on the relative positions of the
several atoms. From this, we may raise the
hypothesis that a change in dimensions of one of
the species will have a profound effect on the
attraction or repulsion between parts of the
species. This leads to the further conclusion
that if two molecules having virtually the same
properties but slightly different dimensions are
substituted, one for the other, in a crystal
lattice with a third material, there should be
differences in energy sufficient to detect by a
difference in the thermal stabilities of the
systems. That is, one molecule might fit very
well, while the other would be under significant
strain.

A logical extension of this hypothesis would
be that if the relative dimensions become sufficiently unfavorable the crystal structure is
unstable and the ions or molecules arrange themselves differently. This can be verified quite
easily from the literature. It is well known
that amongst ions similar in chemistry, for example the halides, the ions of various sizes but
identical charge may enter into different crystal
structures with some other ion. While chloride
and bromide ions generally form the same type of
crystal with a given cation, fluoride usually and
iodide often will form other structures. Or look
at calcium carbonate, which in calcite takes the
rhombohedral sodium nitrate structure along with
magnesium carbonate. However, another common
form of calcium carbonate is aragonite; this has
orthorhombic symmetry like potassium nitrate. In
this form the calcium behaves like the larger
ions of the family, barium and strontium.

The simplest system which can be used to test the hypothesis of relative strain is the water-deuterium oxide substitution in crystalline hydrates. The deuterium oxide molecule is slightly larger, and has, by reason of the increased mass, some differences in properties compared to ordinary water. Nevertheless, it can be expected to enter into most of the hydrate structures. The selection of hydrates for testing the hypothesis must take into account the differences in vapor pressure of the ordinary and heavy water. The simplest way of avoiding any significant vapor pressure effects is by choosing hydrates which undergo either a phase transformation without ejection of water from the lattice or a transformation involving ejection of water from the lattice but without vaporization of the water, that is, a *Solid$_1$ $\leftrightarrows$ Solid$_2$ + liquid* reaction. Two materials falling in the latter group are barium chloride dihydrate and copper sulfate pentahydrate.

Barium chloride dihydrate is a monoclinic crystal (2). When heated under various pressures of water vapor it decomposes in several steps which may or may not be well resolved (3). The first thermal effect does not change in temperature. This shows that it is a phase transition involving loss of water. The literature reports the existence of a monohydrate but Wyckoff (2) points out that the lattice dimensions are such as to cast suspicion on the monohydrate. The work cited (3) indicates that the formula is $BaCl_2 \cdot 1.08\ H_2O$.

The total thermal effect in the vicinity of $100\,^{\circ}C$ at one atmosphere comprises the phase transition releasing liquid water and the vaporization of the water. At higher pressures the vaporization takes place at higher temperatures, so the effects are well-separated. Discontinuities in the heating curve corresponding to the peaks in the differential temperature in DTA may also be used to establish the difference in behavior.

Experimental method

Identical temperature spans were put on both functions of an X_1, X_2, vs time recorder (Speedomax G); each was fed from a 1.0 mm diameter shielded Chromel-Alumel thermocouple. These were on the axes of identical wells, about 6 mm wide and 40 mm deep in an aluminum block. The thermocouple bead was at the center of a 10 mm specimen; the well then being closed at the top by a close-fitting piston to maintain atmosphere control (4,5). Specimens were run in pairs, the hydrate in one well, the deuterium-oxide analog in the other. Upon completion of a run, fresh specimens were introduced into the opposite wells and a new thermocouple obtained. The results were consistent; the two solvates always gave the same relative behavior (Fig. 1).

Results

Upon heating, the two materials increased in temperature quite similarly to a temperature somewhat above $90^{\circ}C$. Then the deuterium oxide solvate transforms, followed by the hydrate transformation 5.2° higher in temperature. Both liquids then vaporize, the vaporization behavior being determined by the solubility characteristics of the solvate-solvent pair. Take note that this behavior is contrary to that which would be predicted from the general isotope effect. The literature gives clear evidence that the heavier isotope could be expected to be more stable (6). Exceptions are known, but the rule is well established.

When concentrated solutions of copper sulfate in ordinary and heavy water are allowed to evaporate, crystals form differently from the two solutions. From D_2O, crystals grow rapidly and well-formed, while from ordinary water the pentahydrate crystals are comparatively

924

irregular (7). (Growing of good pentahydrate crystals is a very slow process.) The two materials have the same crystal structure. Copper sulfate pentahydrate is a triclinic crystal. Both specimens gave the same general X-ray pattern. The spectral properties are quite different, however. Not only is there a difference in intensity of absorbance of light but also a difference in tone (8). Room temperature evaporation yields the same crystal structure but not the same particle shape from the two solvents. The fact that the crystals grow differently could in itself suggest differences in stability. One might raise the hypothesis that the deuterium oxide solvate is more stable. Indeed this has already been concluded by Lange and Sattler (9) from their calorimetric data. But this is in relation to the copper sulfate *solutions*; all we can infer from this concerning the thermal stability is that a difference is probable. From experiments done in the manner described earlier, differences were found (Fig. 2).

Again, although the mass effect would suggest otherwise and solution calorimetry likewise indicates otherwise, the normal hydrate is more stable than the deuterium oxide analog. Again, no inference concerning the later dehydration step is offered.

Discussion

The postulate of relative deformation or strain carries with it the implication that some hydrates may be less stable than their deuterium oxide analogs. Continued investigation is planned. If such materials do not exist, some explanation must be found which is based upon the specific properties of the two isotopic species. This present work, however, shows that experimental results are not in agreement with logical inferences from previous work, so that resolution of this question will lead to a greater understanding of the crystalline state.

Literature Cited

1. McGrath, J.W., and Silvidi, A.A. The measurement of the proton-proton separations in appropriate hydrates by the nuclear magnetic resonance technique. U.S. Dept. Com., Office Tech. Serv., PB Rept. 150,224 (1960).
    McGrath, J.W., and Silvidi, A.A. Structure of the water molecule in solid hydrated compounds. J. Chem. Phys., 34, 322-5 (1961).
2. Wyckoff, R.W.G., Crystal Structures, Vol. 3, Interscience, New York (1965).
3. Garn, Paul D., Hydration States of Barium Chloride Stable at Elevated Pressures of Water Vapor. Division of Physical Chemistry, 151st National A.C.S. Meeting, Pittsburgh, March, 1966.
4. Garn, P.D., and Kessler, J.E., Thermogravimetry in self-generated atmospheres. Anal. Chem. 32, 1563-1565 (1960).
5. Garn, P.D., Thermoanalytical Methods of Investigation, Academic Press, New York 1965.
6. Van Hook, W. Alexander, J. Chem. Phys. 40 3727-8 (1964).
    Matsuo, S., Kuniyoshi, H., and Miyake, Y., Science, 145, 1454 (1964).
    Lietzke, M.H. and Sloughton, R.W., J. Phys. Chem. 68, 3043-7 (1964).
    Wu, C.Y., and Robertson, R.E., Chem. Ind. (London) 1964, 1803B (1964).
    Wheeler, O.H., Can. J. Chem., 42, 706-7 (1964).
7. Garn, P.D., and Wang, J., unpublished measurements, 1966.
8. Chang, J.-C., Spectral shifts arising from deuterium-hydrogen substitution. Master's thesis. The University of Akron, 1968.
9. Lange, E., and Sattler, H., F. Phys. Chem. A179, 427-44 (1937).

The author is grateful to the National Science Foundation for its support through both an institutional grant and a research grant.

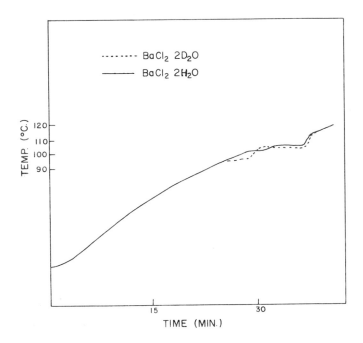

Figure 1.   Heating curves for barium chloride dihydrate and its heavy-water analog. The hydrate is stable to a somewhat higher temperature.

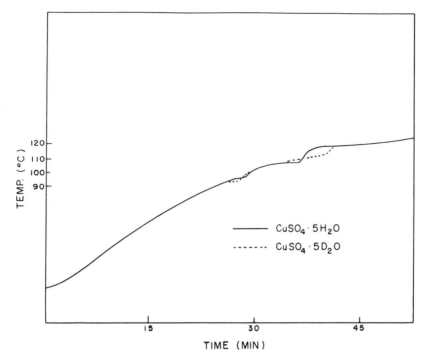

Figure 2. Heating curves for copper sulfate pentahydrate and its heavy-water analog. Again, the ordinary hydrate is stable to a higher temperature.

THE THERMAL DECOMPOSITION OF
$EuFe(CN)_6 \cdot 5H_2O$ AND $NH_4EuFe(CN)_6 \cdot 4H_2O$

P. K. Gallagher and F. Schrey

Bell Telephone Laboratories, Incorporated
Murray Hill, New Jersey

Abstract

The thermal decomposition of $EuFe(CN)_6 \cdot 5H_2O$ and $NH_4EuFe(CN)_6 \cdot 4H_2O$ is investigated by using conventional thermal analysis techniques and the Mössbauer effect. In air or oxygen atmospheres the compounds decompose directly to finely divided and intimately mixed oxides which subsequently react at $600°-700°C$ to form $EuFeO_3$. The decomposition in vacuum or inert atmosphere is far more complex. Unknown species of $Eu(II)$ and (III), Fe_3C and Fe are formed at higher temperatures. A thermobalance having a digital output on punched tape suitable for subsequent computer processing is also described.

Introduction

The thermal decomposition of rare earth hexacyanoferrate(III) and ammonium hexacyanoferrate(II) in air or oxygen has been demonstrated to be an advantageous technique for the preparation of rare earth orthoferrites (1). The mechanism of these decompositions is therefore of practical interest in order to determine the extent of the reaction and to control the particle size and reactivity of the final product. The nature of the decomposition process in vacuum or inert atmospheres is complex and may be expected to result in unique and interesting intermediates.

Seifer (2) and co-workers have investigated the decomposition of a number of cyanoferrates(II). Two studies have dealt directly with samarium (3) and cerium (4)

929

compounds, but there has not been comparable work on the
cyanoferrate(III) compounds. A variety of carbides and
nitrides were reported as intermediates in the cyanofer-
rate(II) decompositions. In summarizing the work
Seifer (2) concluded that the temperature at which the
cyanoferrate(II) ion decomposed was inversely dependent
upon the ionic potential, i.e., charge to radius ratio or
polarizing power of the associated cation. He also noted
that at least in the first transition series, the temperature of initial decomposition was lower when the associated cation has an odd number of d electrons in its
central shell. Chamberlain and Greene (5) have observed
that the alkali and alkaline earth cyanoferrate(III)
compounds decompose more readily than the analogous cyano-
ferrate(II) compounds and they conclude that the ease of
reduction of the metal ion is the critical factor rather
than the stability of the metal-cyanide bond. The closely
related series of rare earth compounds would appear to be
an excellent testing ground for these conclusions.

The europium compounds were selected for a detailed
investigation, prior to surveying the entire series, for
several reasons. Europium is the most readily reduced of
the trivalent rare earths and consequently the chemistry
associated with the decomposition should prove most interesting and there is considerable interest in the electronic
and magnetic properties of divalent europium compounds (6).
In addition, the Mössbauer Effect can be readily utilized
to investigate the rare earth ion in this case as well as
the iron ion. This technique has proved useful in investigations of this type, particularly to follow changes in
oxidation state. The frequent changes in oxidation of iron
associated with the thermal decomposition of alkaline earth
trisoxalatoferrate(III) (7) and the reduction of europium
followed by subsequent reoxidation during the decomposition
of europium(III) oxalate are two such examples (8).

Experimental Procedures and Results

The compounds, $EuFe(CN)_6 \cdot 5H_2O$ and $NH_4EuFe(CN)_6 \cdot 4H_2O$,
were prepared as previously described (1). Table I gives
the results of spectrographic analysis. A Cahn Model RG
vacuum thermobalance was used to obtain the thermogravimetric (TGA) data. The outputs of the balance and the
chromel-alumel thermocouple were converted to digital data
and punched on paper tape for subsequent computer

processing. A block diagram of this apparatus is shown in Fig. 1. The timing cycle for the counter is normally set to count the thermocouple channel for one second and the weight channel for 99 seconds. The apparatus will automatically repeat the cycle indefinitely. The switching time is relatively instantaneous and the data is punched while the counter is operating so that dead time is negligible. The effective use of averaging each reading over these times leads to a reduction of noise which is important for the subsequent computation of the time derivative. The calculation of the derivative is notorious for its noise amplification characteristic. The actual progress of each experiment is simultaneously monitored on an X-Y recorder.

The digital data is transferred from the paper tape to punched cards. The EMF vs temperature tables for the uncompensated chromel-alumel couple were fit by a least square technique to the equation:

$$\overset{\circ}{C} = 22.2877 + 25.7003(mv) - 0.1050(mv)^2 + 0.0017(mv)^3$$

$$(1)$$

This is satisfactory to $\pm 1°C$ over the region of 200-1000°C. A program was composed to compute the average temperature for each pair of consecutive temperature readings and associate this temperature with the average weight readings in the interval between the thermocouple readings. The computer (GE-600) then tabulates and plots both the percent weight loss and the rate of loss (mg/min) as a function of temperature (DTGA). The TGA furnace was programmed at the rate of 100°C/hr. so that the digital readings were at approximately 3°C intervals. The rate of weight loss was simply obtained from the difference in weight of consecutive readings (100 second intervals) and corrected to give mg/min. No further refinement or smoothing of the differential data has been performed yet, although suitable programs are readily available.

Both compounds were run in flowing helium and oxygen using the Cahn flo-thru Vycor tube and in vacuum (approximately 2×10^{-3} Torr). Differential thermal analysis (DTA) was performed on both compounds in static helium and oxygen. The output from the Fisher DTA apparatus was amplified and displayed on an X-Y recorder. Platinel

thermocouples were employed and the standard heating rate
was 10°C/min. The results of the DTGA and DTA are displayed in Figs. 2-4. Tables II and III summarize the
pertinent TGA data.

Samples of both compounds were heated for one-half
hour in air and vacuum (10^{-5} Torr) at approximately 100°C
intervals from 200-1000°C. The samples were cooled rapidly
in the same atmosphere.

X-ray diffraction patterns of these samples were
determined using a GE-XRD-3 diffractometer and CrKα radiation. Selected tracings are shown in Figs. 5-7. The
specific surface areas of these calcined samples were determined by nitrogen absorption using a Perkin-Elmer
Sorptometer. The results are shown in Figs. 8 and 9.

Mössbauer spectra of these calcined samples were
determined at room temperature using both ^{57}Co in pal-
ladium and ^{151}Sm in samarium oxide as sources. The spectrometer is similar to that described by Wertheim (9). Cali-
brations were based upon the ground state splitting of ^{57}Ne
and a value of 3.92 mm/sec obtained from recent NMR and
Mössbauer measurements (10,11), was used. Isomer shifts
for magnetically split spectra were determined from the
centroid of the lines. Samples were prepared as paraffin
suspensions on 3 mil aluminum foil. Selected spectra are
shown in Figs. 10-15.

Discussion

The decomposition of these compounds in oxygen leads
to the formation of the orthoferrite, $EuFeO_3$, in a relatively straightforward manner. Figure 2 shows two weight
losses. The first loss corresponds to most of the water
of hydration. The compounds ignite around 300°C and burn
rapidly to form finely divided intimately mixed
europium(III) oxide and iron(III) oxide. The small particle size can be inferred both from the poor quality of the
X-ray patterns in the 300-500°C region (Fig. 5) and the
Mössbauer spectra (Figs. 10 and 11) which indicate that the
iron oxide is so poorly ordered that it is in a superpara-
magnetic state. The characteristic six-line pattern of
iron(III) oxide which indicates its antiferromagnetic
alignment is absent and instead a doublet is present
having an isomer shift associated with trivalent iron.
This is typical behavior of finely divided or amorphous
iron oxide from a variety of sources (7,12).

In the region of 600°-700°C, or somewhat earlier starting with the iron(II) compound, the oxides react to form the orthoferrite. Both the X-ray pattern and the Mössbauer spectrum of this compound are evident. There is also an exothermic peak in the DTA patterns associated with this reaction. The DTA peaks are at somewhat higher temperature due to the rapid scanning rate, 10°C/min, employed for this measurement.

Changes in the surface areas of the samples calcined in air are consistent with this interpretation. The peak in surface area or minimum particle size occurs after the major decomposition around 300°C. The oxides which are formed then tend to anneal, sinter, and react to reduce their surface area. Around 600° to 700°C there is a slight change in slope caused by the reaction to form the orthoferrite. It would appear that orthoferrites having particle sizes of 0.1 μ or greater can be prepared depending upon the choice of calcined temperature.

The scheme of decomposition in helium or vacuum is clearly more complex due to the absence of oxygen for combustion. A general pattern can be proposed based principally upon the Mössbauer spectra and by analogy with the general work of Seifer (2) on cyanoferrate(II) decomposition. The proposed reactions are given below:

$$EuFe(CN)_6 \cdot 5H_2O \rightarrow Eu(CN)_3 + Fe(CN)_2 + 5H_2O + 1/2(CN)_2 \qquad (2)$$

$$NH_4EuFe(CN)_6 \cdot 4H_2O + Eu(CN)_3 + Fe(CN)_2 + 4H_2O + HCN \qquad (3)$$

$$Eu(CN)_3 \rightarrow Eu(CN)_2 + 1/2(CN)_2 \qquad (4a)$$

$$Eu(CN)_3 \rightarrow EuN + 3C + N_2 \qquad (4b)$$

$$Eu(CN)_2 \rightarrow EuC + N_2 + C \qquad (5)$$

$$Fe(CN)_2 \rightarrow 1/3 \, Fe_3C + N_2 + 5/3 \, C \qquad (6)$$

$$Fe_3C \rightarrow 3Fe + C \qquad (7)$$

The weight loss associated with reactions (2) or (3) is 25.2%. The additional weight loss from reaction 4a or b would make total of approximately 31%. This value is comparable to the values in Tables II and III for the weight loss after the second major decomposition peak in Figs. 3 and 4.

There are no discernible X-ray patterns for the samples calcined in vacuum within this temperature range. The Mössbauer spectra in Figs. 12 and 13 indicate that the iron is still bound as a cyanide type complex in this region. The Mössbauer spectra for europium in Figs. 14 and 15 show the onset of the formation of divalent europium between 300° and 400°C. It is impossible to determine whether this divalent europium is a carbide, nitride, cyanide, or some combination thereof.

At higher temperatures, 600°-800°C, the iron cyanide compound decomposes to form iron carbide. The appearance of a Mössbauer spectrum exhibiting a magnetic hyperfine splitting of 05-210 KOe and having an isomer shift of about +0.05 mm/sec is excellent confirmation. Bernas, et al. (13) give values of 208 KOe and +0.09 mm/sec for Fe_3C. There is no correspondence, however, between any of the X-ray patterns for iron carbides listed in the ASTM files (14), and the principal X-ray lines in Figs. 6 and 7. It is concluded that the X-ray lines at higher temperatures are due to the unknown europium species. It is unfortunate that more X-ray data on rare earth carbides and nitrides are not more readily available.

At temperatures approaching 1000°C the iron carbide decomposes to metallic iron and carbon. The appearance of the Mössbauer spectrum for iron can readily be seen in Figs. 12 and 14. Muir, et al. (15) list an isomer shift of -0.185 and a hyperfine splitting of 330 KOe for metallic iron. This is in excellent agreement considering the probability of dissolved carbon in the decomposition products. The principle X-ray line for iron (68.8°) is also present in the patterns at 1000°C (see Figs. 6 and 7).

The Mössbauer data in Figs. 14 and 15 indicate that the unidentified europium species present at the high temperatures are both divalent and trivalent. It is hoped that infrared spectroscopy (16) and mass spectrographic analysis of the gaseous decomposition products will help elucidate the materials.

The surface area of the samples calcined in vacuum are consistent with the general decomposition scheme proposed. The peak in surface area, Fig. 9, is at higher temperatures and smaller in size because of the absence of the rapid combination. There are apparently minor peaks or inflections at higher temperatures which would be expected due to the multiple decompositions.

Conclusion

The thermal decomposition of $EuFe(CN)_6 \cdot 5H_2O$ and $NH_4EuFe(CN)_6$ in oxygen or air forms a mixture of hematite and europium(III) oxide around 300°C. This mixture forms europium orthoferrite at 600°-700°C. A moderate control of the particle size is obtained by choice of the calcing temperature. In inert atmospheres or vacuum the decomposition is more complex and proceeds to form Fe_3C and eventually metallic iron. The rare earth ion became predominantly divalent around 700°C but the intermediate compounds are presently unknown.

Acknowledgments

The authors are grateful to Messrs. P. M. Bridenbaugh and J. P. Veracco for the computer programming and to Dr. H. H. Wickman for the loan of his ^{151}Sm source.

References

1. P. K. Gallagher, Mater. Resh. Bull., 3, 225 (1968).
2. This is summarized in G. B. Seifer and Z. A. Makarova, Dokl. Akad. Nauk SSR, 169, 358 (1968).
3. G. V. Shevchenko and L. V. Tananaev, Russ. J. Inorg. Chem., 10, 226 (1965).
4. G. B. Seifer, Russ. J. Inorg. Chem., 8, 792 (1963).
5. M. M. Chamberlain and . F. Greene, Jr., J. Inorg. Nucl. Chem., 25, 1471 (1963).
6. J. Danon and A. M. deGraaf, J. Phys. Chem., 5, 214 (1966).
7. P. K. Gallagher and C. R. Kurkjian, Inorg. Chem., 5, 214 (1966).
8. P. K. Gallagher, F. Schrey, and B. Prescott, to be published.
9. G. K. Wertheim, Mössbauer Effect, Principles and Application, Academic Press, Inc., New York, 1964, Chapter 2.
10. J. I. Budnick, L. J. Bruner, R. J. Blume, and E. L. Boyd, J. Appl. Phys., 32, 1205 (1961).

11. R. S. Preston, S. S. Hanna, and J. Herberle, Phys. Rev., $\underline{128}$, 2207 (1962).
12. T. Nakamura, T. Shinjo, Y. Endoh, N. Yamamoto, M. Shiga, and V. Nakamura, Phys. Letters, $\underline{12}$, 178 (1964).
13. H. Bernas, I. A. Campbell, and R. Fruchart, J. Phys. Chem. Solids, $\underline{28}$, 17 (1967).
14. Inorganic Index to the Powder Diffraction File, ASTM Publication PD IS-171, 1967.
15. Mössbauer Effect Data Index, A. H. Muir, Jr., K. J. Ando, and H. M. Coogan, Interscience Publishers, New York, 1966, p. 26.
16. P. K. Gallagher and B. Prescott, to be published.

TABLE I

Results of Spectrographic Analysis

Concentration Wt. %	$EuFe(CN)_6 \cdot 5H_2O$	$NH_4EuFe(CN)_6 \cdot 4H_2O$
0.00X		Ca, Si[*]
0.000X	Ca,[*] Cu,[*] Mg, Si	Al, Cu,[*] Mg

[*] Low

TABLE II

Weight Loss for $EuFe(CN)_6 \cdot 5H_2O$

Products	O₂ °C	% Wt. Loss	He °C	% Wt. Loss	Vacuum °C	% Wt. Loss
$EuFe(CN)_6 \cdot XH_2O$	25–250°	18.2	25–230°	17.8		17.8
Eu_2O_3, Fe_2O_3	250–325°	43.0				
$EuFeO_3$	700°	43.0				
$Eu(III)?$, $Fe(CN)_2$			230–425°	29.5	225–390°	29.9
$Eu?$, $Fe(CN)_2$			425–540°	34.1		
$Eu?$, Fe, Fe_3C			540–900°	41.7	390–850°	40.8

TABLE III

Weight Loss for $NH_4EuFe(CN)_6 \cdot 4H_2O$

Product	O₂ °C	% Wt. Loss	He °C	% Wt. Loss	Vacuum °C	% Wt. Loss
$NH_4EuFe(CN)_6 \cdot XH_2O$	25–200°	14.8	25–200°	13.8	25–110	13.8
Eu_2O_3, Fe_2O_3	200–275°	43.0				
$EuFeO_3$	600°	43.0				
$Eu(III)?$, $Fe(CN)_2$			200–380°	31.0	110–330°	27.3
$Eu(II)?$, $Fe(CN)_2$			380–530°	41.5	330–505°	35.9
$Eu(II)?$, Fe, Fe_3C, C			530–900°	41.0	505–850°	42.9

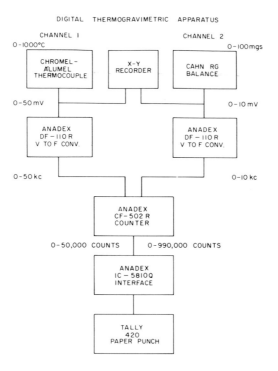

Fig. 1   Block Diagram of Digital Thermogravimetric
Apparatus

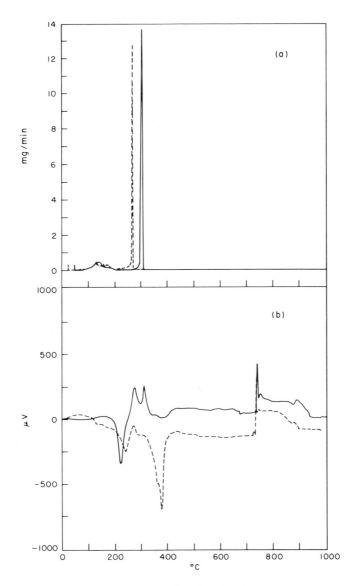

Fig. 2   Thermal Analysis in Oxygen
(a) DTGA ———— $EuFe(CN)_6 \cdot 5H_2O$
(b) DTA   – – – $NH_4EuFe(CN)_6 \cdot 4H_2O$

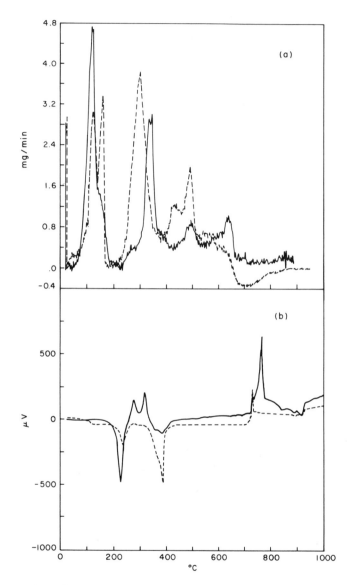

Fig. 3   Thermal Analysis in Helium
(a) DTGA ——— $EuFe(CN)_6 \cdot 5H_2O$
(b) DTA - - - $NH_4EuFe(CN)_6 \cdot 4H_2O$

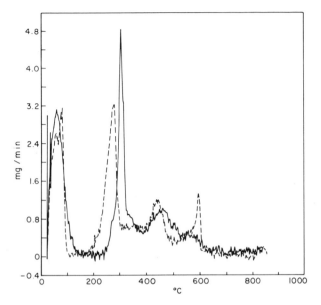

Fig. 4   DTGA in Vacuum
———— EuFe(CN)$_6\cdot$5H$_2$O
- - - NH$_4$EuFe(CN)$_6\cdot$4H$_2$O

941

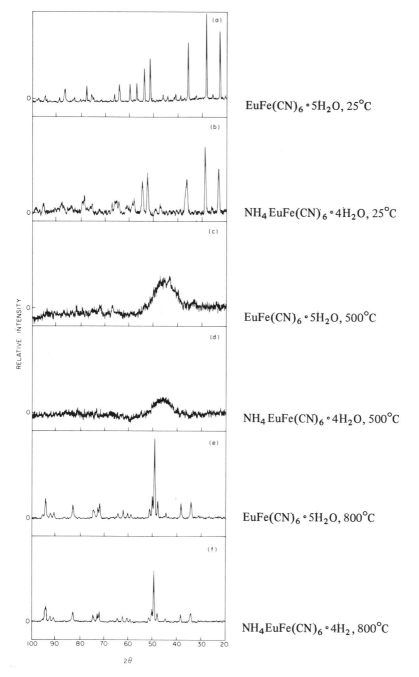

(a)

EuFe(CN)$_6 \cdot 5H_2O$, 25°C

(b)

NH$_4$EuFe(CN)$_6 \cdot 4H_2O$, 25°C

(c)

EuFe(CN)$_6 \cdot 5H_2O$, 500°C

(d)

NH$_4$EuFe(CN)$_6 \cdot 4H_2O$, 500°C

(e)

EuFe(CN)$_6 \cdot 5H_2O$, 800°C

(f)

NH$_4$EuFe(CN)$_6 \cdot 4H_2$, 800°C

RELATIVE INTENSITY

100   90   80   70   60   50   40   30   20

2θ

Fig. 5   X-ray Diffraction Patterns of Air Calcines

942

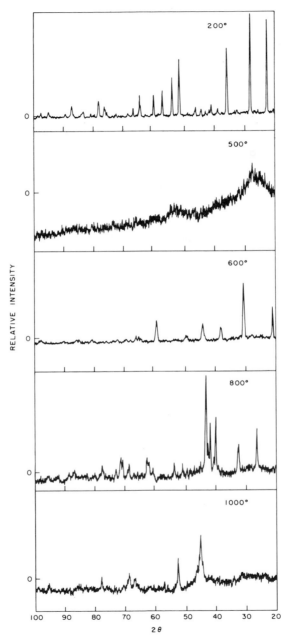

Fig. 6   X-ray Diffraction Patterns of Vacuum Calcined
EuFe(CN)$_6 \cdot 5H_2O$

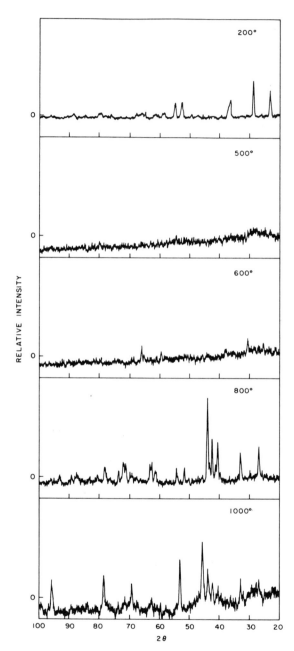

Fig. 7   X-ray Diffraction Patterns of Vacuum Calcined
$NH_4EuFe(CN)_6 \cdot 4H_2O$

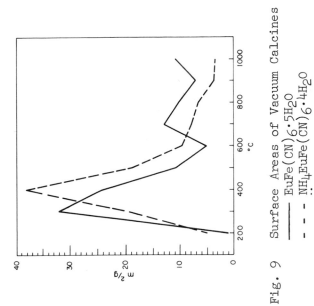

Fig. 9   Surface Areas of Vacuum Calcines
——— EuFe(CN)$_6\cdot$5H$_2$O
– – – NH$_4$EuFe(CN)$_6\cdot$4H$_2$O

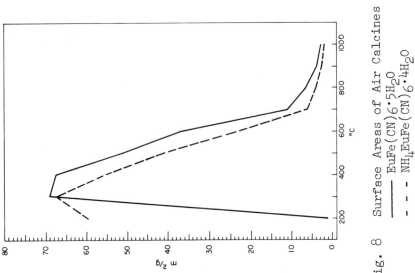

Fig. 8   Surface Areas of Air Calcines
——— EuFe(CN)$_6\cdot$5H$_2$O
– – – NH$_4$EuFe(CN)$_6\cdot$4H$_2$O

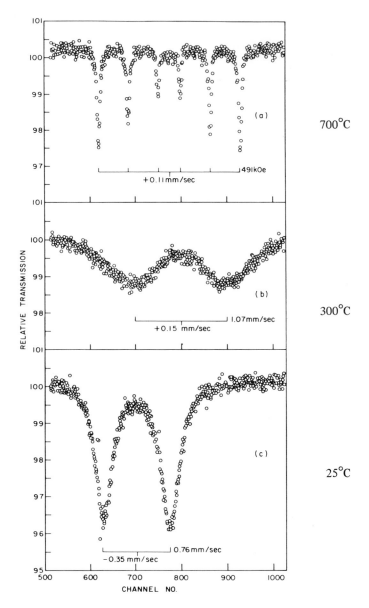

Fig. 10 ^{57}Fe Mossbauer Spectra of Air Calcined
EuFe(CN)$_6 \cdot$5H$_2$O

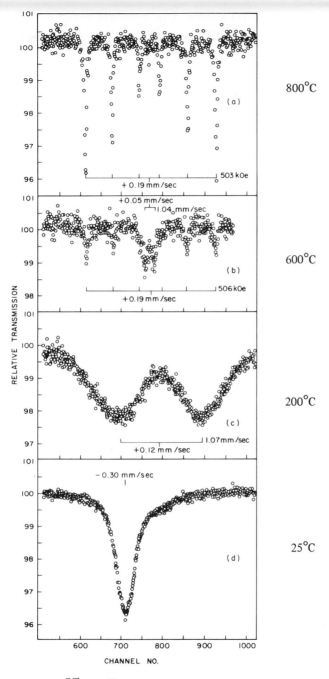

Fig. 11 ^{57}Fe Mössbauer Spectra of Air Calcined
NH$_4$EuFe(CN)$_6$·4H$_2$O

947

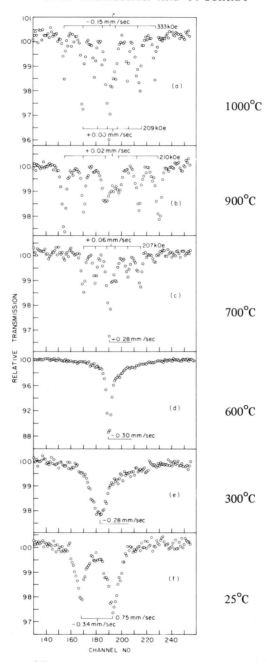

Fig. 12 ^{57}Fe Mössbauer Spectra of Vacuum Calcined
$EuFe(CN)_6 \cdot 5H_2O$

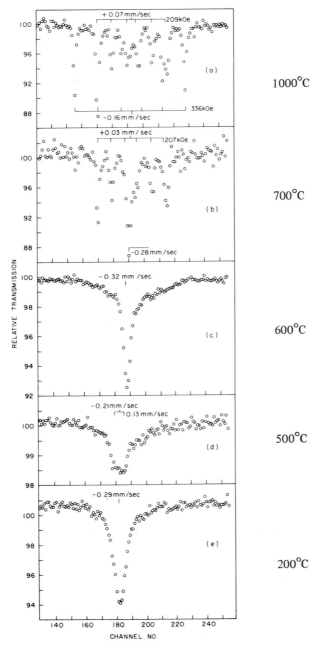

Fig. 13 ^{57}Fe Mössbauer Spectra of Vacuum Calcined
NH$_4$EuFe(CN)$_6$·4H$_2$O

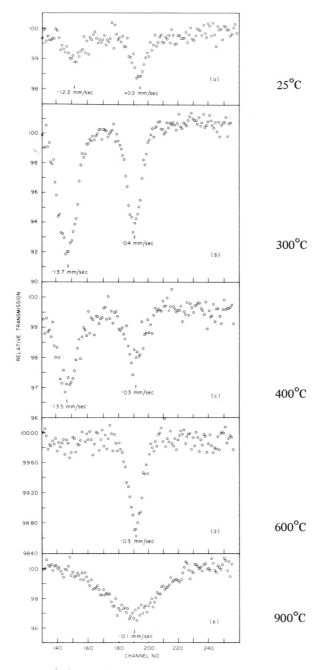

Fig. 14 ^{151}Eu Mössbauer Spectra of Vacuum Calcined
EuFe(CN)$_6$·5H$_2$O

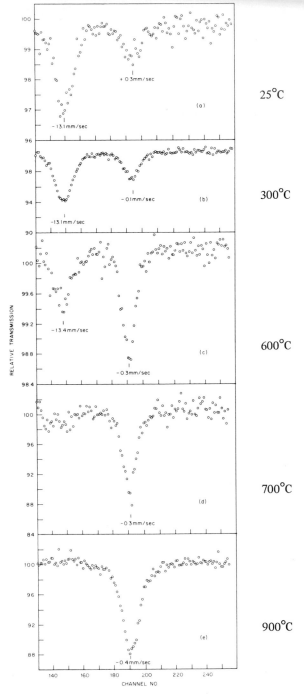

Fig. 15 ^{151}Eu Mössbauer Spectra of Vacuum Calcined $NH_4EuFe(CN)_6 \cdot 4H_2O$

THERMAL ANALYSIS IN STUDIES
OF DEHYDRATION PROCESSES

I.S.Rassonskaya

Institut Obshchei i Neorganicheskoi Khimii
im. N.S.Kurnakova USSR Academy of Sciences,
Moscow

Differential thermal analysis /DTA/ can be used to advantage for studies of dehydration processes.

Differential thermal analysis data, in conjunction with the data obtained by other physico-chemical research techniques, make it possible not only to determine dehydration temperatures, but to ascertain the sequence of dehydration steps as well (1).

Moreover, it appears feasible to evaluate some thermodynamic and kinetic characteristics of the processes under examination from thermal analysis data.

We have resorted to the differential thermal analysis technique for carrying out systematic studies of the behaviour of various salts and minerals subjected to heating.

The following auxiliary techniques have also been used for elucidating the character of transformations and the nature of the formed solid phases: thermogravimetry, X-ray diffraction, crystallooptics, infra-red spectroscopy, density measurements, etc.

Investigations of salt crystallohydrates and zeolites involved, apart from standard DTA curves, also plotting the heating curves at

various external pressures. The latter curves
allowed the dependence of temperature on pressure
to be established and the thermal effects to be
revealed, while on the thermograms plotted at
atmospheric pressure these effects cannot be discerned (4).

The experimental data pointed to the existence of several types of dehydration processes
and also revealed specific features of each
process.

The loss of water from zeolites generally
occurs in a temperature range of 100° to 300°C
and manifests itself on the DTA graphs by an
extended endothermic effect, no changes in the
structure of zeolites being observed. The temperatures of dehydration commencement and termination are somewhat different for various
zeolite types /Fig. 1/. For some synthetic
zeolites, the DTA curves show the dehydration to
be a two-stage process and, hence, corroborate
the assumption that the zeolites contain water
bound in different ways.

The rate and temperature of dehydration
vary with pressure variations, and heating curves plotted at reduced pressures indicate that
the temperature of zeolite dehydration drops as
the external pressure undergoes diminution. The
graph of the dependence of dehydration temperature on pressure plotted in the coordinates lg p
vs. $\frac{1}{T}$ shows a straight-line relationship /Fig.
2/.

Use was made of Piloyan's method (5) to
calculate the energy of activation /E/ for
diverse zeolites from DTA curves and weight loss
curves. Selected results obtained by this
procedure are listed in Table, in which the
values calculated from DTA curves are summarized
in the E_{DTA} column, and those found from thermo-

gravimetric curves are given in the E_{TG} column. Insignificant discrepancies between the data obtained are within the limits permissible for any indirect method.

According to the calculations, the activation energy, E, of zeolite dehydration processes is small, viz., 4-8 kcal/mole.

The order of the reaction was estimated by using the "shape idex" for the thermal effect peak in accordance with Kissinger's empirical equation (6). The dehydration of zeolites in the air was found to proceed as the first-order reaction.

All the experimental data warrant the conclusion that the dehydration of zeolites should be regarded as the diffusion process.

The dehydration of salt crystallohydrates and minerals, but not of zeolites, sets on in the course of heating at a definite temperature which is specific for a given compound. It is not uncommon that, where the crystallization water is abundant, the process of dehydration involves several consecutive stages and the formation of intermediate hydrates.

Two principal groups of compounds can be ascertained on the basis of the behaviour of compounds when heated at different external pressures, which in our experiments varied from 2 to 760 mm mercury. The first group embraces crystallohydrates whose dehydration temperature varies with the pressure, e.g. $Na_2S_2O_3.5H_2O$, $Li_2SO_4 \cdot H_2O$ and $MgSO_4 \cdot 7H_2O$ /Fig. 3/, whilst the second group includes crystallohydrates whose dehydration temperature remains practically constant within the aforementioned pressure range, such as polyhalite, dihydrate of cesium trilithium sulfate (7), etc. /Fig. 4/.

The dissimilar behaviour of these compounds under varying pressure conditions may be ascribed to the dissimilarity of dehydration processes.

In the first group of compounds, dehydration is caused by the dissociation of crystallohydrates, wherein water vapor constitutes an equilibrium phase, whereas in the compounds of the second group dehydration is associated with decomposition.

The process of thermal dissociation is analogous to the process of boiling in that it proceeds at a temperature, at which the dissociation pressure of a crystallohydrate becomes equal to the ambient atmospheric pressure. The temperature of dissociation processes depends upon the pressure in the same manner as does that of any reversible process involving a gas phase. Hence, where the dehydration of a crystallohydrate is accompanied by dissociation phenomena, ambient pressure reduction would result in a substantial lowering of the dehydration temperature and would decrease the number of intermediate hydrates. However, here the probability of metastable phase formation becomes greater. The exothermic effects observed on the DTA curves after the endothermic effects due to dehydration are indicative of the formation of metastable phases. The exothermic effects may be caused by the transition of amorphous phases to the crystalline state or by the rearrangement of the hydrate structure retained in the dehydrated crystallohydrate to yield the structure of the anhydrous salt (4).

For crystallohydrates the graph $\lg p$ vs $\frac{1}{T}$ plotted on the basis of DTA data for various pressures is a straight line inclined in relation to the temperature axis. Where the dissociation is a step-wise process, the graph consists of several straight lines, each line corresponding to a definite equilibrium /Fig. 5/.

$$\text{Solid phase}_I \rightleftarrows \text{Solid phase}_{II} + H_2O(vap.)$$

The process of crystallohydrate dehydration caused by heating may likewise proceed in a different manner, provided the compound undergoes decomposition once the requisite temperature is attained and there occurs water liberation. The removal of the liberated water, i.e., the dehydration proper, is, therefore, the secondary process which proceeds only after the decomposition process.

Here the process of decomposition of the compound is irreversible and takes place in the condensed phase, so that external pressure variations should exert no effect on the decomposition temperature and on the degree of stability of the phases thus formed.

It is of interest to find whether both processes of dehydration discussed above show different kinetics. To elucidate this problem, use was made of the Piloyan method to calculate the activation energies for various crystallohydrates and evaluate the reaction order. The data thus obtained are summarized in part in Table.

For the processes of dissociation of salt crystallohydrates ($LiSO_4 \cdot H_2O$, gypsum, hydroboracite, etc.), the activation energy was found to be 20-35 kcal/mole. Hence, here the loss of water proceeds less readily than the dehydration of zeolites, but the order of the reaction is also close to unity.

As regards the dehydration of compounds, for which the dehydration temperature exhibits little if any, variation with pressure variations /polyhalite, kieserite/, the activation energy was found to be much higher, e.g. 60-100 kcal/mole, and the reaction order is greater than unity.

It is, therefore, feasible to distinguish the nature of dehydration processes occurring in one group of crystallohydrates from that of the other group by noting whether or not the external pressure affects markedly the temperature of dehydration commencement, and also by estimating the activation energy and reaction order.

The present investigation illustrates the usefulness of differential thermal analysis as a research tool for studies of the dehydration processes in zeolites, salt crystallohydrates and minerals. The differential thermal analysis conducted at different pressures makes it possible to establish the dissociation temperature= pressure relationship, whilst the DTA and TG graphs are useful for estimating the kinetic characteristics of the dehydration process. All available data provide a deeper insight into the nature of the processes under consideration and make possible elucidation of the chemistry of the transformations associated with heating.

References

1. L.G.Berg and I.S.Rassonskaya, Trudy Pervogo Sovetshch. po Termografii, AN SSSR, Moscow, 93 (1955).
2. I.S.Rassonskaya and N.K. Semendyaeva, Zhur. Neorg. Khim. 6,1745 (1961).
3. I.S.Rassonskaya and N.K.Semendyaeva, Zhur. Neorg.Khim. 11,1980 (1966).
4. I.S.Rassonskaya, Zhur.Neorg.Khim. 9,2019 (1964).
5. G.O.Piloyan and O.S.Novikova, Zhur.Neorg. Khim. 12, 602 (1967).
6. H.E.Kissinger, Analyt.Chem. 29, 1702 (1957).
7. I.S.Rassonskaya and N.K.Semendyaeva, Zhur. Neorg.Khim. 12, 900 (1967).

TABLE
Activation Energy of Dehydration Processes for Selected Compounds

Compound	E_{DTA}	E_{TG}	n
	kcal/mole		
NaX	3.7	4.3	1.0
CaX	5.1	6.8	0.9
NaA	5.9	6.5	1.0
CaA	6.0	7.2	1.0
Heulandite	8.5	8.3	1.2
$Li_2SO_4 \cdot H_2O$	31.2	30.9	0.9
$CaSO_4 \cdot 2H_2O$	30.2	31.6	1.0
Gypsum	27.6	32.2	1.1
$Rb_2SO_4 \cdot MgSO_4 \cdot 6H_2O$	25.8	27.6	0.8
$Cs_2SO_4 \cdot MgSO_4 \cdot 6H_2O$	36.2	38.2	1.0
$CaC_2O_4 \cdot H_2O$	21.0	19.0	1.0
Polyhalite	50.2	50.8	1.1
Kieserite	65.8	65.8	1.4
$Rb_2SO_4 \cdot 3Li_2SO_4 \cdot 2H_2O$	92.8	106.7	1.8
$Cs_2SO_4 \cdot 3Li_2SO_4 \cdot 2H_2O$	82.8	87.1	1.5

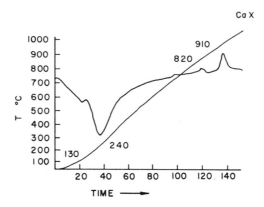

Fig. 1 Heating curve of synthetic zeolite.

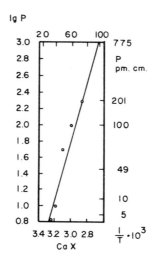

Fig. 2 Dependence of zeolite dehydration temperature on pressure.

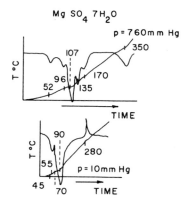

Fig. 3   Heating curves of MgSO$_4$·7H$_2$O at different pressures.

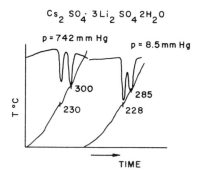

Fig. 4   Heating curves of Cs$_2$SO$_4$·3Li$_2$SO$_4$·H$_2$O for different pressures.

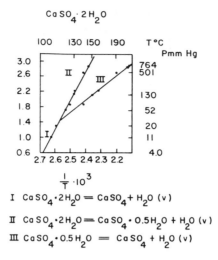

$CaSO_4 \cdot 2H_2O$

I $\quad CaSO_4 \cdot 2H_2O = CaSO_4 + H_2O \, (v)$

II $\quad CaSO_4 \cdot 2H_2O = CaSO_4 \cdot 0.5H_2O + H_2O \, (v)$

III $\quad CaSO_4 \cdot 0.5H_2O = CaSO_4 + H_2O \, (v)$

Fig. 5 lg p vs. $\dfrac{1}{T}$ graph for $CaSO_4 \cdot 2H_2O$

STUDY OF DEHYDRATION OF

MAGNESIUM SULFATE HEPTAHYDRATE

C. E. Locke and R. L. Stone

TRACOR, Inc.
Austin, Texas

Abstract

The dehydration of $MgSO_4 \cdot 7H_2O$ has been studied with thermal analysis techniques. Data were obtained over the temperature range of 25°C to 400°C with DTA, TGA, EGA and X-Ray diffraction. Pressure has been varied from 0.5 to 2300 psig. This study indicates water vapor partial pressure immediately around the sample greatly influences the dehydration reactions. When the water vapor is allowed to diffuse away from the sample, an amphorous structure exists at temperatures of 100°C to 295°C. Possibly a bisulfate structure exists in the 100°C to 295°C range in determinations made with water vapor around the sample. The resulting anhydrous $MgSO_4$ structure is not dependent upon the route or mechanism of formation.

Introduction

Various investigators have used thermal analyses to study the dehydration of magnesium sulfate heptahydrate (1,2,3,4,5,6). These investigators have published a wide variety of conflicting data which have led to much confusion in the literature. Several hydrates of the form $MgSO_4 \cdot XH_2O$ where X is equal to 7,6,5,4,3,2, 1.5 and 1 have been reported. There are only four hydrates listed in the ASTM X-ray diffraction card file. These are for X=7,6,4, and 1. Thermal analysis techniques such as DTA, TGA, EGA, and X-Ray Diffraction have been applied to study the dehydration reactions to produce these hydrates.

Experimental

Samples

Material from a bottle labeled, "Reagent Grade Magnesium Sulfate Heptahydrate", was used for all determinations. As discussed below, this sample was a mixture of $MgSO_4 \cdot 7H_2O$ and $MgSO_4 \cdot 6H_2O$. It was fine, white, needle-like crystals. For the DTA, EGA, and TGA runs, the sample was used as received. For X-ray diffraction patterns, the sample was ground with mortar and pestle to pass through a 300 mesh screen. The 300 mesh material was used for some of the DTA determinations.

DTA

The R. L. Stone Model 202 DTA System was used for all DTA thermograms. This included the LB-202 recorder-controller, JP-202 furnace platform, and F-1D furnace. The SH-11BR2-AL sample holder was used for all runs up to 100 psig. The newly developed SH-15BR2-NI high pressure sample holder was used for all runs above 100 psig.

A sketch of the SH-11BR2-AL sample holder is shown in Figure 1. The ring differential thermocouple was also used in the SH-15BR2-NI. The sample was placed as a thin layer in aluminum pans. Alumina was used as reference material. Gas was flowing around the sample in all runs except the high pressure and vacuum determinations.

EGA

The SH-12CR2-SS sample holder was used for the simultaneous DTA-EGA determination. The R. L. Stone EG/C cell and bridge power supply were used to determine the EGA output.

TGA

The R. L. Stone Model TGA-5B thermogravimetric system was used for all TGA thermograms. TGA operation was controlled by the LB-202 recorder-controller. In one test, the sample was placed in an open pan as a thin layer. A 19-mm flow-through type hang-down tube was used so that nitrogen gas could flow over the sample. In another test, the sample was encapsulated and placed in the pan.

X-Ray

X-ray diffraction patterns were obtained with a
Norelco Diffractometer. A R. L. Stone Model XR-5 controlled atmosphere furnace was used in place of the standard sample holder. The sample was placed on a platinum
plate which served as both the thermocouple and sample
holder. This plate fits directly on the heater. A housing
enclosed the sample so it could be pressured to 40 psig.
Beryllium windows were used in the housing. Copper K-α
radiation was used for the study. The peak locations were
compared with the ASTM X-ray diffraction card file for
sample identification.

Results

DTA

DTA thermograms of magnesium sulfate heptahydrate
obtained at pressures from atmospheric to 100 psig are
shown in Figure 2. The atmospheric thermogram shows four
peaks; two endothermic peaks between ambient temperature
and approximately 70°C, a large endothermic effect which
is not completed until about 250°C, and an exotherm which
peaks at approximately 295°C.

Pressure greatly changes all of this behavior. The
endothermic effects have been divided into several peaks.
The large endotherm (100°C level) has been separated into
five peaks plus two shoulders. The most drastic change is
that the exotherm has been replaced by two endotherms. The
one at the lower temperature is decreased in intensity with
increasing pressure. The other endothermic peak at 350°C
is shifted and increases in intensity between 40 and 70
psig. This peak is broadened between 70 and 100 psig.

The roughness in the peaks at about 150°C in the
40 psig run was probably caused by movement of the sample
particles. This movement could be a result of high rate
of gas evolution from the sample causing agitation.

The DTA thermograms of magnesium sulfate heptahydrate
at pressures from 200 to 2300 psig are shown in Figure 3.
There is a large change in the behavior between the 100 and
200 psig runs. The double endotherm between 150°C and 200°C

965

seen at 100 psig has been changed to a single endotherm with shoulders at 200 psig. The endotherm between 300° and 350°C at 100 psig has been completely replaced by double endotherms between 340° and 420°C.

The endotherm that peaks at 60°C is changed very little. There is a broadening of the next two large endotherms with increasing pressure.

The effect of program rate on the DTA thermograms at atmospheric pressure is seen in Figure 4. The endothermic effects before 70°C have been moved slightly and the second peak is much sharper. The large endotherm has been sharpened and the peak lowered to 75°C. The exotherm has been broadened and lowered about 20 degrees.

The sample container can greatly affect the results if it controls the atmosphere around the sample. The open pans shown in Figure 1 allow the water vapor to diffuse away from the sample. If a closed or "deep well" type holder is used, the water vapor cannot diffuse away so readily.

The effects of sample container shape are seen in Figure 5. One thermogram was with an encapsulated sample and the other with an open pan. The encapsulation was accomplished by folding aluminum foil around the sample, forming it into the dish shape, and then putting a pin hole in the top layer of foil. The results show that where water vapor surrounds the sample, the peaks are shifted.

These thermograms suggest that the increased pressure shown in Figure 2 retarded diffusion of the water vapor away from the sample. The separation of the water evolution into stages is accomplished either by pressure or sample container configuration.

Figure 6 compares DTA thermograms made with a range of water vapor diffusion conditions. An interesting feature is shown in the thermogram made with 40 psig helium. It has been calculated that the diffusivity of water vapor in helium is four times as great as the diffusivity in nitrogen; hence, the water vapor can diffuse away so quickly that the water evolution reactions are not as pronounced.

966

The thermogram made at 0.5-mm was made after the furnace platform chamber was evacuated to the operating pressure. The doublet at about 50°C has been replaced by a single endotherm at a lower temperature. The large endotherm has been shifted so that it starts at approximately the same temperature as the peak seen in the 1°C/min thermogram.

The behavior in the temperature range of 200° to 350°C is also affected by water vapor pressure. The 0.5-mm and one atmosphere dry nitrogen thermograms (10°C/min) show an exothermic peak at 295°C. Reduction of the heating rate to 1°C/min lowers the peak by 20°C.

The 40 psig thermogram illustrates an endotherm followed by an exotherm.

DTA thermograms made with the 300 mesh material are shown in Figure 7. These runs were made at atmospheric pressure and 40 psig. The doublet below 70°C as seen in the "as received" sample has been replaced by a single endotherm. Otherwise, the thermogram with 300 mesh material is very similar to the "as received" material.

The 50°C endotherm in the thermogram made at 40 psig with the "as received" sample is completely absent in the ground sample thermogram at 40 psig. The radical behavior in the 150°C range seen with the "as received" sample has been smoothed in the ground sample.

Figure 8 is a simultaneous DTA-EGA thermogram. Only one of the two DTA peaks below 70°C has water evolved simultaneously with it. The large endotherm has water evolved with it and then, at the temperature of the exotherm, there is a small amount of water evolved.

TGA

The TGA thermograms made with this material are presented in Figure 9. One run was made with the sample encapsulated. The other run was made at 5°C/min in a small open pan. These data indicate the temperature range over which water is evolved rapidly is greater with encapsulation. It is difficult to assign specific hydrate formulas from these TGA results.

These TGA thermograms indicate the "as received" sample consists of both heptahydrate and hexahydrate. The first loss of water is in an amount to indicate only 58.9% of the sample was heptahydrate. A material balance indicates the remaining sample was hexahydrate that does not begin to lose H_2O until $60^{\circ}C$ is exceeded.

X-Ray Data

Powder X-ray diffraction patterns were obtained at atmospheric pressure and at 40 psig. These patterns were obtained while holding temperatures up to $350^{\circ}C$. The results are summarized below.

STRUCTURES DETERMINED BY X-RAY DIFFRACTION

Atmospheric Pressure	40 psig
$25^{\circ}C$ Mixture of $MgSO_4 \cdot 7H_2O$ and $MgSO_4 \cdot 6H_2O$	$25^{\circ}C$ Mixture of $MgSO_4 \cdot 7H_2O$ and $MgSO_4 \cdot 6H_2O$
$41^{\circ}C$ $MgSO_4 \cdot 6H_2O$	$61^{\circ}C$ $MgSO_4 \cdot 6H_2O$
$105^{\circ}C$ No peaks	$98^{\circ}C$ No peaks
	$198^{\circ}C$ No peaks
$347^{\circ}C$ Mixture of monoclinic and orthorhombic forms of $MgSO_4$	$347^{\circ}C$ Mixture of monoclinic and orthorhombic forms of $MgSO_4$

Another set of tests were made with X-ray diffraction using oscillating heating. In this experiment, the sample was heated slowly while the goniometer was oscillated through 3 degrees of $2-\theta$ in the procedure developed by Weiss and Rowland (8). The oscillations covered an angle which included the most intense lines for both the monoclinic and orthorhombic forms of anhydrous magnesium sulfate.

Figure 10 presents a summary of these data. Runs were made at one atmosphere and at 40 psig. The height of the bars roughly indicate the relative intensity of the most intense peaks at the temperatures indicated. These show

968

that the anhydrous material tends to be formed over a wider temperature range and much more slowly at 40 psig than at one atmosphere.

Discussion of Results

The results will be discussed by dividing the thermogram into two sections: (1) the behavior below $70^{o}C$ and (2) the behavior above $70^{o}C$.

Behavior Below $70^{o}C$

The first endotherm(s) must be associated with the evolution of water to go from the heptahydrate to the hexahydrate. Wycoff (7) stated that the seventh water is positioned in voids in the crystal structure and has no covalent bonds between it and any of the metal ions. It is therefore held loosely.

Regarding the doublet at 50-60°C, the EGA and TGA data in Figures 8 and 9 illustrate that gas is evolved simultaneously with the first peak and no gas is evolved nor weight lost with the second peak.

As shown in Figures 2 and 3, pressure forces most, if not all, of the water out that causes the first peak. Apparently, a little grinding and pressure will force all of the water out, as shown in Figure 7.

The X-ray data indicate that the hexahydrate is the only crystalline structure remaining at $60^{o}C$. (The ASTM X-ray diffraction cards report that the heptahydrate structure is orthorhombic and the hexahydrate structure is monoclinic.) Therefore, the second peak at $60^{o}C$ in Figure 2 must necessarily be the transition from the orthorhombic to the monoclinic structure.

To summarize, the two endotherms below $70^{o}C$ in Figures 2 or 4 indicate the evolution of one water of hydration and then the transition, starting at about $45^{o}C$, to the monoclinic hexahydrate structure.

Behavior Above $70^{o}C$

The reactions which occur above $70^{o}C$ are strongly

influenced by the partial pressure of water vapor at the site of the reaction. The presence of water vapor appears to split up the water-evolution reactions into discrete steps. This is evidenced by the fact that the large endotherm (peak at 100° in Figure 2) is replaced by a series of at least 5 distinct endotherms. A means of retaining the water vapor around the sample may be afforded by sample container configuration as shown in Figure 5 or pressure as shown in Figure 2. The diffusion of water vapor away from the sample is inhibited by either case. The influence on the water-evolving reactions of rate of diffusion of the water vapor is illustrated best by Figure 6.

A risky estimation of the species of intermediate hydrates might be made from the TGA results shown in Figure 9. The conditions around the crystals during the TGA run are such that these hydrates are metastable, hence, there are shoulders on the TGA curve. About the best one can say is that there is one step of major water loss, equivalent to four moles of water, occurring below $150^\circ C$ in the encapsulated sample which would leave the dihydrate.

The X-ray diffraction pattern did not indicate the presence of any crystal structure in the 70°-$250^\circ C$ temperature range. Other experimenters have reported structures in this range. Possibly very slow program rates or isothermal procedures must be used for these structures to appear. This approach would more nearly approximate equilibrium conditions.

The X-ray data indicate that the anhydrous $MgSO_4$ structure at $350^\circ C$ was essentially the same under all conditions. However, the route or mechanism is influenced by the amount of water vapor present above about $120^\circ C$.

The exotherm at $295^\circ C$ seen in the atmospheric pressure and 0.5-mm thermograms (Figures 4 and 6) is typical of an amphorous to crystalline transition. The X-ray data have shown only amorphous material above $70^\circ C$. The data in Figure 10 show the rapid formation of the $MgSO_4$ structure at atmospheric pressure at about $290^\circ C$.

The DTA-EGA data shown in Figure 8 illustrate another phenomenon typical of crystalline transitions. Water vapor that is absorbed on or is residual in the amphorous material is "kicked out" when the crystalline material is formed. An amphorous form has been reported by Rassonskaya (5).

The mechanism of formation of the $MgSO_4$ is certainly different when water vapor is present at the site of the reaction. For example, in Figure 5, the exotherm at $295^{O}C$ is completely replaced by endotherms. The same effect is shown by the 40 psig run in Figure 2. The X-ray data in Figure 10 show weak reflections for the crystalline mate. rial at $270^{O}C$ (in the 40 psig run), followed by a 2-step increase at 320° and $350^{O}C$. These temperatures correspond to endothermic effects in Figure 2 and to weight changes in Figure 9.

It is possible that the bisulfate reported by Cho (6) is formed as a material amorphous to X-rays when water vapor is present. The X-ray data showed no evidence of the $MgSO_4$ structure until $270^{O}C$. Cho, however, reported the $MgSO_4$ structure as low as $175^{O}C$. Here, again, an approach to equilibrium and/or time may be necessary for these conditions to exist.

Conclusions

The mechanism for dehydration of magnesium sulfate heptahydrate is fairly complex. The dehydration reactions and the mechanisms are influenced greatly by partial pressure of water vapor, whether influenced by grinding or by pressure. In absence of water vapor, it is possible that an anhydrous amorphous $MgSO_4$ is formed below $250^{O}C$. In the presence of water vapor, possibly a bisulfate, amorphous to X-rays is formed. The manner in which the majority of the water vapor is evolved controls the intermediate structure. However, the crystal structure of the anhydrous material which is seen at the end is essentially the same.

ACKNOWLEDGMENTS

The aid of Bob Duncan in the experimental work is greatly appreciated. We also express appreciation to Dr. Hugo Steinfink for aid in the X-ray diffraction work. The aid of Dr. C. B. Murphy in the literature survey has been invaluable.

References

1. Kamecki, Julian and Palej, Stanislawa (Acad.Mining & Met., Krakow, Poland) Rocznik Chem. 29, 691-704 (1955).

2. Fruchart, Robert and Michel, Andre, Compt. Rend. 246, 1222-4 (1958).

3. Berg, L. G. and Saibova, M. T., Zh. Neorgan. Khim. 7, 91-4 (1962).

4. Berg, L. G. and Rassonskaya, I.S., Dokl. Akad. Nauk SSSR 73, 113-5 (1950).

5. Rassonskaya, I.S., Zh. Neorgan, Khim. 9, 2019-22 (1964).

6. Cho, Jung S., Olson, Ferron A. and Wadsworth, Milton E., Trans. AIME 230 (6), 1419-25 (1964).

7. Wycoff, R.W.G., Crystal Structures, John Wiley & Sons, Inc., New York, 3, 837 (1965).

8. Weiss, E. J. and Rowland, R. A., American Mineralogist 41, 899-914 (1956).

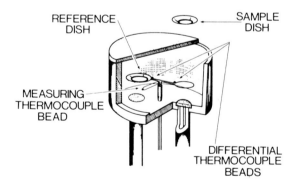

Figure 1   Cutaway Diagram of SH-11BR2 Sample Holder: Differential Thermocouples and Sample Container Configuration

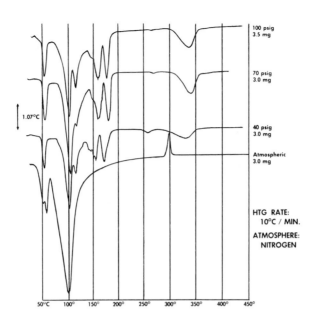

Figure 2   Effect of Pressure on DTA Thermograms of
                  $MgSO_4 \cdot 7H_2O$

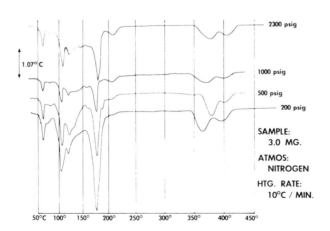

Figure 3   DTA Thermograms of $MgSO_4 \cdot 7H_2O$ Under High
                  Pressure

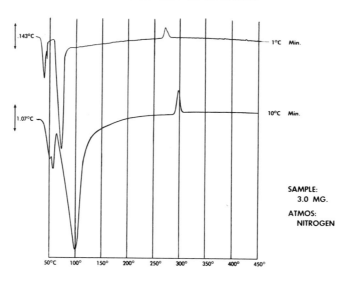

Figure 4   DTA Thermograms of $MgSO_4 \cdot 7H_2O$ at $10^O C/min$ and $1^O C/min$

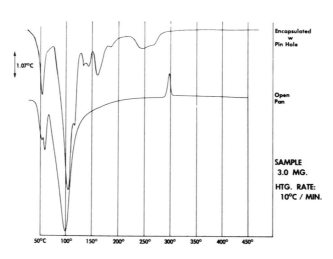

Figure 5   DTA Thermograms of $MgSO_4 \cdot 7H_2O$: Variation of Sample Container

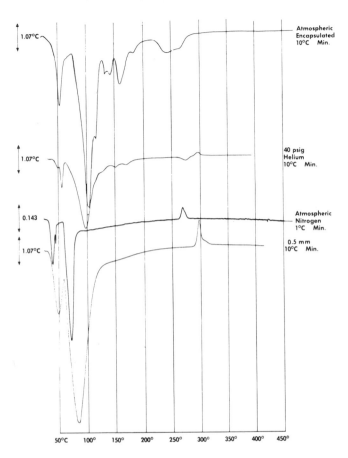

Figure 6   DTA Thermograms of $MgSO_4 \cdot 7H_2O$: Effect of Water Vapor Diffusion

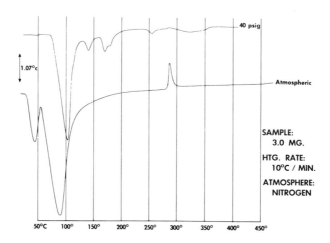

40 psig

1.07°c

Atmospheric

SAMPLE:
3.0 MG.

HTG. RATE:
10°C / MIN.

ATMOSPHERE:
NITROGEN

50°C   100°   150°   200°   250°   300°   350°   400°   450°

Figure 7   DTA Thermogram of $MgSO_4 \cdot 7H_2O$:   Pressure
                  Effect on 300-Mesh Material

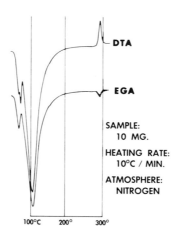

DTA

EGA

SAMPLE:
10 MG.

HEATING RATE:
10°C / MIN.

ATMOSPHERE:
NITROGEN

100°C   200°   300°

Figure 8   DTA and EGA Thermograms of $MgSO_4 \cdot 7H_2O$

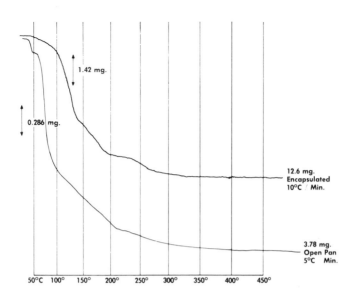

Figure 9   TGA Thermograms of $MgSO_4 \cdot 7H_2O$: Effect of
Heating Rate and of Sample Holder

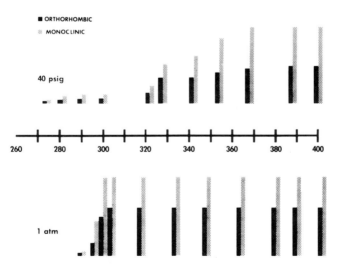

Figure 10   Representation of X-Ray Diffraction
Patterns of $MgSO_4$: Oscillating Heating

DIE ANWENDUNG THERMOGRAPHISCHER METHODEN BEI HOCHTEMPERATURUNTERSUCHUNGEN AN OXIDSYSTEMEN

E. K. Koehler, Prof.-Dr.

(Institut für Silikatchemie der Akademie der Wissenschaften der UdSSR, Leningrad)

ABSTRACT

Thermal analysis has long been used to characterize minerals and other inorganic compounds. It has been assumed that individual minerals in a mixture maintain their thermal characteristics with little or no interaction. However, at high temperatures metal oxides, other oxides, and other inorganic compounds do react with each other. Thus, mixtures of barium carbonate and titanium or zirconium oxides react in the temperature range of 700 to 1200 C to produce titanate or zirconate. In the present work, the reactions and mechanisms involved at elevated temperatures in mixtures including Be, Ce, La, Nb and Nd oxides as well as Ba and Sr carbonates have been studied. Simultaneous analysis by DTA, TGA and DDA was used. The instrumentation is described for this approach, "Komplexe" Thermal Analysis (KTA), which has been employed by the author since 1939.

Die Thermographie findet schon lange als Untersuchungsmethode zur Feststellung des mineralogischen Bestandes von Mineralstoffen Anwendung. Es wird dabei angenommen, dass die für einzelne Mineralien charakteristischen thermischen Effekte in Mineralgemischen ihre Temperaturlage beibehalten und additiv wirken. Wenn es in Wirklichkeit auch beobachtet wird, so is es doch nur im Bereiche verhältnissmäsig nicht hoher Temperaturen und das auch weit nicht immer. Gewöhnlich reagieren Oxyde und andere Verbindung bei höheren Temperaturen aktiv miteinander. Als charakteristisches Beispiel kann die intensive Zersetzung des Bariumkarbonats in Gegenwart von Kieselsäure, Titan- und Zirkoniumoxyd dienen, welche schon bei 700-800°C ansetzt und bei 1100-1200° mit der Bildung entsprechender Silikate, Titanate oder Zirkonate endet (1,2). Demgegenüber ändert sich die Dekarbonisations-temperatur des Kalzium-und Stronziumkarbonates in Gegenwart derselben Oxyde nicht (3,4).

Die Reaktionen beim Erhitzen von Stoffgemischen verlaufen mit Bildung neuer Verbindungen, ihrer Kristallisation, Abgabe oder Aufnahme einer Gasphase (H_2O, CO_2, SO_3, O_2 u.a.), Bildung eutektischer Schmelzen u.s.w. Alle diese Vorgänge sind mit Veränderungen des Energieniveaus des Systems verbunden und werden von Wärmeabgabe oder-aufnahme begleitet.

Leider bedient man sich, bei Untersuchungen an Festkörperreaktionen, ganz ungenügend der thermischen Analyse zur Feststellung der Natur und der Reihenfolge der Reaktionsvorgänge. Gewöhnlich begnügt man sich mit der röntgenographischen oder mikroskopischen Feststellung des Phasenbestandes des Endproduktes der Reaktion bei einer im voraus gewählten Erhitzungstemperatur.

Währenddem ist es, wie zum Verständnis des Reaktionsmechanismus, so auch, besonders, für die technologische Ausarbeitung rationeller Verfahren für die Synthese neuer Materialien und die Herstellung aus ihnen von Erzeugnissen mit gegebenen Eigenschaften höchst wichtig, sich den ganzen Verlauf des Reaktionsprozesses eingehend vorstellen zu können.

Die thermische Analyse kann hierbei grosse Dienste leisten. Besonders weite Möglichkeiten einer eingehenden Untersuchung von Hochtemperaturprozessen bietet die von uns 1939 entwickelte "Komplexe" thermische Analyse. Diese gestattet es, die DTA-, TGA- und DDA - Werte gleichzeitig, in einem Versuch, also in streng identischen Versuchsbedingungen, zu registrieren. (5,6,7,8). Die komplexe thermische Analyse (KTA) wird von uns bestanding bei Untersuchungen an Oxydsystemen und in anderen Gebieten der Silikatforschung verwendet und ist heutzutage in verschiedenen Forschungslaboratorien der Sowietunion weit verbreitet.

Aus der Literatur und aus Unterhaltungen mit meinen ausländischen Kollegen konnte ich die Schlussfolgerung ziehen, dass diese Methode wie in Westeuropa, so auch in den Vereinigten Staaten noch wenig bekannt ist. Ich werde min deshalb erlauben, hier kurz das Arbeitsprinzip einer KTA-Anlage in Erinnerung zu bringen.

Für den Versuch werden aus dem gepulverten Material zwei Zylinderkörper gepresst. Einer davon dient zur DTA und dilatometrischen Messung, der zweite - für die Gewichtsverlustbestimmung. Die Anordung der Proben und des ebenfalls zylindrischen Vergleichskörpers im keramischen Block der Vorrichtung ist in Abb. 1 gezeigt.

Die Differentialtehrmoelemente werden in den Vergleichskörper aus Aluminiumoxyd und den ersten Versuchskörper in entsprechende Hohlbohrungen eingeführt. Zwei Sinterkorundröhrchen, auf die- selben Proben gestützt, verwirklichen die differ- enzielle Uebergabe der linearen Aenderungen der Proben auf das Selbstschreibersystem. Der Gewich- tsverlustprüfkörper ist im Block an einem Platin- drath eingehängt. Alle drei Probekörper befinden sich in völlig gleichen Temperaturbedingungen.

Die weiteren Einzelheiten der Apparatur wer- den hier nicht näher erläutert. Sie können ver- schieden gestaltet werden. So haben wir uns wie eines Kohlegriessofens mit einem rotierenden, den Temperaturausgleich befördernden, schirmenden Karborundumrohr bedient, so auch eines Ofeus mit Platinrhodium-drathwicklung. Es gibt auch Anla- gen, die mit Silitöfen arbeiten. Desgleichen kann auch die Registrierung der Untersuchungserge- bnisse entweder auf Photographischem, oder auf Potenziometrischem Wege stattfinden. Die Auswahl des einen oder des anderen Systems ist von den örtlichen Unständen und von den Untersuchungsauf- gaben abhängig.

Es werden hier einige Beispiele gegeben, wel- che die Anwendung thermographischer Methoden, u.a. auch der KTA, bei der Untersuchung von Hochtempe- raturprozessen in Oxydsystemen erläutern. Diese Beispiele können in zwei Gruppen eingeteilt wer- den:

a) Prozesse, die beim Erhitzen von Naturmi- neralien verlaufen und
b) Prozesse, die sich in Oxydsystemen ab- spielen.

Unter "thermographischen" Methoden verstehen wir hier, wie es auch Paul D. Garn in seinem fundamentalen Werk (9) tut, die Registrierung verschiedener Eigenschaftsveränderungen des Versuchsmaterials als Funktion der Temperatur. Diese Eigenschaften sind hauptsächlich Wärmeeffekte, Gewichtsveränderungen und Volumenveränderungen. Mit Erfolg konnen aber auch Veränderungen der elektrischen (10), mechanischen und anderer physikalischer Eigenschaften, welche mit der Struktur und dem energetischen Zustand des Materials in Verbindung stehen, thermographisch einregistriert werden. In der Regel bedarf die Untersuchung solcher Prozesse in Oxydsystemen einer Erhöhung des Temperaturbereichs der thermischen Analyse bis auf 1400-1500°C, in einigen Fällen Auch höher, da viele, praktisch wichtige Vorgänge sich nur bei hohen Temperaturen abspielen. Zu den Vorteilen der Bestimmung nicht nur thermischer, sondern auch anderer Parameter ist die Unempfindlichkeit der gistrierung letzterer gegen den Zeitfaktor zu zählen, währenddem die langsam verlaufenden thermischen Vorgänge gewöhnlich einer genauen Registrierung, wegen der Wärmezerstreuung, entschwinden.

Die thermographische Untersuchung der Kaolinitumwandlungen beim Erhitzen hat es ermöglicht, interessante Beobachtungen über den Einfluss von Beimengungen auf diese Umwandlungen zu machen (11). In Abb. 2, a) ist das Thermogramm eines kunslichen (durch Gesamtfällung erzeugten) Allophans der Zusammensetzung $Al_2O_3 \cdot 2SiO_2 \cdot n\ H_2O$ wiedergegeben, und in Abb. 2, b) das Thermogramm desselben Allophans mit einem Zusatz von 2% Fe_2O_3. Aus der Gegenüberstellung dieser Thermogramme ist zu ersehen, dass der Fe O - Zusatz eine Ernidrigung der Intensivität der exothermischen Reaktion bei 930 und das Auftreten eines zweiten und

dritten exothermischen Effekts bei 1140 und 1310°
hervorgerufen hat. Röntgenographisch ist festge-
stellt worden, dass im Verlauf des exothermischen
Effekts bei 930-1000° sich im reinen Allophan
Mullit bildet, während es in der Probe mit dem
Eisenzusatz   -Al$_2$O$_3$ist. Der zweite exothermische
Effekt in dieser Probe entspricht der Mullitkris-
tallisation, und der dritte der Cristobalitbildung.
In Abb. 3, a) ist das komplexe Thermogramm des
Kaolins von Prossjanaja wiedergegeben. Röntgenographisch ist die Kristallisation von   -Al$_2$O$_3$
im Verlauf des ersten exothermischen Effekts
(920-980°) und vom Mullit im Verlauf des zweiten
Effekts (1160-1260°) festgestellt worden. Wie aus
Abb. 3, b) zu ersehen ist, ist das Thermogramm des
Kaolins mit einen Zusatz von 2% MgO dem Thermogramm
des reinen Allophans Abb. 2 a) höchst ähnlich. Der
erste exothermische Effekt ist stark vergrössert
und, wie beim Allophan, mit der Bildung von über-
wiegend Mullit verknüpft. Der zweite exothermische
Effekt ist fast verschwunden und in das Gebiet
niedrigerer Temperaturen verschoben (1050-1150).

Es ist von Interesse, dass auch die Schwin-
dungskurven entspechende Aenderungen zeigen:
mehr als um das zweifache ist die Schwindung im
Verlaufe des ersten exothermischen Effekts gewa-
chsen und mehr als um 100° die Temperatur der
Sinterungsschwindung gefallen, welche dem zweiten
exotehrmischen Effekt entspricht.

Es ist hiermit festgestellt worden, das Beimengungen von Eisenoxyd und Magnesiumoxyd, welche
praktisch in allen Kaolinen zugegen sind, die
Phasenumwandlungen des Kaolins wesentlich beein-
flussen. Es wäre damit, wahrscheinlich, der
haupt sächliche Grund der so vielfachen Uneinigk-
eiten erwiesen, welche sich in der Frage der
Kaolinumwandlungen im Laufe von Jahrzehnten beobachten lassen.

Als andere Anwendungsbeispiele der komplexen Hochtemperaturthermographie in der Untersuchung keramischer Rohstoffe können die Thermogramme eines Magnesits (Abb. 4) und eines Kyanits (Abb. 5) dienen. Diese Untersuchungen sind mit der Apparatur mit einem Kohlegriessofen (6,8) welche Arbeitstemperaturen bis zu 1600°C gestattet, durchgeführt werden.

Im ersten Thermogramm (Abb. 4) ist es bemerkenswert, dass die Entfaltung der Haupschwindung in die Periode der Periklaskristallisation fällt, welche durch die exothermische Reaktion bei 1120-1220° gekkenzeichnet ist (und nicht, wei es leicht zu denken wäre, in die Periode der starken Gewichtsabgabe während der Dekarbonisation).

Im Thermogramm des Kyanitkonzentrats II Sorte (Abb. 5) (SiO_2-45, 9%, Al_2O_3-52, 8%, Gewichtsverlust 2, 8%, Feuerfestigkeit 1830°) ist der scharfe Wuchs des Materials (6, 8% linear) zu vermerken, welcher dem Uebergang des Kyanits in Mullit entspricht und von einer deutlichen endothermen Reaktion begleitet ist. Das komplexe Thermogramm gibt auch Anhalt über das Vorhandensein beträchtlicher organischer Beimengungen, welche durch einen Gewichtsverlust von 2, 8% und dementsprechende exothermische Effekte gekennzeichnet werden. Volumenveränderungen werden dabei nicht merkbar. Für technologische Zwecke können solche Thermogramme werte Anhaltspunkte geben.

Bei Untersuchungen an Oxydsystemen kann die Thermographie, besonders die KTA, eine Reihe wertvoller Hinweise erstatten, welche es ermöglichen, den Gesamtumfang der Arbeit beträchtlich zu verringern. Die auf Frund der vorangehenden thermographischen Untersuchung erhaltenen Angaben konzentrieren die Aufmerksamkeit bei den

weiteren Bestimmungen (röntgenographischen, mikroskopischen, chemischen u.s.w.) auf gewisse, schon
festgelegte Temperatur- und Konzentrations-gebiete,
welche durch die oder jene Phasenänderungsmerkmale
thermographisch gekennzeichnet sind. Als Merkmale
können endo- und exothermische Effekte, Gewicht -
und Volumänderungen dienen. In einigen Fällen
können sehr nützliche Hinweise mit Hilfe einer in
den thermographischen Komplex eineschalteten elektrischen Widerstandsmessung erreicht werden (10).
Es gibt, ausserdem, Fälle, wo eben die thermographische Untersuchung selbst schon ausschlaggebende
Schlüsse über die Natur der sich verwirklichenden
Vorgänge zu ziehen vermag. Es ist dies, wenn, zum
Beispiel, der amorphe Zustand der Versuchsprobe es
nicht gestattet, die Röntgenographie zur Feststellung der Phasenneubildungen heranzuziehen. Gewichts
und besonders Volumenänderungen haben gewöhnlich
auch eine grosse sebstständige Bedeutung und können
unmittelbar wissenschaftlich und technisch verwer-
tet werden.

Es werden im Weiteren einige Beispiele der
Anwendung thermographischer Methoden bei der Untersuchung von Hochtemperaturreaktionen in Oxydsystemen gebracht.

Bei der Untersuchung von Festkörperreaktionen
in den Systemen Ln_2O_3 - Nb_2O_3(wo Ln - La, Ce, Pr,
Nd ist) wurde fur La^{3+} und Ce^{3+} die Bildung einer
Verbindung von der gemeinsamen Formel $Ln_2Nb_{12}O_{33}$
festgestellt (Abb. 6). In den Systemen mit Pr
und Nd konnte aber diese Verbindung fur Mischungen
von der Zusammensetzung 1:6 mittels Synthese aus
Oxydgemischen nicht entdeckt werden. Röntgenographisch wurde im System Nd_2O_3-Nb_2O_5 Neodymme-
thaniobat ($NdNb_3O_9$) und freies Niobiumoxyd registriert. Es wurde deshalb eine Untersuchung des
Erhitzungsverhaltens des Niobiumhydroxyds und

eines mittels Gesamtfällung erhaltenen Gels von
der Zusammensetzung Nd_2O_3 : Nb_2O_5 = 1:6 ange-
stellt (Abb. 7).

Ein exothermischer Effekts mit einem Maximum
bei 600° entspricht (Abb. 7, a) der Kristallisation des Niobiumoxyds in der Tieftemperatur "T"-
Form (12). Die von 750° (nach dem ersten exothermischen Effekt) abgeschreckte Probe der Ge-
samtgefällten Mischung (1 Nd_2O_3 +6Nb_2O_5) (Abb. 7,
b) ergab röntgenographisch als Hauptphase ebenso
T-Nb2O5, gemeinsam mit schwachen Linien der
kubischen Form des Neodymorthoniobats ($Nd NbO_4$).
Von 900°, nach dem zweiten exothermischen Effekt
abgeschreckt, enthielt die Probe diese Phasen
schon nicht. Das Röntgenbild zeigte deutliche
Linien der Mitteltemperatur "M"- Form des Niobiumoxyds und schwach ausgedrückte Linien des Neo-
dymmethaniobats ($Nd Nb_3O_9$). Eine Röntgenographi-
sche Untersuchung von Proben, die von 1050°, nach
dem dritten exothermischen Effekt abgeschreckt
waren, erwies die Bildung der Verbindung Nd_2Nb_{12}
O_{33} (1:6). Die Reaktionsfolge kann, demnach, mit
folgendem Schema dargestellt werden: (Nd_2O_3 +
6 Nb_2O_5) $\quad 700^O \quad$ T-Nb O_4+ NdNbO $\quad 850^O$
M-Nb_2O_5 + NdNb$_3$O$_9$ $\quad 1000^O \quad$ $Nd_2Nb_{12}O_{33}$.

Bei weiterer Temperatursteigerung zersetzt
sich die Verbindung $Nd_2Nb_{12}O_{33}$ (ebenso auch
$Pr_2Nb_{12}O_{33}$) im festen Zustand in Neodymmethanio-
bat ($NdNb_3O_9$) und Niobiumoxyd. Die völlige Zersetzung findet bei 1100° im Laufe von 8 Studen
statt. Deswegen kann die Synthese der Vergindun-
gen $Nb_2Nb_{12}O_{33}$ und $Pr_2Nb_{12}O_{33}$ aus Oxydgemischen
nicht verwirklicht werden, da die Wechselwirkungs-
temperatur der Oxyde in diesem Fall über der
Stabilitätsgrenze der Vergindung liegt. Die
Anwendung der DTA hat es, hiermit, ermöglicht,
die Stabilitätsgrenzen der polimorphen Modifika-

tionen des Niobiumoxyds und der Verbindung $Nd_2Nb_{12}O_{33}$ festzustellen un auch die Bildung letzterer über Zwichenphasen zu zeigen (Abb. 8).

Die KTA zeigt überzeugend den stufenweisen Charakter der Bildung fester Lösungen in solchen Systemen, wie ZrO_2 - CaO (13), CeO_2 - SrO (14) und anderen.

Ein komplexes Thermogramm des Gemisches von 50% CeO_2 + 50% $SrCo3$(mol) ist in Abb. 9 wiedergegeben. Der erste endothermische Effekt mit einem Maximum bei 930° entspricht dem Uebergang des Stronziumkarbonats aus der rhombischen in die hexagonale Form, und der zweite, mit einem Maximum bei 1140°, der Zersetzung des Karbonats. Der Anfang dieser Zersetzung, wie es die TGA-Kurve angibt, liegt bei ca 800°, das Ende - bei ca 1200^OC. Der aus der DDA-Kurve ersichtliche deutliche Wuchs des Versuchskörpers bei $1050-1150^O$ ist mit der Bildung des Stronziumcerats ($SrCeO3$) verknüpft.

In Abb. 10 ist das KTA-Bild eines Gemisches von 90% CeO_2 + 10% $SrCO3$ (mol) gegeben. Es enthält alle dieselben thermischen, thermogravimetrischen und dilatometrischen Effekte, welche die Bildung des Stronziumcerats kennzeichnen. Die chemische Analyse (Lösung in $HNO3$), wie auch die Röntgenuntersuchung haben gezeigt, dass bei der Temperatur des maximalen Volumenwuchses (1100°) ca 90% Stronziumoxyd in Stronziumcerat ($SrCeO_3$) gebunden ist. Die Bildung der festen Lösung aber, durch Reaktion zwischen Ceriumoxyd und Stronziumcerat, verwirklicht sich erst bei $1500-1600^O$C. Die analoge Reaktionsfolge im ZrO_2-CaO-System wurde von uns technologisch ausgewertet. Die stabilisierende Zugabe des Kalzium-oxyds wurde in Form von Kalziumzirkonat

eingetragen. Die Unlöslichkeit desselben in
kalter Salzsäure ermöglichte es, das Giessen der
Zirkoniumoxyderzeugnisse aus saurem Schliker dur-
chzuführen und den Ausschuss beim Giessen beträchtlich herabzusetzen.

Mit Hilfe der KTA ist es auch möglich gewor-
den, die Auflockerung des Materials im Laufe der
Kalziumzirkonatbildung zu konstatieren und diese
Angaben bei der Entwicklung Radiokeramischer
Erzeugnisse auf Zirkonatbasis erfolgreich auszun-
utzen.

In Abb. 11 sind Thermogramme von $BaCO_3$-BeO-
Mischungen dargestellt (15). Bild a) enspricht
der Zusammensetzung 2 : 3. Endothermische Effekte
bei 830 und 970° weisen auf den Uebergang des
Bariumkarbonats aus der rhombischen in die hexagonale und weiter in die kubische Form hin. Der
bei 1200° endende grosse endothermische Effekt
entspricht der Zersetzung des Karbonats. Als
Reaktionsergebniss bildet sich, wie es die Ront-
genuntersuchung zeigt, eine Verbindung von der
Formel $Ba_2Be_3O_5$. Eine nachträgliche Erhitzung
(Kurve b) erwies keine thermischen Effekte. Bild
c) entspricht der Zusammensetzung 1 : 3. Ausser
den schon beschriebenen Effekten zeigt dieses
Thermogramm einen neuen endothermen Effekt bei
1280°, welchem ein exothermer Effekt auf der
Kühlungskurve bei 1200° entspricht. Beide diese
Effekte werden auch auf der Kurve einer nach-
träglichen Erhitzung - Kühlung registriert (Kurve
d). Röntgenographisch ist festgestellt worden,
das der endothermische Effekt bei 1280° der Bildung der Vergindung $BaBe_3O_4$ aus $Ba_2Be_3O_5$ und
BeO entspricht, und der exothermische Effekt bei
1200° im Kühlungsverlauf - der rückwärtigen Zersetzung dieser Verbindung. Das BaBe O schmilzt
kongruent bei 1530°. Thermographisch ist es,

989

folglich, gelungen, die Bildung dieser Verbindung, welche nur bei hohen Temperaturen stabilist, im Laufe der Festkörperreaktion festzustellen.

Noch viel komliziertere Fragen konnten in grossem Masze mit Hilfe der KTA, bei der Untersuchung von Festkörperreaktionen im dreifachen System $BaO-TiO_2$ $-ZrO_2$ gelöst werden (16).

Erfolgreich war die Anwendung dieser Methode bei der Untersuchung der Wirkung von B_2O_3 als Mineralisator beim Sintern des Kalziumzirkonats (17), bei Forschungsarbeiten an Tantalaten der seltenen Erden (18), bei der Erforschung des Bildungsprozesses von Zirkonaten der seltenen Erden (19) und in vielen anderen Arbeiten, wie im Institut für Silikatschemie der Akademie der Wissenschaften, so auch in anderen Forschungslaboratorien der keramischen, zement- und chemischen Industrie.

Zuletzt möchte ich noch auf einige Anwendungsgebiete der Präzisions - TGA bei der Untersuchung von Reaktionen zwischen Festkörper und Gas hinweisen. Die klassischen Arbeiten auf diesem Gebiet benehmen sich häuptsächlich entweder mit des Untersuchung der Zersetzung von Salzen, oder mit Wechselreaktionen zwiøschen Metallen und Gasen.

Die neuheitlichen Erfolge auf dem Gebiete der Elektronentechnik und Vervollkommungen in der Hochtemperaturtechnik ermöglichten es, ein System zu schaffen, welches instande ist, Gewichtsänderungen mit einer präzision von 1.10^{-5} Gr. im Temperaturbereich bis zu $1600^{O}C$ in gewünschten Gasmedia zu registrieren.

Solch ein Systemen gestattet es schon, die Buildung von Zwischenphasen im Laufe komilizierter

vielstufiger Reaktionen zu verfolgen (20), die
Quantitätsänderung der unbesetzten Anionenposten
in Oxyden zu schätzen, die Messung der Hall-Kon-
stante in oxydischen Halbeitern (in Verbindung
mit Elektrizitätleitfahigkeitsmessungen) durch-
zuführen (21) u.s.w.

Als Beispiel kann Ceriumchromit betrachtet
werden (22). Es wird angenommen, dass die Bildung dieser Verbindung aus Oxyden nach der Reaktion $2CeO_2 + CrO_3 \quad 2CeCrO_3 + 1/2 \, O_2$ verlaüft.

Das Ceriumchromit hat die Struktur des Perovskit-Typus. Seine elektrischen Eigenschaften
können aber nicht auf Grund der kristallchemischen
Theorie, welche auf der Vorstellung von der Perov-
skit-Struktur beruht, erklärt werden. Das
Ceriumchromit hat eine erhöhte Leitfähigkeit,
zeigt einen deutlich ausgeprägten Einfluss auf
dieselbe des parzialen Sauerstaffdrucks der um-
gebenden Gasphase und eine anomale Abhängigkeit
der Leitfähigkeit von der Temperatur.

Die Erläuterung dieser Widersprüche wurde mit
Hilfe der Präzisions - TGA gefunden.

Aus Abb. 12 ist ersichtlich, dass das Produkt
der Synthese an der Luft Unstabil ist und mit
Sauerstoff in awei Stadien reagiert:

$$CeCrO_{3-x} + X/2 \, O_2 \quad \xrightarrow{450-550^\circ} \quad CeCrO_3$$

$$2CeCrO_3 + 1/2 \, O_2 \quad \xrightarrow{750-1150^\circ} \quad 2CeO_2 + Cr_2O_3$$

Die mittels der TGA-Untersuchung bestimmte
Defektheit des Anionengitters des Ceriumchromits
und die beobachtete Zersetzung des Chromits gestat-
ten nicht nur eine bestimmte Interpretation der
erwähnten elektrischen Anomalitaten (22) und die

991

Shätzung einiger wichtigen physikalischen Konstan-
ten dieser Verbindung, sondern geben auch die
Möglichkeit, die Schlussfolgerung zu ziehen, dass
die Ceriumchromitbildung in Wirklichkeit nach der
folgenden Reaktion verläuft:

$$2\ CeO_2 + Cr_2O_3 \quad 2CeCrO_3 + 1/2\ O_2 +$$
$$+\ \frac{x}{2}\ O_2,\ wo\ \ O\ \ X\ \ 0,2\ ist.$$

Man kann behaupten, dass die Thermographie,
im Besondern die komplexe Thermographie, bei
Hochtemperaturuntersuchungen viel Zeit und Geld
an Forschungsarbeiten sparen kann. Ausserdem ist
es auch oft möglich, Erscheinungen zu entdecken,
welche ohne Anwendung der thermographischen Methoden nicht an'den Tag zu bringen wären, wie,
zum Beispiel, die Bildung von Zwischen - und me-
tastabielen Phasen, die Feststellung der Existen
gebiete unstabiler Verbindungen u.s.w.

Literatur

1. E. K. Koehler, V. B. Glushkova. Die Bildungs-
bedingungen der Bariumsilikate. Zh. neorgan.
chimii Vol. 1, Heft 10, 1956, S. 2283-2293.

2. N. B. Karpenko, E. K. Koehler. Die Wechsel-
wirkung von $BaCO_3$ mit TiO_2 und ZrO_2 bei hohen
Temperaturen. Zh. Neorgan. Chimii, Vol. V, Heft
6, 1960, S. 1267-1282.

3. E. K. Koehler, N. A. Godina, A. K. Kuznetzov,
A. B. Andreeva. Die Wirkung von Mineralisatoren
auf den Sinterungsprozess der Erdalkalizirkonate.
Zr. prikladn. chimii, Vol. XXX, 1957, S. 682/689.

4. E. K. Koehler, A. K. Kuznetzov. Die Synthese
und die physikalisch-technischen Eigenschaften der
Stronzium- und Bariumzirkonate. Zh. prikladn. chimii, Vol. XXXIV, 1961, S. 2146-2153.

5. E. K. Koehler. Trudy III Wsessojuznogo Ssowestshanija po ogneupornym materialam. Yzd. ANSSR, 1947, S. 173.

6. E. K. Koehler, Thermomechanische Eigenschaften der Alumosilikatischen feuersten Materialien Metallurgizdat, M-L., 1949.

7. E. K. Koehler, A. K. Kuznetzov. Die Anwendung der komplexen thermischen Analyse in physikalisch-chemischen und technischen Untersuchungen. Zh. neorgan. chimii. Vol. I, Heft 6, 1956, S. 1292-1295.

8. E. K. Koehler. L'analyse thermique complexe et son utilisation dans les recherches physico-chimiques et techniques. Bull. Soc. France. Deramique 1958, D-51, p. 3-10.

9. Paul D. Garn. Thermanalytical methods of investigation. Academic Press, New York-London, 1965.

10. G. N. Voronkov. Trudy IV Ssowestshanija po experimentalnoj mineralogii i petrografii, Heft 2, Izd. ANSSSR, Moskva, 1958.

11. E. K. Koehler, A. I. Leonov. Der Einfluss der Beimengungen im Kaolin auf sein Benehmen beim Erhitzen. Dokl. A.N. SSSR, 1955, Vol. 101, Heft 1, S. 137-139.

12. G. Brauer, Z. anorg. u. allgem. Chem., 1941, 1, S. 248.

13. E. K. Koehler, N. A. Godina. Vom Mechanismus der Bildung harter Lösungen im System ZrO_2-CaO. Dokl. ANSSSR, 1955, Vol. 103, N 2, S. 247-250.

14. E. K. Koehler, N. A. Godina. Die Bildungs-bedingungen harter Lösungen im System CeO_2-SrO, Zh. neorgan. chimii., Vol. II, Heft 1., 1957, S. 209-211.

15. E. N. Isupova, E. K. Koehler. Die Wechsel-wirkung im System BaO-BeO. Zh. neorg. chimii., Vol. IX, Heft 2, 1964, S. 394-4-2.

16. N. B. Karpenko, E. K. Koehler. Die Wechsel-wirkung zwischen $BaCO_3$, TiO_2 und ZrO_2 bei hohen Temperaturen. Zh. neorg. chimii. Vol. V., Heft 6, 1960, S. 1267-1282.

17. A. K. Kuznetzov. Von der Wechselwirkung des Kalziumzirkonas mit dem Mineralisator - B_2O_3. Zh. prikladn. chimii, Vol. XXXI, 1958, S. 1799-1805.

18. N. A. Godina, E. P. Savtschenko, E. K. Koehler. Die Bildungsbedingungen und Eigenschaf-ten der Lantan, -Cerium, -Praseodym- und Neodym-orthotan-talate, Zh. neorg. mater., Vol. IV, Heft 3, 1968, S. 389-394.

19. A. K. Kuznetzov, E. K. Koehler. Die Zirkona-te der Seltenerdenelemente und ihre physikalisch-chemischen Eigenschaften. Izv. ANSSSR, Ser. chimitsheskaja, 1966, N 12, S. 2073-2079.

20. A. I. Leonov, V. S. Rudenko, E. K. Koehler. Trudy VI Ssowestshanija po eksperimentalnoj i technitsheskoj mineralogii i petrografii. Moskva, 1962.

21. A. I. Shelykh, K. S. Artemov, V. S. Shvaiko-Shvaikovskii. Elekrical properties of cobaltous-oxide single crystals at high temperatures and their dependence on the partial pressure of oxy-den. Soviet-Phisiks-Solid State. Vol. 8, N 3, Sept. 1966.

22. V. E. Shvaiko-Shvaikovskij, A. I. Leonov,
A. K. Shelykh. Elektrische und thermograwimetri-
sche Untersuchungen an Ceriumtitanat,- chromit und -
aluminat, mit der Struktur vom Perovskit-Typus.
Zh. Neorg. mater., Vol. I, N 5, 1965, S. 737-742.

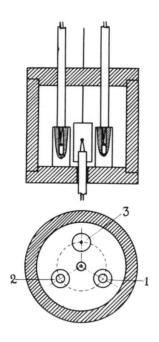

Fig. 1.   DTA-TGA Sample Holder

1.   Reference Material
2.   DTA Sample
3.   TGA Sample

995

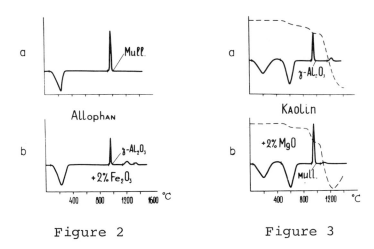

Figure 2

Figure 3

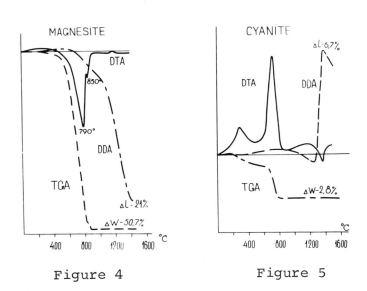

Figure 4

Figure 5

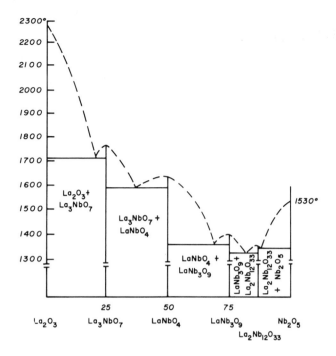

Figure 6

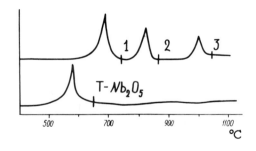

Fig. 7. 1. $T-Nb_2O_5 + (NdNbO_4)$

2. $M-Nb_2O_5 + (NdNb_3O_9)$

3. $Nd_2Nb_{12}O_{33}$

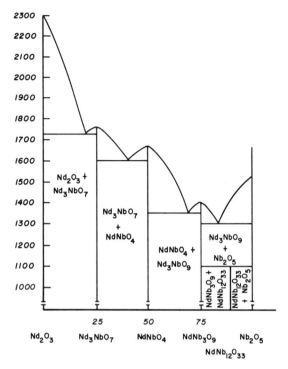

Figure 8

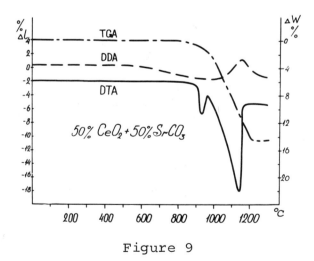

Figure 9

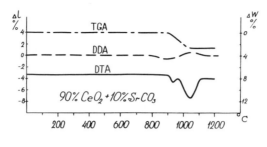

Figure 10

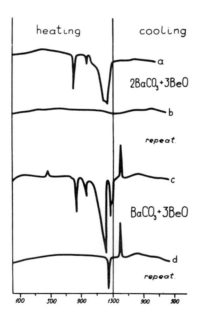

Figure 11

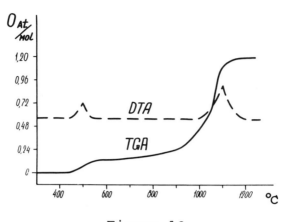

Figure 12

SECTION 4

PHYSICAL CHEMISTRY

Chairmen:

J. H. Flynn
T. R. Ingraham
J. Sestak

THE SIMULTANEOUS DETERMINATION OF THE KINETICS AND THERMODYNAMICS OF DECOMPOSITION BY ISOTHERMAL DTA

T. R. Ingraham and P. Marier

Mines Branch, Department of Energy,
Mines and Resources, Ottawa, Canada

Abstract

Thermodynamic and kinetic parameters were resolved for the decomposition of $CaCO_3$, $Ca(OH)_2$, $BaCl_2 \cdot H_2O$ and $NiSO_4$. The heats of decomposition were obtained by calibrating a DTA cell against a known heat of decomposition. Reaction rates were determined from the time required to complete the decomposition. Temperature corrections were made for the cooling of the sample during its reaction period.

Introduction

Differential thermal analysis (DTA) is a dependable and widely used technique for the discovery and identification of any exothermic and/or endothermic processes that occur when a material is subjected to a slow (1-10°C/min) heating or cooling program (1). When a carefully standardized procedure is used, a DTA apparatus may be calibrated and used as a semi-quantitative calorimeter for estimating heats of crystal transition (2).

A number of attempts have been made to define kinetic parameters by DTA (3,4,5,6). Each of the suggested procedures is based on the assumption that the rate of heat adsorption or evolution during a reaction is proportional to the rate of that reaction at the temperature at which it is measured. A number of different methods have been devised to determine the rate of heat change in a sample. Kissinger (3) assumed that the thermal properties of the reacting mass in a DTA cell could be standardized and that the rate of heat change would be directly reflected as a change in temperature within the sample. Correlating the temperature at which the maximum DTA deflection occurred with the rate of heating of the sample, he derived acceptable values for both the activation energy and frequency factor for several clay mineral dehydrations. More recently, Tateno (4) made an electrical simulation of DTA peaks and confirmed that the area under a peak is proportional to the heat change. He used heat transfer functions to describe a DTA curve and to estimate the activation energies and frequency factors for the three stages in the decomposition of calcium oxalate. Reich (5) estimated a rate of reaction from the fraction of the total heat exchanged in a specific period during a DTA run. Piloyan et al. (6) made essentially the same analysis, but they used the temperature displacement, instead of a narrow band of area, as representing the rate of reaction.

In each of the foregoing methods, geometric features related to sample size, gas flow and packing (all of which are known to affect the rate of decomposition) (7) are neglected. Moreover, each method uses, as its peak temperature, the temperature in the reference material at the time when the peak is developed in the sample. Depending on the intensity of the heat effect, the sample and reference temperatures may differ by as much as 20°C. Hence, any conclusions based on the assumption that the temperature in the reference material is the reaction temperature at the time of the peak, are likely to be in error.

We have found that there is a relatively simple solution to the problem of obtaining kinetic parameters from DTA data, for those endothermic reaction systems in which the reaction rate can be controlled by the presence of a product gas. This paper will describe experiments in which "isothermal" DTA runs were made at different temperatures and the rate of reaction at each temperature was estimated from the length of time required for the heat exchange to be completed. The procedure avoids geometric complications and is based on the actual temperature at the reaction interface.

Materials, Apparatus and Procedure

Materials

Reagent-grade $CaCO_3$ was used, as purchased, without

drying. Calcium hydroxide was prepared from reagent-grade $CaCO_3$ by first decomposing it at 900°C and then hydrating it with CO_2-free distilled water under conditions which excluded CO_2 absorption. The material was dried under vacuum at 150°C and its composition confirmed by X-ray diffraction analysis. Anhydrous $NiSO_4$ was prepared by heating $NiSO_4 \cdot 6H_2O$ in a muffle furnace at 420°C for 5 hours. Barium chloride monohydrate was prepared by mixing stoichiometric amounts of $BaCl_2 \cdot 2H_2O$ and $BaCl_2$ and heating them together in a sealed pyrex tube at 125°C for 20 hours.

Apparatus

A Model 12BC2 DTA unit supplied by the Robert L. Stone Division of Tracor Incorporated was used in the experimental work. The inconel sample-holder (SH1-8A) was fitted with Pt-Pt/10% Rh thermocouples and was used with the carbonate, hydrate and hydroxide samples. A boron nitride cell of similar design was used to study the sulfate decomposition. The DTA peaks were recorded on a Moseley Model 7100B strip chart recorder. Temperature programs were selected with a Model 240 R programmer made by the F & M Division of Hewlett-Packard.

Procedure

The sample materials were ground to pass through a 200-mesh sieve and packed lightly into the DTA cell with a 1/4 x 5-inch glass rod. The quantity of sample required to fill the cell was slightly different for each compound. The amount used was determined by differential weighing. The samples were brought to the selected reaction temperature in an atmosphere of their decomposition product gas. Steam was used for the hydrate and hydroxide, and cylinder-grade CO_2 for the carbonate. A 2-to-1 mixture of SO_2 and O_2, equilibrated at the reaction temperature over platinum, was used to study the sulfate decomposition. The runs were begun by switching the product gas mixture to a 45 cc/min stream of tank-grade argon.

Results and Discussion

Calcium Carbonate

In the first group of experiments, calcium carbonate

samples were used to establish the temperature profile
within the sample during its decomposition. Three experiments were done at 755°C and three at 818°C. In the first
experiment at each temperature, the differential thermocouple was placed at 25% of the distance between the lower
and upper surfaces of the sample. In the second experiment,
the thermocouple was placed in the center of the sample.
In the third experiment at each temperature, the thermocouple was placed at 75% of the distance between the lower
and upper surfaces of the sample. The results obtained at
each temperature were similar; those at 818°C are shown in
Figure 1.

From the rapid initial cooling indicated by each
thermocouple, it is evident that when decomposition is
initiated it takes place generally through the sample and
not at a well-defined interface which advances through the
sample in the direction of the gas flow. The maximum
amount of cooling caused by the reaction varies within the
sample from bottom to top, as shown in Table I.

From the data in Table I, the temperature profiles
were constructed. They are shown in Figure 2. The slope of
the curves indicates that as the reaction progresses, the
sample continues to cool. The maximum amount of cooling
occurs at about 75% of the distance from the bottom of the
sample. From the differences in cooling shown by the curves
for the 775 and 818°C experiments, it is evident that the
amount of cooling is directly related to the temperature at
which the decomposition reaction is initiated. The most
important point to be resolved from the curves is that
despite a constant sample temperature at the onset of
decomposition, the decomposition process does not occur at
any single temperature. The temperature at which parts of
the sample decompose may vary by as much as 7.5°C when the
starting temperature is 775°C, to as much as 17.7°C when
the starting temperature is 818°C.

To obtain the mean temperature deviation from the
starting temperature, Simpson's rule was used to integrate
the areas under the curves in Figure 2. The mean deviation
calculated from the area was compared with the maximum
deviation indicated by a thermocouple placed in the center
of the sample. For the 775°C experiment, the mean was 75%
of the peak value recorded, and for the 818°C experiment it
was 80%. The average of these two means, 77.5%, was
considered representative and was used throughout the

remaining experiments to calculate the mean decomposition temperature during a run. From the results of previous experimental work on heats of transition (2), there was no reason to believe that the 77.5% figure would be altered by the slight changes in thermal conductivity occasioned by using samples of different compounds. For this reason the temperature profile experiments were not repeated for each new sample.

The data from the foregoing experiments were also analyzed to determine the effect of thermocouple position on magnitude the DTA response from a sample. The results are shown in Table II.

The data in Table II indicate that a thermocouple placed at the 25% position responds to only about 80% of the heat change recorded by thermocouples at the 50 and 75% positions. Within experimental error, the thermocouples at the 50 and 75% positions "see" the same amount of heat change.

The heat of decomposition of $CaCO_3$ is well established (8,9,10,11). At the mid-point temperature in the decomposition range, the average value of the heat of decomposition is 39.5 ± 1 kcal/mole. This value was used to obtain a calibration factor of 5.3×10^{-4} kcal/deg.min for the SH1-8A cell and 4.9×10^{-4} kcal/deg.min for the boron nitride cell.

The curves shown in Figure 1 for a typical DTA run depart sharply from the base line when the reaction begins and return sharply to it when the reaction is complete. Because of this, it is possible to make a reasonably precise measurement of the length of time required for the completion of a run at a specified temperature. A typical group of curves for $CaCO_3$ are shown in Figure 3. The data calculated from them is shown in Table III.

From the results shown in Table III, it is evident that the peak area is essentially the same for a variety of starting temperatures. The relative reaction rates at each temperature are proportional to the reciprocal of the time required for reaction. From the logarithm of the relative reaction rates and the reciprocal of the mean absolute temperature of reaction, the Arrhenius graph shown in Figure 4 was constructed. A least squares fitting of the best straight line through the points gave a value of 47 ± 2 kcal for the activation energy of decomposition of $CaCO_3$. This is within the experimental error of most of the values previously reported (7).

Calcium Hydroxide

A similar series of experiments was done to estimate the heat of decomposition of $Ca(OH)_2$. A value of 23.6 ± 0.8 kcal/mole was obtained. This is in good agreement with 24.9 kcal/mole obtained by Halstead and Moore (12), and 25.2 kcal/mole by Mikhail et al. (13). From the length of time required to complete the decomposition at a series of temperatures, an activation energy of 35 ± 2 kcal was estimated. At flow-rates of nitrogen from 10 to 60 cc/min at STP through the sample, the activation energy is independent of flow rate.

The value of 35 kcal obtained by this method is in good agreement with values of 36.5 kcal and 38.5 kcal reported by Dave and Chopra (14). It is in substantial disagreement with a value of 14.9 kcal reported by Mikhail et al. (13) for a two-stage decomposition process of $Ca(OH)_2$.

Barium Chloride Monohydrate

Experiments similar to those done on $CaCO_3$ and $Ca(OH)_2$ were made with $BaCl_2 \cdot H_2O$. From the area under the isothermal DTA peak, a heat of 15.3 ± 1 kcal/mole was estimated for the decomposition reaction. This is in agreement with 15.3 kcal/mole reported by Yatsimirskii (15) and 16.6 ± 0.7 kcal/mole reported by Ingraham and Rigaud (16). The estimated activation energy for the decomposition was 18.0 ± 1.0 kcal. This is within the experimental error of the value of 20 ± 4 kcal estimated by Ingraham and Rigaud (16).

Nickelous Sulfate

When the DTA area and time-duration experiments were repeated with anhydrous nickel sulfate in a boron nitride DTA cell, the heat of decomposition to NiO, SO_2 and O_2, relative to a $CaCO_3$ standard, was estimated as 75 ± 2 kcal/mole. This agrees well with a value of 75.5 ± 2 kcal/mole estimated recently by Ingraham (17) from decomposition pressure measurements. An activation energy of 60.5 kcal was estimated for the decomposition of $NiSO_4$ to NiO and SO_3. This agrees well with an earlier estimate, of 61 ± 3 kcal, made by the authors (18) when using a standard thermogravimetric method.

Conclusions

When a simple chemical reaction can be retarded by its product gases, the heat of its decomposition and the overall activation energy of the reaction may be estimated from a few "isothermal" DTA runs. It is significant that the DTA method makes it possible to calculate the activation energies based on the temperature prevailing at the reaction site.

Acknowledgments

Mr. P. Belanger made the X-ray diffraction analysis required to confirm the composition of the compounds used in the experiments.

References

1. M. C. B. Hotz and T. R. Ingraham, Can. Met. Quart. 5, 237 (1966).
2. T. R. Ingraham and P. Marier, Can. Met. Quart. 4, 169 (1965).
3. H. E. Kissinger, J. Res. Nat. Bur. Std. 57, 2712 (1956).
4. Jun Tateno, Trans. Faraday Soc. 62, 1885 (1966).
5. L. Reich, Polymer Letters 4, 423 (1966).
6. G. O. Piloyan, I. D. Ryakchikov and O. S. Novikova, Nature 5067, 1229 (1966).
7. T. R. Ingraham and P. Marier, Can. J. Chem. Eng. 41, 170 (1963).
8. K. K. Kelley and C. T. Anderson, U. S. Bur. of Mines Bull. 384 (1935).
9. M. Zawistowski, Cement-Wapno-Gips 10, 46 (1954).
10. G. Sabatier, Bull. Soc. Franc. Mineral 77, 953 (1954).
11. I. G. Murgulescu, Bul. Inst. Nat. Cercetari 1, 21 (1946).
12. P. E. Halstead and A. E. Moore, J. Chem. Soc., 3873 (1957).
13. R. Sh. Mikhail, S. Brunauer and L. E. Copeland, J. Col. and Int. Sc. 21, 394 (1966).
14. N. G. Dave and S. K. Chopra, J. Am. Ceram. Soc. 49, 575 (1966).
15. K. B. Yatsimirskii, J. Gen. Chem. USSR 17, 2019 (1947).

16. T. R. Ingraham and M. Rigaud, Can. Met. Quart. 4, 247 (1965).
17. T. R. Ingraham, Trans. Met. Soc. AIME 236, 1064 (1966).
18. T. R. Ingraham and P. Marier, Trans. Met. Soc. AIME 236, 1067 (1966).

TABLE I

Temperature as a Function of Thermocouple Position

Position of Thermocouple	Maximum Temperature Deviation	
	775°C Expt.	818°C Expt.
25%	5.0°C	13.6°C
50%	6.5°C	16.8°C
75%	7.5°C	17.7°C

TABLE II

Peak Area as a Function of Thermocouple Position

Position of Thermocouple	Area (Arbitrary Units)	
	775°C Expt.	818°C Expt.
25%	0.81	0.81
50%	1.00	1.00
75%	0.94	1.05

TABLE III

Duration of DTA Runs at Various Starting Temperatures

Starting Temperature	Time (min)	Area (deg.min/mole)	ΔT at Peak (°C)	Mean Position Temperature
752.0	31.7	96400	5.3	748
776	21.2	93700	7.6	770
798	14.3	90700	11.4	789
819	9.5	91800	15.5	807
841	6.7	93200	22.4	823

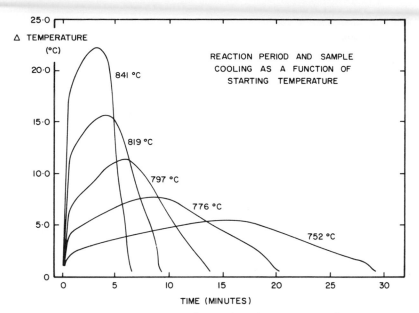

Fig. 1 - Sample Cooling during reaction, as indicated by thermocouples placed at 25, 50 and 75% of the distance from the bottom to the top surface of the $CaCO_3$ sample.

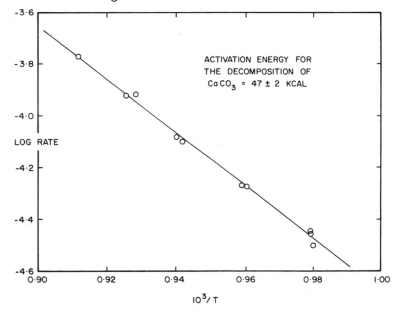

Fig. 2 - Temperature profile within $CaCO_3$ sample during decomposition.

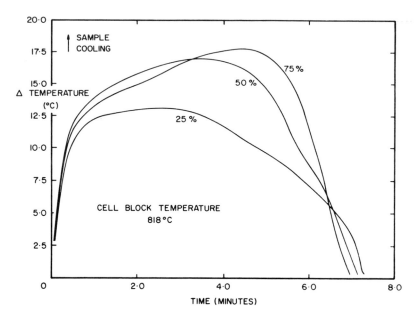

Fig. 3 – Variation of reaction period with
temperature of initiation.

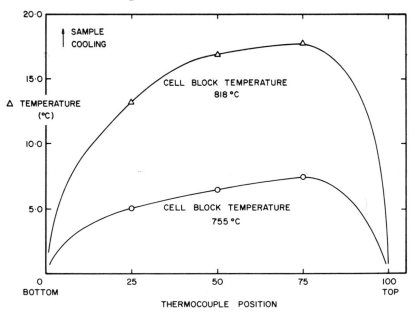

Fig. 4 – Arrhenius plot of log rate versus
reciprocal temperature for CaCO$_3$.

Kinetics of the Reaction between $MgSO_4$ and Cr_2O_3

Samuel F. Hulbert
Department of Ceramic Engineering
Clemson University
Clemson, South Carolina

Abstract

Thermogravimetric analysis was used to study the kinetics of the reaction between $MgSO_4$ and Cr_2O_3, in the temperature range 900°C to 1000°C, as a function of sample mass and processing procedures. The measured kinetics are influenced by the reversible nature of the reaction. Pelletization, or increasing the sample mass, retards the reaction by increasing the partial pressure of SO_3 developed within the powdered compact. The effect of processing pressure on the kinetics of the reaction is dependent on the sample mass.

The kinetics of the reaction were found to be described by a nuclei growth equation with (m) equal to 1.25.

Introduction

Reactions of the type Solid A + Solid B→Solid C +→ Gas↑ are often used to form titanates, zirconates, ferrites, and other materials of technological importance. The reaction between $MgSO_4$ and Cr_2O_3 was examined in an attempt to gain a better understanding of solid state reactions in which one of the product phases is a gas. To accomplish this objective, the kinetics of this reaction were studied with elaboration on: (a) the rate equation which best fits the experimental data, i.e., the fraction reaction completed versus time data; (b) whether the reaction is phase boundary or transport controlled; (c) whether the transport mechanism is uni - directional solid state diffusion, Wagner[1], Hauffe[2], vapor, etc.; (d) the distribution of product phase with respect to the reactant phase (continuous product layer surrounding one reactant phase, nuclei distributed at random in one reactant phase, etc.); and (e) the effect of sample mass, pelletization, and processing pressure.

Experimental Procedure

The reaction between $MgSO_4$ and Cr_2O_3 to form $MgCr_2O_4$ plus SO_3 was studied isothermally, between 900°C and 1000°C, using thermogravimetric analysis to monitor the fraction reaction completed versus time. The thermogravimetric analysis apparatus consisted of a Kanthal furnace, a temperature controller capable of maintaining a constant temperature of ±3°C, a temperature recorder, and an Ainsworth recording balance. From the recorded weight loss curve, the fraction reaction completed (x for $MgSO_4 + Cr_2O_3 \rightarrow MgCr_2O_4 + SO_3\uparrow$) was calculated as the ratio of the weight loss at time (t) to the theoretical total weight loss.

The $MgSO_4$ was prepared by heating Baker analyzed $MgSO_4$ $7H_2O$ at 400°C in a platinum crucible for 2 hours. Optical microscopy and x - ray analysis showed complete conversion to $MgSO_4$. The individual particles were estimated microscopically to range in size from 1 to 10 microns with the majority being between 3 and 5 microns. Baker's c.p. grade chromic oxide was used. The chromic oxide had an average particle size of one micron; the largest particle size observed was 5 microns.

Stoichiometric proportions of chromic oxide and magnesium sulphate were throughly mixed by first tumbling the dry powders together for three hours and then blending with a mortar and pestle. The powder mixture was examined under a binocular microscope. The white magnesium sulphate was observed to be uniformly distributed throughout the green chromium oxide background.

Presentation and Discussion of Results

The effect of temperatures on the fraction reaction completed versus time curve for the reaction between $MgSO_4$ and Cr_2O_3 is shown in Figure 1. The effect of sample mass on the velocity of the reaction is illustrated in Figure 2 and the effect of processing pressure in Figure 3. Note in Figures 1, 2, and 3 that the fraction reaction completed versus time curves have a signoid shape. This may be interpreted as arising from the production of nuclei at a localized active center in one of the reactants, the growth of these nuclei and, beyond the point of inflexion, the decay

of the reaction as nuclei overlap and the area of the interface between reactant and product phases decreases.

A van't Hoff differential analysis[3] was made to see if
the kinetics of the reaction can be classified as to a reaction order, see Figure 4. The van't Hoff plot can be
broken into four distinct regions. In region A (from 0 to
approximately 15 to 20 percent completion), the rate of
reaction is increasing which represents an induction period
or nucleation period. In region B (from approximately 15
to 60 percent completion), the velocity of the reaction is
practically constant and thus, the kinetics in this region
can be classified as zero order. In region C (from approximately 60 to 85 percent completion) the rate of reaction
rapidly decays. This suggests that the majority of the
nuclei comes into contact when the reaction is approximately
60 percent completed. During the final stage of the reaction (region D) the rate constant slowly decays. The first
three stages of the reaction are readily identified in
Figures 1,2, and 3, however, with the time scale employed,
it is difficult to distinguish the third stage from the
fourth stage. The non - linearity of the van't Hoff plot
shows the entire reaction cannot be classified as to a
reaction order.

The van't Hoff analysis and fraction reaction completed
versus time plots both indicate that a nuclei growth equation ought to give the best mathematical representation of
the data. A nuclei growth analysis[4,5] was performed on each
set of data using an IBM 360 Model 40 computer, see Figure 5.
The linearity of the nuclei growth plots showed that the
entire reaction could be represented by a nuclei growth
equation. The values of (m) in the general nuclei growth
equation

$$(kt)^m = - \ln (1-x) \qquad (1)$$

for the reaction between $MgSO_4$ and Cr_2O_3, range from 1.14
to 1.32 with an average value of 1.25. [3] Plots of rate constants calculated using equation

$$(kt)^{1.25} = - \ln (1-x) \qquad (2)$$

versus the fraction of reaction completed were nearly horizontal while rate constants calculated using other nuclei
growth equations (m = 1 and 3/2) drifted with time, see

1015

Figure 6.

The isothermal reaction data was subjected to the equation derived by Jander[6], Kroger - Ziegler[7,8], Zhuravlev - Lesokhin - Tempel'man[9], Ginstling - Brounshtein[10], Dunwald - Wagner[11], and Carter[12] - Valensi[13]. Rate constants, calculated using the foregoing showed a pronounced drift with time, see Figure 6, indicating that models based on diffusion through a continuous product layer are invalid for analyzing the reaction between $MgSO_4$ and Cr_2O_3.

Rate constants calculated using the nuclei growth model (with m = 5/4) were used in constructing an Arrhenius plot. An apparent activation energy of 69 kcal/mole and a frequency factor of $2.6 \times 10^{10} \frac{1}{(minutes)}$ was observed for 0.25 gram samples pressed at 8,000 psi.

The fact that the reaction between $MgSO_4$ and Cr_2O_3 is dependent on sample mass, see Figure 2, indicates that the reverse reaction limits the kinetics of the overall process. The rates of reaction for the decomposition of many carbonates have been found to be sharply dependent upon the partial pressure of carbon dioxide[14,15]. Spencer and Topley[15] expressed the rate of reaction (R) for the decomposition of silver carbonate powder as a function of partial pressure of CO_2 (PCO_2) in the following manner:

$$R = \frac{R\circ(P°CO_2 - PCO_2)}{P°CO_2 + KPCO_2} \qquad (3)$$

where ($P°CO_2$) is the equilibrium partial pressure, ($R\circ$) the rate of decomposition when ($PCO_2 = 0$), and (K) the ratio of the rate constants for the forward and reverse reactions. According to equation (3), if a constant pressure of CO_2 is maintained, the observed overall rate constant will not change with time. The model applicable for the reaction between $MgSO_4$ and Cr_2O_3, over the range of boundary conditions employed, was found to be independent of processing pressure and sample size. This suggests that a certain internal pressure of SO_3 is rapidly developed within the sample and is maintained until the final stages of the reaction. Pelletization and increasing the sample mass retards the reaction by increasing the partial pressure of SO_3 developed within the powdered compact.

The effect of processing pressure on the kinetics of the reaction is more complex. Loose powders were always

observed to react faster than pressed pellets. When the
sample mass was below one gram, the pellets pressed at
16,000 psi reacted faster than those pressed at 8,000 psi,
see Figure 3. However, when the sample mass was above one
gram the samples pressed at 8,000 psi reacted faster than
those pressed at 16,000 psi. A possible explanation for
the observed phenomena is that in a mixture of fine powders,
the number of contact points between two components has an
important effect on the rate of the reaction, which proceeds
through the contact points between particles. Increasing
the processing pressure increases the number of contact
points between reactants which in turn increases the rate
of the reaction. Increasing the processing pressure also
makes it more difficult for the SO_3 created during the
reaction to be evolved from the powdered compact thus decreasing the rate of reaction. This latter effect becomes
more pronounced as the sample mass increases.

When indirectly measuring the rate of formation of the
product phase, as by change in weight due to gas evolution,
there always exists the question of whether or not the
measurement actually represents the rate of the reaction
being studied or if it is, rather, the rate of decomposition of one substance in the presence of a second phase.
X - ray patterns of the product formed by the reaction
between $MgSO_4$ and Cr_2O_3 showed $MgCr_2O_4$ to be the only phase
present. X - ray patterns of partially reacted compacts
revealed the presence of $MgCr_2O_4$, $MgSO_4$, and Cr_2O_3. The
absence of MgO indicated that the SO_3 evolution was associated with the reaction between $MgSO_4$ and Cr_2O_3 to form
$MgCr_2O_4$ and not with the decomposition of $MgSO_4$ to MgO.

A sudden decrease in furnace temperature of a partially reacted compact would lead to weight gain if decomposition had occurred. In the temperature range for which
the kinetic data is reported (900 - 1000°C) no weight was
observed with reduction in furnace temperature. Reactions
at temperatures deliberately high enough to independently
decompose magnesium sulphate (1100°C) gave large weight
gains with sudden temperature reduction into the stability
range of magnesium sulphate.

Conclusions

1. The kinetics of reaction between $MgSO_4$ and Cr_2O_3 are
found to be described by the nuclei growth equation with

(m) equal to 1.25.

2. The measured kinetics are influenced by the reversible nature of the reaction. Pelletization, or increasing the sample mass, retards the reaction by increasing the partial pressure of SO_3 developed within the powdered compact.

3. The overall effect of processing pressure on the kinetics of the reaction is dependent on the sample mass.

4. Consideration of sample mass, pelletization, and processing pressure must be included in the designing of any process involving reactions of the type Solid A + Solid B $\longrightarrow$ Solid C + Gas$\uparrow$.

Acknowledgements

This work was supported by the General Refractories Company.

The writer thanks George D. MacKenzie, of the General Refractories Baltimore Research Laboratories, for the particle size determination.

References

1. C. Kooy, Reactivity of Solids, edited by G. M. Schwab, 21-28, Elsevier Publishing Co., New York (1965).
2. K. Hauffe, Reaktionen in und an Fester Stoffen, p. 582, Springer Verlag (1955).
3. K. J. Laidler, Chemical Kinetics, 15-17, McGraw - Hill, Inc., New York (1965).
4. J. W. Christian, The Theory of Transformation in Metals and Alloys, Pergaman Press, New York (1965).
5. S. F. Hulbert and J. J. Klawitter, Jour. Am. Cer. Soc., 50 484 (1967).
6. W. Jander, Z. Anorg, Allgem, Chem., 163 (1927).
7. C. Kroger and G. Ziegler, Glastech. Ber. 26 346 (1953).
8. C. Kroger and G. Ziegler, ibid., 27 199 (1954).
9. V. F. Zhuravlev, I. G. Lesokhin, and R. G. Tempel'man, Jour. Appl. Chem. USSR (English Transl.) 21 887 (1948).
10. A. M. Ginstling and B. I. Brounshtein, Jour. Appl. Chem. USSR(English Transl.) 23 1327 (1950).
11. H. Dunwald and C. Wagner, Z. Physik. Chem. (Leipzig) B24 (1934).
12. R. E. Carter, Jour. Chem. Phys. 34 2010 (1961).
13. G. Valensi, Compt. Rend., 202 (1936).

14. I.B. Cutler, Kinetics of High-Temperature Processes, edited by W. D. Kingery 294-300, John Wiley & Sons, Inc., New York (1959).
15. W. D. Spencer and B. Topley, Jour. Chem. Soc., 2633 (1929).

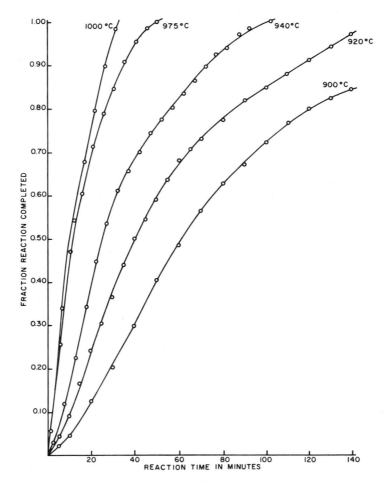

Figure 1. Isothermal reaction rate curves showing effect of temperature on the reaction $MgSO_4 + Cr_2O_3 \longrightarrow MgCr_2O_4 + SO_3\uparrow$ (0.25 gram specimens pressed at 8,000 psi).

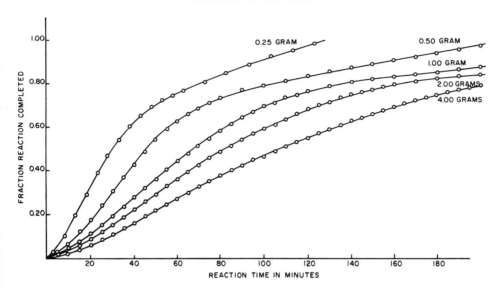

Figure 2. Reaction rate curves for $MgSO_4 + Cr_2O_3 \rightarrow MgCr_2O_4$ + $SO_3\uparrow$ at 950°C showing the effect of sample mass (specimens pressed at 8,000 psi).

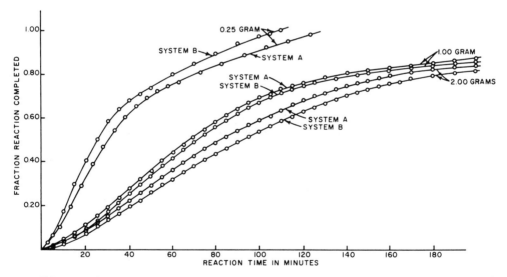

Figure 3. Reaction rate curves for $MgSO_4 + Cr_2O_3 \rightarrow MgCr_2O_4$ + $SO_3\uparrow$ at 950°C showing the effect of processing pressure (System A consists of pellets pressed at 8,000 psi, System B, pellets pressed at 16,000 psi).

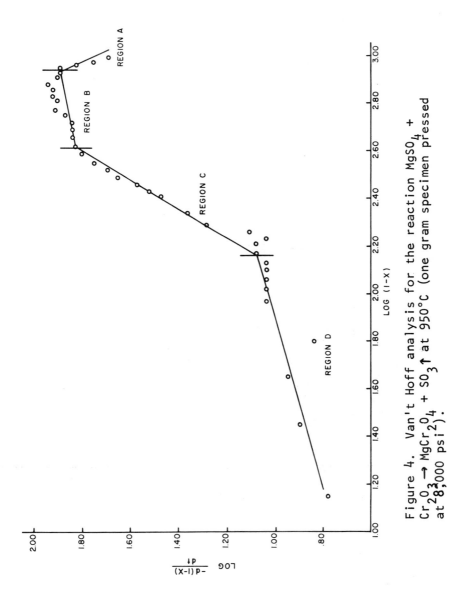

Figure 4. Van't Hoff analysis for the reaction $MgSO_4 + Cr_2O_3 \rightarrow MgCr_2O_4 + SO_3\uparrow$ at 950°C (one gram specimen pressed at 8,000 psi).

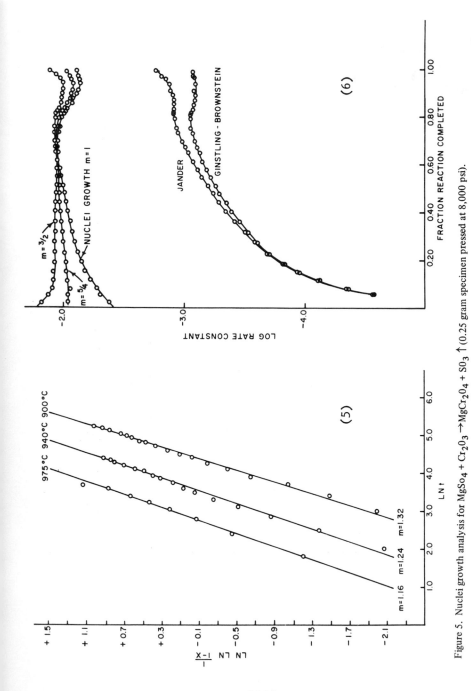

Figure 5. Nuclei growth analysis for $MgSO_4 + Cr_2O_3 \rightarrow MgCr_2O_4 + SO_3 \uparrow$ (0.25 gram specimen pressed at 8,000 psi).

Figure 6. Analysis of rate equations for the reaction $MgSO_4 + Cr_2O_3 \rightarrow MgCr_2O_4 + SO_3 \uparrow$ (one gram specimen pressed at 8,000 psi reacted at 950°C).

SURFACE AREA EFFECTS ON THE
OXIDATION KINETICS OF PYROLYTIC GRAPHITE

Milton Levy

Army Materials and Mechanics Research Center
Watertown, Massachusetts 02172

Abstract

The oxidation kinetics of pyrolytic graphite was studied as a function of temperature, air velocity, and surface area. The transition temperature between chemical and diffusion control may be significantly increased or decreased by decreasing or increasing the surface area of pyrolytic graphite. Kinetic theory calculations showed that the maximum reaction rate in the diffusion-controlled region is 50,000 times the observed rate for specimens having the smallest surface area.

Symbols

K_R = equilibrium constant
n = number of collisions of oxygen/sqcm/sec
$\dfrac{dn}{dt}$ = reaction rate in atoms C/sqcm/sec
$\dfrac{dw}{dt}$ = reaction rate in grams/sqcm/sec

Introduction

Pyrolytic graphite is a specialized polycrystalline form of graphite deposited from a carbonaceous vapor at temperatures above 3635 F on a suitable substrate, resulting in a buildup of layers having the graphitic structure. According to the supplier, pyrolytic graphite is impermeable to both liquids and gases, has greater strength than normal commercial graphite, and exhibits a greater degree of anisotropy in its thermal and electrical properties than single-crystal natural graphite. The microstructure of pyrolytic graphite is typical of vapor-deposited materials (fibrous in nature) and shows an unusually high degree of preferred orientation.

1023

Figure 1 illustrates the columnar structure of pyrolytic graphite. Localized regions within the grains have different preferred orientations which are due to the fact that the basal planes in the cones are not parallel to the specimen length but are curved instead. The varying degrees of curvature result in a grain structure of conical configuration. This curvature is indicative of strain. Frozen-in stresses exist because of the thermal expansion and contraction that occur in the deposition process. Although this is typical of other graphites it is so to a lesser degree because of the less preferred orientation in normal graphite. Pyrolytic graphite has a high density compared to commercial graphite and has been prepared with measured densities as high as 2.22 grams per cubic centimeter.

The susceptibility of graphite to oxidation, beginning at comparatively low temperatures and becoming progressively more severe with increasing temperature, limits its usefulness as a high temperature material in spite of its several very favorable properties.

Oxidation may be studied readily by observation of chemical composition, penetration rate, structure of the oxide layer formed, and by the change in weight of the material during oxidation. Graphite is less reactive to oxygen than many metals. However, its oxides are gaseous and provide no protective film or layer. The formation of these gaseous products produce a loss in weight which, when carefully recorded in relation to time, offers a means for studying the rate of oxidation.

Equilibria calculations may be made on several reactions to determine the thermodynamic feasibility of the secondary reactions and the stability of the reaction products.

The pertinent reactions involving graphite, oxygen, carbon dioxide, and carbon monoxide are contained in Table I along with values of the equilibrium constant K_R.

The equilibrium constants for reactions (1,2,3) show that both carbon dioxide and carbon monoxide are stable to decomposition. Carbon monoxide can be oxidized at all temperatures between 1100 and 2200 F according to reaction (3), whereas the reaction of carbon dioxide with graphite

1024

(4) is possible anywhere above 1200 F. The dissociation of oxygen molecules, reaction (5), is not appreciable at all temperatures in Table I.

The overall heterogeneous reaction of O_2 and C may be envisaged as involving the transport of the gaseous reactants to the surface, the reaction on the surface, and the transport of the gaseous products from the surface. Thus, the controlling factors of the reaction would be diffusion or chemical reactivity, depending on which is the slower process.

In an earlier investigation, Levy (1) studied the oxidation of pyrolytic graphite in quiescent air between 1250 and 1850 F. A break in the Arrhenius plot occurred at 1550 F. This break may have been due to a change in controlling mechanism, but could not be ascertained in a quiescent system. Later, Levy and Wong (2) studied the oxidation kinetics of pyrolytic graphite between 1400 and 1800 F at air velocities of 25 to 100 cm/sec and atmospheric pressure and for a specimen area of 3.024 sq cm. A transition from chemical to diffusion control occurred between 1500 and 1600 F. The existence of a change in mechanism of reaction at approximately 1600 F was reported for normal graphite and carbon by Tu, Davis, and Hottel, (3), Kuchta, Kant, and Damon, (4), Blyholder and Eyring, (5), and Gulbransen, Andrew, and Brassart (6). Gulbransen also found that the transition between chemical and diffusion control depends on pressure, sample size, and the nature of the reaction system. Since these earlier investigators also reported transition temperatures near 1600 F, their reaction system, specimen areas, and oxidation conditions were probably similar. This report presents a study of the effect of specimen surface area on the oxidation kinetics of pyrolytic graphite for a given reaction system.

Apparatus and Experimental Procedure

An automatic weighing and recording reaction system (Aminco Thermograv) was used for obtaining the rates of oxidation of pyrolytic graphite. The weight sensitivity of the system was 0.2 mg. The furnace temperature was regulated by a calibrated chromel-alumel furnace thermocouple which controlled the power input to the furnace. An additional calibrated chromel-alumel thermocouple placed ad-

jacent to the sample was used to maintain the desired temperature within ± 3.5 F during the oxidation runs. This
assured that the difference between the temperature of the
sample and the furnace would be minimized as much as possible under the experimental conditions.

Air was introduced at the bottom of the reaction chamber,
dried with Drierite, and measured with flow meters.

According to the supplier (Raytheon Co., Waltham, Mass.),
the pyrolytic graphite was deposited from methane on a synthetic graphite substrate at 3812 F and had a density of
2.20 g/cc. Specimens had surface areas of 6.27 sq cm,
0.927 sq cm, and 0.394 sq cm, were rinsed with ethyl alcohol,
and dried to constant weight. Specimens had a fairly constant ratio of exposed basal plane surface to edge surface
to minimize anisotropy effects.

The oxidation of pyrolytic graphite was studied as a
function of time, temperature, air velocity, and surface
area. Runs were made at 1400, 1500, 1600, 1700, and 1800 F
at air flow rates of 25, 50, 75 and 100 cm/sec for each
temperature and surface area.

Results and Discussion

A plot of reaction rate versus 1/T for four air velocities and a specimen surface area of 0.927 sq cm is shown
in Figure 2. Limiting tangents at the longer exposure
times were employed for the determination of reaction rate
constants. The temperature of oxidation was then at constant value for each exposure. The initial portion of the
curves between 1400 and 1700 F clearly represents a region
in which chemical resistance is controlling, since the effect of velocity is overshadowed by that of temperature. For
this region an energy of activation of 38 Kcal/mol was
calculated. At 1700 F and above, a change is observed in
oxidation kinetics at all gas velocities. In this region
an energy of activation of 5 Kcal/mol was calculated.

The effect of velocity for several temperatures and a
specimen surface area of 0.927 sq cm is shown in Figure 3a,
both scales of which are logarithmic. Below 1700 F the
curves are parallel to the velocity axis, showing a lack of

dependence of rate on air velocity because of the predominant effect of chemical resistance at the surface. The slopes of the isotherms increase at 1700 F and above, where the rate is substantially independent of temperature. The substantial parallelism of the curves for this temperature region indicates that chemical resistance appears to have no importance between 1700 and 1800 F when the combustion rate is defined as containing two additive terms, the first of which corresponds to a diffusional resistance and the second to a chemical resistance. (3) If the reaction is in the diffusion-controlled region, one would expect the reaction rate to increase with increasing air velocity, which was the case at 1700 and 1800 F.

Figures 3b and 3c show similar curves for specimens having surface areas of 6.27 sq cm and 0.394 sq cm. By increasing the specimen surface area, the transition temperature between chemical and diffusion control decreases to 1600 F. Conversely, decreasing the specimen surface area increases the transition temperature to above 1800 F.

Figure 4 shows the effect of surface area on reaction rates at temperatures of 1400 to 1800 F and an air velocity of 25 cm/sec. It is important to note that the reaction rate is the highest for the small surface areas at the same temperature. This indicates that surface area itself has an effect on reaction rate independently of other variables. In other words, for the same air velocity and temperature a sample having a smaller surface area oxidizes more rapidly than one having a larger surface area. In the region of the smallest area, the curves become steeper and at 1800 F the curve was very steep, indicating an enormous reaction rate for a very small area. The effect of increasing air velocity on reaction rate is evidenced by a shifting of the curves upward for each increase in air velocity. For the reaction rates at higher velocities, the slopes of the curves were similar, however, the reaction rate curves begin to rise sooner than for the lower velocities.

Studies on the diffusion-controlled oxidation of graphite are more meaningful when the rates of reaction are related to the chemical-controlled reaction and to the values calculated from kinetic theory. Table II contains the number of impacts (n) of oxygen molecules with a square centimeter of surface area per second at temperatures of 1400 to 1800 F and atmospheric pressure, calculated from kinetic theory. If CO is formed, each collision results in reaction with two atoms of C. Therefore, the theoretical value of dn/dt, expressed as atoms of carbon per square centimeter per second, will be twice the number of collisions per square centimeter per second. The values for dn/dt are also contained in Table II.

Table III shows the effect of surface area on the rates of oxidation which are expressed as dw/dt (g/sq cm/sec) and dn/dt (atoms C/sq cm/sec) calculated by using Avogadro's number (for air velocity of 25 cm/sec). The sample area was varied by a factor of 16 to determine the transition between chemical and diffusion control. Since the value of dn/dt increased on reducing the specimen size, the reaction is still under diffusion control for the smaller sample. Reaction rates up to 5.00×10^{18} atoms C/sq cm/sec were measured.

Figure 5 contains a plot of log dn/dt versus $1/T$ (K) at an air velocity of 100 cm/sec for samples having surface areas of 0.394, 0.937, and 6.27 sq cm. The linear portions of the curves represent chemical-controlled oxidation with an energy of activation of 38 Kcal/mol. Reaction rates to the right of these linear portions represent diffusion-controlled oxidation where temperature has a minor effect on the reaction rate. The important variable is the surface area. The maximum measured rate of oxidation for a 0.394 sq cm sample at a furnace temperature of 1800 F was 5.00×10^{18} atom C/sq cm/sec. Kinetic theory calculations contained in Table II indicate a maximum reaction rate of 2.7×10^{23} atoms C/sq cm/sec at 1800 F. This value is 50,000 times the observed value for a 0.394 sq cm specimen area.

The transition temperature between chemical and diffusion-control depends on the specimen area and the nature of the reaction. By decreasing the specimen area it was possible to increase the transition temperature from 1600 F to above 1800 F.

References

1. M. Levy, Oxidation of Pyrolitic Graphite in Air between 1250 and 1850 F. Ind. Eng. Chem., Prod. Res. and Dev., 1, 19, (1962).

2. M. Levy and P. Wong, Oxidation of Pyrolitic Graphite at Temperature of 1400 to 1800 F, and at Air Velocities of 25 to 100 Centimeters per Second. J. of Electrochemical Society, III, (1964).

3. C. M Tu, H. Davis, and M C. Hottel, Combustion Rate of Carbon. Ind. Eng. Chem. 26, 749, (1934).

4. J. M. Kuchta, A. Kant, and G. H. Damon, Combustion of Carbon in High Temperature High Velocity Air Streams. Ind. Eng. Chem. 44, 1559, (1952).

5. G. Blyholder and H. Eyring, Kinetics of Graphite Oxidation. J. of Phys. Chem. 61, 682, (1957).

6. E. A. Gulbransen, K. F. Andrew and F. A. Brassart, The Oxidation of Graphite at Temperatures at 600 to 1500 C, and at Pressures of 2 to 76 Torr of Oxygen. J. of Electrochemical Society, 110, (1963).

TABLE 1
Equilibrium Data For Reactions Of Pyrolytic Graphite

Temperature (deg)		$Log_{10}K_R$				
K	F	(1)	(2)	(3)	(4)	(5)
873	1112	11.27	23.64	12.37	-1.10	-11.725
1073	1472	10.05	19.25	9.20	+0.85	- 8.92
1273	1832	9.20	16.27	7.07	+2.13	- 6.97
1473	2192	8.55	14.04	5.49	+3.06	- 5.56

(1)	$C(S) + 1/2\ O_2(g)\ \cdot\ \cdot\ \cdot\ \cdot\ CO(g)$
(2)	$C(S) + O_2(g)\ \cdot\ \cdot\ \cdot\ \cdot\ \cdot\ \cdot\ CO_2(g)$
(3)	$CO(g) + 1/2\ O_2(g)\cdot\ \cdot\ \cdot\ \cdot\ CO_2(g)$
(4)	$CO_2(g) + C(S)\cdot\ \cdot\ \cdot\ \cdot\ \cdot\ 2CO(g)$
(5)	$1/2O_2(g)\ \cdot\ \cdot\ \cdot\ \cdot\ \cdot\ \cdot\ \cdot\ \cdot\ .O(g)$

TABLE 2
Molecular Collision Data Calculated From Kinetic Theory

Temperature (deg)		N (number of collisions of oxygen/sq cm/sec)	dn/dt (atoms C/ sq cm/sec)
F	K		
1400	1033	1.47×10^{23}	2.9×10^{23}
1500	1089	1.44×10^{23}	2.9×10^{23}
1600	1144	1.40×10^{23}	2.8×10^{23}
1700	1200	1.37×10^{23}	2.7×10^{23}
1800	1255	1.33×10^{23}	2.7×10^{23}

TABLE 3
Effect Of Surface Area On Rates Of Oxidation
Air Velocity - 25 cm/sec

Temp. (deg F)	Sample Area (sq cm)	dn/dt (atoms C/sq cm/sec)	dw/dt (g/sq cm/sec)
1400	6.270	1.10×10^{17}	2.2×10^{-6}
1400	0.927	3.31×10^{17}	6.6×10^{-6}
1400	0.394	3.66×10^{17}	7.3×10^{-6}
1500	6.270	2.56×10^{17}	5.1×10^{-6}
1500	0.927	9.04×10^{17}	1.8×10^{-5}
1500	0.394	1.10×10^{18}	2.2×10^{-5}
1600	6.270	4.02×10^{17}	8.0×10^{-6}
1600	0.927	1.51×10^{18}	3.0×10^{-5}
1600	0.394	1.71×10^{18}	3.4×10^{-5}
1700	6.270	5.54×10^{17}	1.1×10^{-5}
1700	0.927	2.16×10^{18}	4.3×10^{-5}
1700	0.394	2.56×10^{18}	5.1×10^{-5}
1800	6.270	6.025×10^{17}	1.2×10^{-5}
1800	0.927	2.36×10^{18}	4.7×10^{-5}
1800	0.394	5.00×10^{18}	1.0×10^{-4}

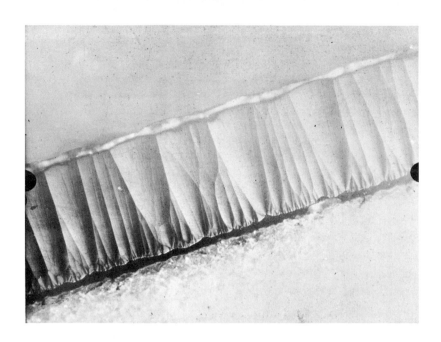

Fig. 1.   Pyrolytic Graphite Microstructure Mag. 80X

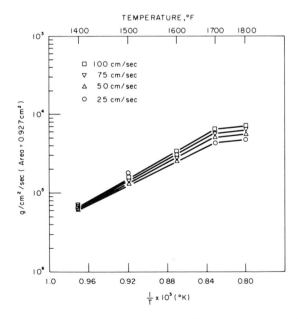

Fig. 2.   Effect of Temperature on Reaction Rate of Pyrolytic Graphite (Surface Area
0.927 sq cm)

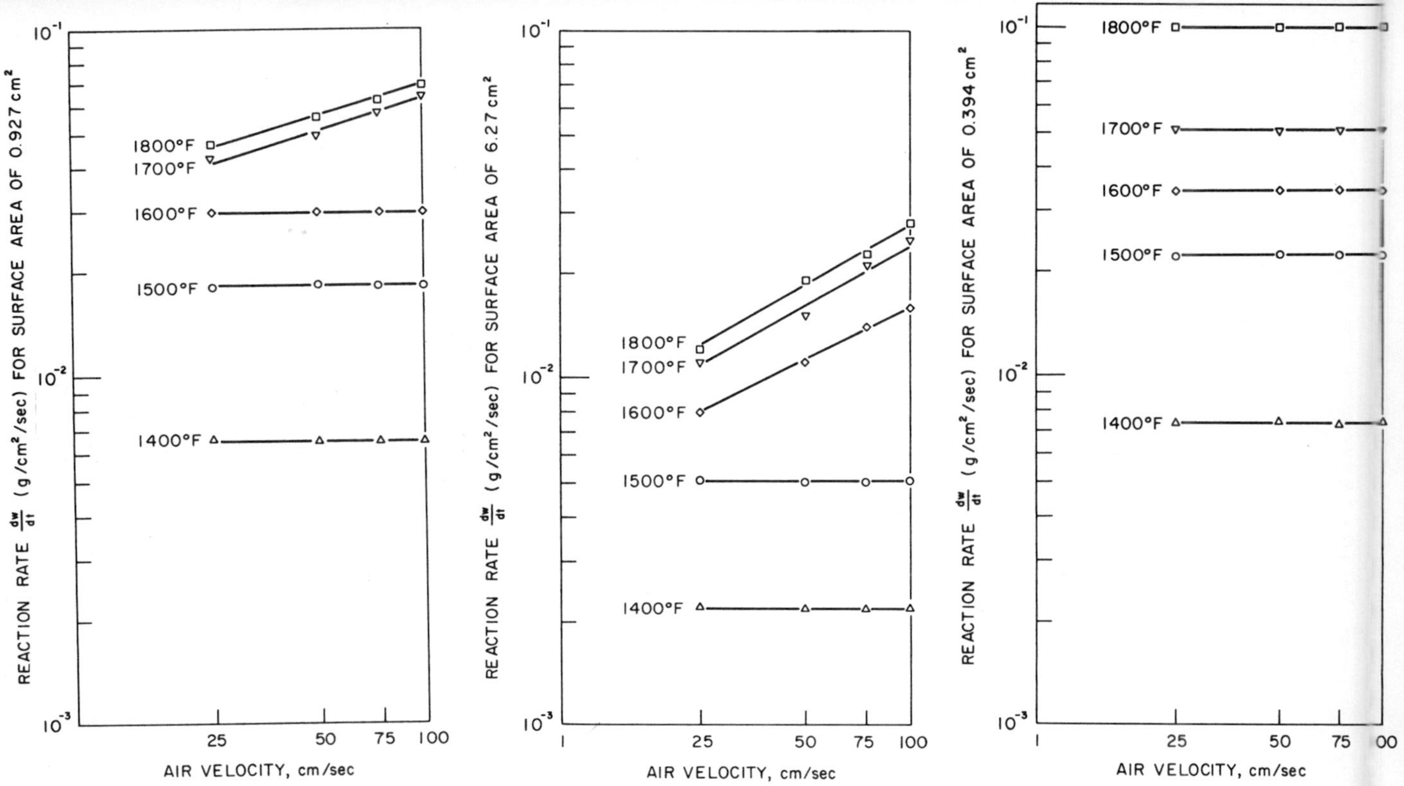

Fig. 3. Effect of Air Velocity on Reaction Rate for Several Temperatures (a) Specimen Surface Area 0.927 cm² (b) Specimen Surface Area of 6.27cm² (c) Specimen Surface Area of 0.394 cm²

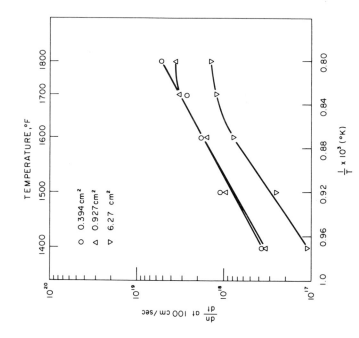

Fig. 5. Effect of Surface Area on Reaction Rates at Several Temperatures and an Air Velocity of 100 cm/sec

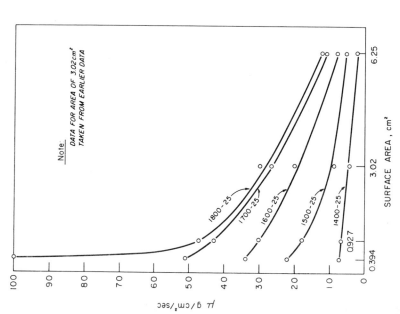

Fig. 4. Effect of Surface Area on Reaction Rates at Temperatures of 1400 to 1800 F and an Air Velocity of 25 cm/sec

NOTE ON THE ALGORITHMISATION OF KINETIC DATA COMPUTATION FROM THERMOGRAVIMETRIC TRACES WITH INCREASING TEMPERATURE

J.Šesták[x], A.Brown, V.Řihák[xx], G.Berggren

Aktiebolaget Atomenergi, Studsvik, Nyköping, Sweden

The report considers mathematical methods
for the derivation of kinetic data from
non-isothermal TG traces using computer
techniques. Two published programmes are
compared as regards computed results. A
flow diagram of the proposed course of
algorithmisation is given.

Symbols used

f	= represents a function	x	= variable of function
α	= degree of decomposition	m_o	= initial weight
t	= time	Q	= constant time interval of scanning
T	= temperature		
k	= Arrhenius constant	w	= weight loss
E	= activation energy	index max	= maximum
$n\ (m)$	= reaction order	index $\overline{i}$	= inflection point
Z	= frequency factor	index $\overline{j}$	= arbitrary point
$d\alpha/dt\,(=DW)$	= rate of decomposition	err x	= error in value of x evaluated by the method of least squares
Φ	= heating rate		

[x] On leave from Institute of Solid State Physics of the
Czechoslovac Academy of Sciences, Cukrovanická street 10,
Prague.
[xx] Address: University of Chemical Technology, Technická
street 5, Prague, Czechoslovakia.

Introduction

The kinetics of decomposition processes can be analysed by two different mathematical methods $|1,4,6|$:

(i)   From assumptions as to the mechanism involved in the reaction a series of kinetic equations $|1,2,3|$ can be written, subsequent comparison with experimentally obtained data being used to select the most appropriate equation and the most suitable mechanism. As regards mathematical evaluation this approach is tedious and a simplified method is therefore used $|4,5,6|$ in the form of a differential equation.

(ii)   Application is made of the general form of the kinetic equation which describes all the mechanisms involved in decomposition $\left(e.g. d\alpha/dt = k'f(\alpha) \, f^-(1-\alpha) \, f^{--}(t)\right)$. This approach is also difficult to handle mathematically and a simplification of the equation usually valid for the intermediate stage of decomposition is commonly employed. This assumes that the decomposition process follows the equation $d\alpha/dt = k(1-\alpha)^n$ or $d\alpha/dt = k\alpha^m$.

Both these methods become applicable to kinetic analysis when a digital computer $|3|$ is employed for the tedious and time consuming treatment of the experimental data. The first method seems to be most valuable for the direct evaluation of mechanism(e.g. by using a modified Bratton and Bridley half-time method $|15|$). It has however, a mathematical basis which is mainly applicable to isothermal measurements.

For experiments with increasing temperature the method which treats the mathematical solution of simplified kinetic equations is preferable. It can be applied in the following ways:

(i)   Integral methods: these are the most accurate with errors of evaluation limited to about $\pm6\%$ $|6,12,16|$

(ii)   Differential methods: only these are capable of yielding parallel values of $\underline{E}$ and $\underline{n}$ in a single calculation $|6,11,16|$

(iii) Approximation methods: these are the least accurate as regards the precise location of inflection points, but previous determination of these points may serve to provide a rough value of $\underline{n}$ (e.g. from equation $\ln\alpha_i = (\ln n)/(1-n)$) |6,14,16|

The best approach seems to be to start from a preliminary evaluation which yields the value of $\underline{n}$ and then to derive precise kinetic parameters by testing (of $\underline{n}$) with an integral method.

This method of evaluating kinetic data is, mathematically, a somewhat formal description of a process; the derived constants (referred to as kinetic parameters) may, however, serve as preliminary information as to the kinetics of the observed process. This approach is suitable for obtaining a measure of the change in the kinetical processes when comparing a series of experiments conducted under different conditions |7|.

Data input and output

An accumulation of recorded strip charts is the characteristic result of a thermal analysis experiment |17|. Owing to the practice of manual data-logging, the choice of suitable charts is somewhat arbitrary. In this instance two alternative types of input data are possible:

(i)   a recorded TG trace $\alpha = f(t)$,

(ii)   as above together with a plot of the electronically obtained derivative $d\alpha/dt = f'(t)$.

These require that the data be scanned and then assembled for treatment. Furthermore some numerical method must be devised for obtaining the best derivative curve, preferably by means of a computer programme. The uncertainties inherent in such methods of data collecting will be demonstrated in the final results.

A more reliable and time-saving approach is to use a digital voltmeter combined with a data-logging system (iii):

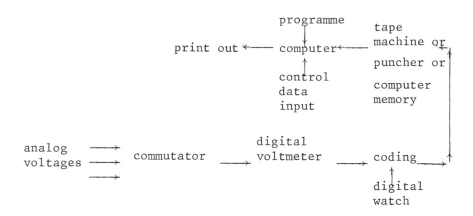

The commutator selects the impulses in a suitable order and transmits them to the voltmeter, which converts the ana log voltage into digital form. The coder transmits the information together with a time code to a tape machine, or puncher (or directly to the computer). This information may be combined with a suitable programme for the empirical correction of experimental measurements |13|, if a quantitative solution is to be obtained and for the computation of kinetic data |8,9| (analogue programme |10|).

Output data should consist of all the calculated kinetic parameters and a list of points obtained from the calculated TG trace comprising degree of decomposition, temperature and derivative. In addition a check of the accuracy of the evaluated kinetic parameter can be included using a comparison of the observed values of the degree of decomposition and values derived by back calculation. The results can be presented in tabular form and also in the form of a plot.

Programmes published

There are two programmes which make use of the basic equation $d\alpha/dt = \exp(-E/RT)(1-\alpha)^n$ and evaluate its kinetics parameters $\underline{E}$, $\underline{Z}$ and $\underline{n}$ by means of differential methods.

The method of Schempf et al. |8| is written in FORTRAN II and is applicable only to the first order reaction. The method utilizes a least squares polynomial fit of TG trace (time-sample weight) with a j-th order polynomial ($\alpha = A_0 + A_1 x + \ldots + A_j x^j$, where $\underline{j}$ is about 13 and $\underline{A}$ are constants obtained from the least square fit of experimental data) for obtaining the correct derivative curves. The method

method can be extended to finding the location of inflection points from the second derivative ($d^2\alpha/dt_i^2 = 0$).

Using the method of least squares, the Arrhenius factor $\underline{k}$ for each temperature is evaluated and from its temperature plot the kinetic parameters ($\underline{E}$ and $\underline{Z}$) are obtained.

The temperature increase is computed from separately introduced data for temperature-time dependence. From a rough knowledge of $\underline{n}$ (e.g. by estimating the inflection point $|14|$ or using Freeman and Carroll methods $|11|$) this method can be extended to other values of $\underline{n}$ by testing several values in the neighbourhood of the estimated value. Thus the best straight line is obtained as regards the minimum error of $\underline{k}$ (or $\underline{E}$).

The second method $|9|$ proposes the use of the simplest means for obtaining a derivative of an observed TG curve (time-weight loss $\underline{w}$) by numerical derivation using the first three terms of a series

$$(d\alpha/dt)_j = (w_{j+1}-w_{j-1})/2 - \ldots + $$
$$+(w_{j+3}-4w_{j+2}+5w_{j+1}-5w_{j-1}+4w_{j-2}-w_{j-3})/60 - \ldots + \ldots)/Qw_{max}.$$

This is applied in the form of a programme written in ALGOL 60. Temperature dependence is given by the initial temperature of decomposition and heating rate, and is formed by scanning with intervals of constant time. For a parallel evaluation of $\underline{E}$ and $\underline{n}$ the Freeman and Carroll derivative method $|11|$ is used. The parameter $\underline{Z}$ is derived from the original curve, using a subroutine for calculating exponential integrals $|5,6,7|$ and the previously calculated $\underline{E}$ and $\underline{n}$ values. The least square method is used throughout; errors in data evaluation are computed at various stages to indicate the level of accuracy attained.

The derivative plot obtained is not sufficiently smooth, because of experimental uncertainties and precise re-reading of weight loss data is therefore necessary. The programme accordingly requires a derivative fit (by a polynomial or Gauss curve plot) which, however, complicates the procedure. An iterative least squares refinement of linear coefficients should therefore be applied to exclude points which lie outside the permitted limit.

The result obtained by computing the test data of Ref. $\underline{8}$ and $\underline{9}$ with these programmes (programme 1: FORTRAN IV version and IBM 360/30 computer, and programme 2: ALGOL ELLIOTT version and Elliott 4120 computer) are compared in Table 1 with results obtained by manual calculation.

The discrepancy which occurs can be explained by differences in the requirements for input data. The input data published in Ref. 8 are given with less accuracy and this seems to lead to larger values for errors in programme 2. Thus discrepancy between calculated values for E in the two programmes corresponds to the error in E calculated in programme 2. The corresponding discrepancy between values for Z may be attributed to differences in the value derived for n; Z in programme 2 is expressed as $Z^{\sim} = Z (m_o/$ mol.weight$)^{(1-n)}$, $x)$, see Table I.

Flowchart

The diagram is based upon the operational sequence of the second of these programmes which is probably more suitable as regards the parallel evaluation of E and n and the possibility for on-line computation. The scheme is divided into four parts:

(i)   Description of subroutines and input data (Table II)

(ii)   Derivative evaluation of kinetic parameters and selection of appropriate equation $d\alpha/dt = k (1-\alpha)^n$ or $d\alpha/dt = k \alpha^m$ (Table III)

(iii)   Integral evaluation of kinetic parameters (Table IV)

(iiii) Print out of data used and test values (Table V)

Part (ii) can be replaced by a modified version of the programme described in Ref. 8 as outlined above.

Versions of this programme in FORTRAN IV and in ALGOL 60 are in course of preparation and will be published separately.

Acknowledgements

Authors thank to Mr. J. Patočka for his assistance at the computing, Miss G. Hjorth and Miss B. Nygren for typing.

References

1.   Garner, W.E., Chemistry of the Solid State, Butterworth Sci. Publ., London 1955.
2.   Young D.A., Decomposition of Solids, Pergamon Press, London 1966.

3. Higgins, J., Use of Computers, in Friess, S.L., Lewis, E.S., Weissberg, A., Investigation of Rates and Mechanisms of Reactions, Intersc. Publ. Inc., New York 1961.

4. Murgulescu, I.G., Segal, E., St. Cerc. Chim. Tom. 15, 261 (1967).

5. Šatava, V., Silikáty 5, (1961).

6. Šesták, J., Silikáty 11, 153 (1967).

7. Šatava, V., Šesták, J., Silikáty 8, 134 (1964).

8. Schempf, J.M., Freeberg, F.E., Royer, D.I., Angeloris, F.M., Anal. Chem. 38, 521 (1966).

9. Šesták, J., Šatava, V., Řihák, V., Silikáty 11, 315 (1967).

10. James, G.E., Pardue, H.L., Anal. Chem. 40, 769 (1968).

11. Freemen, E.S., Carroll, B., J. Phys. Chem. 62, 394 (1958).

12. Coats, A.W., Redfern, J.P., Nature 20, 88 (1964).

13. Soulen, J.R., Anal. Chem. 34, 137 (1962).

14. Horowitz, H.H., Metzger, G., Anal. Chem. 35, 1646 (1963).

15. Braton, R.J., Bridley, G.W., Trans. Far. Soc. 61, 1017 (1965).

16. Šesták, J., Talanta 13, 567 (1966).

17. Murphy, C.B., Anal. Chem. 40, 380R (1968).

Experimental data used	Kinetic data	Manual evaluating (graphically)			Computer evaluating	
		Derivative $|11|$	Integral $|12|$	Frequency factor $|7|$	Programme 1 $|8|$	Programme 2 $|9|$
Weight loss scanned from theoretically evaluated and plotted TG trace using the following kinetic parameters (from Ref. 16): $E=27 \cdot 10^3$, $n=1$, $Z=7 \cdot 10^{11}$, $\Phi=3.18°C/min$, $m_o=0,13$ g, $Q=37.8$ sec, $T=392°K$, mol.weight= $=145.15$, weight loss: 15.7, 18.9, 22.8, 27.1 32.2, 38.1, 45, 52.8, 61.6, 71.3, 81.9, 93.4 105.5, 118.1, 131, 143.3, 154.5, 164.6, 173.9, 181.2, 186.6	E $\cdot 10^3$	27.7 (± 2.2)	27.5 (± 0.8)	(27.5)	27.63	26.82 (err 1.22)
	n	1.06	(1)	(1)	(1)	0.939 (err 0.251)
	Z	-	-	7.17 $\cdot 10^{11}$	7.67 $\cdot 10^{13}$	$5.79 \cdot 10^{11}$ (err $1.9 \cdot 10^9$)

TABLE I

Cont.

Cont.

Experimental data used	Manual evaluating (graphically)				Computer evaluating	
	Kinetic data	Derivative $\lfloor 11 \rfloor$	Integral $\lfloor 12 \rfloor$	Frequency factor $\lfloor 7 \rfloor$	Programme 1 $\lfloor 8 \rfloor$	Programme 2 $\lfloor 9 \rfloor$
Experimental data for calcium oxalate decomposition (loss of carbonyl e.g. kinetic data from Ref. $\lfloor 11 \rfloor$ E= $=74 \cdot 10^3$, n=0.7) taken from Ref. $\lfloor 8 \rfloor$: $\Phi=2.85°$/min, $m_0=74$ mg, Q=75 sec, T=689°K, mol. weight=128.1, weight loss: 0.4, 0.6, 0.8, 1.3, 1.6, 2.2, 2.9, 3.6, 4.7, 6.1, 7.4, 9.4, 11.7, 14.3, 16.9, 19.6, 22.2, 24.4, 26.3 28.5, 29.5	E $\cdot 10^3$	67 ($\pm$ 15)	74.1 ($\pm$ 3.5)	(74)	72.1	58.67 (err 13.5)
	n	0.6	(1)	(1)	(1)	0.591 (err 0.461)
	Z	–	–	3.8 $\cdot 10^{22}$	4.03 $\cdot 10^{20}$	$(9.17 \cdot 10^{14})$ **x** (err $1.1 \cdot 10^{13}$) $1.1 \cdot 10^{18}$

TABLE I

TABLE II

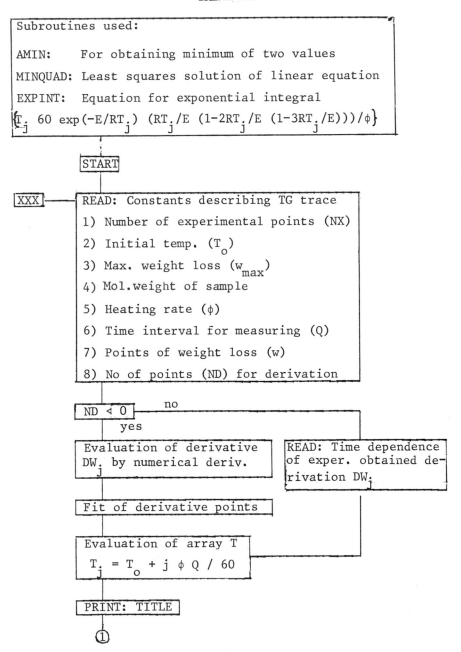

Subroutines used:

AMIN: For obtaining minimum of two values

MINQUAD: Least squares solution of linear equation

EXPINT: Equation for exponential integral

$$\{T_j \; 60 \; \exp(-E/RT_j) \; (RT_j/E \; (1-2RT_j/E \; (1-3RT_j/E)))/\phi\}$$

START

XXX —— READ: Constants describing TG trace

1) Number of experimental points (NX)

2) Initial temp. (T_o)

3) Max. weight loss (w_{max})

4) Mol.weight of sample

5) Heating rate (ϕ)

6) Time interval for measuring (Q)

7) Points of weight loss (w)

8) No of points (ND) for derivation

ND < 0 ——— no

yes

Evaluation of derivative DW$_j$ by numerical deriv.

READ: Time dependence of exper. obtained derivation DW$_j$

Fit of derivative points

Evaluation of array T

$$T_j = T_o + j \; \phi \; Q \; / \; 60$$

PRINT: TITLE

①

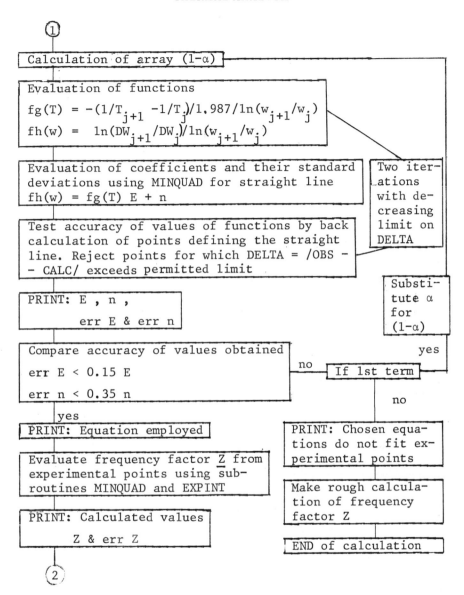

①

Calculation of array (1-α)

Evaluation of functions

$$fg(T) = -(1/T_{j+1} - 1/T_j)/1.987/\ln(w_{j+1}/w_j)$$
$$fh(w) = \ln(DW_{j+1}/DW_j)/\ln(w_{j+1}/w_j)$$

Evaluation of coefficients and their standard deviations using MINQUAD for straight line
$$fh(w) = fg(T) \, E + n$$

Test accuracy of values of functions by back calculation of points defining the straight line. Reject points for which DELTA = /OBS - - CALC/ exceeds permitted limit

Two iterations with decreasing limit on DELTA

PRINT: E , n ,
      err E & err n

Substitute α for (1-α)

Compare accuracy of values obtained
$$err\ E < 0.15\ E$$
$$err\ n < 0.35\ n$$

yes

no   If 1st term

no

yes

PRINT: Equation employed

PRINT: Chosen equations do not fit experimental points

Evaluate frequency factor $\underline{Z}$ from experimental points using sub-routines MINQUAD and EXPINT

Make rough calculation of frequency factor Z

PRINT: Calculated values
      Z & err Z

END of calculation

②

TABLE III

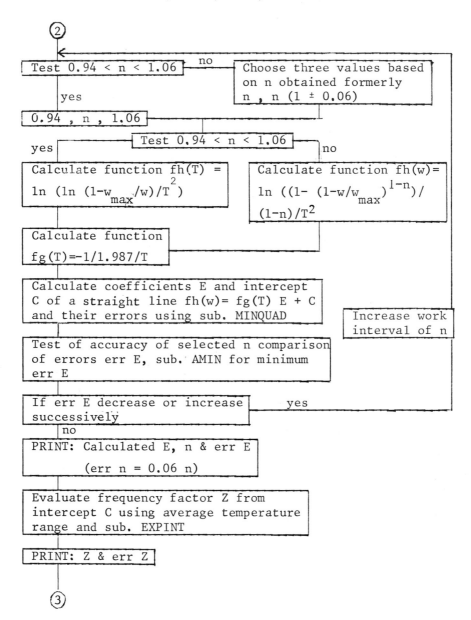

TABLE IV

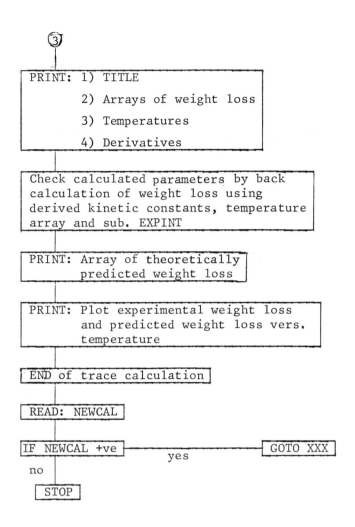

TABLE V

CALCULATION OF ACTIVATION ENERGY OF DECOMPOSITION REACTIONS FROM THERMOGRAVIMETRIC ANALYSIS

S.R.Dharwadkar and M.D.Karkhanavala

Chemistry Division
Bhabha Atomic Research Centre
Trombay, Bombay
India

Abstract

A number of equations are available to calculate the activation energy of decomposition reactions from an analysis of the thermogravimetric curve. However, the values calculated are influenced by various experimental parameters, though the exact dependence is not known.

The effect of sample size and heating rate on the values of activation energy for the dehydration of calcium oxalate monohydrate of uniform particle size has been evaluated using the method of Horowitz and Metzger. The large variations observed have been traced to the inherent limitations in the method of calculation.

The equation has, therefore, been suitably modified so as to yield values of activation energy which are independent of the variation in sample size and heating rate. For first order kinetics the modified equation is

$$\ln \ln (1-\alpha)^{-1} = \frac{E^*}{RT_i^2} \cdot \frac{100}{(T_f - T_i)} \cdot \theta + C$$

Symbols

α = Fraction reacted

a = Heating rate

c = Constant

E^* = Activation energy

R = Gas constant

T_i = Temperature of inception of reaction

T_f = Temperature of completion of reaction

T_s = Temperature at point of inflection in thermogravimetric curve

θ = Difference between T_s and temperature under consideration ($T-T_s$)

φ = Difference between T_i and temperature under consideration ($T-T_i$)

W_o = Initial weight

W_f = Weight at temperature under consideration

W_t = Final weight

Z = Frequency factor

Introduction

In recent years there has been increasing interest in determining the rate dependent parameters of decomposition or oxidation reactions in the solid state, from an analysis of the thermogravimetric (T.G.) curve. Several equations has been proposed (1-11) to analyse a T.G. curve and obtain values of the kinetic constants. The advantages of this method over the conventional isothermal method have been discussed by a number of workers (1,3,8,12).

In spite of the advantages, the drawback remains that the results are not very consistent (5,13,14,15,16). This is largely due to the fact that the shape of the T.G. curve as well as its position on the temperature axis, vary with a number of experimental parameters, such as heating rate, particle size, sample size, furnace atmosphere etc. Some of these have been pointed out and discussed by one of us (16). Subsequently these have been discussed more fully by Garn (17). Sestak (18) has discussed the influence of the kinetic constants on the shape and position (on the temperature axis) of the T.G. curve.

It was, therefore, felt necessary to undertake a programme, (a) to establish the extent to which the activation energy for one and the same reaction, calculated from any one equation is altered due to changes in experimental parameters, and (b) to evaluate the applicability and accuracy of equations proposed by different authors. For this purpose, the effect of sample weight and heating rate on the dehydration of $CaC_2O_4 \cdot H_2O$ of uniform particle size was chosen for a detailed study; the effect of the particle size having been studied earlier (16). The method of Horowitz and Metzger (2) has been studied first, since it is the simplest of the graphical methods.

As the experimental factors were found to have a profound influence on the results obtained, and further as these results could not be satisfactorily explained on any theoretical basis, an analysis was made to determine the causes for these discrepancies. On the basis of this analysis a modified equation has been proposed which yields results that are found to be almost independent of the heating rate and sample size.

Experimental

Calcium oxalate monohydrate was prepared by dissolving B.D.H. AnalaR grade $CaCO_3$ in HNO_3 (AnalaR), boiling off the excess acid and precipitating calcium oxalate from the hot solution using 0.1M pure oxalic acid. The precipitate was filtered, washed thoroughly and dried at 100°C for 12 hours. It was crushed and sieved. The fraction between −240 and +300 B.S.S. was used. Enough $CaCO_3$ was used to give about $\frac{1}{2}$ kg of $CaC_2O_4 \cdot H_2O$.

Thermogravimetric curves were obtained using the Stanton thermobalance (high temperature model) of 1 mg sensitivity. Three different heating rates (2,4 and 8°C/min) were employed. Sample sizes were chosen so as to give weight loss of 20, 50, 80, 150, 220 and 300 mg for the dehydration reaction

$$CaC_2O_4 \cdot H_2O \longrightarrow CaC_2O_4 + H_2O \qquad (1)$$

Representative thermograms for different heating rates and sample sizes are shown in Figs. 1 and 2. Generally, a minimum of four runs were taken for each set to evaluate the reproducibility in the values of (a) temperature, (b) weight loss and (c) the activation energy. In one or two cases, however, only one run was taken.

The samples were packed in platinum crucibles in as identical a manner as possible. The temperatures were recorded using a platinum vs. platinum-13% rhodium thermocouple placed near the crucible but not in the sample. The temperatures recorded on the chart of the thermobalance were also measured by means of portable thermocouple potentiometer (Honeywell Model No.126W3) using an ice bath as cold junction.

The decomposition was also studied under isothermal conditions. For these experiments, the furnace was heated to the desired temperature and was maintained at that temperature by switching off the programme motor. At the appropriate temperature, the furnace was fully lowered over the specimen. The weight loss was then recorded as a function of time on the thermobalance.

Results

Table I summarizes the temperatures of inception, peak and the completion of the reaction as determined from the T.G. curves obtained under different experimental conditions. The mean deviations for each measurement is also given. It is seen that though the inception temperatures are not markedly influenced by the changes in the heating rate and sample size, the peak and final temperatures differ considerably for one and the same reaction. This is in agreement with the earlier work by Karkhanavala and Rege (16) and Paulik et al (19).

The overall order of reaction was determined by the method of Horowitz and Metzger (2) and was found to be very near one. Accordingly the activation energy E* for the decomposition reaction was calculated using their equation for first order kinetics:

1052

$$\ln \ln \frac{W_o - W_t^f}{W - W_t^f} = \frac{E^*}{RT_s^2} \theta \qquad (2)$$

The left hand side of the above equation can be simplified in the form of α to give

$$\ln \ln (1-\alpha)^{-1} = \frac{E^*}{RT_s^2} \theta \qquad (3)$$

In the subsequent discussion, the equation is used in this form, as this is much more convenient.

The plot of $\ln \ln (1-\alpha)^{-1}$ vs θ yielded reasonably good straight lines, from the slope of which the activation energy was calculated. However, the first few points (initial 15 to 20% of the reaction) did not fall on the line. This is expected since the decomposition of solids is known not to obey first order kinetics in the initial stages (20,21). Typical $\ln \ln (1-\alpha)^{-1}$ vs θ plots are shown in Fig.3.

Table II and Fig.4(a) summarize the values of the activation energies calculated for the reaction under different experimental conditions. It is seen that the activation energy decreases (a) with increasing sample size at a constant heating rate and (b) with increasing heating rate for the same sample size.

From the isothermal experiments, the specific reaction rate constant k for different temperatures was calculated assuming first order kinetics. The activation energy was then calculated using the well known Arrhenius relation. For a 20 mg total loss the value of E^* is found to be 12.4 kcal/mole. This value is considerably lower than that obtained (Table II) even under near equilibrium conditions of 20 mg weight loss and at 2°/min. However, such differences have been observed also by other workers (22).

Discussion

The Observed Variation of Activation Energy

For a constant heating rate, the activation energy can be expected to increase with the sample size. The atmosphere in the thermobalance furnace is essentially static and it can be reasoned that a larger amount of the sample will result in an accumulation of the released gases — water vapour in the present case — in the vicinity of the decomposing solid. As the partial pressure of water vapour inside the sample approaches the dissociation pressure at a given temperature, the decomposition process will be slowed down. It would even be interrupted when the dissociation pressure is attained and exceeded. Also when a larger sample is taken, the released gases would have a longer diffusion path to escape out of the container and therefore would be retained to a greater extent within the sample. In the case of smaller samples, the depth of the sample layer being sufficiently small the gases would readily escape. As a result, the apparent activation energy for small sample sizes can be expected to be lower than that for the larger ones. The observations are just the converse.

Further since the activation energy is the amount of energy required per mole of the substance to transform to the product, there seems to be no reason why it should increase with decreasing heating rate.

There is thus no theoretical explanation for the observed variations viz. decrease in activation energy with increasing sample size and/or heating rate. The explanation for this effect has therefore to be sought in the method of calculation.

Analysis of the Horowitz and Metzger's Equation.

The activation energy is calculated by multiplying the slope of the straight line obtained from $\ln \ln (1-\alpha)^{-1}$ vs θ plots by the term RT_s^2. Thus there is an implicit assumption that both T_s and the slope are independent of the experimental parameters and depend only on the reaction studied.

As can be seen from Table I and Figs. 1 and 2, T_s increases with increasing heating rate and sample size. The calculated values of activation energy must therefore increase considerably with increasing sample size and heating rate since the square term, T_s^2 would increase very rapidly.

However, what is observed is the contrary. This can happen only if values of the slopes decrease so markedly as to offset the enhancement due to increase in values of T_s^2. It can be seen from Table III, col.3 that the slopes do decrease very considerably with increasing sample size and heating rate. Thus at a constant heating rate of 2°/min, the slope is 0.085°C^{-1} for a weight loss of 20 mg but 0.039°C^{-1} for a weight loss of 300 mg. Similarly for a constant weight loss of 20 mg the slope which is 0.085°C^{-1} for a heating rate of 2°/min, decreases to 0.056°C^{-1} at 8°/min. Such steep decrease in the slope more than compensates for the increase due to the term RT_s^2, and results in decreasing values of activation energy with increasing sample size as well as heating rate.

It is obvious therefore that the observed variations in E* are not due to any fundamental variations in the processes taking place, but arise mainly due to variations in the values of the slope and to a lesser extent due to variations in the values of T_s^2.

The Modified Equation
Correction For T_s

In the derivation of the Horowitz and Metzger equation T_s is arbitrarily chosen as the reference temperature, since such a choice leads to simplification of the final equation. However, the increase in the value of T_s with increasing sample size and heating rate constitutes a disadvantage.

There is a further disadvantage, since T_s does not truly represent the sample temperature when the reaction rate is maximum. This is because T_s is derived from a plot of dw/dT vs T and corresponds to the point where dw/dT is a maximum. The values of T on the temperature axis are taken from a thermocouple located outside the sample. Often this temperature is not truly respresentative of the actual sample temperature which could be considerably higher or lower due to self-heating or self-cooling as a result of the heat of reaction (23). This difference would be maximum when the rate of reaction is maximum.

It is nevertheless, possible to choose any other temperature in the course of the reaction as reference point. It was therefore decided to select such a point as would not vary with the experimental parameters.

The temperature of inception of the reaction $-T_i$, is known (16,19) to be insensitive to these variables. This has been confirmed in the present study also. Moreover T_i would be truly representative of the sample temperature, because even if it is determined from a thermocouple located outside the sample, it will not significantly differ from the sample temperature since the reaction would have barely commended. In view of these advantages T_i, the inception temperature is chosen as the reference point. Any other temperature on the thermogram can then be expressed in terms of T_i, as

$$T = T_i + \varphi \tag{4}$$

If the derivation of Horowitz and Metzger is repeated for the first order kinetics using T_i instead of T_s, then

$$\ln \ln (1-\alpha)^{-1} = \frac{E^*}{RT_i^2} \cdot \varphi + \left[\ln \frac{Z}{a} \cdot \frac{RT_i^2}{E^*} - \frac{E^*}{RT_i} \right] \tag{5}$$

The second term on the right hand side, involves quantities which are characteristic of the reaction and constant, except for 'a' the heating rate. But at a constant heating rate, the entire term is a constant and the equation reduces to the form

$$\ln \ln (1-\alpha)^{-1} = \frac{E^*}{RT_i^2} \cdot \varphi + C \tag{6}$$

The only effect, therefore, of the different heating rates would be to yield a series of parallel lines with different intercepts. The slope however would remain unaltered.

Further, in equation (5) the term $\dfrac{E^*}{RT_i^2}$ is truly constant under different experimental conditions since as seen before, T_1, the inception temperature does not vary significantly with either the heating rate or the sample size. Thus the variations in the slope should be dependent only on E*.

Though in the present consideration T_s has been replaced by T_1, yet the determination of T_s is essential to evaluate the order of reaction and hence the appropriate function of α .

Correction For Slope
As seen above, the slope varies considerably with the experimental parameters and these variations in the slope have a profound influence on the calculated values of E*. Now since the modified term RT_1^2 is quite constant, E* would remain constant only if the slope does not vary with the experimental parameters.

The slope of the line represented by equation (5) or (6) is

$$\text{slope} = \frac{\Delta \ln \ln (1-\alpha)^{-1}}{\Delta \varphi} \tag{7}$$

$\Delta \varphi$ is the difference between the two temperatures T_2 and T_1 corresponding to any two selected values of α. The slope would therefore be constant if for the same difference in the values of α the value of $\Delta \varphi$ remains constant. But as seen from Table IV and Fig.5 the temperature span (φ_f) for complete decomposition (T_f-T_i) varies considerably with the sample size and heating rate. Thus for samples with a 20 mg weight loss the span increases from 47° to 87° i.e. by 40° as the heating rate is increased from 2°/min to 8°/min. For samples with 300 mg weight loss this difference is much more, 146° to 220° i.e. 74°. These wide variations in φ and hence in $\Delta \varphi$, lead to marked variations in the slope (Table III, col.3).

This is because while the Y-coordinate i.e. ln ln $(1-\alpha)^{-1}$ is being normalized (since the fraction decomposed is considered), the X-coordinate φ is not. Therefore, in addition to substituting T_1 for T_s it is necessary to normalize the X-coordinate $-\varphi$, also. This can best be done by considering any particular value of φ corresponding to any given α, as percent of the entire temperature span in which the reaction occurs. Thus, the normllized function would be $\varphi \cdot 100/T_f - T_i$. The values of the slopes calculated after this normalization do not vary to any appreciable extent (Table III column 4).

Equation (6) can now be written as

$$\ln \ln (1-\alpha)^{-1} = \frac{E^*}{RT_i^2} \cdot \varphi \cdot \frac{100}{(T_f - T_i)} + C \qquad (8)$$

The quantity φ can as well be substituted by the function θ devised by Horowitz and Metzger, since for obtaining the slope

$$\Delta\varphi = \Delta\theta = T_2 - T_1 \qquad (9)$$

Hence equation (8) can also be written as

$$\ln \ln (1-\alpha)^{-1} = \frac{E^*}{RT_i^2} \cdot \theta \cdot \frac{100}{(T_f - T_i)} + C \qquad (10)$$

As seen before, the constant 'C' which would be numerically different for different heating rates, would have no effect on the slope and hence on the activation energy.

The activation energy can also be computed from the slope of the original Horowitz-Metzger plot by incorporating the correction terms

$$E^* = \text{slope} \cdot \frac{T_f - T_i}{100} \cdot RT_i^2 \qquad (11)$$

These modifications though made for the equation for first order kinetics, apply equally well in the other cases also.

Recalculation of Activation Energy
For evaluating the applicability of the proposed

equation, the activation energies were recalculated (a) after normalizing only the value of θ in Horowitz and Metzgers equation and (b) using equation (11).

It can be seen (Table V and Fig.4b) that when only the θ values are normalized the value of E^* obtained under near equilibrium conditions is closest to that obtained by the isothermal method. However, the activation energy increases with increasing sample size mainly due to increasing values of T_s and hence T_s^2. Though this increase in activation energy with the increasing sample size can be understood to some extent on the basis of the arguments presented earlier, the extent of the increase is considered to be quite large for the desired applicability.

When equation (11) is used the results (Table VI and Fig.4c) show that the activation energy is almost insensitive to heating rate and sample size. Thus the modified equation gives much more consistent results, which are also closer to the results of the isothermal runs, over widely varying heating rates and sample sizes. The slightly smaller values of E^* obtained (Fig.4c) with the smaller sample weights can be readily understood on the basis of the reasons discussed earlier. In a recent study on the dehydration kinetics of kaolinite (12) it has been shown that the activation energy for dehydration as determined by both thermogravimetric and isothermal methods increases slightly with increasing partial pressure of the enviromental water vapour upto a certain limit (4 mm Hg) beyond which the activation energy tends to be nearly constant. If the partial pressure of water vapour is due only to the water released in dehydration then the partial pressure would be proportional to the sample size and hence E^* could be expected to increase slightly with the sample size, and after a certain limit remain constant. This is in agreement with the observations reported here.

Conclusion

The present study has shown that the values of E^* vary considerably with the experimental conditions. Hence conclusions with regards mechanism of reaction, based on these values of E^* should be drawn with great care. It is very necessary to examine carefully the equation employed to obtain E*. Though some authors (24) believe that the disagreement in the values of the kinetic parameters obtained by thermoanalytical methods emanates from the ill defined terms 'kinetic order' and 'activation energy' for solid state reactions, yet the experimental variables have much to contribute in vitiating the results. Unless the equations are modified suitably to take into account the discrepancies arising due to experimental variables, the values of kinetic parameters would have very little meaning.

This difficulty is overcome by the modified equation, which gives consistent values of E* which are independent of the heating rate and sample size.

Acknowledgements

The authors express their sincere thanks to Shri A.B. Phadnis for his help in taking T.G. runs and in computation. The authors also thank Dr. J. Shankar, Head, Chemistry Division, for his interest and encouragement,

References

1. E.S.Freeman and B.Carrol, J. Phys. Chem. 62, 394, (1958).
2. H.H.Horowitz and G.Metzger, Anal. Chem. 35, 1464, (1963).
3. A.W.Coats and J.P.Redfern, Nature 208, 68, (1964).
4. P.Kofstad, Nature 179, 1362 (1957).
5. N.G.Dave and S.K.Chopra, Z. Physik Chem. 48, 257, (1966).
6. P.K.Chatterjee, J. Polymer Sc. Part A(3), 4253, (1965).
7. R.M.Fuoss, I.O.Salyer and H.S.Wilson, J. Polymer Sc. Part A(2), 3147, (1964).
8. T.Ozawa, Bull. Chem. Soc. Japan 38, 1881, (1965).
9. L.Reich, Polymer Letters 2, 621, (1964).
10. B.M.Moiseev, Z. Fiz. Khim. 37, 685, (1963).
11. J.H.Flynn and L.A.Wall, Polymer Letters 4, 323, (1966).
12. B.N.N.Achar, G.W.Brindlay and J.H.Sharp, Proceedings of the International Clay Conference 1, 67, (1966).
13. V.V.Subba Rao, R.V.G.Rao and A.B.Biswas, J. Inorg. Nucl. Chem. 27, 2525, (1965).

14. V.M.Padmanabhan, S.C.Saraiya and A.K.Sundaram, J. Inorg. Nucl. Chem. <u>12</u>, 356, (1960).
15. R.P.Agarwala and M.C.Naik, Anal. Chem. Acta <u>24</u>, 128, (1961).
16. M.D.Karkhanavala and S.G.Rege, Paper No.13, Symposium on Rate Processes, Bombay, Jan. 1960, J. Indian Chem. Soc. <u>40</u>, 459 (1963).
17. P.D.Garn, Thermoanalytical methods of investigation, Academic Press Inc. New York 1965
18. J.Sestak, Talanta <u>13</u>, 567, (1966).
19. J.Paulik, F.Paulik and L.Erdey, Anal. Chim. Acta, <u>34</u>, 419, (1966).
20. P.W.M.Jacobs and F.C.Tompkins, Chemistry of the Solid State, pp.188 Ed.W.E.Garner,(Butterworth Scientific Publication, London 1955).
21. A.W.Coats and J.P.Redfern, J. Polymer Sc. Part <u>3(B)</u>, 917, (1965).
22. G.Metzger and H.H.Horowitz, Paper presented before A.C.S.Division of Petroleum Chemistry, Preprint 8(3), 57–62, (1963) N.Y. City, Sept. 1963.
23. A.E.Newkirk, Anal. Chem. <u>32</u>, 1558, (1960).
24. J.M.Thomas and T.A.Clarke, J. Chem. Soc. (A) No.<u>2</u>, 457, (1968).

Table I

Inception, peak and final temperature of the dehydration reaction for different heating rates and sample sizes.

Heating rate in °C/min.	Sample sizes in mgs. (wt. loss in bracket)	Inception Temperature T_i °K	Peak temperature T_s °K	Final temperature T_f °K
2	162 (20)	433 ± 2	470 ± 1	480 ± 3
	405 (50)	432 ± 2	484 ± 2	501 ± 2
	648 (80)	431 ± 2	490 ± 3	515 ± 2
	1215 (150)	433 ± 2	515 ± 5	541 ± 7
	1782 (220)	431 ± 2	528	565
	2430 (300)	431*	536*	577*
4	162 (20)	432 ± 2	484 ± 4	499 ± 4
	405 (50)	433 ± 2	504 ± 4	526 ± 2
	648 (80)	432 ± 2	515 ± 3	546 ± 2
	1215 (150)	435*	520*	565*
8	162 (20)	431 ± 2	500 ± 8	518 ± 4
	405 (50)	431 ± 2	516 ± 3	553 ± 5
	648 (80)	431 ± 2	536 ± 3	582 ± 4
	1215 (150)	434 ± 2	548	614 ± 4
	1782 (220)	436 ± 2	588 ± 5	646 ± 8
	2430 (300)	435	593 ± 3	655

*Only one run

Table II

Activation energy calculated by Horowitz and Metzger's equation for different heating rates and sample sizes

Heating rate °C/min.	Weight loss (mgs)					
	20	50	80	150	220	300
2	38.3	30.8	27.8	24.7	24.1	22.5
4	32.6	27.1	24.5	23.0		
8	27.7	22.0	23.0	19.0	19.3	17.4

The average mean deviation — 0.7 Kcal/mole.

Table III

Slopes of the ln ln $(1-\alpha)^{-1}$ vs θ plots before and after normalisation.

Heating rate in °C/min.	Weight loss in mg	Slope Before normalisation	Slope After normalisation
2	20	0.085	0.044
	50	0.061	0.050
	80	0.056	0.053
	150	0.047	0.051
	220	0.043	0.057
	300	0.039	0.056
4	20	0.069	0.049
	50	0.054	0.049
	80	0.047	0.054
	150	0.043	0.055
8	20	0.056	0.047
	50	0.040	0.047
	80	0.039	0.057
	150	0.032	0.054
	220	0.028	0.056
	300	0.024	0.054

The average mean deviation — 0.0015

Table IV

Temperature span (°C) for completion of the reaction

Heating rate °C/min.	20	50	80	150	220	300
2	47	69	84	108	134	146
4	67	93	114	130		
8	87	122	151	180	210	220

Table V

Activation energy calculated for different heating rates
and samples sizes after normalisation of θ.

Heating rate in °C/min.	Weight loss (mgs)					
	20	50	80	150	220	300
2	19.6	24.2	26.2	31.7	31.7	34.4
4	22.9	24.4	28.2	30.0		
8	23.6	25.6	32.2	32.8	38.7	38.2

The average mean deviation — 0.8 Kcal/mole.

Table VI

Activation energy after normalisation of θ and substitution of T_i for T_s.

Heating rate in °C/min.	Weight loss (mgs)					
	20	50	80	150	220	300
2	16.5	18.9	19.6	19.5	21.3	21.0
4	18.2	18.2	20.0	21.0		
8	17.7	17.7	21.2	20.6	20.8	20.4

The average mean deviation — 0.5 Kcal/mole.

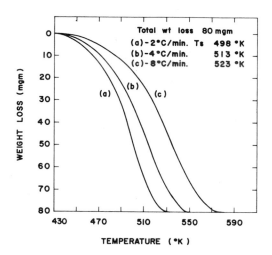

Fig.1. Typical thermograms for constant weight loss and different heating rates. T_s value for each curve are given.

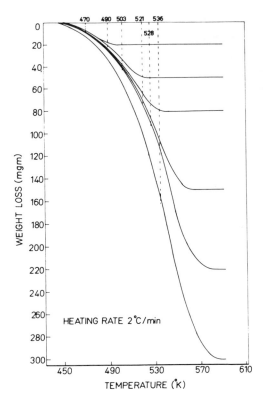

Fig.2. Typical thermograms for constant heating rate and different weight losses. Values of T_S are marked for each curve.

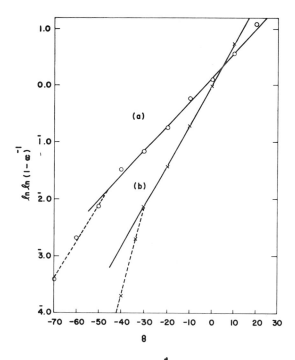

Fig.3. Typical ln ln $(1-\alpha)^{-1}$ vs θ plots according to Horowitz and Metzger, at the heating rate of 2°C/min. and for the sample sizes (a) 150 and (b) 20 mg.

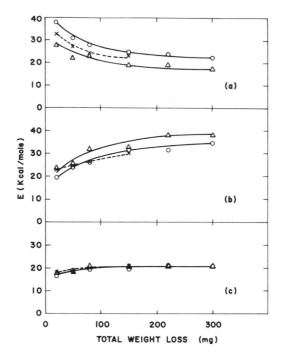

Fig.4. Variation of activation energy E* with sample size
(a) calculated according to Horowitz and Metzger
(b) calculated after normalization of Θ and (c)
calculated according to the modified equation.

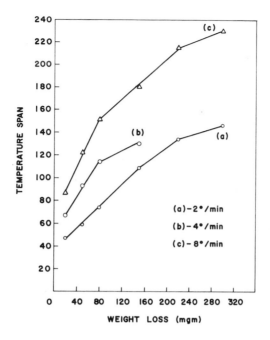

Fig.5. Variation of the temperature span (T_f-T_i) for completion of the reaction with sample size and heating rate.

KINETIC INVESTIGATION OF POLYMERIZATION REACTION WITH DIFFERENTIAL SCANNING CALORIMETER

Hirotaro Kambe, Itaru Mita, and Kazuyuki Horie

Institute of Space and Aeronautical Science
University of Tokyo
Komaba 4, Meguro-ku, Tokyo, Japan

Synopsis

The curing reaction of unsaturated polyester with styrene and the copolymerization of diethyl fumarate with styrene as a model reaction are investigated with differential scanning calorimeter operated at isothermal conditions. Heat of polymerization was determined by comparison of total heat evolved with monomer consumption. The rate of reactions is directly shown by the DSC curves as the rate of heat evolution. The rate of cure of unsaturated polyesters with various compositions of fumarate and succinate units could be followed over the whole range of conversion at isothermal conditions. The reduced rate curves obtained for these curing reactions by using the initial rate of model copolymerization show a distinct gel effect.

INTRODUCTION

The measurement of the rate of polymerization is an indispensable step for the kinetic investigation of polymerization reactions. In the usual chemical method, polymers are isolated from the reacting systems and weighed to determine the degree of conversion of monomer to polymer. In some cases polymerization is also followed by the change of a physical property of the system, such as specific volume, refractive index, ultraviolet or infrared absorption, dielectric or viscoelastic properties. However, physical

1071

methods are essentially relative and limited in application.

In the ordinary kinetic investigations, polymerization is suppressed within a very low degree of conversion for the rate of polymerization to be considered as a constant. In these cases usual methods can be applied successfully. However, when polymerization proceeds in a viscous medium where the rate constants change (so-called the gel effect), the rate cannot be measured accurately by the usual method or by conventional dilatometry and other physical methods. The rate of cure of thermosetting polymers is also difficult to be measured by the simple isolation method. The measurement of the rates at higher conversions needs some other means. The graphical differentiation used in the ordinary method also makes it difficult to follow delicate variations of the rate in the course of polymerization.

Calorimetry is a powerful method for the direct measurement of the rate of exothermic polymerization. Andersen(1), using an isothermal kinetic calorimeter, has revealed several changes in the polymerization rate in emulsion polymerization. A method of measuring the temperature rise with a thermocouple inserted into a reacting system is applicable even for the solidified system (2). By such a simple method however, it is impossible to follow a continuous change of the rate of polymerization with time.

Differential scanning calorimeter (DSC) (3) may be used to determine the rate of polymerization directly and continuously even in a gelled or solidified state. As to the thermosetting polymer, Johnson, Hess and Miron (4) have determined the relative degree of cure by the differential thermal analysis (DTA). This method is based on the exothermic peak during the temperature scanning. On the other hand, DSC measures the absolute degree of cure over the whole range of conversion and in particular it has especial features that it can be used in a strictly isothermal condition.

We have shown in a previous paper (5) that the change in the rate of the diffusion-controlled polymerization of methyl methacrylate and styrene can be followed easily and accurately by the isothermal operation of DSC. The present paper is concerned with the applicability of DSC to the kinetic investigation of curing reaction of thermosetting unsaturated polyester prepolymer with the crosslinking agent. Diffusion-controlled polymerization and copolymerization as a model reaction of curing reaction are shown for comparison. The DSC method is satisfactory to determine the rate up to the final conversion.

EXPERIMENTAL

Procedure

The major distinctive device of DSC varied from traditional DTA is the differential temperature control, which corrects any temperature difference between the reference and the sample. This device makes it possible to detect the heat of reaction in a strictly isothermal condition.

Polymerization reactions were carried out in a modified sample pan with a Perkin-Elmer differential scanning calorimeter (DSC-1) operated isothermally. The modified pan was made of two standard aluminum pans, bonded face-to-face by a heat-resistant adhesive, Araldite AV-8. The sample was injected into the closed pan with a syringe; then the hole made by the syringe was closed with a cellophane tape. The modified pan holds a sample up to about 70 mg. Polymerization in solution as well as in bulk can be conducted in it. The loss of the sample due to volatilization was kept within several per cent by weight using modified pan, while with standard pan it amounted to 20-30%.

It was found that the baseline of the DSC curves obtained in isothermal operations did not show a substantial drift even after the completion of the polymerization. By addition of a small amount of benzoquinone as an inhibitor it was possible to obtain the baseline before the onset of polymerization. This effect is shown in the DSC curve for the polymerization of styrene in Fig. 1. The initial baseline coincides perfectly with the final one. In subsequent experiments the baseline was established by the backward extrapolation of the final flat line appeared at the final stage of polymerization. The deflection of the DSC curve from the baseline expresses the rate of heat evolution and then is proportional to the rate of polymerization at every instant.

To calibrate the average temperature control, melting points of nine compounds were used between 40 and 100°C. The energy was calculated from peak area with a conversion factor calibrated between 40 and 150°C. by heats of fusion (6) of eight non-volatile compounds. The conversion factor seems to be unchanged in this range of temperature.

Materials

The monomers were methyl methacrylate, styrene and diethyl fumarate, which were freed of inhibitor, dried, and purified by distillation under nitrogen at a reduced pressure.

Two samples of polyester prepolymers with different degree of unsaturation were prepared by the condensation of diethylene glycol with mixtures of fumaric and succinic acids in different compositions. The monomer compositions and the number-average molecular weight of the prepolymers are shown in Table 1, together with the composition of styrene used for crosslinking.

Polymerizations were initiated by benzoyl peroxide (BPO) or 2,2'-azobisisobutyronitrile (AIBN), which had been recrystallized in a usual manner.

RESULTS AND DISCUSSION

DSC curves of isothermal polymerization of methyl methacrylate are shown in Fig. 2. Typical DSC curves for isothermal copolymerization of diethyl fumarate with styrene are shown as a model reaction of the cure of unsaturated polyester in Fig. 3, and curves for curing reaction in Fig. 4.

Polymerization and Copolymerization

In the polymerization of methyl methacrylate a remarkable gel effect is observed. The rate of polymerization increases up to eightfold the initial rate as the polymerization proceeds, decreases subsequently, and finally becomes zero. In the course of its decrease, an inflection or peak in the rate curve has been found out with DSC (5). The gel effect appears in the rate curve for bulk polymerization of styrene, but not for homopolymerization of diethyl fumarate and its copolymerization with styrene.

The final conversion was calculated from the content of residual monomers, determined with a Shimadzu IV-50A recording spectrophotometer. Absorbance was measured at 212 mμ for methyl methacrylate, at 214 mμ for diethyl fumarate and at 248 mμ for styrene in ethanol-acetone (99:1 or 199:1) mixture.

The enclosed area of an exothermic peak with baseline devided by the number of moles of reacted monomers at the final conversion gives the heat of polymerization. The values of the heat of polymerization obtained by DSC are in good agreement with those in references (7) as compared in

Table 2.

The heat of copolymerization of diethyl fumarate with styrene varies with the monomer composition as shown in Fig. 5. These values are quite reasonable in comparison with that of diethyl fumarate with vinyl acetate given by Tong and Kenyon (8) also plotted in Fig. 5. The initial rate of polymerization measured with DSC coincided also with literature values (5).

Curing Reaction

The final conversion of curing reactions has hardly been determined by conventional methods because of insolubility of the resulting polymers with network structure. For crosslinked unsaturated polyester Hamann, Funke and Gilch (9) have proposed hydrolysis method, transforming the crosslinked polyester to linear copolymer of fumarate with styrene. The final conversion can be determined far more simply and with the same degree of accuracy by using DSC. It is noteworthy that DSC can determine the final conversion of all kinds of exothermic curing reaction, independent of the existence of special functional groups such as ester group.

The final conversion of the curing reaction of unsaturated polyester with styrene was calculated from the area of an exothermic peak in DSC curves devided by the heat of copolymerization of diethyl fumarate with corresponding amount of styrene, determined by the model reaction.

After an isothermal cure in DSC had been completed, a temperature scanning at 8°C./min. was carried out on the same sample up to 200°C. An exothermic peak due to the postcure of remained monomers began just at the temperature of isothermal cure. The final conversion of isothermal cure and the conversion added by the temperature scanning are shown in Table 3.

The final conversion of isothermal cure increases with the temperature. The glass transition temperature of the cured unsaturated polyesters should be far below the curing temperature (10). However, the temperature scanning could not bring the reaction up to the completion. It is of interest that the total conversion by isothermal and subsequent scanned curings is about 80-85% independent of the temperature of isothermal curing and the content of the fumarate unit in unsaturated polyester.

Diffusion–Controlled Polymerization

The distinguished features of calorimetric method with DSC operated isothermally will be exhibited by the diffusion-controlled polymerization where the rate of reaction is determined by the diffusion processes of polymeric radicals and monomer molecules because of the increase in the viscosity of the system. At the final stage of polymerization the system composed of monomer–polymer mixture solidifies sometimes.

The rate of polymerization R_p of methyl methacrylate was devided by the concentration of monomer [M] for eliminating the effect of monomer consumption. Then in order to clarify the gel effect, the rate per unit concentration of monomer is reduced with its initial value, and plotted against conversion as shown in Fig. 6, where the subscript 0 indicates the initial state. The shoulder in the later stage of polymerization appeared in Fig. 2 becomes more distinct in Fig. 6 and it must play an essential role in discussing the kinetics of the gel effect. The detailed kinetics based on Fig. 6 of the diffusion–controlled polymerization of methyl methacrylate has already been discussed (5).

The curing reaction of unsaturated polyester with styrene is known to be diffusion-controlled from the onset of the reaction. However, the rate of cure in the wide range of conversion has scarcely been discussed because of the experimental difficulties due to insolubility of the cross-linked polymer. The gel time is an ordinary measure for the rate of cure. Electrical resistivity (11,12) and broad–line NMR (13) techniques are also proposed to follow the curing reaction of unsaturated polyester with styrene. These methods are useful, however, only for the relative and rough estimation of curing rate and inadequate for the kinetic investigation. Infrared spectrometry (14) seems a reliable method in comparison with the above techniques, but it is insufficient for accuracy and inconvenient for continuous measurement.

The change in the rate of cure of unsaturated polyester with styrene over the whole range of conversion was illustrated in Fig. 7. To observe the gel effect separately in the rate curves, the rate of cure, namely the rate of monomer consumption R_c was devided by the total concentration [M] of styrene monomer and unreacted fumarate units in polyester. The reduction was carried out also in this case

1076

with the initial rate of copolymerization per initial total concentration of monomers in model reaction, that is, copolymerization of diethyl fumarate with styrene. The reduced curves for the rate of cure against conversion, shown in Fig. 8, have remarkable features in some respects. The reduced rate curves vary with curing temperature in the same way as for the diffusion-controlled polymerization of methyl methacrylate, shown in Fig. 6. A shoulder is also noticed in the later stage of cure. The gel effect is enhanced as the curing temperature lowers. The increase in the content of fumarate unit in the polyester prepolymer which means the higher degree of crosslinking results only in the increase in the rate of cure and does not affect the trend of the rate curves with conversion. The detailed analysis on the kinetics of curing reaction of unsaturated polyester with styrene will be given elsewhere.

CONCLUSION

It is ascertained from the above results that the polymerization reactions, especially diffusion-controlled polymerization and the curing reactions which proceed in viscous media or even in a soft solid state can be successfully followed with DSC operated isothermally. The direct and continuous measurement with DSC of the rate of polymerization over the whole range of conversion will be expected to bring many valuable informations to the kinetic investigation of the polymerization reactions.

References

1. H. M. Andersen, J. Polymer Sci. A-1, 4, 783 (1966).
2. P. Hayden and H. Melville, J. Polymer Sci. 43, 201 (1960).
3. E. S. Watson, M. J. O'Neill, J. Justin and N. Brenner, Anal. Chem. 36, 1233 (1964).
4. G. B. Johnson, P. H. Hess and R. R. Miron, J. Appl. Polymer Sci. 6, S 19 (1962).
5. K. Horie, I. Mita and H. Kambe, J. Polymer Sci. A-1, 6, (9) in press (1968).
6. Landolt-Börnstein, Zahlenwerte und Funktionen, Vol. 2, Part 4, Springer-Verlag, Berlin, 1961, p. 179.
7. G. E. Ham, Vinyl Polymerization, Part 1, Marcel Dekker, New York, 1967, p. 461.

8. L. K. J. Tong and W. O. Kenyon, J. Am. Chem. Soc. 71, 1925 (1949).
9. K. Hamann, W. Funke and H. Gilch, Angew. Chem. 71, 596 (1959).
10. K. Shibayama and Y. Suzuki, J. Polymer Sci. A 3, 2637 (1965).
11. R. W. Warfield and M. C. Petree, S. P. E. Trans. 1, 3 (1961).
12. N. C. W. Judd, J. Appl. Polymer Sci. 9, 1743 (1965).
13. V. F. Chuvaev, L. V. Ivanova and P. I. Zubov, Vysokomol. Soedin. 6, 1501 (1964).
14. T. Imai, J. Appl. Polymer Sci. 11, 1055 (1967).

Table 1. Compositions of unsaturated polyesters cured with styrene

	Unsaturated polyester prepolymer				Styrene, mole
	Fumaric acid, mole	Succinic acid, mole	Diethylene glycol, mole	Number-average mol. wt.	
PES 1	0.30	0.70	1.05	3,300	1.00
PES 2	0.60	0.40	1.05	2,800	1.00

Table 2. Heat of polymerization, kcal/mole

Monomer	Temperature, °C.	Heat of polymerization	
		with DSC	by others (7)
Methyl methacrylate	70	12.7 ± 0.4	
	80	13.3 ± 0.2	12.9–14.0
	90	13.1 ± 0.4	
Styrene	90	15.9 ± 0.4	
	100	16.3 ± 0.2	16.1–17.7
Diethyl fumarate	100	15.5 ± 0.2	—

Table 3. Curing reaction of unsaturated polyester with styrene

Sample	Isothermal cure		Conversion by temperature scanning, %	Total conversion, %
	Temperature, °C.	Final conversion, %		
PES 1 – St	60	66.3	14.1	80.4
	70	75.5	7.1	82.6
	80	77.6	2.7	80.3
	90	78.5	4.7	83.2
	100	83.5	0	83.5
PES 2 – St	60	70.0	10.1	80.1
	70	77.7	9.0	86.7
	80	77.1	6.9	84.0

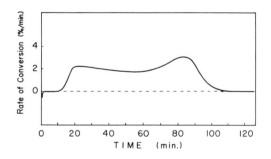

Fig. 1. DSC curve for bulk polymerization of styrene at 100°C. with 0.10 mole/l. BPO and 8.4×10^{-3} mole/l. benzoquinone.

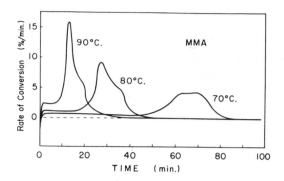

Fig. 2. DSC curves for isothermal bulk polymerization of methyl methacrylate with 0.05 mole/l. AIBN at various temperatures.

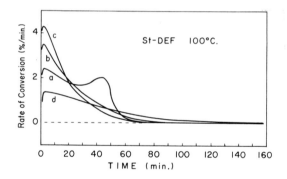

Fig. 3. DSC curves for polymerization and copolymerization of styrene (St) and diethyl fumarate (DEF) at 100°C. with 0.09 mole/l. BPO. Monomer compositions: a, St 100%; b, St 77%, DEF 23%; c, St 50%, DEF 50%; d, DEF 100%.

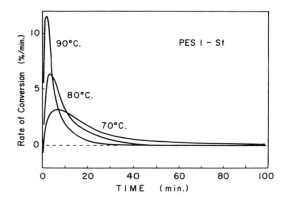

Fig. 4. DSC curves for isothermal cure of unsaturated polyester (PES 1) with styrene with 0.09 mole/l. BPO at various temperatures.

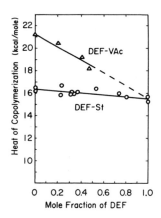

Fig. 5. Heat of copolymerization of diethyl fumarate (DEF) with styrene against mole fraction of DEF in copolymer. Data for DEF with vinyl acetate (8) are indicated for reference.

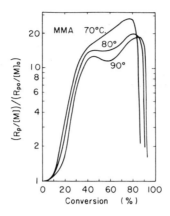

Fig. 6. Reduced rate curves with conversion for the polymerization of methyl methacrylate at various temperatures.

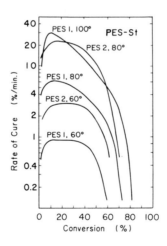

Fig. 7. Rate of cure with conversion for the isothermal cure of unsaturated polyesters with styrene at various temperatures.

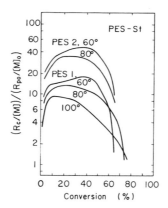

Fig. 8. Dependence of reduced rate on curing temperature and degree of crosslinking for isothermal cure of unsaturated polyester with styrene.

A THERMOGRAVIMETRIC METHOD APPLIED TO THE STUDY OF SOLID STATE DEHYDRATION KINETICS IN VACUUM

Jaroslav Šesták

Institute of Solid State Physics[x]
The Czechoslovak Academy of Science
Prague

Experimental arrangements for TG measurements using infrared heating are described. To programme temperature control a simple combination of a photosensitive transistor regulator with a mechanical continuous regulator was used. Special attention is directed towards precise temperature measurement using two geometrically similar cells with very small heat inertia and without direct contact. The method has been successfully tested on the kinetics of solid state dehydration.

Introduction

It has been shown that large errors in kinetic analysis are introduced by poor temperature measurements and control [1,2,3,4]. These errors are even aggravated when working in vacuum owing to insufficient heat transfer, especially at intermediate temperatures. In such circumstances the use of inversion thermogravimetry seems to be useful since the solid sample can be decomposed under exactly defined conditions. We have found, however, that this method was not suitable for investigation of dehydration kinetics because of condensation and of the delay in adsorption of water vapour on the adsorbent [5]. The current way of heating the sample is by placing an evacuated vessel into a furnace [10]. This has the disadvantage of a great temperature gradient between the programmed furnace and the sample, particularly at lower temperatures. The use of high frequency

[x]Address: Prague 6, Cukrovarnická street 10, Czechoslovakia

eddy-current heating has the drawback of complicating the accurate weighing of the sample as well as the temperature control.

A heater operated by infrared thermal energy is here proposed and examined. For this purpose it was necessary to use a suitable sample holder geometry to ensure good radiation adsorption and exact temperature measurement by a satisfactory sensing element. When observing small weight changes it is impossible to measure the temperature by direct contact (between the temperature detector and the sample) without disturbing the sensitivity and the accuracy of weighing. The temperature measurement by a thermocouple junction placed near the sample [3,4,10] is not sufficiently precise [1,2] even if heat transfer by conduction and convection takes place (as in gaseous environment). The greater the difference between the heat transfer characteristics of the sample holder and the sensing device, the greater the difference between their respective temperatures. The heat transfer in vacuum is taking place mainly by radiation and the temperature of an object will depend on its radiated surface, the energy of radiation (per unit time), and the degree of its adsorption. Also the velocity of heat loss by radiation and by conduction through the measuring equipment may affect the measured temperature. The temperature difference between the sample holder and the sensing element will depend on their geometrical similarity, their heat capacities, the blackness of their surfaces, their position with regard to the direction of rays, and the velocity of the heat loss.

Experimental arrangement
(i) Infrared heating and its control

For heating, two infrared lamps were used with a maximum temperature of 350 ^{O}C (500 W[*]) with an approximately homogeneous axial distribution of radiation intensity. The two lamps were placed horizontally at an equal distance of 5 cm from the heated sample which was suspended inside an evacuated glass tube (see Fig. 2). The temperature gradient in the centre of the heated area did not exceed $\pm$ 2 ^{O}C at a distance of $\pm$ 1 cm perpendicular to the radiation axis.

---

[*]Using infrared rays focusation it is possible to attain higher temperatures.

The infrared lamps and the detection cell were fixed during measurements.

For the control of the sample temperature a three-position regulator [5] operating on the principle of a photosensitive device combined with transistors was used. Its input voltage was programme-controlled by a continuous regulator [14], consisting of an autotransformer with a motorized sliding contact (see Fig. 1). As temperature detector a thermocouple "Pallaplat" (45.5 mV/1000 °C) was employed, being circuited so that its emf was substracted from the emf of a potentiometer driven by a clock work [13]. The controlled system oscillated between ± 0.3 °C from the average value (see Fig. 3) and the amplitude of these oscillations was given mainly by the dead play of the regulator [5] due to the negligible heat inertia of the measuring detector.

Other temperature control systems can by used, e.g. based on a magnetic amplifier controlled by a dc amplifier which balances the difference between the wanted and the real voltage of the thermocouple [15]. However, their evaluation was not the aim of this work.

The above described heating method can be used for isothermal as well as for non-isothermal techniques. In isothermal investigations [5], the sample is initially heated by full possible radiation and after the working temperature has been attained, the temperature is maintained by switching between minimum and average input power (marked with min and 1/2, see Fig. 2). Even if heating up is much faster in this case [5] than other possible methods [3,4], it does not fully remove the difficulties connected with determining the onset of the decomposition [6]. Therefore further development will be made with respect to non-isothermal methods [6] by using lineary increasing temperature. The intermediate control position corresponds approximately to a chosen temperature rise given by the continuous regulator (synchronised with the time base); the temperature differences of the measuring cell are compensated by small changes of radiation by switching to maximum or minimum control position (see Fig. 1 and 3).

(ii) Temperature measurements by means of two geometrically similar cells

The problem of precise temperature measurement was solved by using two similar cells, one as sample holder and the other for temperature sensing and measurements. Nearly identical cylindrical cells (diameter 2.2 cm, height 0.8 cm and weight 1.8 g) were made from an Ag-foil (thickness 0.05 mm, or from a Cu-foil with thickness 0.1 mm) by soldering. Their outside surfaces were blackened by platinum electro-plating and firing.

Three thermocouple wires were symmetrically soldered on to the brim of one of the cells in order to obtain repre-sentative temperature values. This temperature sensing and controlling cell was positioned in the vacuum chamber close-ly underneath the sample holder. The emf of these thermo-couples did not change. In order to find the deviation of the temperature of the sample holder, several cells were equipped with thermocouples and the temperature measured simultaneously with the sensing cell. For the following ex-perimental work the sample holder with the least temperature deviation was chosen. Then both sample holder and sensing cell were charged with equal amounts of a sample powder spread thinly over the inner surface [1,2] and the calibra-tion repeated. The temperature deviation over the whole tem-perature range is proportional (σ) to the temperature (T) and can be expressed (at the chosen heating rate ϕ) by the following equation

$$T_{real} = T_m \cdot \sigma$$

$$(\phi_{real} = \phi_m \cdot \sigma)$$

(where real stands for temperature of sample holder and m is the measured temperature of the sensing cell). The thermo-couple wires were then cut and used for suspending the sam-ple holder from the thermobalance wire (see Fig. 2) in or-der to keep analogous conditions of heat loss through con-ductivity of thermocouple wires.

With decomposition occurring in vacuum already at room temperature calibration and measurements have to be related to a standard temperature at the cold junction of the ther-mocouple below 0 $^\circ$C (e.g. – 70 $^\circ$C for mixture of solid CO_2 with diethylketon etc.). Before evacuation the glass chamber containing the sample must be cooled below the sample's de-composition temperature.

Application of the described method

To test the system outlined above the thermal dehydration of $CaSO_4 \cdot 0.5 \ H_2O$ was chosen in line with our earlier work [8,9]. An adapted microbalance [5] (Sartorius) was used with full automatic recording. An example of a thermogram obtained is shown in Fig. 3; the error in the temperature increase obtained by plotting a straight line through the temperature curve is much smaller than the amplitude of the temperature oscillations.

Kinetic data computed on the digital computer ELLIOTT NE 803 B [7] agree with our earlier measurements [8,9] as well as with results in Ref. [12]. The data and their interpretation will be published in a separate paper [16].

Conclusions

It has been shown that using two almost similar cells (one as sample holder and the other for temperature sensing) with negligible heat inertia will considerably improve TG investigation applied to thermal decomposition of solids in vacuum with regard to precise temperature measurements. It can serve for kinetic analysis of processes, particularly at lower temperature, as well as for higher temperature ranges if welded platinum cells are employed [11]. The use of infrared heating as described makes it possible to compensate the temperature drop occurring during thermal decompositions due to self-cooling [1,2] of samples. The sensitivity of temperature control achieved in vacuum in this work is comparable to the sensitivity usually obtainable in gaseous atmosphere [3,4,10].

Acknowledgements

The author expresses his thanks to Prof. Dr. V. Šatava, Prof. Dr. R. Bárta, Mr. V. Hulínský, Mr. P. Týle (Prague University of Chemical Technology), Dr. P. Kaul, Mr. G. Berggren (Aktiebolaget Atomenergi, Studsvik, Sweden), Dr. A. Bergstein and Mr. P. Holba (Institute of Solid State Physics) for their interest in his work.

References

1. Šesták, J., Silikaty 7, 125 (1963), Effect of Temperature Phenomena on Accuracy of Kinetic Data Obtained by TG Method.
2. Šesták, J., Talanta 13, 567 (1966), Errors of Kinetic Data Obtained from TG Curves at Rising Temperature.

3. Wendlant, W.W., Thermal Methods of Analysis, Interscience Publisher, New York 1964.
4. Garn, P.D., Thermal Analysis of Investigation, Academic Press, New York 1965.
5. Šesták, J., Hulínský, V., The lecture at Conference on New Laboratory Techniques in Silicate Chemistry, Brno (Czech.), July 1967. Utilization of Infra-heating in Vacuum Thermogravimetry (Proceedings p. 90-95).
6. Šesták, J., Silikaty 11, 153 (1967), Review of Methods of Mathematical Evaluation of Kinetic Data from Non-isothermal and Isothermal TG Measurements.
7. Šesták, J., Šatava, V., Řihák, V., Silikaty 11, 315 (1967), Algorithm for Evaluation Kinetic Data from Non-isothermal TG Trace.
8. Šatava, V., Šesták, J., Silikaty 8, 134 (1964), Kinetic Analysis of TG Measurements.
9. Šatava, V., Šesták, J., The lecture at the First International Conference on Thermal Analysis, Aberdeen 1965. The Effect of Experimental Conditions on Activation Energy Values Found through Thermogravimetric Methods.
10. Vacuum Microbalance Technique, Plenum Press (New York), Volume I, 1960 (Katz, J.M.), Volume II, 1962 (Walker, R.F.), Volume IV, 1965 (Waters, P.M.).
11. Hulínský, V., Šesták, J., Czechoslovak Letter Patent Applied for.
12. Mc Adie, H.G., Can. J. Chem. 42, 792 (1964), Effect of Water Vapour upon the Dehydration of $CaSO_4 \cdot 2 H_2O$.
13. Šatava, V., Trousil, Z., Silikaty 4, 272 (1960), Simple Construction of Apparatus for Automatic DTA.
14. Šatava, V., Silikaty 1, 204 (1957), Temperature Programme Controllers for Thermal Analysis.
15. Blažek, A., Unpublished work.
16. Šatava, V., Šesták, J., Kinetic Data of Thermal Decomposition of $CaSO_4 \cdot 0.5 H_2O$, prepared for publication.

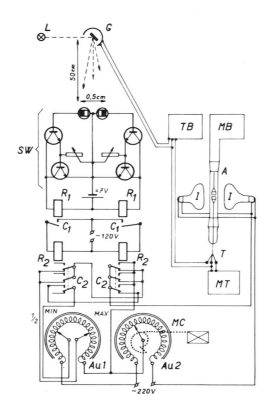

FIGURE 1

Simple temperature control circuit
using infrared heating.

(SW) Light transistor switch, (R₁) Relays I and their
breaker contacts (C₁), (R₂) Relays II and their breaker contacts (C₂), (AU₁) Autotransformer with two set sliding contact mechanically controlled (MC), (I) Infrared lamps, (G)
Galvanometer, (L) Light, (TB) Time base, (MB) Microbalance,
(A) Apparatus for thermal decomposition, (T) Thermocouples,
(MT) Compensation temperature measurements.

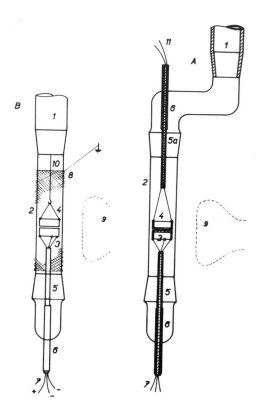

FIGURE 2

Arrangement for temperature measurements
by means of two almost identical cells.

A) Calibration of temperature differences
B) Arrangement for TG investigation

(2) Glass tube connected by a glass–metal joint to the
body of thermobalance (1), (3) Cell for temperature sensing
(4) Crucible for sample weighing, (5) Corundum three-capil-
lary (two-capillary 5a) tube vacuum sealed (6), (7) Two
thermocouples with a common pole, (8) Cu-net cage, (9) Infrared lamps, (10) Thermobalance wire (11) Thermocouple for
temperature calibration.

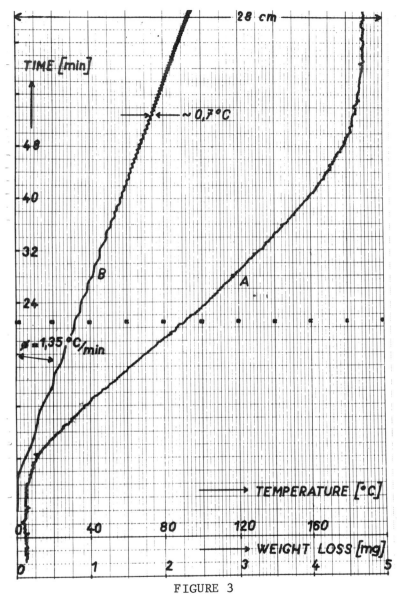

FIGURE 3

Experimentally obtained thermogram of the $CaSO_4 \cdot 0.5\ H_2O$ decomposition using infrared heating.

A) Thermogravimetric trace (Initial weight 76 mg, vacuum between 10^{-3} and 10^{-4} mm Hg)

B) Temperature record (correction factor $\sigma = 0.976$)

DETERMINATION OF THE ACTIVATION ENERGY CHANGE OF $CaCO_3$ UNDER INFLUENCE OF VARIOUS ENVIRONMENTAL GASES

Abund O. Wist

Fisher Scientific Company
Pittsburgh, Penna.

Abstract

The change of activation energy of $CaCO_3$ under the influence of pure He, CO_2, CO, H_2, O_2 and H_2O was studied under atmospheric pressure with a new single run method.

If the activation energy is calculated according to the formula

$$\log \frac{a\, \alpha}{A_N\, T^3} = \frac{E}{2.3R} \cdot \frac{1}{T} + \log ki$$

significant changes from value of E occur especially if CO_2, (232 kcal) CO (56 kcal), or H_2 (61 kcal) is added to the He stream. Calculating in the prohibitive effect of CO_2 on the reaction rate with the proposed formula

$$\log \frac{a\, \alpha}{A_N\, T^3} = \frac{E}{2.3R} \cdot \frac{1}{T} +$$
$$+ \log \left[1 - p \cdot \frac{1}{1 - RE} \cdot e^{+\frac{Al}{T} - B_1} \right] + \log k_1{}'$$

shows that in any CO_2 (or CO) atmosphere the activation energy is not elevated.

Adding a diffusion term to basic Equation 2 reduces the elevated activation energy for H_2 to 40 kcal as it can be seen in the following proposed equation:

$$\log \frac{a \cdot \alpha}{A_N \, T^3} = - \frac{E}{2.3R} \cdot \frac{1}{T} + {} + \log \left[1 + \sqrt{c} \cdot \frac{1}{1 + \frac{RE}{A}} \cdot e^{-\frac{A2}{T} + B_2} \right] + \log k_2'$$

The gases investigated can also be classified according to the results very clearly into inhibitory (CO_2, CO) and non-inhibitory (O_2, H_2O, H_2).

Symbols

a = Rate of temperature increase 2°C/min.
α = Molefraction of offcoming gas
A_N = Normalized surface area
k_i = Constant
E = Activation energy
R = Gas constant
P = Pressure
Po = CO_2 equilibrium pressure
A_1 = Constant in p_{CO_2} equation
B_1 = Constant in p_{CO_2} equation
A_2 = Constant in diffusion term
B_2 = Constant in diffusion term
d = Diameter of pellet
h = Height of pellet
b = Flatness factor $b = \frac{h}{d}$
Vo = Total volume
V = Reacted volume
c = Concentration

Introduction

The influence of external gases on the reaction rate of calcium carbonate has been investigated by several people (1, 2, 3). Ingraham (4) first suggested a single run method for the study of the activation energy of calcium carbonate in

helium. A modified version of this method, which
was presented by the author at the Pittsburgh
Conference (1968) is used exclusively in this
study (5). The great time and cost reduction and
high accuracy of this method made this study
possible.

The method consists basically of allowing
helium gas to flow over a pressed calcium powder
pellet, located in a closed container (EGA head)
which can be temperature programmed. The offcoming gas is analyzed in a thermoconductivity
cell and recorded on a standard recorder. For
this study the gas to be investigated was injected
just before the helium stream enters the thermoconductivity cell.

Experimental Results

Some typical gas evolution curves are shown
in the first seven Figures.

The helium (Figure 1), water (Figure 2), and
hydrogen (Figure 3) curves seem to start around
800°K, whereas the oxygen, (Figure 4) carbon
monoxide (Figures 5 and 6) and carbon dioxide
(Figure 7) (970°K) curves start significantly
later.

The hydrogen curve shows the earliest end
(967°K) whereas the carbon dioxide has the highest
reaction end (1060°K).

The calculation of the activation energy
using formula 2 in Figure 8 results in 45 kcal for
helium. Not to different values are obtained for
water (41 kcal 0.5%   45 kcal 3%) and oxygen
(48 kcal for both concentrations).

A significant deviation from 45 kcal results
from the carbon dioxide curve with 232 kcal at
990°K according to Equation 2 (Figure 8).

If the CO_2 pressure dependence of the reaction according to Bretsznajdar and Zawadzki (6) $V = K (p - p\circ)$ is incorporated in Equation 2, the Equation 6 (Figure 8) follows. Inserting in this equation for $E = 40$ kcal and $p = 2.34$ mm Hg the dotted curve in Figure 15 follows. This indicates that the activation energy in the partial CO_2 atmosphere did not change its value from the assumed 40 kcal. Values for the equilibrium pressure p$\circ$ were taken from Hill and Winter (7).

The small difference between the theoretical and experimental curve in their latter parts corresponds to the constant ln ki in Figure 15. As some factors in this constant are not too well known only an estimate can be made; but choosing reasonable values, the value of this constant is very close to the observed value of ln ki.

The reaction of $CaCO_3$ in a CO atmosphere shows a similar behavior to the reaction of $CaCO_3$ in CO_2; only a much higher concentration of CO is needed to achieve a similar amount of inhibition of the reaction of $CaCO_3$.

The Figures 13 and 14 show that choosing a pco$_2$ value of 0.65 mm Hg for 3.3% CO curve and 1.25 mm Hg for 15.2% CO curve and for $E = 40$ kcal a close fit to the experimental values can be achieved. This indicates that the inhibiting agent is probably CO_2 built up somehow from CO and O_2. It should be noted that the relationship $\sqrt{3.3\%} : \sqrt{15\%} = 0.6$ mm Hg : 1.21 mm Hg seems to hold true.

A quite different picture presents the H_2 curve (Figure 10). Adding a diffusion term to the basic equation results in the following new expression:

$$\log \frac{a\,\alpha}{A_N\,T^3} = \frac{E}{RT} + \log \left[1 + \sqrt{c'} \cdot \frac{1}{1 + \frac{RA}{E}} \cdot e^{\frac{-A2}{T} + B_2} \right] + \log k_2$$

Choosing for $A_2 = 28,000$ and for $B_2 = 31$, the theoretical curve (circles in Figure 10) is obtained.

The A_2 value is for all practical purposes identical to the diffusion activation energy of CO_2 molecules through a $CaCO_3$ lattice as found by Haul and Stein (8).

Several experimental curves with three different concentrations of H_2 in He (2%, 15%, 30%) were run, to establish the square root factor of the concentration of H_2 in He.

Discussion

The experimental curves and the suggested theoretical interpretation in Figure 7 for CO_2 indicate 1) that the reaction rate is directly proportional to the difference between the CO_2 pressure before and after the reaction zone 2) adding CO_2 to the helium gas does not change the activation energy from its assumed value around 40 kcal.

Similar suggestions may hold true for CO if it is assumed that the inhibitory action comes from CO_2, as the results in Figures 13 and 14 suggest, and some process exists which transforms the CO to CO_2. It should be noted that in our limited investigation, the CO_2 concentration increase is less than linear with the CO concentration (approximately with the square root.) The CO_2 concentration is much higher (1:1000) than expected from the CO_2 (and O_2) concentration alone in the He and CO zero gases used in this investigation (~ 1 ppm O_2, CO_2.)

The results in Figure 10 suggest that the mobile H_2 atoms are capable of transferring much additional energy to the $CaCO_3$ (CO_2) molecules in the reaction zone and probably beyond. This increases the CO_2 output, making diffusion more and more the rate determining factor. This would, otherwise, occur only at higher temperatures.

This activation by the surrounding gas is assumed also in a lesser amount to hold true for the larger He atoms. The activation energy is, therefore, increased to 45 kcal (Figure 9) from an assumed true value of around 40 kcal for this temperature.

From the foregoing the following short summary can be made:

A certain number of CO_2 molecules move around in the $CaCO_3$ sample at each temperature.

As the activation energy of moving around in the sample (58 kcal) is quite higher than the activation of dissociation of the CO_2 molecules (40 kcal as found in this study), they must come from where the $CaCO_3$ lattice ends and not from the inside of the sample. This clearly creates a definite and thin reaction zone and prohibits a volume reaction.

Surface activation by a surrounding gas (like H_2 and He) may increase the outflow of CO_2 to such an extent that at a much lower temperature than normal, the diffusion becomes rate determining and the reaction thus gets partly volume controlled. This can also be visualized as a vast increase in the thickness of the reaction zone.

Deviation from the theoretical curves below 1%, in Figure 10 seems to indicate that the assumed zero order reaction law does not hold true here and another reaction law governs the reaction. The lower reaction rate at this range is probably due to nucleation which does not cover the whole surface of the sample. An exception can be seen here in Figure 15 (CO_2^- run) where probably because of the high temperature, this phase (nucleation) is being bypassed, as the zero order reaction law seem to hold true for the whole curve.

1100

According to Figures 13 and 14 it seems that the decomposition of $CaCO_3$ is less inhibited during nucleation than in a reaction zone.

The foregoing study suggests that only one reaction zone exists in the $CaCO_3$ decomposition in which gradually the CO_2 pressure changes from its value inside the sample (Po CO_2) to its value outside the sample (pco$_2$). The thickness of this zone is very thin in vacuum (depending on the porosity of the sample.

Under influence of H_2 or He this reaction zone widens greatly from its initial small value, proportional to the concentration of these gases.

Summary

The change of the activation energy of the decomposition of $CaCO_3$ was studied under the influence of H_2, H_2O, He, O_2, CO, CO_2.

It was found that the activation energy does not change under the influence of various con-centrations of these gases within the precision of these experiments (± 2.5 kcal.)

For the interpretation of the CO_2 (CO) experiments an additional term corresponding to $V = k (p - po)$ was added to the Equation 2 Figure 8. The H_2 (He) experiments can be inter-preted by adding an diffusion term to Equation 2 Figure 8.

The gases could be easily classified according to their evaluation curves as inhibitory (CO_2, CO) and not inhibitory (H_2, He, H_2O) with O_2 having a somewhat intermediate position.

H_2 has a catalytic effect on the reaction rate. To a lesser extent this seems to be true of He and also H_2O.

1101

References

1. Hyatt, E.P., Cutler, I.B., and Wadsworth, M.E., J. Am. Ceramic Soc. 41, 70 (1958).

2. Bischoff, F., Z. anorg. Chemie., 262, 18 (1950).

3. Huttig, G.F., and Heinz, H., Z. anorg. Chemie. 255, 15 (1948).

4. Ingraham, T.R., Proceedings of the Second Toronto Symposium on Thermal Analysis (ed. McAdie) p. 21 (1967).

5. Wist, A.O., Lecture (#9) given at the Pittsburgh Conference on Analytical Chemistry and Applied Spectroscopy (1968).

6. Zawadzki, J., and Bretsznajder, S., Z. fur Physikalische Chemie 22 (1933).

7. R. Hill and E. Winter, Journal of Physical Chemistry, Vol. 60, (1956) p. 1361.

8. A. Haul and L. Stein, Journal of the Faraday Soc. Transactions, p. 1280 (1955).

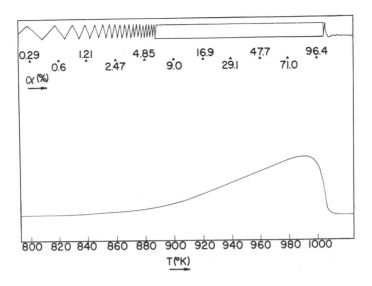

Fig. 1.   EGA–RUN: 35mg CaCO₃ Pellet, 66cc/Min. Hel, 2C/Min. 7.5″/Hour, Sens. 2

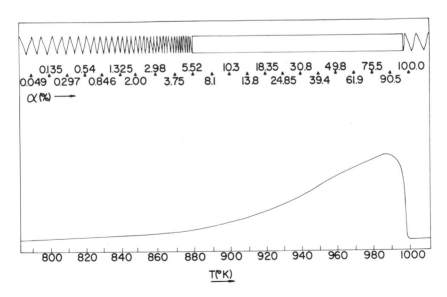

Fig. 2.   EGA –RUN: 35mg CaCO₃ Pellet, 66cc/Min. Hel, 14. 7cc/Min. Hel. Satur.
H₂O(25) 2C/Min. 10″/Hour, Sens. 3

1103

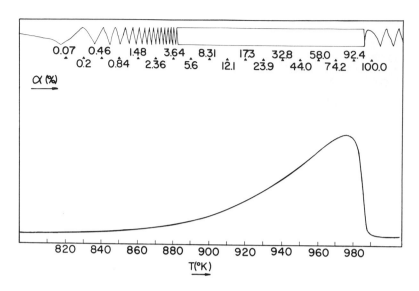

Fig. 3.   EGA–RUN: 35mg CaCO₃ Pellet, 66cc/Min. Hel, 1.7cc/Min. H₂ 2C/Min. 10″/Hour, Sens. 3

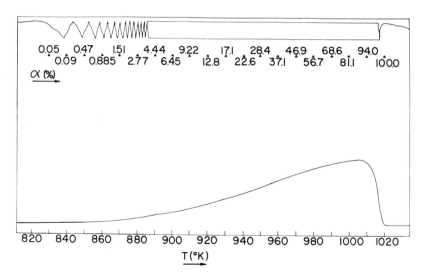

Fig. 4.   EGA–RUN: 35mg CaCO₃ Pellet, 66cc/Min. Hel, 13.4cc/Min. O₂ 2C/Min. 10″/Hour, Sens. 3

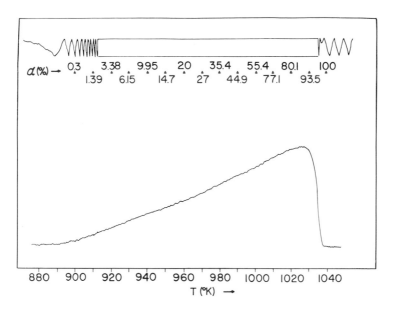

Fig. 5. EGA-RUN: 35mg CaCO₃ Pellet, 66cc/Min. Hel, 2.25cc/Min. CO 2C/Min. 10″/Hour, Sens. 3

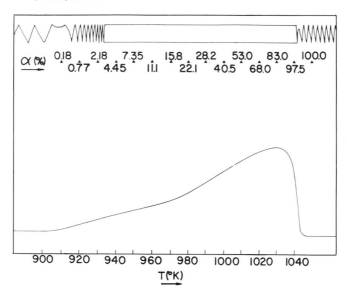

Fig. 6. EGA-RUN: 35mg CaCO₃ Pellet, 66cc/Min. Hel., + 12.2cc/Min. CO 2C/Min. 10″/Hour, Sens. 3

1105

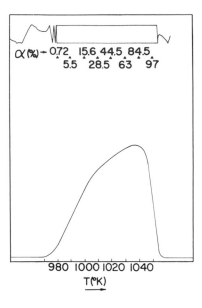

Fig. 7. EGA–RUN: 35mg $CaCO_3$ Pellet, 66cc/Min. Hel, 0.32cc/Min. CO_2 2C/Min. 7.5″/Hour, Sens. 2

1) $\frac{dn}{dt} = C.A.K.$

2) $\log \frac{a\alpha}{AnT3} = -\frac{E}{2.3R} \cdot \frac{1}{T} + \log ki$

3) $An = 1 - \frac{4b-b^2}{1\,2b}\alpha$

4) $b = \frac{h}{d}$

5) $\alpha = \frac{Vo-V}{Vo}$

6) $\log \frac{a}{AnT3} = -\frac{E}{2.3R} \cdot \frac{1}{T} + \log \left[1-P\cdot\frac{1}{1-\frac{RA}{E}}\cdot e^{\frac{A}{T}-B}\right] + \log ki$

Fig. 8. Formulas for Calculation of Activation Energy

1106

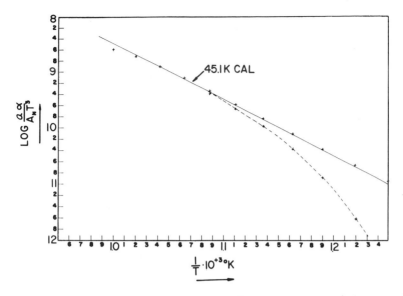

Fig. 9. Evaluation: 35mg CaCO₃ Pellet, 66cc/Min. Hel, 2C/Min. 7.5″/Hour, Sens. 2

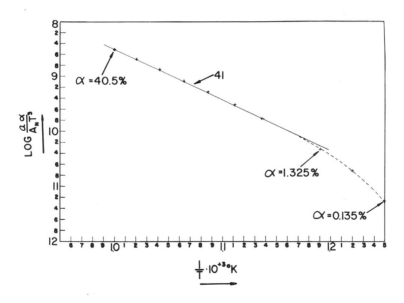

Fig. 10. Evaluation: 35mg CaCO₃ Pellet, 66cc/Min. Hel, 14.7cc/Min. Hel. Satur. H₂O
(25) 2C/Min. 10″/Hour, Sens. 3

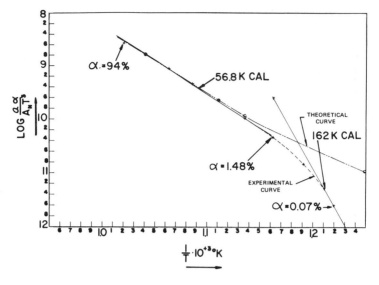

Fig. 11. Evaluation: 35mg $CaCO_3$ Pellet, 66cc/Min. Hel, 1.7cc/Min. H_2 2C/Min. 10″/Hour, Sens. 3

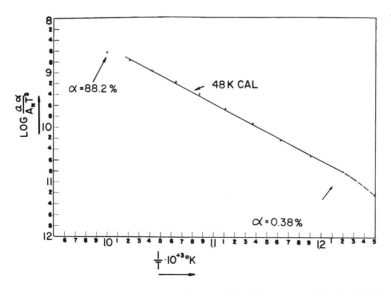

Fig. 12. Evaluation: 35mg $CaCO_3$ Pellet, 66cc/Min. Hel, 13.4cc/Min. O_2 2C/Min. 10″/Hour, Sens. 3

1108

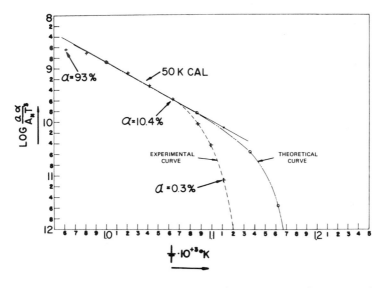

Fig. 13. Evaluation: 35mg $CaCO_3$ Pellet, 66cc/Min. Hel, 2.25cc/Min. CO 2C/Min. 10″/Hour, Sens. 3

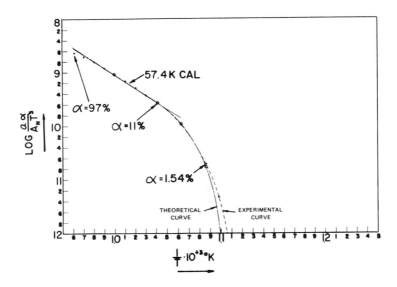

Fig. 14. Evaluation: 35mg $CaCO_3$ Pellet, 66cc/Min. Hel., +12.2cc/Min. CO 2C/Min. 10″/Hour, Sens. 3

1109

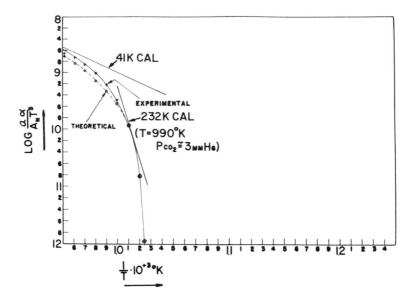

Fig. 15. Evaluation: 35mg CaCO₃ Pellet, 66cc/Min. Hel, 0.32cc/Min. CO₂ 2C/Min. 7.5″/Hour, Sens. 2

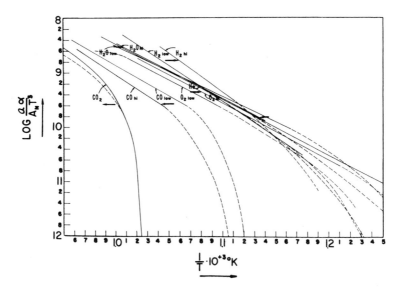

Fig. 16. Overlay of ten evaluation curves showing the influence of external gases on the reaction rate of CaCO₃

THE HISTORICAL DEVELOPMENT OF APPLIED
NONISOTHERMAL KINETICS

Joseph H. Flynn

Polymer Chemistry Section
Polymers Division
Institute for Materials Research
Washington, D. C. 20234

Abstract

In spite of a surprisingly extensive literature prior
to 1950 on nonisothermal kinetic methods, this field was
long ignored by chemical kineticists who were preoccupied
with simple systems in the gas phase or in homogeneous
solution. In such systems, the equations of state of each
involved species change with temperature so that isothermal restrictions were often necessary.

However, the advent of wide interest in thermogravimetric techniques applied to condensed phase volatilization reactions has helped the kineticist shake off the
shackles of isothermicity and has fostered the development
of new and powerful methods of kinetic analysis.

The neglected early literature is reviewed briefly in
light of modern developments. Generalized techniques for
determining kinetic parameters under isothermal, isoconversional and isokinetic conditions are outlined and
illustrated.

1111

Introduction

The use of non-isothermal experimental techniques for the determination of kinetic parameters of reactions measured by loss in weight of a condensed phase species has received considerable attention in recent literature. Many of the papers published between 1950 and 1966 have been critically reviewed (1).

However, there exists a large body of pioneering work in non-isothermal kinetics which has remained relatively neglected or unknown. We will review some of these works in the following section. This will be done not only to give just credit to these scientists whose achievements have been rediscovered independently during the past decade, but also to gain from them a broader understanding of the extent of investigative possibilities opened up by non-isothermal methods. We find these parallel developments in as diverse fields as, for example, fluorescent glow curves at liquid nitrogen temperatures, oxidation of metals, adiabatic reactor design and homogeneous kinetics in solution, as well as the usual inorganic and polymeric systems of thermogravimetry.

Historical Survey

The use of thermal analysis to measure reaction rates dates back, at least, to 1911 in work attributed to P. Bruylants (2) who followed the isomerization of isobutyl bromide to tertbutyl bromide from the cooling curve of the two isomers.

Horiba (3), in 1927, measured reaction velocity from changes in properties of a gaseous system resulting from heat of reaction. Horiba's "Thermal Analysis of Reaction Velocity" method was later applied to homogeneous gaseous and liquid systems (4, 5).

The development of the thermo-balance by Honda (6) in 1915 lead to the first non-isothermal kinetic analysis. In an investigation of the effect of temperature on cellulosic insulating materials, Kujirai and Akahira (7), in 1925, had found from a series of isothermal weight-loss

1112

experiments that a plot of log t, the time to reach a percent weight-loss, w, vs. $1/T$, the reciprocal absolute temperature, resulted in a series of parallel iso-gravimetrics, w_1, w_2, w_3, ..., shown in Fig. 1. This confirmed the applicability to this case of the iso-thermally integrated form of eq. 1,

$$\frac{dw}{dt} = Ae^{-E/RT}f(w) \qquad (1)$$

where A exp(-E/RT) is the usual Arrhenius equation.

Akahira (8) later pointed out that the independence of $f(w)$ from T in eq. 1 may be tested by cycling abruptly between two temperatures T_1 and T_2 and comparing these curves with the isothermals. He defined an equivalent temperature, T_e, for a cycling system,

$$T_e = \frac{E/R}{\ln[\frac{1}{\tau}\int_o^{\tau} e^{-E/RT}dt]} \qquad (2)$$

where τ is the period and $T = \varphi(t)$. In 1929, Akahira (9) published tables of e^{-x}/x and $\int_x^{\infty} e^{-u}/u \, du$ for the nonisothermal kinetically useful range x = 20 to 50. He suggested their use for evaluating not only the Arrhenius temperature integral, but also the temperature dependence of an electric current in dielectric materials and the Schottky-Dushman equation in thermionic emission.

A parallel development of nonisothermal kinetic methods in the study of luminescent materials was begun the following year, 1930. Urbach (10) obtained for the equation at the maximum of the glow curve

$$\frac{W}{k} = JT^2 \Big/ \left(L \frac{dT}{dt}\right) ,$$

where $J = h\nu \, dn'/dt$ and $L = n'h\nu$. These equations are identical to the often evoked (11) equation for first order kinetics,

$$\frac{E}{R} = \frac{T_i^2 \left(\frac{dC}{dt}\right)_i}{\beta_i (1-C)_i} \tag{3}$$

where E is the activation energy, R, the gas constant, β, the heating rate, C, the conversion and the subscript, i, refers to inflection point values.

Three independent works on nonisothermal kinetics were published in the mid-thirties.

P. Vallet (12), in 1935, utilized the van't Hoff expression for temperature dependence of the reaction rate, $K'^{\alpha\theta}$, where θ is the temperature in degrees Celsius. He justified the use of this by the near linearity between θ and $1/T$ in the usual temperature range and by the easy integrability of the van't Hoff formulation contrasted with the necessity of evoking tables of exponential integrals for the similar integration of the Arrhenius expression. Vallet (13) has shown that the van't Hoff expression is equivalent to a two term Taylor's expansion of the Arrhenius equation about a reference temperature. Thus Vallet (12) found that, at a sufficiently high θ,

$$\ln F(C) = \ln \int_0^C \frac{dC}{f(C)}$$

is linear with θ and plots of $\ln \ln 1/C$ vs. θ were used to determine activation energy for first order reactions as shown in Fig. 2. Nearly identical "reference temperature" methods have appeared in recent literature (14).

Vallet's method was applied to a chemical reaction -- the reduction of ferric oxide by hydrogen--by Olmer (15) in 1943.

Sherman (16), in 1936, evaluated the Arrhenius temperature integral by transforming the exponential integral into a more conveniently computable function.

1114

The integral was evaluated for linear, exponential, sinusoidal and polynomial time-temperature relationships. The results were applied to several industrial processes.

Brietmann (17), in 1937, also formulated the temperature integral and discussed the use of simpler empirical expressions than the Arrhenius function for approximating effects of temperature variations in industrial applications. The area of the time-temperature curve (in °C), $\int \theta \, dt$, often could be correlated with the time-temperature variation of the properties of a process.

In a series of papers on the phosphorescence of solids, Randall and Wilkins (18), in 1945, developed a theory of glow curves in which the number of electrons, n, leaving a trap is related to the emission intensity, I, by

$$I = C \, \frac{dn}{dt} = -Cnse^{-E/RT}, \qquad (4)$$

where C and s are constants, so at a constant heating rate, β,

$$\log n/n_o = - \int_o^t \frac{1}{\beta} \, se^{-E/RT} dT. \qquad (5)$$

Several expressions involving the temperature at the maximum were suggested for the calculation of E for first and second order kinetics. Garlich and Gibson (19), in 1948, compared experimental glow curves with calculated ones.

Horton (20), in 1948, used a numerical approximation method to evaluate the exponential integral during the theoretical development of the effect on kinetics of a lag in reaching reaction temperature.

The simplest and most direct method for determining kinetic parameters--an Arrhenius plot of the logarithm of the nth order rate constant, k_n, vs. 1/T--was used by Segawa (21) in 1948. He calculated activation energies from the equation,

$$\log k_n = \log \left[\frac{(\frac{dC}{dt})}{(1-C)^n}\right] = \log \frac{A}{\beta} - \frac{E}{2.303RT} \quad (6)$$

for thermal analysis studies on limestone, clay and quartz.

The independent development in various unrelated scientific areas of similar nonisothermal kinetic methods has continued to the present. We shall review briefly a few such papers which may not have received attention from scientists oriented toward thermal analysis.

Considerable attention continues to be given to glow curves resulting from the escape of electrons from traps in phosphors. Bohun (22), in 1954, was probably the first investigator to use eq. 7,

$$-\frac{E}{R} = \frac{\Delta \ln \beta_i/T_i^2}{\Delta(1/T_i)} \quad (7)$$

in which E may be determined from the variation of the temperature at the maximum, T_i, with the heating rate, β_i.

A comprehensive review and development of nonisothermal kinetic methods in this field has been published by Hoogenstraaten (23).

Gaenssen and Makenzie (24), in 1955, concerned themselves with the "freezing" or quenching gaseous reactions. They calculated values for the exponential integral for the range X = -E/RT = 5 to 100, and treated cases in which the temperature decreases exponentially, linearly and inversely with time. These authors also developed numerical solutions of differential equations for nonisothermal reversible reactions.

Articles applying nonisothermal kinetics to engineering problems continue to appear in literature. A few examples are Kodama et al. (25) on the temperature distribution in self-heat-exchanger reaction chambers, A. P. Zinov'eva (26) on nonisothermal processes in nuclear reactors, and Hanna and Kapner (27) on the nonisothermal kinetics of industrial reactor systems.

Discussion

The history of extensive development and redevelopment of nonisothermal kinetics in many diverse scientific disciplines during the past forty years has been outlined in the preceding section.

The fact that most investigators were in widely unrelated fields--analytical chemistry, chemical engineering, various branches of physics, etc.--can explain to some extent the amazingly repetitive nature of these theoretical developments. However, it does not explain the failure of chemical kineticists to initiate or even collect and unify these diverse developmental works.

The answer seems to lie in the preoccupation of chemical kineticists with systems in the gas phase or homogeneous solution, where obvious analogs for mechanisms were readily available. The ingenuity of the applied chemical kineticist was challenged by the task of fitting and interpreting the $F(C)$, extent of reaction, term which might take a multitude of possible analytical forms. Therefore, kineticists tended to focus on the extent-of-reaction function and attempted to hold all other reaction variables constant. The universally accepted and unexciting Arrhenius temperature function was considered only in afterthought.

There are other factors which contributed to the lack of popularization of nonisothermal techniques. In gas phase or homogeneous solution systems by which kineticists were engrossed, the equation of state of each reactant, intermediate or product species changed in an individualistic manner with temperature. This made it prohibitively difficult to translate measured physical or chemical properties into units of concentration at changing temperature.

On the other hand, in solid phase reactions or bulk volatilizations, the density of the reacting substrate can usually be assumed to be almost invariant with change in temperature, thus allowing greater thermal flexibility in both experimental and kinetic analyses. Therefore, it has been the recent interest in these condensed phase systems which has mainly fostered the development of nonisothermal kinetics.

New Developments in Applied Nonisothermal Kinetics

This concluding section contains a brief description of a few new simple methods and an outline of a generalized treatment of nonisothermal kinetic analysis.

The experimental rate may be expressed, for purposes of curve-fitting, as a product of separable functions of conversion and temperature plus conversion-temperature cross terms, i.e.,

$$\frac{dC}{dt} = f(C)k(T)g(C,T). \qquad (8)$$

If it is assumed that $f(C) = (1-C)^n$, $k(T) = Ae^{-E/RT}$ and $g(C,T) = 1$, where n is the reaction order, the method of van't Hoff may be applied which, in its most primitive form, involves the solution of eq. 9.

$$\left[\ln (1-C)_i\right]n - (1/T_i)E/R + \ln A = \ln (dC/dt)_i \qquad (9)$$

at three sets of the points--$\left[(1-C)_i, T_i, (dC/dt)_i\right]$--for the three parameters n, E/R and ln A (28). Solutions to eq. 9 may be simplified by taking points of isokinetic degeneracy, $(dC/dt)_1 = (dC/dt)_2$, or allowing the sample to heat and cool so points of isothermal degeneracy may be utilized (28). Combination of the equation at the inflection point,

$$\frac{E}{nR} = \frac{T^2_i (\frac{dC}{dt}_i)}{\beta_i (1-C)_i} \qquad (10)$$

with eq. 9 for a single additional set of points will also effect a solution. Applications and limitations of these and similar methods will be discussed elsewhere (28).

For many solid state and most polymer volatilization reactions the above assumptions are unjustified over-simplifications. What one may do is assume $g(C,T) = 1$ and critically test the assumption in the following general manner.

Under isothermal conditions, $T = T_1$,

$$\frac{dC}{dt} = f(C)k(T_1) \tag{11}$$

or

$$F(C) = \int \frac{dC}{f(C)} = \int k(T_1)dt = k(T_1)t$$

Thus traditional isothermal methods are most appropriate for determining the form of $f(C)$.

However, the parameters of $k(T)$ are best determined under isoconversional conditions, $C = C_a$, where

$$\frac{dC}{dt} = f(C_a)k(T)$$

or

$$F(C_a) = \int k(T)dt = \int \beta^{-1}k(T)dT \tag{12}$$

Due to the temporal nature of conversion, iso-conversional conditions can not be maintained in a single run. However, they may be approached by several techniques.

If the temperature is changed rapidly from T_1 to T_2, as in Fig. 3, the rates may be extrapolated to the same degree of conversion at different temperatures. If one assumes

$$k(T) = Ae^{-E/RT}, \quad g(C,T) = 1,$$

then

$$\frac{E}{R} = \frac{\ln\left[(\frac{dC}{dt})_1 / (\frac{dC}{dt})_2\right]}{1/T_2 - 1/T_1} \tag{13}$$

$$(C = const)$$

If the temperature is varied in a slow harmonic cycle, e.g., $T = T_o + T_A \sin \omega t$, as in Fig. 3, the rates at temperature $T_1 = T_o + T_A$ and $T_2 = T_o - T_A$ may be obtained at constant conversion from the upper and lower envelopes of the curve. These methods have the advantage that there is no sample variation and they give instantaneous values of the parameters. Practical considerations require ΔT to be small, but other sets of temperatures may be tested at a number of conversions in this manner.

The constancy of the parameters of $k(T) = Ae^{-E/RT}$ may be tested at various constant conversions from several runs at different heating rates by either a differential method (29) based on,

$$\log \left(\frac{dC}{dt}\right) = \log Af(C_a) - \frac{E}{2.303RT} \quad (14)$$

or an integral method (30-32),

$$\log F(C_a) \cong \log \frac{AE}{R} - \log \beta_1 - 2.315 - 0.457 \frac{E}{RT} \quad (15)$$

In order to corroborate the assumption, $g(C,T) = 1$, $f(C)$ should be determined at several isothermals and $k(T)$ at several isoconversionals, or an isokinetic comparison made.

Systems of suspected complexity should be compared over a whole mosaic of C and T values.

Such a comparison might be made between one isothermal experiment and several experiments of programmed heating rate, $\beta_1, \beta_2, \beta_3, \ldots$, or, as in the example given below, at one TG of constant β and several isothermal runs.

If $k(T) = Ae^{-E/RT}$ and $g(C,T) = 1$, then the TG may be described by eq. 15 and the isothermal experiments by

$$\left.\begin{array}{l} T = T_1 \\ \qquad \log F(C_a) = \log A + \log t - \dfrac{E}{2.303RT_1} \\ T = T_2 \\ \qquad \log F(C_a) = \log A + \log t - \dfrac{E}{2.303RT_2} \end{array}\right\} (16)$$

For various degrees of conversion, C_a, C_b, C_c, C_d,..., selected over the whole thermogram, the temperatures $T_{\beta a}$, $T_{\beta b}$, $T_{\beta c}$, $T_{\beta d}$,..., are determined, and the times to reach the same degrees of conversion, t_{1a}, t_{1b}, t_{1c}, t_{1d},... t_{2a}, t_{2b}, t_{2c}, t_{2d},..., ..., are also

determined from the isothermals. From a plot of log t vs. 1/T as in Fig. 4, from eq. 15 and 16, the slopes of the isothermals are

$$\frac{d \log t_{iso}}{d \, 1/T_{\beta}} = \frac{\log t_{a1} - \log t_{b1}}{1/T_{\beta 1b} - 1/T_{\beta 1a}} \cong 0.457 \, \frac{E}{R} \tag{17}$$

and the distance between isothermals along iso-conversionals will be the usual Arrhenius equation,

$$\log t_{a1}/t_{a2} = (1/T_2 - 1/T_1) \, \frac{E}{2.303R} \tag{18}$$

One may test the separability of a single Arrhenius temperature function by this method over a broad mosaic of C and T values. Any region of deviation from the hypothesis will manifest itself by a difference in E/R values obtained from eqs. 17 and 18, a break in the slope of the isothermals, and/or a deviation from their parallel character.

A more complete exposition of this general treatment is in preparation (28) as well as its application to polymeric systems (33) and to some relatively simple models of composite reaction kinetics (28).

References

1. J. H. Flynn and L. A. Wall, J. Research NBS 70A, 487 (1966).
2. G. Baume, J. Chim. Phys. 9, 442 (1911) (footnote 5); ibid, Rev. Gen. Sci. 25, 252 (1914).
3. S. Horiba and T. Ichikawa, The Sexagint, p. 73, Kyoto (1927).
4. S. Horiba, Sci. Rept. Tohoku Univ. 1st ser., p. 420 (1936); Rev. Phys. Chem. Japan 11, 189 (1937).

5. H. Matsuyama, Proc. Imp. Acad. Tokyo, 14, 343 (1938).
6. K. Honda, Sci. Rept. Tokohu Univ. 4, 97 (1915).
7. T. Kujirai and T. Akahira, Sci. Papers Inst. Phys. Chem. Research (Tokyo) 2, 223 (1925).
8. T. Akahira, ibid., 9, 165 (1928).
9. T. Akahira, ibid., Table No. 3, 181-215 (1929).
10. F. Urbach, Sitz. ber. Akad. Wiss. Wien math.-naturw. Klasse, Ab. IIa 139, 362 (1930).
11. Ref. 1, pp. 495, 507.
12. P. Vallet, Comp. Rend. Acad. Sci. 200, 315 (1935), Annales de Chemie 7, 298 (1937).
13. P. Vallet, "Integration of Rate Constants with Respect to Temperature", Gauthier-Villars et cie, Paris (1961).
14. Ref. 1, p. 501.
15. F. Olmer, J. Phys. Chem. 47, 313 (1943).
16. J. Sherman, Ind. and Eng. Chem. 28, 1026 (1936).
17. W. M. Breitmann, ibid., 29, 1202 (1937).
18. J. T. Randall and M. H. F. Wilkins, Proc. Roy. Soc. (London) A184, 366 (1945).
19. G. F. J. Garlick and A. F. Gibson, Proc. Phys. Soc. (London) 60, 574 (1948).
20. W. S. Horton, J. Phys. and Colloid Chem. 52, 1129 (1948).
21. K. Segawa, J. Japan Ceram. Assoc. 56, 7 (1948).
22. A. Bohun, Czech. J. Phys. 4, 91 (1954).
23. W. Hoogenstraaten, Phillips Research Reports 13, 515 (1958).
24. H. Gaensslen and H. A. E. Makenzie, J. Appl. Chem. 5, 552 (1955).
25. S. Kodama, K. Fukui, K. Takagi and K. Tame, J. Chem. Soc. Japan (Ind. Chem.) 53, 273 (1950).
26. A. P. Zinov'eva, Khim. i Tekhnol. Topliv. i Masel 3, 34 (1958).
27. O. T. Hanna and R. S. Kapner, Ind. and Eng. Chem. Fund. 6, 116 (1967).
28. J. H. Flynn (to be published).
29. H. L. Friedman, J. Poly. Sci. 6C, 183 (1965).
30. T. Ozawa, Bul. Chem. Soc. Japan 38, 1881 (1965).
31. J. H. Flynn and L. A. Wall, Polymer Letters 4, 323 (1966).

32. C. D. Doyle, "Techniques and Methods of Polymer Analysis", Ed. P. E. Slade and L. T. Jenkins, Vol 1, <u>Thermal Analysis</u>, p. 206 (Marcel Dekker, Inc. New York, 1966).

33. J. H. Flynn and L. A. Wall, to be published.

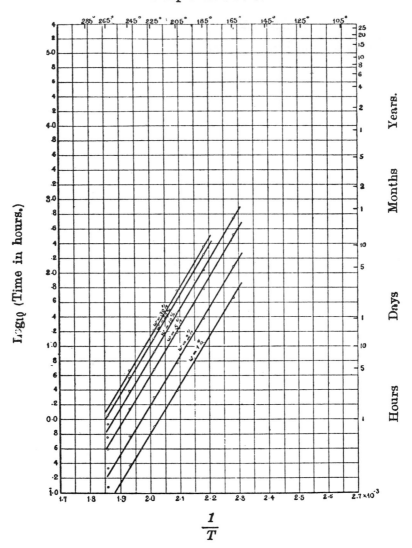

Figure 1 - Parallel isogravimetrics for thermal
degradation of filter paper (ref. 7).

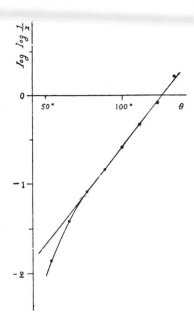

Figure 2 - ln ln C plotted against θ for dehydration of

$CdSO_4 \; + \; \dfrac{8}{3} \; H_2O$ (ref. 12).

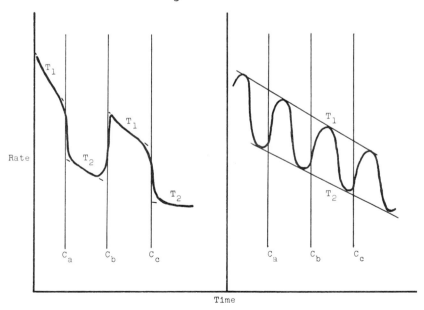

Figure 3 - Rate plotted against time for cyclic methods.

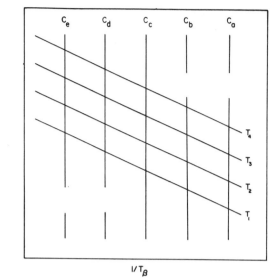

Figure 4 - Logarithm of isothermal reaction time vs. reciprocal temperature at which conversion took place on the TGA.

C_i isoconversional

T_i isothermals

slope of isothermals $\cong \dfrac{-0.457E}{R}$

distance between isothermals

$$= \frac{0.4343}{R} - (\frac{1}{T_i} - \frac{1}{T_j})E.$$

A CONTRIBUTION TO THE KINETICS AND MECHANISM OF THE THERMAL DECOMPOSITION OF ALKALI METAL PICRATES

Manfred Stammler

University of California, Los Alamos Scientific Laboratory
Los Alamos, New Mexico 87544

Abstract

The thermal decomposition of alkali metal picrates was studied at heating rates of from 2-50°C/min with a differential thermal analyzer (DTA) and at heating rates of ~ 10^{8}°C/min by injection of single crystals into the flame of a methane-air flat flame burner. In addition, isothermal decompositions were carried out in a helium atmosphere at temperatures below 300°C. These results were compared with those obtained from cesium 2,6-dinitrophenoxide. Decomposition without melting (below 300°C) of all nitrophenoxides studied produces a water soluble (alcohol insoluble) solid residue whose empirical formula is believed to be $M^{+}[C_2NO_3]^{-}$ (for M = Na, K, Rb, Cs). This material (probably oxalatomononitrile oxide) loses oxygen and hydrolyzes to yield, among other products, a mixed ammonium oxalate. The gaseous products formed are identical for all the picrates but are different for 2,6-dinitrophenoxides. The first order rate constants for these two groups of compounds are also different.

Decomposition with melting (T > 300°C) always results in the explosion of the picrates. The activation energy for this reaction - as determined from self heating rates and induction time measurements - is 30 kcal/mole for the alkali metal picrates. A tentative reaction mechanism for the decomposition is proposed although it was not possible to identify the presumed intermediate products.

Introduction

Salts of picric acid, in particular the alkali metal

1127

salts, offer several advantages for a kinetic and mechanistic study of the thermal breakdown of aromatic nitro compounds:

1. Their low volatility permits the use of thermogravimetric techniques to study the kinetics of the solid phase decomposition.

2. The presence of a relatively heavy alkali metal ion permits the isolation of solid decomposition products which help in establishing a reaction path for the solid decomposition.

3. Ignition time studies of single crystals in flames can be performed because of the intense emission of light of the alkali metal ion upon thermal breakdown of the aromatic anion.

The thermal decomposition of picric acid and picrates has recently been the subject of studies by K. K. Andreyev and co-workers.[1, 2] The authors decomposed the compounds isothermally in a closed system and recorded pressure changes and reaction times in the temperature range between 183°C and 270°C.

For the vapor phase decomposition of picric acid (1) they observed 5 decomposition stages, which were distinguished by the rate of gas evolution. The first stage, prominent in the low temperature region, is characterized by an induction period during which no gases are generated. At temperatures above 230°C, no induction period was detected. The second decomposition phase is an acceleratory period which is immediately followed by a first order reaction (stage 3). During the 4th decomposition phase the rate of gas evolution passes through a 2nd maximum of lower intensity than the preceding one; this is succeeded by a sharp deceleratory period (phase 5).

An Arrhenius plot, using the first order rate constants k_1^3 of decomposition phase 3 in the temperature interval 183-250°C, yields the following temperature dependence:

$k_1^3 = 10^{11.6} e^{-38.600/RT}$ [min^{-1}]. No reaction products were identified during this investigation, but it was determined that 4.8-5.4 moles of gaseous products are released per mole of picric acid.

The decomposition of ammonium picrate[2] was carried out in the temperature range of from 200 to 270°C. In contrast to the picric acid decomposition, a black and brown solid residue remained in the reaction vessel at the end of each ammonium picrate decomposition experiment. The pressure-time curves of the ammonium salt showed a longer induction period than the free acid, which is followed by a first order reaction. When the material was approximately 50% decomposed, the rate of gas evolution decreased abruptly and became deceleratory only. From each mole of ammonium picrate 5.6-5.8 moles of unidentified gaseous products were formed. For the initial 1st order reaction (from 11 to 45% decomposition) an activation energy of 57.2 kcal/mole was obtained with a relatively high preexponential factor of $\approx 10^{19}$. The reaction which proceeds above 50% decomposition requires an activation energy of only 32.2 kcal/mole.

The pressure-time curves for potassium picrate in the temperature range of from 250-300°C are similar in shape to those of ammonium picrate. However, a longer induction time was observed and the reaction stopped abruptly near 50% decomposition. Approximately 3.8 moles of gaseous products are released per mole of potassium picrate. At the end of the reaction a black powder remained in the reactor. Neither gaseous nor solid products were analyzed. Activation energies were calculated from 1st order rate constants and induction times and were found to be 41.2 and 42 kcal/-mole, respectively.

From these investigations no conclusions can be drawn about the reaction path of the picrate decomposition or to which reactions the determined activation energies can be attributed.

A reinvestigation of the kinetics of the picrate decomposition, using different experimental techniques, was therefore desirable. In addition, it was hoped that a knowledge of the nature of the gaseous and solid decomposition products might shed some light on the various reactions involved.

Alkali metal salts of picric acid were chosen for the present investigation because of their low vapor pressure in the decomposition temperature range. This permits the use of thermogravimetric techniques in an open system. The gaseous reaction products can be immediately removed from the reaction zone and quenched to room temperature, thus avoiding, to a large extent, the possibility of secondary reactions. These isothermal studies have been supplemented by differential thermal analysis (DTA) and flat flame burner experiments.

1129

Experimental

1) Preparation of compounds

Picrates of Na, K, Rb, and Cs were prepared by neutralization of an aqueous solution of picric acid with the corresponding base. The following description of the preparation of sodium picrate will serve as an example for the preparation of all the compounds made during this study. 0.025 moles of picric acid was dissolved in 100 cm^3 of water containing 30% alcohol. (The alcohol was added to reduce the surface tension.) The solution was heated to the boiling point and 25 cm^3 of 1N NaOH was added. Immediately a precipitate was observed, which was redissolved by adding a few cc of solvent to the solution, which then was again heated to the boiling point. After the solution was cooled with ice water, the precipitate was filtered and washed with ice water. After a second crystallization from water, the material was dried and stored in a vacuum desiccator over silica gel.

2) Properties of the Picrates

The thermal properties of the alkali metal picrates were determined by differential thermal analysis at heating rates of 10-35°C/min. Densities were determined at room temperature by the flotation method and each value given represents the average of 2 or 3 experiments. These data are summarized in Table 1.

3) Isothermal Decomposition of Picrates (without melting)

The isothermal decomposition of picrates was studied at 250-300°C with sample sizes ranging from 5-25 mg per experiment. No sample size effect could be detected on the weight-loss vs time curves. The decomposition curves are characterized by an induction time which is followed by a first order decomposition reaction. The latter comes to a sharp stop after 39.4, 45.3, 52.1, and 53.0% weight loss for Cs, Rb, K, and Na picrate, respectively. A water-soluble, alcohol-insoluble black residue remains which is hygroscopic. Based on weight gain measurements, the equivalent of 1 mole of water is added. It can be removed by reheating the sample to 110°C. The elemental analysis of the black residue was irreproducible, possibly because of partial hydrolysis during the transfer of the sample from the reactor to the analyzer. Based on weight loss measurements, the residue corresponds to the empirical formula

$$M^+ \left[C_2NO_3\right] \quad [M = Cs, Rb, K, Na].$$

Typical weight-loss vs time curves for alkali metal picrates are shown in Fig 1. If the picrates are heated to temperatures above 300°C for any extended period of time, they deflagrate after several minutes. It has been stated earlier that Andreyev et al(2) observed a similar decomposition - time curve for potassium picrate and ammonium picrate. According to their findings the reaction essentially ceases after approximately 50% decomposition is achieved. This is in good agreement with the value of 52.1% decomposition for potassium picrate obtained in this investigation. For ammonium picrate, Andreyev et al reported a 2-5 fold drop in the decomposition rate after approximately 50% decomposition. If we assume - in analogy to the alkali metal picrates - the formation of a solid product with the formula $NH_4 \left[C_2NO_3\right]$, the reaction of ammonium picrate is complete at 57.5% decomposition. Here, however, the solid reaction product can undergo rearrangement reactions. Our most extensive kinetic studies have been made on cesium picrate. Typical first-order rate plots are shown in Fig 2. The induction time τ for cesium picrate was obtained as the intercept of the first-order region with the time axis. From these graphs, the temperature dependence of the first-order rate constants k, and of the induction times τ_{iso}, has been obtained (Fig 3 and 4). They closely obey the following equations:

$$\ln \tau_{iso} = -35.5 + \frac{(43 \pm 3)\ 10^3}{RT} \quad [min]$$

and

$$\ln k_1 = 71.4 - \frac{(84 \pm 5)\ 10^3}{RT} \quad [min^{-1}].$$

The extremely large value for the "frequency factor" and the high "activation energy" of the first-order rate constant may in part be caused by experimental errors arising from autocatalysis and self-heating of the material. Both would tend to increase the preexponential factor as well as the activation energy. Some evidence that self-heating is effective in the higher temperature region, i.e., at 285°C and above, is indicated by the observation that a runaway reaction occurs (the sample deflagrates) at the end of the induction time. The temperature at which deflagration occurs decreases with increasing sample size when more than 50 mg are used. In the lower temperature region (below 275°C) variation of the sample size from 5-20 mg did not change the shape of the decomposition curve within the experimental error. Between 258° and 275°C autocatalytic effects appear to be more important than self-heating since the addition of 5% of partially decomposed cesium picrate to a fresh sample resulted in a reduction of the induction period and an increase in the first-order rate constant. A plot of the rate of weight-loss vs time is shown in Fig 5. The shape of this curve, which is typical for all picrates under investigation, is characterized by only one sharp maximum.

The Induction Period

During the induction period no detectable heat release (as determined by DTA measurements) or weight loss occurs. This may best be explained by assuming an intramolecular rearrangement into an intermediate compound which in turn decomposes as described above, or catalyzes the decomposition of unchanged picrate.

The following observations indicate that a rearrangement takes place during the induction time:

1. At the end of the induction time, the sample has changed color from bright yellow to a greenish-brown. The greenish-brown compound, which is present in small quantities (less than 1%), can be isolated from the yellow cesium picrate by dissolving the latter in acetonitrile, in which the other compound is less soluble. Both products yield the same IR spectrum.

2. The induction time has a memory (more than 4 days), indicating that either irreversible changes have occurred or the reverse reaction is very slow.

3. If fresh Cs picrate is coprecipitated from acetonitrile with 0.3% of the greenish-brown compound, the induction period is suppressed (Fig 6) and decomposition starts immediately, suggesting that this intermediate product has catalytic activity.

Material which has been heat treated to the end of the induction time is completely soluble in warm water, from which it can be recrystallized. The product from the recrystallization is yellow and behaves thermally in a manner identical to the original material.

These results suggest that during the induction period a rearrangement occurs in which a product is formed which catalyzes the decomposition of the picryl ion. The nature of this rearrangement is unknown. The apparent activation energies E_a of the induction time reactions of potassium, rubidium, and cesium picrate were found to be identical within the experimental error (Table 2), suggesting that the same reaction occurs in all three compounds. The actual induction times, however, tend to decrease in the order K, Rb, Cs (Table 3). Apparently the rate of the induction time reaction (at constant temperature) increases rapidly with increasing radius of the cation.

The First Order Reaction

From the first order part of the cesium picrate decomposition curve an apparent activation energy of 84 kcal/mole has been determined. This value is about twice as high as that found by Andreyev[2] et al for potassium picrate (E_a = 41.2 kcal/mole). From the induction time determination of potassium picrate a value of 42 kcal/mole was calculated. It is possible that the induction time reaction in the case of potassium picrate is the rate determining reaction, which would result in an identical activation energy value for the first order reaction. [Potassium picrate has, in the temperature range between 270 and 295°C, an approximately 6 times longer induction period than cesium picrate (Table 3)]. Consequently, it may be assumed that the first order rate of cesium picrate (in the same temperature range) is slower than the preceding rate of the induction time reaction. The higher E_a value of the first order decomposition of cesium picrate can thus be reasonably explained.

Product Analysis

Decomposition products were determined during the isothermal decomposition experiments by sweeping the gases into an absorption liquid with helium (100 cm^3/min). If the gaseous products are absorbed in water, the absorption liquid became slightly acidic (pH 4-5). Further experiments were carried out using 0.1 N KOH as absorption liquid. After the decomposition was completed, the absorption liquid was tested for formaldehyde, formic acid, NO_2^-, NO_3^-, CN^-, CO_3^{2-}, and NH_4^+ ions. Only CN^- and CO_3^{2-} ions could be detected in relatively large amounts. A confirmation of these results was obtained by decomposing alkali metal picrates in the mass spectrometer. The main decomposition products observed were CO_2, HCN, CN^-, and H_2O.

The solid products were also analyzed. The originally bright yellow compounds are discolored at the end of the induction period and turn black after approximately 3% weight loss. This material consists mostly of undecomposed picrate. If the decomposition is interrupted after 16-19% weight loss, the IR spectrum shows, besides the absorption bands of undecomposed picrate, an additional weak band at 1710 cm^{-1} which could be caused by a carboxylic acid. A test for formic acid was negative; however, oxalic acid was found to be present in small amounts. Other absorption bands appear in the IR spectrum at 2210 and 2270 cm^{-1} when the decomposition is carried out at 270°C or below. These bands indicate the presence of OCN or CNO groups.

If the decomposition is carried to completion, the 2210-2270 cm^{-1} bands increase in intensity and shift to 2150 cm^{-1} upon raising the temperature to 285°C. In this region, nitriles, isonitriles, and inorganic cyanates have their characteristic absorption.* The black decomposition residue is water soluble and alcohol insoluble. The NMR spectrum in D_2O of this material shows no proton resonance. The calculated weight losses for the reaction

$$M \left[C_2NO_3 \right] + gas \qquad M = Na, K, Rb, Cs$$

are in excellent agreement with the experimental values (Table 4). Although the solid reaction products could not clearly be identified owing to their high reactivity, these results, together with the analytical tests, suggest that the end product is probably an oxynitrile derivative of oxalic acid,

Upon exposure to air the end product of the cesium picrate

* Identical shifts of the C ≡ N absorption bands were found when salts of the cyanoacetic acid were heated to 285°C.

decomposition rapidly adds 1 mole of water, which is lost when the material is heated to 100°C. It decomposes slowly above 280°C, probably with loss of $\frac{1}{2}$ mole of oxygen, resulting in a total weight loss (based on cesium picrate) of 43.7%. Several reaction mechanisms can be postulated. Two reaction paths are outlined below, but others may occur concurrently.

1)

Calc wt loss 7.4%, found 6.9% CO_2 + MCN

test for NH_4^+ positive
test for $(COOH)_2$ positive

ninhydrin test positive

2)

CO_2 positive   +   MOCN   IR absorption at 2150 cm^{-1}

Analytical evidence for the proposed possible reaction paths has only been obtained for the end products, i.e., oxalic acid, CO_2, CN^-, and NH_3. The suggested intermediate products are based on infrared evidence and weight loss measurements. However, in conjunction with the weight loss measurements the proposed reaction mechanisms appear plausible.

4) Cesium Picrate Decomposition Under Temperature Transient Conditions (decomposition in the melt).

The decomposition of cesium picrate was studied at heating rates of from 2-50°C per minute with the differential thermal analyzer (DTA), and at the methane-air flame temperature of a flat flame burner with an estimated heating rate of 10^8°C/min.

From the slopes of the DTA traces of the deflagration exotherms at various heating rates, the rates of self-heating, r_s (2 mg samples), were determined, together with the temperature at which the exotherm begins. (It is assumed that the heat release is proportional to the reaction rate.) At heating rates below 4.5°C/min it was found that slow decomposition without melting occurred and the samples did not deflagrate. Therefore, only experiments at which the

heating rates were greater than 4.5°C/min are considered in
the following discussion. In the DTA experiments, the beginning of the exothermic reaction was found to be between
308° and 360°C. The average values of 3 experiments are
summarized in Table 5 and the experimental self-heating rates
are compared with values calculated from the equation

$$\ln r_s = 29.09 - \frac{32,500}{RT} \; [°C/min]. \qquad (1)$$

The agreement between the experimental and calculated r_s
values in Table 5 is satisfactory.

When cesium picrate crystals (particle size $\sim$ 50-100µ)
were injected into the center of the methane-air flame
(methane mole fraction $m_f = 0.228$) of a 5 cm diameter flat-
flame burner, the ignition of particles was found photo-
graphically to occur between 3.9 and 2.1 cm above the burner, depending upon the injection jet velocity V_I, which varied from 0.93 · 10^4 cm/sec to 0.52 · 10^4 cm/sec, respectively. From this an average induction time, τ, of 4.1 · 10^{-4}
sec is derived. If it is assumed that the flame is a perfect thermostat, with the surface of the injected particle
being heated instantaneously to the flame temperature (1400°C)
in the luminous zone, a theoretical estimate of the induction time can be obtained by the procedure of Zinn and
Mader (3). Using the kinetic parameters from Eq. (1), with
$\ln QZ/c = 29.09$ and $E = 32,500$, we obtain $\tau \cong 6 \times 10^{-5}$ sec.
In view of the various assumptions, the agreement with the
experimental value of 4×10^{-4} is quite good, and, in particular, the discrepancy is in the expected direction.

Another attempt was made to reduce the data by assuming that τ_e and the temperature at the point of ignition of
the sample obey the empirical relation*

----

* Time to explosion, τ_e, in the DTA experiments was determined at heating rates of from 5-50°C/min, as the time required to heat the sample from room temperature to the
temperature of explosion, T_e. For a first order reaction
and constant heating rate, it can be shown that

$$\ln \tau_e \cong \ln \frac{E}{RT_e} - \ln A + \frac{E}{RT_e}$$

$$\tau_e = B \cdot e^{E/RT_e} .$$

The experimental τ_e values are in good agreement with those calculated from the equation

$$\ln \tau_e = -22.22 + \frac{30,500}{RT_e} \text{ [min]} \qquad (2)$$

(Table 6).

In all these experiments the sample melted prior to deflagration. The activation energies obtained from self heating rates and induction times can be considered equal within the experimental error. However, by comparing the E values from the isothermal experiments, it becomes apparent that a change in the reaction mechanism occurs if the sample melts prior to decomposition. Little solid residue could be collected after the deflagration of alkaline metal picrates; most of it consisted of elemental carbon. It may be assumed that cesium oxide is another end product of this reaction.

Decomposition of Cesium 2,6-Dinitrophenoxide (Cs 2,6-DNP)

Isothermal decomposition experiments were also carried out with Cs 2,6-DNP in order to compare the solid residues with the solid cesium picrate decomposition product. In the temperature range between 273°C and 293°C a decomposition-time curve similar to that of cesium picrate was obtained; however, the rate of weight loss decreases abruptly after 27.0%. The black decomposition residue consisted of 1 mole carbon/mole Cs 2,6-DNP and a water soluble, alcohol insoluble product which yielded an IR spectrum identical to that of the solid cesium picrate decomposition residue. The fact that the solid residue of Cs 2,6-DNP contains carbon (not present in the cesium picrate residue) suggests that the gaseous decomposition products are different from those of the picrate, which would be expected owing to the lack of the para NO_2 group in Cs 2,6-DNP. The decomposition of Cs 2,6-DNP in the mass spectrometer yielded HCN and relatively large quantities of CO_2, NO (NO_2), and some water. A difference is also observed in the kinetic parameters of Cs 2,6-DNP and Cs picrate. The temperature dependence of k_1 is

represented by $\ln k_1$ Cs(DNP) $= 36.3 - \dfrac{42,200}{RT}$ $[\text{min}^{-1}]$
with both the preexponential factor and the activation ener-
gy approximately half the values of Cs picrate. The activation energy from induction time measurements was found to be
47 kcal/mole, and is thus, within the experimental error,
the same as for Cs picrate. These results indicate that the
induction time reaction for both cesium salts is the same,
while the first order reactions are different.

Discussion of Results

The experimental evidence suggests that the decomposition mechanism differs in the melt and in the solid.

The decomposition of the solid (258-285°C) is characterized by an induction period during which no weight loss
occurs. Activation energies which have been calculated from
induction time determinations are equal for potassium, rubidium, and cesium picrates, although the actual value of
the induction time at a given temperature decreases with increasing radius of the cation (from K to Cs). The induction
period has a memory (at least 4 days) which can only be removed by recrystallization. A probable explanation for
these observations is a molecular rearrangement of the
picrate ion. The back reaction is very slow at room temperature, resulting in the induction time memory. The rate of
this reaction apparently depends upon the size of the cation
and increases from K^+ to Cs^+. If, at the end of the induction time, the heat treatment is continued, a decomposition
reaction starts, which has been interpreted as first order
reaction. Both the induction time reaction and the succeeding first order decomposition reaction can be considered as
consecutive reactions which explains that for potassium picrate the activation energies for the induction time reaction
and the decomposition reaction are the same $(r_1 < r_2)$ while
they differ considerably for cesium picrate $(r_1 > r_2)$. At
the end of the first order reaction the decomposition rate
decreases abruptly for all alkali metal picrates investigated.
Weight loss measurements agree well with the reaction:

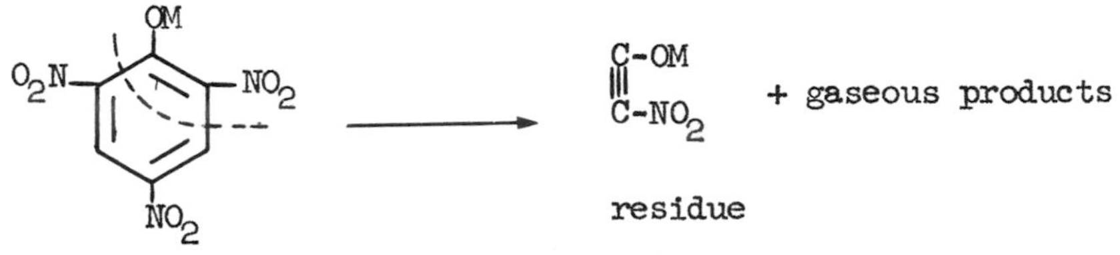

It can be assumed that the residue rearranges rapidly to form oxalatomononitrile oxides. The latter absorbs rapidly one mole of water when exposed to humid air and, upon re-heating to 290°C, water and the equivalent of 1/2 mole oxygen are lost. The cyanoformate can undergo several reac-

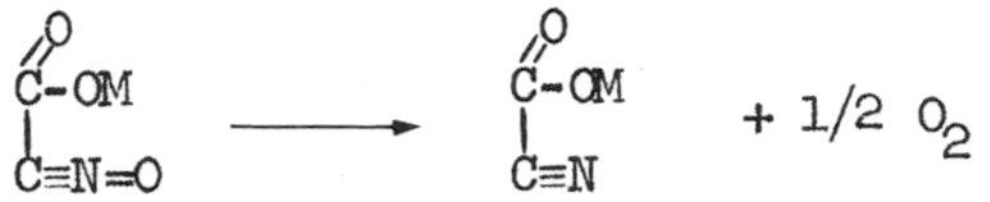

tions; it trimerizes readily to paracyanoformate which hy-drolyzes to yield $\begin{matrix} COOM \\ COONH_4 \end{matrix}$ or it decomposes directly into $MCN + CO_2$. All four ions ($(COO)_2^{2-}$, NH_4^+, CN^-, and CO_3^{2-} have been detected after acid hydrolysis of the residue.

As gaseous decomposition products, only HCN and CO_2 could be detected. Andreyev et al (2) found that approximately 3.8 moles of gases are liberated during the slow decomposition of potassium picrate. This suggests that the remainder of the aromatic ring decomposes according to:

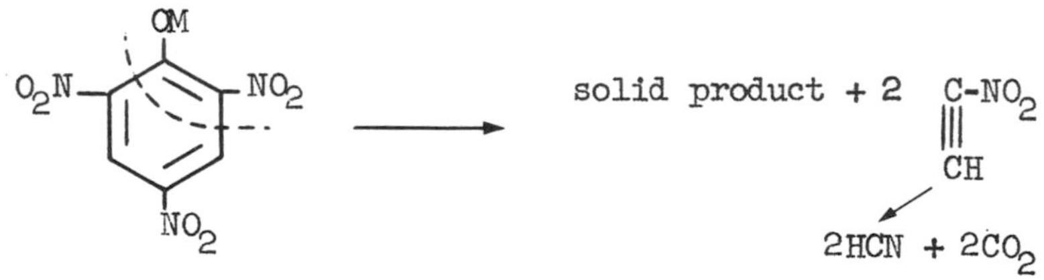

From this a total of 4 moles of gaseous products, HCN and CO_2, are expected, which is in reasonable agreement with the experimental value of approximately 3.8 moles. For the decomposition with melting, a different reaction path has to be assumed since not only the reaction products are different (elementary carbon is formed) but the reaction also results in an explosion which is accompanied by a sharp noise. The end product analysis is rather meaningless and no intermediate product could be identified. The overall activation energies for the decomposition with melting (as determined from self-heating rates and induction time determinations) were found to be 32.5 and 30.5 kcal/mole, respectively. It is experimentally extremely difficult to determine intermediate products for such fast reactions and reaction mechanisms can only be speculated on.

Acknowledgment

The author is indebted to Dr. L. C. Smith for many helpful discussions.

This work was performed under the auspices of the U.S. Atomic Energy Commission.

References

1. "The thermal decomposition of picric and styphnic acid". K. K. Andreyev and Liu Pao-feng: Teoriya vzryvchatykh veshchestv. **Sbornik** statey. 349-363, (1963). English translation: Theory of Explosives, 493-512 (1963).
2. "Thermal decomposition of ammonium, potassium, and lead salts of picric and styphnic acid." K. K. Andreyev and Liu Pao-feng: same source as (1), 363-401 (1963). English translation: Theory of Explosives, 513-567 (1963).
3. J. Zinn and C. L. Mader, J. Appl. Phys. 31, 323 (1960).

TABLE I

PROPERTIES OF ALKALI METAL PICRATES

Picrate	Moles of water of hydration	1st phase transf. (°C)	2nd phase transf. or melt. (°C)	Density (g/cm³)
Na	1 H_2O	- 1H_2O at 165°	275° (d)[*]	-----
K	0	250°	≈ 330° (d)	1.955
Rb	0	243°	323°[**] (expl 350°)	2.295
Cs	0	280°	320°[**] (d)	2.527

[*] d = decomposition

[**] Transition is only observed at heating rates > 25°C/min.

TABLE II

INDUCTION TIME AT 285°C AND ACTIVATION ENERGIES

	τ 285°C	E_a
Na-pic	melts with decomp.	---------------------
K-pic	130 (ref 2)	42 kcal/mole (ref 2)
Rb-pic	70	42 kcal/mole
Cs-pic	20	43 kcal/mole

TABLE III

COMPARISON OF INDUCTION TIMES
OF POTASSIUM AND CESIUM PICRATE

| | τ [minutes] | |
Temperature (°C)	K pic	Cs pic
259	---	100
270	320	55
281	170	27
285	130	20
290	100	15
295	55	9

TABLE IV

EXPERIMENTAL AND CALCULATED WEIGHT LOSSES
FOR ALKALI METAL PICRATES

| | % Weight Loss | |
Cation	Experimental	Theoretical for $M[C_2NO_3]$ endproduct
Cs^+	39.4	39.4
Rb^+	45.4	45.5
K^+	52.1	52.0
Na^+	54.3	53.4

TABLE V

SELF HEATING RATES r_s OF CESIUM PICRATE

α [°C/min]	T_e [°C]	r_s [°C/min]$_{exp}$	r_s [°C/min]$_{calc}$
5	308	2.40	3.20
10	315	4.45	4.44
15	325	8.95	6.69
30	335	10.00	10.10
40	340	20.0	14.1
50	360	30.0	31.2

α = heating rate [°C/min]

T_e = temp. of beginning exotherm

r_s = self heating rates

TABLE VI

CESIUM PICRATE INDUCTION TIMES τ

T_e [°K]	T_e [min]		$\dfrac{10^3}{T}$ [°K^{-1}]	α [°C/min]
	Experiment	Calculation		
586	53.0	45.7	1.709	5
598	29.5	26.4	1.672	10
608	20.0	17.9	1.645	15
618	11.0	11.7	1.618	30
623	8.5	9.58	1.605	40
633	6.7	6.56	1.580	50
1683	$6.67 \cdot 10^{-6}$	$1.97 \cdot 10^{-6}$	0.595	$\approx 10^8$

1143

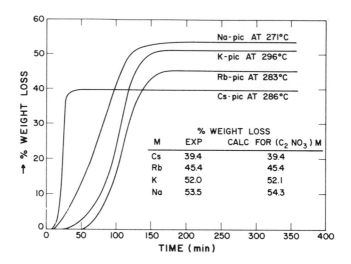

Fig 1 - Isothermal alkali metal picrate decomposition curves.

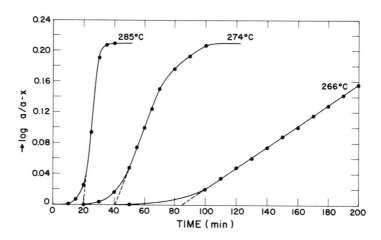

Fig 2 - 1st order rate plots of Cs-pic decomposition.

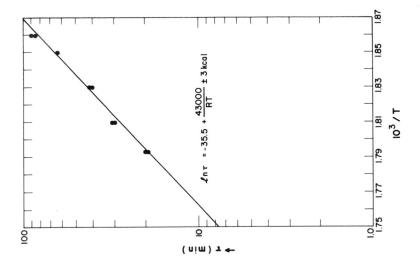

Fig 4 – Cs-pic decomposition. Temperature dependence of the induction time.

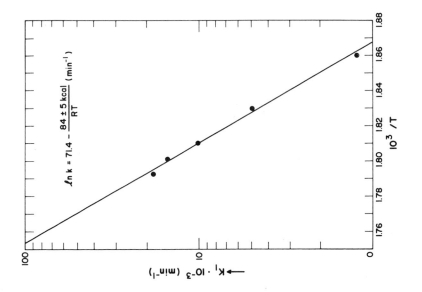

Fig 3 – Cs-pic decomposition. Temperature dependence of k_1.

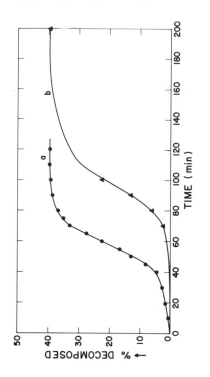

Fig 6 – Cs-pic decomposition at 268°C. a) Cs-pic coprecipitated with ≈ 0.3% acetonitrile insoluble crystals obtained from Cs-pic which was heated to the end of induction period. b) Fresh sample.

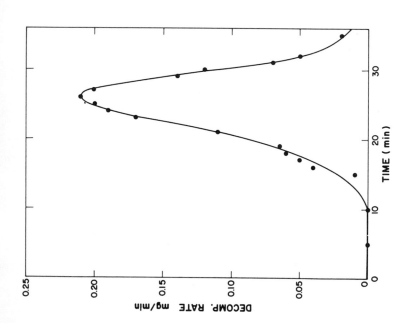

Fig 5 – Cesium picrate. Decomposition rate vs time at 285°C.

THE CALORIMETRIC OBSERVATION OF SOLID STATE
REACTIONS IN ALUMINUM ALLOYS

D. S. Thompson

Reynolds Metals Company
Richmond, Virginia

Abstract

Precipitation processes in both Al-Cu and Al-Zn-Mg
alloy systems have been detected by DTA.   Work on the early
stages of precipitation (G.P. zone formation) and reversion
of these zones has shown that reversion is dependent upon
both the initial zone size and the heating rate.   Consequently, the concept of a G.P. zone solvus for an alloy is
questionable, though some limiting value must exist.   Substructure and other parameters such as heating rate, quench
rate and composition were shown to have a major influence
on the DTA thermogram.   These effects were interpreted in
terms of precipitation models.

Introduction

Precipitation of intermetallic particles from a supersaturated solid solution is the most effective method of
hardening aluminum alloys;   though careful control of the
precipitation process is necessary to obtain optimum
properties (1,2).   Prior to achieving equilibrium the
precipitated second phase can be of some metastable form,
and it is actually these non-equilibrium precipitates which
are the most effective hardening agents.   It is thus of
considerable importance to understand the kinetics of the
various stages of the precipitation sequence.
Typically, the thermal practice necessary to obtain
the desired precipitate distribution consists of a solution
heat treatment at a temperature sufficiently high to place
all solute atoms into solid solution, followed by a quench

1147

to retain a supersaturated solid solution, and finally
aging at one or more temperatures to cause precipitation.
The amount, size and type of the precipitate depend upon
aging temperature and time. At low aging temperatures the
solute atoms initially cluster in certain regions while
still occupying matrix lattice sites. That is, these
clusters or Guinier-Preston zones (G.P. zones) are coherent
with the matrix, the interfacial energy is low so that the
minimum metastable size is small. At higher temperatures
or longer times G.P. zones can act as nuclei for intermediate metastable precipitates (3) which have a distorted
equilibrium lattice and are partially coherent with the
matrix. These intermediate precipitates are larger than
G.P. zones and are not as effective hardeners but have
other benefits. Without the prior presence of G.P. zones
this intermediate phase is not nucleated (3,4) homogeneously
and will have very little hardening effect. At still
higher temperatures and longer times the equilibrium second
phase can be formed. This phase is incoherent and is of
little practical value.

The complete precipitation sequence is usually of the
form:

G.P. zones $\longrightarrow$ Metastable phase $\longrightarrow$ Equilibrium phase
(coherent   (partially   (incoherent)
with matrix)   coherent with
                        matrix)

The higher the aging temperature or the longer the aging
time, then the larger the precipitates and the larger the
volume fraction of solute atoms precipitated. That is
provided the aging temperature is such that the equilibrium
solubility is small compared to the solute concentration.

Two aspects of DTA applied to the precipitation
process will be considered:

(1) The use of DTA to follow the progress of precipitation
     either during the DTA heating scan or by pre-aging
     specimens and then scanning to establish the extent
     of precipitation during the pre-aging process.

(2) To derive kinetic data for the various stages of
     precipitation.

Precipitation Kinetics

The rate of precipitation from a supersaturated solid solution depends upon the degree of supersaturation, the complete time-temperature history of the sample since complete solid solutionizing was last achieved, and the particular solute and matrix atoms involved (1). More recently (2) the excess vacancy concentration retained during quenching has been shown to play a prominent part during nucleation (3,4) and in the early stages of growth (2). It is well established that the kinetics of the early stages of G.P. zone formation are controlled by vacancy diffusion or the diffusion of vacancy-solute atom complexes (2,5-8). Initially, clustering takes place very rapidly, even at room temperature, and later decreases. The diffusion rate in these later stages is still greater than would be expected if the vacancy concentration had fallen to the equilibrium value as observed in pure Al.(2). Consequently excess vacancies are still available for the later stages of the precipitation process.

The kinetics of the later stages of precipitation, including the formation of metastable intermediate phases and the equilibrium phase, have not been examined in great detail with the exception of the Al-Cu and Al-Ag systems (9-12). In general the activation energy of the various stages of precipitation increase as equilibrium is approached; typically .4 - .7 eV for G.P. zone formation (effectively the activation energy for vacancy migration) and approaching the activation energy for bulk diffusion in the final stages. Beyond these systems there is very little information about the mode or kinetics of precipitate transformations. Some previous DTA investigations of precipitation have been reported (13-26) though they have dealt mainly with the determination of the heat of precipitation or re-solution in the Al-Cu system. None have attempted to derive kinetic data.

Various isothermal precipitation rate relations have been proposed and have been reviewed by Hardy and Heal (1) and others (27,28) none of which have proved to be universally applicable (27,29), but the simplest form of many is a first order rate equation. In the present, work such an equation is adequate since the rate equation is principally used as a means of displaying the kinetic data. It is shown, however, that using this rate equation the present work is in good agreement with previous isothermal kinetic data of at least two stages of precipitation in the Al-Cu system. This rate equation can be written as:

$$df/dt = k(1 - f) \tag{1}$$

where f is the fraction of precipitate formed after a growth time t and k is a temperature sensitive constant (the rate constant). The temperature variation of k is given by:

$$k = Ae^{-E/RT} \tag{2}$$

where A is the frequency factor which is assumed to be constant for a given reaction and E is the activation energy of the process. The kinetic parameters necessary to completely describe the system are the values of E and A in equation 2. It is more informative, however, to plot ln k against 1/T, as an Arrhenius plot.

Some confirmation of the general validity of this approach has been provided by Borrelius and his co-workers (18,30). DTA provides realistic conditions under which to study precipitation since the heating rates used (1-40°C/min.) lie in the middle of the range of values used during aging (10^{-1}-10^{4}°C/min.). However, since only the transient effects are associated with precipitation the method does not lend itself to isothermal observations at typical aging temperatures due to the long times involved (typically 10-50 hrs.).

The Derivation of Kinetic Parameters from DTA Results

Two analyses of the DTA results have been used; the first, due to Borchardt and Daniels (31), determines the variation of k across a single DTA curve, while that due to Kissinger (32,33) involves a single determination of k at the peak of the curve so that several different heating rates must be used to evaluate the variation of k with temperature. This last analysis is particularly useful for small ill-defined peaks or where two independent peaks interfere with one another. The Borchardt and Daniels analysis can only be used on large well-defined peaks. The Borchardt and Daniels analysis, together with comparison to known kinetic data, was used to test the validity of

1150

Kissinger's method.   In its simplest form Borchardt and
Daniels analysis leads to the relation:

$$k = \Delta T/a \qquad (3)$$

where a is the area of that portion of the DTA curve lying
at temperatures above that at which ΔT was measured.   An
assumption of this derivation was that the ratio (α) of
heat capacity of the specimen to the coefficient of heat
transfer between specimen and heating block is small.   In
the present work this is true since the ratio, which has
the dimension of time, is small (approximately 9 sec.).
The value of α is a measure of the time response of the
system;   it decreases with decreasing heat capacity and
increasing rate of heat transfer.   Also, the high
conductivity of the sample and its small dimensions
minimise any appreciable thermal gradients within the
specimen, another assumption of the analysis.
     Kissinger's (32,33) analysis is based on the
erroneous assumption that d^2f/dt^2 is zero at the peak of
the DTA curve,   i.e. when $d\Delta T/dt = 0$.   Reed, Weber and
Gottfried (34) and Bohon (35) have shown that the maximum
reaction rate never occurs at the peak of the DTA curve.
However, under certain experimental conditions, it has
been shown (36) that the point of maximum reaction rate
approaches the peak as the value of α decreases,   i.e. as
the effective time response of the system is reduced.
Reed et al. showed that:

$$\alpha(d^2\Delta T/dt^2)_m = -(d\Delta T/dt)_m \qquad (4)$$

where the subscript m refers to the maximum precipitation
rate.   At the peak temperature (T_p), the term on the left
hand side of equation 4 is a maximum and the one on the
right is zero, hence an equality is impossible at the peak.
If, however, α is sufficiently small, then T_m approaches
T_p.   Such conditions prevail in the present experimental
arrangement, where α is an order of magnitude smaller than
in the experiments of Reed et al.   To a first approximation a plot of $d\Delta T/dt$ was found to be linear so that
equation 4 will be satisfied at a time α before the peak.
In terms of temperature this is approximately .15°C for a
heating rate of 1°C/min. or 1.5°C for a heating rate of
10°C/min.   Therefore, the errors introduced by using

Kissinger's analysis will be small and generally less than the experimental error introduced in determining the peak temperature.

Kissinger showed that:

$$Ae^{-E/RT}_p = E\lambda/RT_p^2 \tag{5}$$

where λ is the heating rate of the DTA scan. Combining equations 2 and 5 gives:

$$k = E\lambda/R \; T_p^2 \tag{6}$$

or taking natural logarithms, equation 5 can be written:

$$\ln \frac{\lambda}{T_p^2} = -E/R.1/T_p + \ln AR/E \tag{7}$$

Hence a plot of $\ln \dfrac{\lambda}{T_p^2}$ against $1/T_p$ has a slope of $-E/R$

which can be substituted in equation 6 to obtain a value of k at the temperature T_p.

Experimental Methods

The heating block assembly of the DuPont 900 Differential Thermal Analyser used in the present investigation is shown schematically in Fig. 1. Cylindrical alloy and reference samples (4.0mm. diameter and 10.0mm. long), anodized to form a 20 micron coating to provide thermal and electrical resistance, fit into the cylindrical silver heating block.

A direct estimate of α was made by observing how the specimen temperature approaches equilibrium when the rest of the system is heated isothermally. This was accomplished by attaining isothermal equilibrium in the heating block and in both the sample and the reference material. The specimen was then removed and allowed to cool some $10^{\circ}C$. It was then replaced in the heating block and ΔT observed as a function of time. Heating was Newtonian, i.e. ΔT varied linearly with log t, and gave a value of $\alpha = 9.0 \pm .3$ sec.

In all experiments Al-Cu alloys were solution heat

treated at 540 $\pm$ 2°C for about 1 hr. and 7000 series alloys
for a similar time at 470° $\pm$ 5°C.   All specimens were
quenched into ambient temperature (23 $\pm$ 2°C) water.

Comparison of Thermograms with known Precipitation Behaviour of Al-Cu Alloys

According to X-ray and electron microscopy investigations (1,2), the precipitation sequence for the Al-Cu
system is:

$$G.P. \text{ Zones} \longrightarrow \theta'' \text{ (or G.P.II)} \longrightarrow \theta' \longrightarrow \theta \ CuAl_2$$

A typical DTA thermogram for a solution heat treated and
cold water quenched Al-4.6Cu* binary sample is shown in
Fig. 2 and, with one exception, is similar to those of
other workers (16,19,24,26).   The principal features are:
three exothermic peaks A, D and E, an endothermic peak B,
the solvus F and the plateau C, which will be referred to
below.   The exceptional feature is the peak A;   most
investigators have not reported this peak.   The three exotherms, A, D and E will be shown to be related respectively
to the formation of G.P. zones, θ' and θ.   The exotherm E
is actually in a large endotherm representing re-solution
which is complete at F the solvus.   The endotherm B is due
to the reversion of G.P. zones.   These identifications can
be demonstrated by aging solution heat treated and quenched
DTA specimens for 24 hrs. at 130°C, 6 hrs. at 177°C and
24 hrs. at 218°C which, according to other workers (1,10)
tend to complete the precipitation of G.P. zones, θ'' and θ'
respectively.   The thermograms obtained on such specimens
are shown in the lower three curves of Fig. 3.   The upper
curve is the thermogram of a quenched sample and is similar
to that shown in Fig. 2.   From the curve marked "G.P.
zones" it can be seen that peak A of Fig. 2 is no longer
present, consequently peak A can be identified with the
formation of G.P. zones.   The endotherm (B of Fig. 2) is
now somewhat greater in area, but occurs over nearly the
same temperature range as in the "as-quenched" sample.
The third curve of Fig. 3 was obtained on a sample aged to
the completion of the precipitation of θ'';   no peak which

* 4.6% Cu by weight.   All compositions reported are by
weight and the % symbol will be omitted.

occurred in the G.P. zone curve has been eliminated. The endotherm has, however, shifted some 50°C to 235°C. The significance of this will be discussed later, though it appears that the endotherm represents reversion or re-solution of either larger G.P. zones or θ" precipitates. The peak temperature of the endotherms in the G.P. zone and θ" curves correspond closely to the solvus temperatures reported by Beton and Rollason (37) for G.P. zones and θ" respectively. The lower curve of Fig. 3 shows the thermo-gram developed after the DTA specimen was pre-aged to form θ'. It can be seen that both the large exothermic peak (D of Fig. 2), and the endotherm have disappeared, and no new endotherm has been introduced. It is evident that this large peak was associated with the formation of θ'. Also, since no new endotherm has been introduced, peak E can be identified with the transformation $\theta' \longrightarrow \theta$, which has been reported to be an allotropic transformation (38) and hence no endotherm would be expected. Further confirmation of the identity of peaks A, D and E is given in the discussion of kinetics below.

So far, the only feature of Fig. 2 not identified is the plateau C. Since the position of the base line is uncertain, this could be a small exotherm due to the form-ation of θ", however, it occurs at approximately the same temperature as the endotherm of the θ" curve in Fig. 3. This endotherm was supposedly due to the reversion of θ", and it is most unlikely that both reversion and formation could occur at the same temperatures. It must be concluded that the plateau C is, in fact, a portion of the base line.

Thus no exothermic peak can be associated with the formation of θ", though ample opportunity for nucleation was permitted. In particular the thermogram shown as the second curve in Fig. 3 was pre-aged to form G.P. zones which, in the light of recent work on other systems (3,4), should constitute a copious supply of nuclei for θ" form-ation. It is possible that the heating rates used were high, so that insufficient growth of θ" was possible before reversion and transformation to θ' occurred. However, it appears that, at least as far as heating at the rates used in this investigation are concerned, the formation of θ" is not a separate and distinct process but rather is a continuous transformation; possibly due to the addition of planes of Cu atoms to G.P. zones to increase their thick-

ness together with an increase in diameter. No peak would
be observed if the thickening occurs by a process of
competitive growth; where G.P. zones are reverted to
supply solute atoms for the growth with little nett change
in energy. The reversion experiment results shown in
Figs. 4 and 5 are also relevant to the transformation G.P.
zones $\rightarrow$ θ".

In Fig. 4, note that the energy absorbed in the endothermic reaction is approximately constant while the
position of the peak moves to steadily higher temperatures
with increasing pre-age time. The only factor introduced
in pre-aging which could influence reversion is the zone
size which increases with time (2,29). An increase in the
density of zones (number per unit volume) would increase
the size of the endotherm but would probably not change the
temperature range over which it occurs. The effect of pre-
aging at room temperature for various times is shown in
Fig. 5. Two stages of reversion are evident, the first
near $100^{\circ}C$ and a second at approximately $200^{\circ}C$. The
latter is similar to those seen with no pre-aging (Fig. 2)
and is most likely due to the reversion of zones which grew
during the early stages of the DTA scan. The lower
temperature endotherm is due to the reversion of zones
formed during the pre-age at $23^{\circ}C$. The temperature range
over which reversion takes place steadily increases with
increasing aging time. Mean G.P. zone diameters
estimated from the work of Baur and Gerold (29) are marked
in Fig. 5. Nearly all previous investigations have used a
single aging practice to form the precipitates for
reversion. It is not surprising, therefore, that a single
value (or small range of temperature) has been found for
the G.P. zone solvus. In the present work, many starting
conditions were investigated and each thermogram
represented a complete reversion experiment. Reducing the
heating rate of the DTA scan lowers the reversion
temperature; which effect is discussed in the section on
Al-Zn-Mg alloys. Thus both the initial size and the
heating rate determine the reversion temperature or the
range of temperature over which reversion occurs.

Hirano et al. (26) in their calorimetric investigation
of the Al-Cu system did not detect reversion of θ" and they
concluded that the single peak D of Fig. 2 included the
G.P. zone $\rightarrow$ θ" and θ" $\rightarrow$ θ' transformations. Polmear and
Hardy (19) drew similar conclusions, though according to

Graf's (39) X-ray work, the formation of θ' is a distinct
process from the formation of θ". However, Graf's work
was conducted under isothermal conditions which may not be
applicable to heating at a linear rate. That is, at a
given temperature the two processes could be distinct, but
if observed while the temperature is increasing, the
processes could easily overlap. However, as stated
previously, it is unreasonable to expect precipitation of
θ" at temperatures at or above those at which reversion of
the same phase occurs.

  With the exception of De Sorbo et al. (5) and
Borrelius et al. (30) previous calorimetric work has not
detected peak A of Fig. 2. This is somewhat surprising;
however, it may be due to G.P. zone formation in the period
between quenching and starting the heating scan. Due to
the cumbersome nature of most calorimetric apparatus the
minimum delay time can be several hours, which is sufficient
to eliminate the first peak.

  Three types of kinetic data are shown in the
Arrhenius plot of Fig. 6. These are the individual DTA
results calculated by Kissinger's method and shown by the
open symbols for three binary Al-Cu alloys; results from
the peaks identified as A, D and E in Fig. 2 are indicated
as G.P. zones, θ"→ θ' and θ'→ θ respectively. Results due
to other workers are also shown. The short lines among the
θ"→ θ' results were determined from the present results by
the Borchardt and Daniels method, which could only be
applied to the well-defined large peak (D). To within
experimental error the methods of analysis lead to the same
values. The lines due to the Borchardt and Daniels
analysis lie within the scatter band for the Kissinger
results. It is evident that the biggest danger in
interpreting kinetics from DTA data is in making
measurements over a small range of temperature or heating
rates and extrapolating the results.

  The results of other workers are all in good agreement
with the present results. Very little data pertaining to
the rate constant for G.P. zone formation is contained in
the literature, though many determinations of the
activation energy of zone formation have been reported and
reviewed (2). A calorimetric result of De Sorbo et al.
(5,40) and one from the X-ray data of Baur and Gerold (29)
are represented by solid diamond shaped symbols in Fig. 6.
The E value used for the slope of the line through the G.P.

zone formation results is .51 eV (2) and is drawn as the best fit to both De Sorbo's et al. and Baur and Gerold's values of ln k.

The results for the transformations to form θ' and θ as shown in Fig. 6 were derived from many sources. Some were direct observations such as Graf's (39) and Nileshwar's (9) X-ray determinations, while others are less direct, such as the dilatometric measurements of Lankes and Wasserman (12). Results due to Laird et al. (41), Borreluis et al. (30), Guinier (11) and Hardy (42) are included. The recent work of Hornbogen (43) was not included due to his widely spaced experimental results; however, this investigation appeared to be in general agreement with the present work.

It must be concluded that the simple rate equations assumed in the above analyses do adequately represent all three precipitation processes. That is, the same equation could adequately describe the formation of coherent, partially coherent and incoherent precipitates in the Al-Cu system.

Al-Zn-Mg alloys (7000 series)

These alloys include the strongest aluminum alloys and consequently are of considerable importance. The precipitation sequence has been reported (44) to be:

$$\text{G.P. zones} \rightarrow \text{metastable } MgZn_2 \rightarrow \text{equilibrium } MgZn_2$$
$$(\eta' \text{ or } M') \qquad\qquad (\eta \text{ or } M)$$

An ordering stage within G.P. zones has also been reported (45,46).

Typical thermograms of alloys containing 5Zn, 3Mg and three levels of Cu are shown in Fig. 7. The principal features are the single central peak of the commercial purity 7039 which corresponds to two peaks in the high purity version and yet another peak which appears when about .7% or more Cu is added. At high heating rates 20-40°C/min. two or more of these peaks may merge to form a single peak. The rather ill-defined low temperature peak (60-90°C) is due to the formation of G.P. zones. This peak is not readily detectable in Cu free material but becomes increasingly more well-defined as the Cu content is increased. It will be shown below that Cu plays an

1157

important role in the nucleation of G.P. zones and the later stages of precipitation though it apparently has little effect on the rate of growth of G.P. zones.

Three other peaks, marked 2, 3 and 4, can be seen in Fig. 7. Their identity will be discussed below after considering the kinetics of their formation.

Kissinger's analysis was used to derive the Arrhenius plot for a Cu bearing 7000 series alloy shown in Fig. 8. Borchardt and Daniels analysis could not be used since the central peaks overlapped. The numbers refer to the peaks shown in Fig. 7. The values of the activation energies are consistent with a vacancy controlled process for peaks 1 and 2 and a higher value for peak 4. Peak 3, which it will be remembered occurs only when the Cu content is about .7% or greater, does not fit into the pattern of increasing activation energy with successive stages of the precipitation sequence. This suggests that a different process, perhaps involving the precipitation of a different phase such as an Al-Cu-Mg phase, is involved. Electron microscopy of samples removed from the DTA at various points along the thermogram on peaks 2, 3 and 4 has so far failed to identify such a phase. Across all three peaks the only obvious difference in the precipitates is one of size. Preliminary examination showed no evidence in the Cu bearing alloy of the presence of more than one precipitating species; the precipitates were always roughly equiaxed. Had an Al-Cu-Mg phase been precipitated then discs, possibly with an associated strain field, might have been seen; neither were evident. It is possible that peak 3 represents the diffusion of Cu into the precipitate formed in peak 2 and hence no drastic change in morphology is experienced.

From the particle size and morphology it seems evident that at least towards the high temperature limits of peak 4 the M phase was formed. It was not possible to identify the precipitate associated with the early stages of peak 4 nor peak 3. The precipitates associated with peak 2 were apparently G.P. zones and hence this peak could be due to growth or 'ripening', or possibly an ordering process within zones. A connection between peaks 1 and 2 is in fact suggested in Fig. 7 where it can be seen that as peak 1 either appears or becomes more well defined, then peak 2 becomes less distinct. Thus it would appear that the role of Cu is to nucleate and stabilize the early

stages of G.P. zone formation. These considerations will
be continued after some data on reversion is presented.

The influence of pre-aging at room temperature on the
DTA thermogram is shown in Fig. 9 for a Cu bearing alloy
(7075) and in Fig. 10 for a Cu free alloy (7039). The
upper curve in both figures is for the essentially as
quenched material. As previously reported peak 1 can only
be seen in the case of the Cu bearing commercial purity
alloy. With increasing times at room temperature, endotherms appear in the temperature range 75-150°C and steadily
shift to higher temperatures. The large 250°C exothermic
peak of 7075 is not influenced by pre-aging while that of
7039 moves to lower temperatures with increasing aging time;
suggesting difficult nucleation in the case of 7039. After
about 5-8 days this shift stops; which period corresponds
to the incubation times which have been found to be
necessary to achieve maximum mechanical properties with
7039 type alloys. This behaviour is consistent with the
non-appearance of peak 1 for 7039, i.e. G.P. zones are not
formed, consequently nucleation of the later stages of the
precipitation sequence is difficult and so occurs at higher
temperatures (3). Both alloys behave in a similar manner
as far as the effect of varying aging time on reversion is
concerned. Since the major effect of time at room temperature is on the size of precipitates it is reasonable to
assume that growth occurs at approximately the same rate in
7039 and 7075, i.e. Cu plays no major role in G.P. zone
growth but is important to achieve nucleation of G.P. zones.
The influence of the DTA scanning rate on reversion is shown
in Fig. 11. The reversion temperature decreases with
decreasing heating rate, indicating that reversion has a
greater opportunity to occur at lower temperatures given a
long enough time, however, less is reverted. At very low
heating rates growth occurs at a greater rate than reversion.

A summary of the above reversion results together with
50°C and 100°C results for 7039 and results for some high
purity alloys are shown in Fig. 12. At room temperature
reversion behaviour of all the alloys investigated was
similar, though there is an apparent increase in slope with
increasing Cu content. It is apparent that reversion is
more sensitive, at least in the case of 7039, to pre-aging
temperature rather than time. It takes some 20 days at
23°C to achieve the same reversion temperature (and
presumably a similar precipitate size distribution) as

5 hrs. at 50°C.

The most important information from these experiments is the fact that the growth of G.P. zones at room temperature is independent of the alloy, which might be expected if vacancies control the kinetics of zone growth. Yet, in view of the difficulty of nucleation experienced with 7039, Cu must play a vital role in the nucleation or very early stages of zone growth.

Two final aspects of 7000 series DTA data which are related to the above observations are the influence of trace elements and the heating rate used for the DTA scan. As was shown in Fig. 7 trace elements can produce considerable differences, cf. 7039 and the 5Zn 3Mg alloy. The effects of further variations in trace elements are shown in Fig. 13. It is possible but unlikely that the trace elements, per se, are responsible for the differences between the thermograms. Cr and Mn are added to these alloys to retard recrystallization (Cr is the more effective) and it is the retained substructure which acts as a sink for vacancies and hence influences precipitation (47), that is the most probable cause of the variations shown in Fig. 13. The commercial alloy contained .18% Cr and .23% Mn and had the smallest subgrain size. The Cr bearing alloy was slightly coarser, the Mn alloy was a mixture of large equiaxed grains and some unrecrystallized regions while the high purity 5Zn 3Mg alloy had a large grained fully recrystallized structure. It is likely that a loss of vacancies to the grain boundaries occurs either during or soon after quenching with a subsequent reduction in the initial rate of growth of G.P. zones. The vacancy concentration must still be high enough to continue the growth process since it was shown in the discussion of Fig. 12 that all the alloys considered showed essentially similar reversion behaviour, i.e. they contained approximately the same size zones, though perhaps not the same density of zones. The alloy 7075 also had an unrecrystallized structure but its thermogram was apparently not sensitive to structure. This can only be explained in terms of the formation of Cu containing complexes which retain the vacancies on quenching. Although space precludes presentation of any data it should be mentioned that low quenching rates after solution heat treatment has been found to result in the reduction in the number of peaks observed. For example, the lower curve of Fig. 13

on quenching slowly leads to a single peak similar to that
of alloys with a fine substructure.   On further reduction
of the quench rate the single peak shifts to higher temperatures, indicating more difficult nucleation.   Again, this
can be interpreted in terms of vacancy loss to subgrain or
grain boundaries during the quench.

Conclusions

From the present work the following conclusions may be
drawn:

1.   In the case of Al-Cu alloys the kinetic analysis
        described is consistent with data obtained by other
        means for the formation of G.P. zones, θ' and θ.
2.   That reversion is a process which depends upon the
        initial precipitate size and on the heating rate
        used to attain the reversion temperature.
3.   That the formation of θ" is not a separate and distinct
        process.   It is possibly a continuation of G.P. zone
        growth simply extended to the third dimension
        together with growth in the plane of the original
        G.P. zone.
4.   That the precipitation sequence in Cu bearing Al-Zn-Mg
        is more complex than previously thought.
5.   That the substructure of Al-Zn-Mg alloys, the quench-
        ing rate from solution heat treating and the heating
        rate of the DTA scan all have major effects on the
        nature of the thermograms.
6.   That Cu in Al-Zn-Mg alloys plays an important role in
        the nucleation of G.P. zones but has little
        influence on the growth of G.P. zones.

References

1.   Hardy, H.K. and Heal, T.J., Prog. Metal Physics. 5,
        143 (1954).
2.   Kelly, A. and Nicholson, R.B., Prog. Materials Science.
        10, 151 (1963).
3.   Lorimer, G.W. and Nicholson, R.B., Acta Met. 14, 1009
        (1966).
4.   Embury, J.D. and Nicholson, R.B., Acta Met. 13, 403
        (1965).
5.   De Sorbo, W., Treaftis, H.N. and Turnbull, D., Acta

Met. 6, 401 (1958).

6. Zener, C., Proceedings of the International Conference on the Physics of Metals, 117 (Amsterdam, 1948).

7. Seitz, F., L'Etat Solide, Inst. Internat. Phys. Solvay, 401, (Stoops, Brussels, 1952).

8. Federighi, T., Acta Met. 6, 379 (1958).

9. Nileshwar, V.B., J. Inst. Met. 92, 241 (1963-64).

10. Silcock, J.M., Heal, T.J. and Hardy, H.K., J. Inst. Met. 82, 239 (1953-54).

11. Guinier, A., Z. Electrochem. 56, 468 (1952).

12. Lankes, J.C. and Wassermann, G., Z. Metallk. 41, 381 (1950).

13. Kokubo, S., Sci. Rep. Tohoku Imp. Univ. 20, 268 (1931).

14. Fraenkel, W., Metallwirtschaft. 12, 583 (1933).

15. Luznikov, L.P. and Berg, L.G., Zavodskaya Laboratoruja 14, 824 (1948). Fulmer Research Institute Translation No. 37.

16. Swindells, N. and Sykes, C., Proc. Roy. Soc. A168, 237 (1938).

17. Suzuki, T., Sci. Rep. Res. Inst. Tohoku Univ. (A) 1, 183 (1949).

18. Borelius, G., Andersson, J. and Gullberg, K., Ing. Vetenskaps Akad. Handlingar, 169 (1943).

19. Polmear, I.J. and Hardy, H.K., J. Inst. Met. 83, 393 (1954-55).

20. Jones, F.W. and Leech, P., J. Inst. Met. 67, 9 (1941).

21. Dichtl, H.J., Radex-Rundschau , 608 (1967).

22. Koster, W., L'Etat Solide, Inst. Internat. Phys. Solvay 235 (Stoops, Brussels, 1952).

23. Koster, W. and Schell, H.A., Z. Metallk, 43, 454 (1952)

24. Dehlinger, U. and Knapp, H., Applied Scientific Research 4A, 231 (1954).

25. Hirano, K., J. Phys. Soc. Japan. 8, 603 (1953).

26. Hirano, K. and Iwasaki, H., Trans. Japan Inst. Met. 5, 162 (1964).

27. Christian, J.W., The Theory of Transformations in Metals and Alloys (Pergamon, London 1965).

28. Burke, J., The Kinetics of phase transformations in metals, (Pergamon Press, New York 1965).

29. Baur, R. and Gerold, V., Z. Metallk. 57, 181 (1966).

30. Borelius, G. and Strom, L., Arkiv. Mat. Astron. Fysik 21, 32 (1945).

31. Borchardt, H.J. and Daniels, F., J. Phys. Chem. 79, 41 (1957).

32. Kissinger, H.E., J. Res. Nat. Bur. Stds., 57, 217 (1956).
33. Kissinger, H.E., Analytical Chem., 29, 1702 (1957).
34. Reed, R.L., Weber, L. and Gottfried, B.S., Ind. Eng. Chem. Fundamentals, 4, 38 (1965).
35. Bohon, R.L., Proc. 1st Toronto Symp. Thermal Analysis, (Chem. Inst. Canada, 1965).
36. Thompson, D.S., Ind. Eng. Chem. Fundamentals. 5, 286 (1966).
37. Beton, R.H. and Rollason, E.C., J. Inst. Met., 86, 77 and 85 (1957-58).
38. Gayler, M.L.V., Proc. Roy. Soc., A173, 83 (1939).
39. Graf, R., J. Inst. Met. 86, 534 (1957-58).
40. Turnbull, D., Rosenbaum, H.S. and Treatfis, H.N., Acta Met. 8, 277 (1960).
41. Laird, C. and Aaronson, H.I., Acta Met. 14, 171 (1966).
42. Hardy, H.K., J. Inst. Met. 79, 321 (1951).
43. Hornbogen, E., Aluminium 43, 163 (1967).
44. Thomas, G. and Nutting, J., J. Inst. Met. 88, 81 (1959-1960).
45. Guinier, A., Solid State Physics, 9, 294 (Academic Press, 1959).
46. Mondolfo, L.F., Gjostein, N.A. and Levinson, D.W., Trans. AIME 206, 1378 (1956).
47. Holl, H.A., Met. Sci. J. 1, 111 (1967).

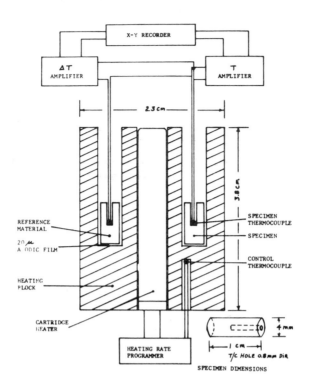

FIG. 1   Schematic Arrangement of Heating Block and Samples.

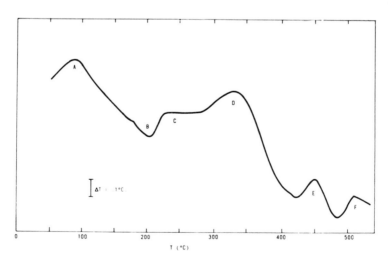

FIG. 2   Typical Thermogram of an Al-Cu Binary Alloy.
Heating Rate = 15°C/min.

1164

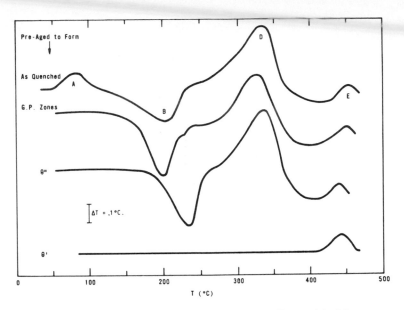

FIG. 3   Al - 4.6% Cu Alloy Pre-Aged to Essentially
          complete the Precipitation of the Indicated Phase.
          Heating Rate = 10°C/min.

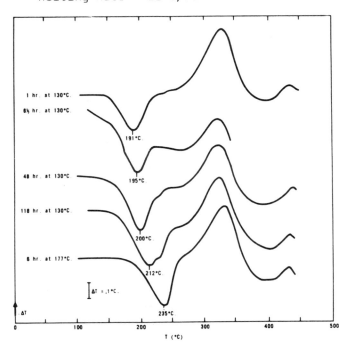

FIG. 4   Thermograms of an Al-Cu Alloy Pre-Aged under the
          Indicated Conditions.   Heating Rate = 10°C/min.

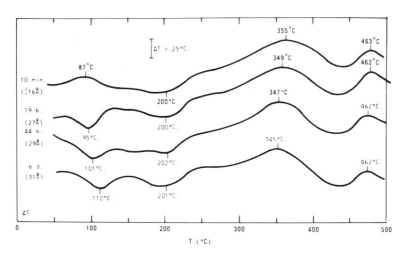

FIG. 5   Al - 4.8 Cu Alloy Pre-Aged at 23°C for the Indicated
          Time.   Numbers in Parentheses are Baur and Gerolds
          Estimate of G.P. Zone Diameter after Pre-Age.
          Heating Rate = 20°C/min.

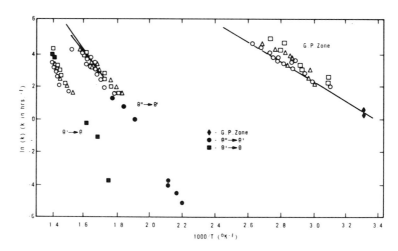

FIG. 6   Arrhenius Plot for Various Al-Cu Alloys.   DTA Results
          analyzed using Kissinger's Method and (for the
          formation of θ') Borchardt and Daniels Method.   The
          Results of other workers using other Experimental
          Techniques are included.

1166

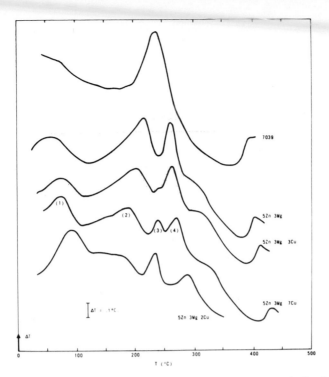

FIG. 7   Typical DTA Thermograms of Cu free and Cu bearing
7039 type Alloys.   Heating Rate = 10°C/min.

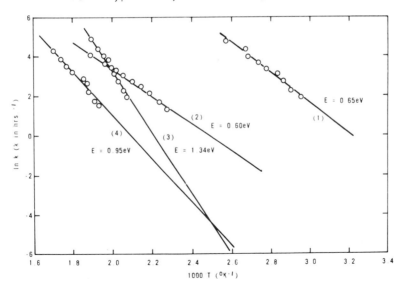

FIG. 8   Arrhenius Plot for a 7Zn - 2.5Mg - 1.5Cu High Purity
Alloy.   The numbers identify the peaks shown in
Fig. 7.

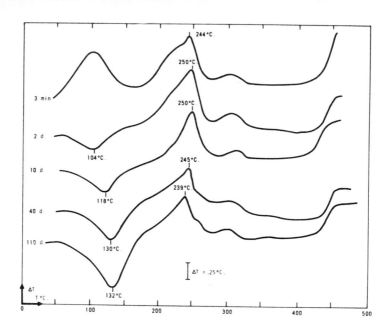

FIG. 9   7075 Alloy Pre-Aged at Room Temperature (23°C) for
          Indicated Times.   Heating Rate = 20°C/min.

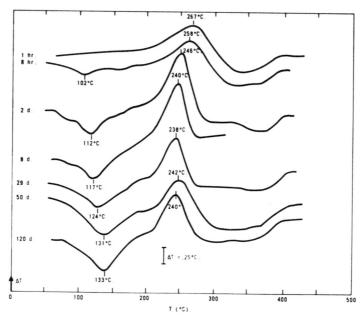

FIG. 10   7039 Alloy Pre-Aged at Room Temperature (23°C) for
          Indicated Times.   Heating Rate = 20°C/min.

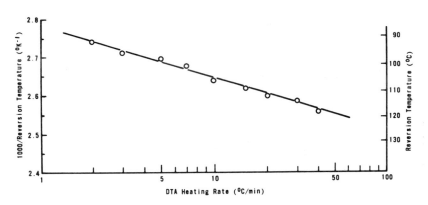

FIG. 11   The Influence of Heating Rate of DTA Scan on Reversion
Temperature of a 5Zn 3Mg Alloy.

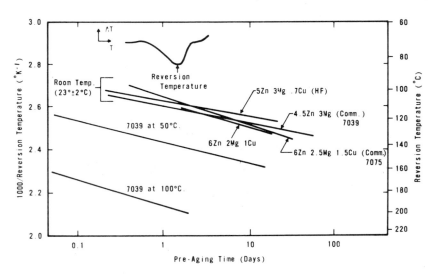

FIG. 12   Influence of Pre-Aging Time at Room and Elevated
Temperatures on the Reversion Temperature (Peak of
the Endotherm) for various Commercial Purity (Comm.)
and High Purity (HP) Alloys.   Heating Rate = 20°C/min.

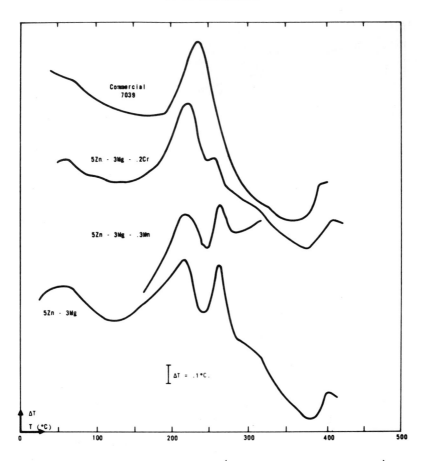

FIG. 13 The Influence of Purity (or grain substructure) on DTA
Thermograms.   Heating Rate = 20°C/min.

ISOTHERMAL PRECONDITIONING FOR
QUANTITATIVE THERMAL ANALYSIS

Bernard Miller

Textile Research Institute
Princeton, New Jersey

Introduction:

The very early portion of a thermally induced transition or reaction is least susceptible to dynamic thermoanalytical scanning. Most
practitioners in the field accept the limitation
that measured peak areas are not proportional to
the total enthalpy change, but rather to a somewhat lesser value which excludes the heat involved before there is any apparent deviation from
the base line. In at least one case, a correction
factor based on the assumption that this lost
amount of heat was constant (for a fixed set of
scanning conditions) has been used to improve the
use of heat of fusion data for purity determinations (1).

The cause of this limitation is inherent in
the nature of dynamic thermoanalysis and in the
limiting sensitivity of the apparatus used.
Activation energies for most processes will cause
a small initial rate of enthalpy change, and it is
this rate that actually is responsible for the
generation of a differential signal in both DTA
and DSC units.

Thermal and kinetic data for this pre-peak
region would be of considerable value in that it
could reveal induction periods, separate

1171

overlapping processes, and, in general, extend
the practical use of thermal analysis. This report describes the use of systematic isothermal
preconditioning before thermal scanning as a means
of obtaining such data. While many investigators
have pre-heated materials to impose a known
thermal history on their samples, little quantitative use has been made of this technique.

Experimental Procedure:

The general procedure in this work has been
the following. A sample, weighed and encapsulated in the aluminum cup used for differential
scanning calorimetry, is brought quickly to the
desired temperature, held isothermally for a
definite time, and then quenched to ambient temperature. To facilitate this procedure a small
furnace mounted on a platform jack was equipped
with a multiple sample holder and appropriate
control and sensing components (see Figure 1). If
this assembly was first allowed to heat up and
the samples then introduced, the latter could be
brought to temperature in a matter of a few minutes. Cooling of the samples was accelerated by
blowing gas over them after the furnace was lowered. The entire pre-conditioning thermal history was available on a strip chart recorder connected to the thermocouple. A typical heating-
cooling plot is included in Figure 1. The multiple sample holder made it convenient to perform replications, and there was no observable
difference incurred by the vertical stacking of
the samples. After cooling, the samples were
reweighed (if pertinent) and then scanned in a
DSC unit.* The area under the peak of interest

---

*Of the three experimental cases reported here,
the first two were performed with the Perkin
Elmer Differential Scanning Calorimeter and the

was measured with a planimeter. Rate process data for each temperature could be obtained by appropriate analysis of the dependence of peak area on preconditioning time, as will be illustrated in the following examples.

(A) Thermal Transformation of Trimethylolmelamine:

Trimethylolmelamine (TMM) undergoes two overlapping endothermic processes between 100 and 200° C; one or both are coincident with a partial weight loss (see Figure 2). No combination of controllable experimental variables (e.g. sample size, scanning rate, etc.) was capable of resolving these events with direct thermal scanning. Instead, isothermal preconditioning was carried out at temperatures of 110, 120, 130, 140, 150, and 160°C. for various periods of time. Each conditioned sample was then scanned at 10 degrees per minute using a sensitivity setting of 8 millicalories per sec. on the Perkin Elmer instrument. The results are shown in Figure 3, in which the relative peak area per gram is plotted logarithmically against conditioning time. The data for the lowest four temperatures reveals that the first process accounts for between 60 and 70% of the total enthalpy change and does not show first order rate behavior. Heating to 150°C or higher brings on the second process and coincides with the disappearance of the first peak from the thermogram, leaving only the second which appears at 162°C. and ends at 188°C. When the reciprocals of the areas are plotted as a function of time (Figure 4), the linear relationships for the first process seem to indicate a second order reaction, with the straight lines extrapolating to the unheated control value. The discontinuity at

---

*third with the DuPont 900 Differential Thermal Analyzer with a DSC cell attachment.

the end of the first stage is clearly evident from
the tailing-off of the values for 130 and 140°C
and from the magnitude of the changes for 150°C.
When samples were heated to 160°C for as little as
five minutes, over 90% of the peak area vanished
and no further studies were done at this temperature.

(B) <u>Crystallization of Quenched Poly(Ethylene
Terephthalate)</u>

Amorphous poly (ethylene terephthalate) (PET)
will crystallize spontaneously upon heating above
its glass transition temperature. Thus, on DTA
or DSC scanning, an exotherm will appear in the
range 130-160°C. However, it is known that this
crystallization can occur at as low as 96.5°C.,
as reported by Mayhan et.al. (2) from light
transmission measurements using amorphous films.
To study this lower temperature range, PET yarns
were placed in aluminum sample containers,
heated to slightly above their melting points and
quenched. The same heating and quenching conditions were used for all samples once it was established that maximum non-crystallinity could be
achieved in this way. Isothermal preconditioning
was then carried out for each sample at temperatures between 95 and 115°C followed by scanning
at 20 degrees per minute in the Perkin Elmer instrument. The scan was carried up through the
melting range of the polymer and therefore it was
possible to quench again and re-use the same
sample. Samples were recycled and used as long
as they showed no weight loss.

In this case there is some question as to
how the control (maximum) peak area should be
evaluated. The largest exotherm will, of course,
be obtained for a quenched but unconditioned
sample. However this will be an inaccurate

estimate of the heat of crystallization since it
will not include the pre-peak enthalpy change.
On the other hand, the total amount of crystallinity should be nearly proportional to the area
under the melting peak and this could be considered as a more proper value for the maximum
area of crystallization. The alternatives are
shown schematically in Figure 5. In a previous
publication (3) both versions were compared and
proved to be relatively equivalent for obtaining
rate constants and activation energies, but did
not show good agreement in revealing induction
periods at each temperature. To achieve a better
series of comparable crystallization areas two
somewhat more detailed analyses have been considered.

The following quantities are defined:

A_f = area of the melting endotherm for a sample

A_x° = crystallization area of unconditioned sample

A_x = crystallization area of conditioned sample

A_{tx} = true total crystallization area (including
portion not detectable during scanning)

One possible approach is to expect that the
pre-peak crystallization area ($A_{tx} - A_x$) would be
proportional to the observed exotherm:

$$A_{tx} - A_x = k\ A_x$$

For the unconditioned sample we then assume that
this missing portion is the difference between
the melting and the crystallization areas, and,
to be consistent, we must allow for a similar
missing portion in the melting peak. This would
be a constant amount, however, and can be

included in the evaluation of the proportionality
constant:

$$(A_f + c) - A_x^o = k\, A_x^o$$

(where c is the pre-peak lost area for
the melting endotherm)

$$k = \frac{(A_f + c) - A_x^o}{A_x^o}$$

The corrected total exothermic area for any scan
would then be:

$$A_{tx} = \left(\frac{A_f + c - A_x^o}{A_x^o}\right) A_x + A_x = \left(\frac{A_f + c}{A_x^o}\right) A_x$$

Thus the measured exotherm should be mul-
tiplied by the ratio of the true heat of fusion
to the maximum heat of crystallization. Since
this ratio will be constant for a given sample
it would not be needed for the relative comparison used in most rate studies. However, to
detect and measure induction periods it is necessary to evaluate the fraction of uncrystallized
polymer remaining after preconditioning, which
would be:

$$\frac{A_{tx}}{A_{tx}^o} = \left(\frac{A_f + c}{A_x^o}\right)\frac{A_x}{A_f + c} = \frac{A_x}{A_x^o}$$

Therefore the correct fraction should be obtainable from the exotherms alone. Figure 6 shows
plots of the logarithm of this ratio versus preconditioning times, indicating first order kinetic
behavior, and the existence of temperature dependent induction periods. Cobbs and Burton (4)
have reported induction times for PET for temperatures above 120°C. and their data has here
been extrapolated to the temperatures used in

this work. Table I shows the comparison with the results obtained herein. Figure 7 is a plot of rate constants as a function of temperature resulting in an activation energy of 44 kcal./mole.

A second approach to this problem depends on the alternate assumption that the missing prepeak exotherm area is constant and therefore:

$$A_{tx} - A_x = \text{constant} = (A_f + c) - A_x^{\circ}$$

or:

$$A_{tx} = A_x - A_x^{\circ} + (A_f + c)$$

The fraction of uncrystallized polymer will then be:

$$\frac{A_{tx}}{A_{tx}^{\ell}} = \frac{A_x - A_x^{\circ}}{A_f + c} + 1$$

This expression is sensitive to the value of (c) and, since we have as yet no means of evaluating this quantity, useful values for induction periods cannot be obtained by this analysis.

TABLE I

Induction Times for Crystallization
of Polyester

Temperature	From This Study	From Cobbs & Burton Data
100°C.	18.0 min.	12.9 min.
105	9.0	9.4
110	3.0	6.7
115	2.0	4.9

(C)   Non-oxidative Pyrolysis of Cotton

A comparable study of the feasability of
following the thermal decomposition of cotton
cellulose at temperatures where the first stage
reactions are not too rapid has involved the same
preconditioning technique. Cotton fabrics, yarns,
and ash-free filter paper have been heated and
scanned, this time with the DSC attachment of a
DuPont 900 analyzer. A typical set of pyrolysis
curves are shown in Figure 8 for heating at 280°C,
considerably below the minimum temperature of the
appearance of a peak. When this data and similar
results for 300°C. are plotted according to simple first order kinetics, straight line plots are
found; extrapolating back to give a maximum
pyrolysis area of 6.0 - 6.1 square inches. This
extrapolated value is strongly supported by a
series of four control runs made on the same
starting material which gave an average value of
6.02 + 0.05. More detailed rate studies on
cellulose pyrolysis are currently in progress.

Conclusions

Isothermal preconditioning is capable of
extending the use of quantitative thermal analysis
to temperature regions below the conventional peak
generating ones. The experimental procedures are
simple and seem to produce reliable data. Applications other than those shown herein are obvious.
One would expect that a parallel monitoring of
weight loss after preconditioning, when compared
with the rate of dimunution of peak area, might
be a means of distinguishing two overlapping
processes where there was only one involving loss
of weight.

Acknowledgement

The author would like to acknowledge the cooperation of Professor J. K. Gillham of the Department of Chemical Engineering at Princeton University in helping to obtain some of the data for this study.

References

(1) Gray, A. P., Thermal Analysis Newsletter, No.6 Perkin Elmer Corp.
(2) Mayham, K. G., James, W. J. and Bosch, W., J. Appl. Polymer Sci., 9, 3605 (1965)
(3) Miller, B., J. Appl. Polymer Sci., 11, 2343 (1967)
(4) Cobbs, W.H. and Burton, R. L., J. Polymer Sci., 10, 275 (1953)

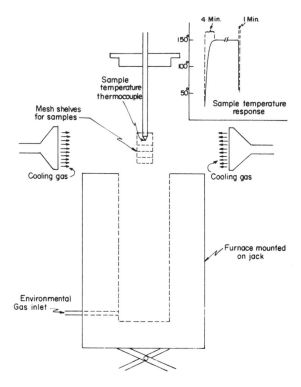

Fig. 1 - Apparatus for Preconditioning Samples

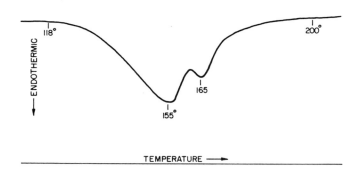

Fig. 2 - Thermogram of Trimethylomelamine;
scanning rate = 10°/min., N₂ atm.,
range = 8 millical./sec.

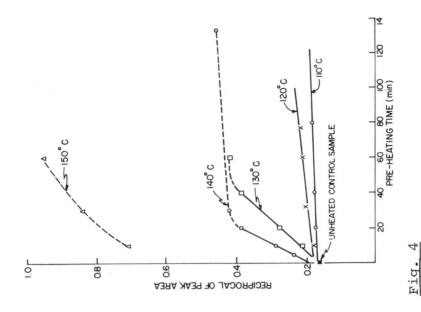

Fig. 4

Reciprocal Rate Plots for Thermal
Reactions of Trimethylolmelamine

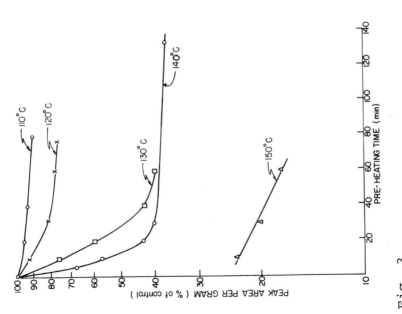

Fig. 3

Rate Plots for Thermal Reactions of
Trimethylolmelamine

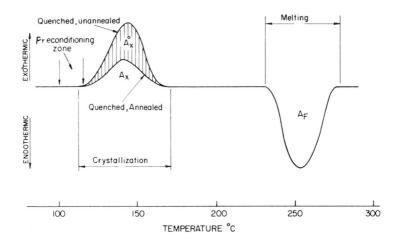

Fig. 5 - Reduction of Crystallization Exotherm
of PET on Preconditioning

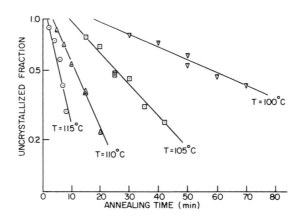

Fig. 6 - Rate Plots for Crystallization of PET

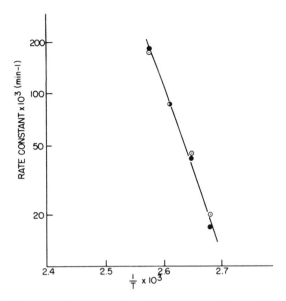

Fig. 7 - Rate Constants as a Function of
Temperature

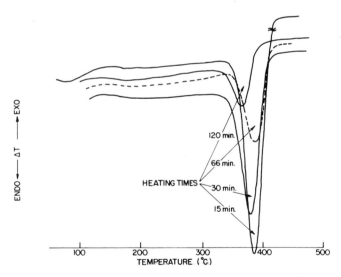

Fig. 8 - Effect of Pre-heating at 280°C. on
Thermal Behavior of Cotton Cellulose;
scanning rate = 20°/min., N$_2$ atm.

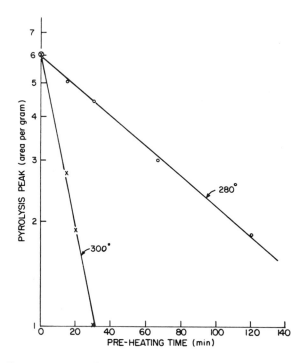

Fig. 9 - Rate Plots for Cellulose Pyrolysis
in N_2

APPLICATION OF DIFFERENTIAL THERMAL ANALYSIS TO THE QUANTITATIVE MEASUREMENT OF ENTHALPY CHANGES

B.R. Currell

(Dept. of Chemistry, Northern Polytechnic,
Holloway Road, London, N.7.)

Summary

It is reported that the "miniblock" assembly of the Standata 625 may be used for the quantitative measurement of enthalpy changes without the need to take into account the variation in sample thermal characteristics (thermal conductivity etc.).

Introduction

The classical differential thermal analysis (DTA) involves the sample and reference materials being held within cells cut from a block (metallic or ceramic). Thermocouples are placed at the centre of each cell. This arrangement allows heat to flow from the sample to the reference material or vice versa. With the thermocouple beads within the material, the differential temperature depends not only on the quantity of heat evolved or absorbed by the material but also on the transport of heat across the material to the block. This dependence of the differential temperature upon the sample thermal characteristics (thermal conductivity etc.) has, with the present state of the art, made impossible the development of a treatment with general applicability for the quantitative measurement of enthalpy changes (H values) using the classical differential thermal analysis arrangement.

Differential calorimetry is an approach
which enables H values to be obtained without knowledge of the sample thermal
characteristics. Boersma (1) suggested
this approach in which sample and reference
materials are isolated from each other,
i.e. there is no heat flow between sample
and reference materials. This is the
design of the Du Pont Calorimeter Cell.
The area under the peak is then directly
proportional to the value of H irrespective
of the sample thermal characteristics.

The disadvantage of the differential
calorimeter is that as heat escape from the
sample holder is slow, peaks are very broad
and H values associated with two closely
neighbouring peaks may not be measurable.

Garn (2) has reviewed the attempts at
quantitative interpretation of DTA and
differential calorimetry results.

Experimental

The results reported below were obtained
using the "miniblock" assembly of the Standata
625.

Alumina was used as the reference material,
the samples and the alumina were both contained
in platinum crucibles (height 8mm, diameter
6·2mm) supported in a stainless steel block
(width, 10mm; length, 20mm; height, 13mm).
The crucibles were a close fit in the block.
Sample weights varied considerably but in
most cases the crucible was less than half
full. Runs were carried out at a nominal
heating rate of 10°/min. The complete area
under each peak was measured using tracing
paper, then cutting out the shape of the peak
and weighing.

Depending on the size of each peak various
chart speeds and amplifier sensitivities were
used; for the purpose of calculation, however,
these areas were corrected to be equivalent
to that obtained on a chart speed of 24 ins.

per hour and an amplifier sensitivity of 50 uV.

The results were treated assuming a direct relationship between peak area and H, a calibration coefficient was then calculated as shown below:-

$$g = \frac{H\,m}{A}$$

A   area of peak (sq. cms.).

m   weight of sample (gms.).

H   literature value of heat of fusion or transition (cals. gm^{-1}).

g   calibration coefficient (cals. cms^{-2}).

Results

Table 1 shows the average calibration coefficient value obtained from each sample. The coefficient values given are the averages of results obtained with at least two different sample weights and a number of runs with each sample weight. The mean deviation of individual results from the average calibration coefficient values for each sample is, with the exception of the potassium nitrate peaks, approximately 2%. In the case of the potassium nitrate peaks this variation is about 9%, potassium nitrate is obviously "peculiar" in this respect as is shown by the very wide variation in reported H values in the literature for the transition and fusion.

A plot of the calibration coefficient (g) against peak temperature (t) gives a straight line.

Equation $g = -1.3 \times 10^{-4}t + 0.2200$

standard deviation = 0.0047

Table 2 shows the coefficients calculated using different sample weights.

Discussion

These results indicate that, after suitable calibration, the Standata 625 miniblock assembly may be used to measure H values. We have of course so far only studied fusions and solid — solid transitions but it is intended to study the application to reactions involving loss of volatile matter. The very wide range of samples studied so far show that this method of treating the results is independent of the sample thermal characteristics (thermal conductivity etc.). Similar results have been obtained by Ingraham and Marier (3) for a range of sulphates using the R.L. Stone apparatus.

In explaining these results and their independence of the sample thermal characteristics it is important to note that this assembly differs from the classical DTA arrangement in that the thermocouples are not in direct contact with the sample or reference materials; it would appear that the sample is acting solely as a producer of heat and that we are measuring a temperature difference produced by the flow of this heat through the block. In the classical DTA arrangement the temperature difference is measured across both the block and the sample.

References

(1)   S.L. Boersma, J. Am. Ceramic Soc.
                38,   281 (1955).

(2)   P.D. Garn, Thermoanalytical Methods of
       Investigation, Academic Press, New York,
                                    1965.

(3)   T.R. Ingraham and P. Marier, Can. Metall.
                Quart., 4, 169 (1965).

Table 1: Values of calibration coefficient determined using transitions of known H value

Sample	Peak temp. °C	H lit. value cals. gm.$^{-1}$	Calibration coeff. cals. cms^{-2}
Palmitic acid	77 *	39.2 (3)	0.200
Stearic acid	83 *	47.6 (3)	0.200
Benzoic acid	136 *	33.9 (3)	0.198
Ammonium nitrate	140 —	12.6 (1)	0.185
Potassium nitrate	146 —	12.06 (1)	0.198
Silver nitrate	179 —	3.49 (4)	0.191
Ammonium nitrate	181 *	16.2 (1)	0.180
Silver nitrate	226 *	16.24 (1)	0.177
Tin	248 *	14.2 (1)	0.178
Potassium nitrate	346 *	22.7 (1)	0.166
Potassium dichromate	411 *	28.9 (2)	0.156

* fusion
— solid — solid transition

(1) American Institute of Physics Handbook, 2nd Edition McGraw Hill

(2) Selected Values of Chemical Thermodynamic Properties, Circular 500 National Bureau of Standards (1952).

(3) Handbook of Chemistry and Physics, 35th Ed., Chemical Rubber Publishing Co., Ohio (1953).

(4) A. Arell in J.P. Redfern. Thermal Analysis 1965, p. 58, Macmillan, London (1965).

Table 2: Measurement of calibration coeff. with different weights of sample

KNO$_3$ transition at 146°C. Tin fusion at 248°C.

Sample wt. mgm.	Calibration coeff. cals. cms.$^{-2}$	Sample wt. mgm.	Calibration coeff. cals.cms.$^{-2}$
18	0.209	61.9	0.177
22	0.200	158.2	0.183
23	0.198	168.6	0.178
35	0.191	193.9	0.180
47	0.203		
48	0.188		
51	0.202		

THE REDUCTION OF QUANTITATIVE DIFFERENTIAL THERMAL ANALYSIS DATA TO BASIC THERMODYNAMIC AND KINETIC QUANTITIES

D. M. Speros

Lighting Research Laboratory, General Electric Company
Nela Park, Cleveland, Ohio 44112

Abstract

In order to define the enthalpy, H, of a substance, it is necessary to specify its temperature. Likewise, in order to define its change, ΔH, for a reaction, it is necessary to define the reaction temperature. However reactions measured by Quantitative Differential Thermal Analysis ([1-3]) generally take place over a temperature interval: T_a-T_b. The problem then consists in correlating the heat H_o evolved or absorbed over T_a-T_b with the thermodynamic quantity ΔH_T, the change in heat content per mole of reaction at reference temperature T.

In addition to H_o, Q.D.T.A. determines dH/dt, the rate of heat absorption or evolution which is related to the rate of the reaction by means of the equation

$$\frac{dH}{dt} = \frac{H_T}{N} \frac{dx}{dt} \tag{1}$$

where dx/dt is the rate of the reaction in moles per unit time and $H_T/N = \Delta H_T$ the heat of the reaction per mole at temperature T. Since however ΔH_T is changing with temperature the relationship between dH/dt and dx/dt is changing and ΔH_T must be expressed as a function of temperature if equation (1) and those in which it is incorporated are to yield meaningful kinetic quantities such as the activation energy, ΔE, of the reaction.

The reduction of the raw data of Q.D.T.A. to basic thermodynamic and kinetic quantities is accomplished by numerical integration which incorporates basic concepts of chemical thermodynamics and kinetics. A sample application of this reduction or correction to a well characterized Q.D.T.A. result is given. It is shown that the correction is usually small and/or can be approximated. Hence most past Q.D.T.A. results can stand uncorrected. However, this reduction is conceptually important because, in answering the questions raised above, it contributes to the fundamental validity of Q.D.T.A. results.

1. Introduction

This paper describes how the heat evolved or absorbed in a process or reaction studied by Quantitative Differential Thermal Analysis (Q.D.T.A.) (1-3) over a temperature interval $(T_a - T_b$ in Figs. 1,2) may be related to the enthalpy of the process or reaction at a single reference temperature. This is necessary because in order to define the thermodynamic quantity enthalpy or heat content, H, of a substance, it is necessary to specify the temperature of the substance. Likewise, in order to define the change in this quantity, ΔH, for a reaction or process, it is necessary to define the temperature at which the process or reaction takes place. However the Q.D.T.A. measurement consists of the determination of the total heat, H_o, evolved or absorbed, by the reaction of N moles, from T_a to T_b. The problem then consists of correlating the quantity H_o/N with the thermodynamic quantity ΔH_T: the change in heat content per mole of reaction at temperature T.

In addition to H_o, Q.D.T.A. determines dH/dt, the rate of heat absorption or evolution which is related to the rate of the process or reaction by means of the equation:

$$\frac{dH}{dt} = \frac{H_T}{N} \frac{dx}{dt} \tag{1}$$

where dx/dt is the rate of the reaction in moles per unit time, and $H_T/N = \Delta H_T$, the heat of the reaction per mole at temperature T.

Equation (1) is incorporated in the appropriate rate law in order to evaluate the reaction kinetics. Since however ΔH_T is changing with temperature, (Fig. 3 gives an example of such change), the relationship between dH/dt and dx/dt is changing, and ΔH_T must be expressed as a function of temperature if equation (1), and those in which it has been incorporated, are to yield meaningful kinetic quantities such as the activation energy, ΔE, of the reaction.

In conclusion, it appears that an appropriate treatment of the raw data of Q.D.T.A. is necessary in order to reduce it to basic thermodynamic and kinetic quantities.

2. Thermodynamics

The reaction between T_a and T_b is to be referred to temperature T_R. Deciding at the outset on a method of numerical integration in order to accomplish this, the range T_a to T_b is divided into n equal intervals ΔT, Fig. 1. Then each product of ΔT_i and the ordinate $(dH/dt)_i$ at the ith interval from the beginning will represent an element of area

$$\left(\frac{dH}{dt}\right)_i \frac{\Delta T_i}{A'} \tag{2}$$

which represents the heat of the reaction of Δx_i moles at ΔT_i. A' is the heating rate or $\Delta T/\Delta t$. The heat of each element (2) may be referred to a reference small interval of temperature ΔT_R by using the thermodynamic relation:

$$\Delta H_R - \Delta H_i = \int_{T_i}^{T_R} \Delta C_p dT \tag{3}$$

where $\Delta C_p = \Sigma C_p$ (products) $- \Sigma C_p$ (reactants).

Applying (3) to each element in turn and summing we obtain:

$$\left(\frac{dH}{dt}\right)_{R,1} \frac{\Delta T_R}{A'} - \left(\frac{dH}{dt}\right)_1 \frac{\Delta T_1}{A'} = \Delta x_1 \int_{T_1}^{T_R} \Delta C_p dT$$

$$\left(\frac{dH}{dt}\right)_{R,2} \frac{\Delta T_R}{A'} - \left(\frac{dH}{dt}\right)_2 \frac{\Delta T_2}{A'} = \Delta x_2 \int_{T_1}^{T_R} \Delta C_p dT$$

$$\cdot \ \cdot \ \cdot \ \cdot \ \cdot \ \cdot \ \cdot \ \cdot \ \cdot \ \cdot \ \cdot \ \cdot \ \cdot \ \cdot \ \cdot \ \cdot \ \cdot \ \cdot \ \cdot \ \cdot$$

$$\left(\frac{dH}{dt}\right)_{R,n} \frac{\Delta T_R}{A'} - \left(\frac{dH}{dt}\right)_n \frac{\Delta T_n}{A'} = \Delta x_n \int_{T_n}^{T_R} \Delta C_p dt$$

$$H_R - H_o = \sum_{i=1}^{i=n} \Delta x_i \int_{T_i}^{T_R} \Delta C_p dT =$$

$$= \Sigma \Delta Q_T \qquad (4)$$

Thus the sum of all area elements $\left(\frac{dH}{dt}\right)_i \frac{\Delta T_i}{A'}$ approximates the total area under the curve, H_o. The sum of all reference elements $\left(\frac{dH}{dt}\right)_{R,i} \frac{\Delta T_R}{A'}$ approximates an area H_R at ΔT_R, differing from H_o by the right hand side of equation (4)

T_R, in principle, can be any temperature. However, consider the case in which T_R is such that the right hand side of equation (4) becomes equal to zero. This means that the sum of all $\Delta x_i \int_{T_i}^{T_R} \Delta C_p dT$ terms for $T_i < T_R$ equals the sum of all terms for which $T_i > T_R$. Then $H_R = H_o$

i.e. the area under the curve is replaced by an equal area at ΔT_R of width ΔT_R.

In order to set the right hand side of equation (4) equal to zero and solve for T_R, Δx must be defined. Since the heat per unit reaction is not constant between T_a and T_b a unit area at T_i, for example, involves a different number of moles Δx than the same area at T_n. Thus one mole reacting at T will cause the absorption or evolution of ΔH_T calories; Δx_T moles reacting at T will cause the evolution or absorption of $\dfrac{dH}{dt}_T$ ΔT_T calories. From simple proportionality then:

$$\Delta x_T = \frac{\left(\dfrac{dH}{dt}\right)_T \dfrac{\Delta T_T}{A'}}{\Delta H_T} \tag{5}$$

and from (3)

$$\Delta x_T = \frac{\left(\dfrac{dH}{dt}\right)_T \dfrac{\Delta T}{A'}}{\Delta H_R - \displaystyle\int_T^{T_R} \Delta C_p dt} \tag{6}$$

The heat energy, ΔQ_T, necessary to bring these Δx_T moles of reaction to T_R then will be

$$\Delta Q_T = \Delta x_T \int_T^{T_R} \Delta C_p dT \tag{7}$$

or, from (6) and (7):

$$\Delta Q_T = \frac{\left(\dfrac{dH}{dt}\right)_T \dfrac{\Delta T_T}{A'}}{\Delta H_R - \displaystyle\int_T^{T_R} \Delta C_p dT} \int_T^{T_R} \Delta C_p dT \tag{8}$$

1195

Equation (8) must be applied to each element $\left(\dfrac{dH}{dt}\right)_T \dfrac{\Delta T_T}{A'}$ from ΔT_1 to ΔT_n using known heat capacity data. According to (4), $\Delta H_R = H_o/N$ and therefore known. Thus each application of (8) results in an equation in T_R. Then all equations (8) are added and the resultant summation is equated to zero and solved for T_R.

Simplifications, Application and Discussion

In practice, it is simpler to introduce to the sum of all equations (8) a trial value for T_R and thus find a numerical result in calories which, of course, is in general different from zero. This result is plotted as a point on a plot of the sum of all equations (8), $\Sigma \Delta Q_T$, versus temperature. A repetition of this process for other values of T_R gives a line on the plot. The temperature at which this line crosses the abscissa $\Sigma \Delta Q_T = 0$ is the true T_R.

This process is applied, as an example, to the dissociation of $CaCO_3$. The Q.D.T.A. result for this reaction (2) is reproduced on Fig. 2. Values of ΔH_{298} and heat capacity data (4,5) lead to Fig. 3 which gives the variation of ΔH_T for the reaction with temperature. For the variation of ΔC_p with temperature the equation

$$\Delta C_p = -2.57 - 2 \times 10^{-3} T + 2.5 \times 10^5 \frac{1}{T^2} \tag{9}$$

is derived from literature data (4) and applied to $\Sigma \Delta Q_T$ for a number of values of T_R. The results are plotted on Fig. 4. It is seen that the line of $\Sigma \Delta Q_T = f(T)$ crosses the abscissa $\Sigma \Delta Q_T = 0$ at $T_R = 1043^\circ K$, $(770^\circ C)$.

Consideration of Fig. 3 indicates that ΔH_T, from $630^\circ C$ where the reaction begins (Fig. 2) to $820^\circ C$ where it ends, varies by approximately 2%. Under favorable circumstances, such as minimum base line drift, the experimental error in the value of H_o/N will amount to approximately $\pm$ 1%. Hence the assignment of a T_R at random between T_a and T_b (Fig. 1) can, in the case of Fig. 2, cause an error in ΔH_R of the same order of magnitude as the experimental error. Therefore the determination of T_R as indicated here is worthwhile. Usually however reactions cover a range less than 200°C and the necessity for the exact determination of T_R is less. Thus in many cases T_R could be approximated with sufficient accuracy by considering as T_R the temperature that divides the Q.D.T.A. peak into two halves of approximately equal area. Had this been done in the case of Fig. 2, T_R would have been found to be equal to 1053°K instead of 1043°K. From Fig. 3 it is seen that the difference in ΔH_T between these two temperatures is only 40 cal or approximately 0.1% of ΔH_{1043}.

Equation (8) is greatly simplified if two approximations can be made:

$$1. \quad \Delta C_p \cong const. = \alpha$$

$$2. \quad \Delta H_R \gg \int_{T_i}^{T_R} \Delta C_p dT$$

The first approximation leads to a linear variation of ΔH_T with temperature, equation (3) acquiring the form $\Delta H_T = A + BT$. Consideration of Fig. 3 between 900°K and 1100°K, the range in which the reaction used here as an example took place, indicates that indeed the change of ΔH_T with temperature is nearly linear. This behavior is not unusual for reactions at high temperatures and the validity of the first approximation may be quite general.

The second approximation may also be of general validity. In the example used here it was seen that ΔH_R is larger than the integral of ΔC_p by at least two orders of magnitude.

Then it can be shown readily that:

1. T_R is coincident with the center (or axis) of gravity of the Q.D.T.A. peak.

2. T_R is independent of the magnitude of ΔC_p (i.e. ΔC_p need not be known).

Equation (8) can now be written as:

$$\sum_{i=1}^{i=n} \Delta Q_{T_i} = \frac{\alpha}{\Delta H_R} \sum_{i=1}^{i=n} \left(\frac{dH}{dt}\right)_i \frac{\Delta T_i}{A'} \cdot (T_R - T_i) = 0 \qquad (9A)$$

where $\left(\dfrac{dH}{dt}\right)_i \dfrac{\Delta T_i}{A'}$ = area element = ΔS_i

Solving (9A) for T_R:

$$T_R \sum_i \Delta S_i = \sum_i T_i \Delta S_i$$

and

$$T_R = \frac{\sum\limits_i T_i \Delta S_i}{\sum\limits_i \Delta S_i} \qquad (9B)$$

which is the definition of center of gravity. Indeed by cutting out a tracing or Xerox copy of Fig. 2 and balancing it on a knife edge - held parallel to the ordinate - it is found that the figure is balanced to within one or two degrees of T_R at $1043^{\circ}K$ $(770^{\circ}C)$.

Rewriting equation (9A) in general form for any T_y:

$$\sum_i \Delta Q_{T_i} = \frac{\alpha}{\Delta H_R} \left(\sum_i \Delta S_i\right) T_y - \frac{\alpha}{\Delta H_R} \sum_i T_i \Delta S_i$$

A plot of $\sum \Delta Q_{T_i}$ vs. T_y will give a straight line (Fig. 4) with slope $(\alpha/\Delta H_R)\sum\limits_i \Delta S_i$. As before, $T_y = T_R$ is given by equation (9B) which does not contain α.

This conclusion is shown to be true by repeating the calculations that led to the plot of Fig. 4, i.e. utilizing again equation (8), but using only the first term of equation (9) for ΔC_p, namely -2.57. The result is the dashed line on Fig. 4. It is seen that the value of T_R thus determined is undistinguishable from that obtained by utilizing the entire expression of equation (9). It is to be noted that the same values for each $(dH/dt)_i (\Delta T_i/A')$

1198

element were used for both sets of calculations, hence this agreement is not due to fortuitous compensation of errors.

The non-dependence of T_R on ΔC_p is demonstrated again (and equation (9A) further simplified) by redetermining T_R using $\Delta C_p = \alpha = -1$. It is seen on Fig. 4 that the same value of T_R is obtained.

3. Kinetics

Equation (1) is incorporated in whatever rate law is deemed applicable in order to evaluate the kinetics of the reaction or process. Thus in each different case the treatment of Q.D.T.A. data will be different. However all cases will involve the necessity of finding the correspondence between H and dH, and the kinetic parameter under study such as x and dx (moles) or 1 and dl (length of interface migration).

An example of the determination of such correspondence is given below. In another investigation (2) the kinetic rate law $dx/dt = k(a-x)^n$ (10) was used in order to obtain, in conjunction with equation (1), the relation $k = (dH/dt)/[\Delta H_R^{1-n}(H_0-H)^n] = A\exp(-\Delta E/RT)$ (11)

The application of (11) as it stands, implies that the heat per "unit" reaction represented by a unit area under the curve of Fig. 1 is constant with temperature from T_a to T_b. As was shown in the past section this is not correct. Hence (11) must be re-derived taking the findings of the previous section into consideration.

Deciding once again on the same method of numerical integration, equation (10) is approximated as follows: $\Delta x/\Delta t = k(\alpha-x)^n$ (12). Δx at temperature T, Δx_T, had been

given by equation (6). Hence

$$\Delta x_T/\Delta t = (dH/dt)_T/[\Delta H_R - \int_T^{T_R} \Delta C_p dT] = F \quad (13)$$

where $A' = \Delta T_T/\Delta t_T$ i.e. the heating rate of the Q.D.T.A. experiment in $^\circ C/sec$. x in equation (12) is simply the number of moles that have reacted up to time t and is therefore given by:

$$x = \sum_{T=T_a}^{T=T} \Delta x_T \tag{14}$$

$$x = \sum_{T=T_a}^{T=T} (dH/dt)_T (\Delta T_T/A') \Big/ \Big[\Delta H_R - \int_T^{T_R} \Delta C_p dT \Big] \tag{15}$$

Likewise

$$a = \sum_{T=T_a}^{T=T_b} (dH/dt)_T (\Delta T_T/A') \Big/ \Big[\Delta H_R - \int_T^{T_R} \Delta C_p dT \Big] \tag{16}$$

Incorporating (13), (15) and (16) into (12), solving for k and equating to the Arrhenius equation the final result is obtained:

$$k = F \Big/ \sum_{T=T}^{T=T_b} [F(\Delta T_T/A')]^n = A\exp\left(-\frac{\Delta E}{RT}\right) \tag{17}$$

Application and Discussion

Equation (17) contains the expressions used for the determination of T_R in the previous section. Hence the treatment of both the kinetic and thermodynamic results from a given Q.D.T.A. experiment can be done in one operation.

In general the magnitude of the correction, i.e. the difference between equations (11) and (17), will depend on the magnitudes of ΔCp, n, $(T_a - T_b)$ and k. It is expected that, in the usual case, this correction will be unnecessary and that the results of most past Q.D.T.A. investigations can stand uncorrected. For example, application of both equations (11) and (17) to the results of Fig. 2 gave Arrhenius plots (using n = 0.2) on Fig. 5 that are indistinguishable at the scale of the figure. However, re-application of these equations to the same results, but using a value of n = 1 instead of 0.2, resulted in the plot of Fig. 6 showing significant differences between corrected (equation (17)) and uncorrected (equation (11)) points, the difference increasing with increasing values of k.

4. Conclusions

The thermodynamic and kinetic reduction of Q.D.T.A. data described here will be necessary only in special cases. However from the conceptual or fundamental point of view it is important because, in answering the basic questions raised in the introduction section, it contributes to the fundamental validity of Q.D.T.A. results.

Although the derivation of relations (8) and (17) is straight forward their application to actual experimental data is laborious and complex. However part of the labor involves operations normally performed in the routine evaluation of the kinetic data (numerical integration) and part of the complexity may be avoided by applying the simplifications indicated. It is interesting to note that even at their complete form these reductions represent a fraction of the labor and complexity usually associated with the reduction of calorimetric results as for example the application of the "Washburn Correction" (6,7) to results obtained by bomb calorimetry.

As is usual with numerical integration methods, the calculated maximum additive error in applying the correction can exceed the error introduced by choosing a random T_R.

Acknowledgments

The collaboration of R. H. Springer is gratefully acknowledged. E. O. Davis did the computational work involved. Thanks are due to A. E. Newkirk, D. A. Butter and W. E. Smyser for discussions and assistance.

References

1. R. C. Wilhoit, J. Chem. Educ. <u>44</u>, A853, A863 (1967).

2. D. M. Speros and R. L. Woodhouse, a) Nature <u>197</u>, 1261
    (March 1963), b) J. Phys. Chem. <u>67</u>, 2164 (1963),
    c) U.S. Patent No. 3,319,456, May 16, 1967, d) A Study
    of the Reaction $CaCO_3 \rightleftarrows CaO + CO_2$, J. Phys. Chem. <u>72</u>,
    Aug. (1968).

3. D. M. Speros, R. L. Hickok and J. R. Cooper; A Study
    of the Reaction $2"CaHPO_4" \rightarrow Ca_2P_2O_7 + H_2O$, 6th
    International Symposium on the Reactivity of Solids
    (August 1968).

4. O. Kubaschewski and E. L. Evans, "Metallurgical
    Thermochemistry", Pergamon Press, New York, N.Y., 1958.

5. K. K. Kelley, U.S. Bureau of Mines Bulletin 584, U.S.
    Government Printing Office, Washington, D.C., 1960.

6. E. W. Washburn, J. Research Natl. Bur. Standards <u>10</u>,
    525 (1933).

7. N. W. Hubbard, D. W. Scott, and G. Waddington, J. Phys.
    Chem. <u>58</u>, 152 (1954).

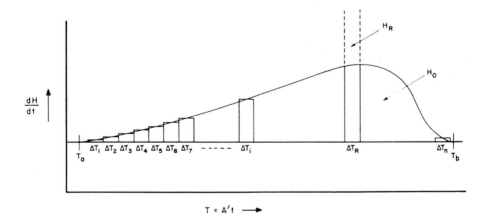

Fig. 1. Numerical integration of Q.D.T.A. peak.

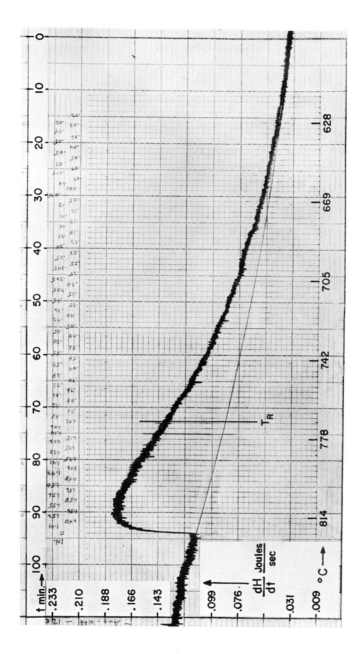

Fig. 2. Q.D.T.A. record of the thermal decomposition of $CaCO_3$.

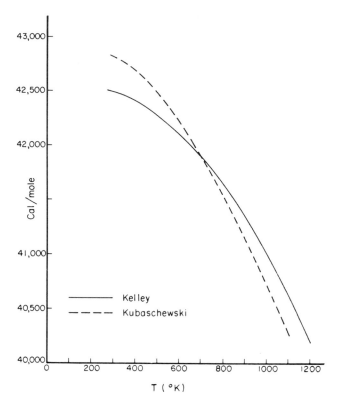

Fig. 3. The change of ΔH_T with temperature for the decomposition of $CaCO_3$.

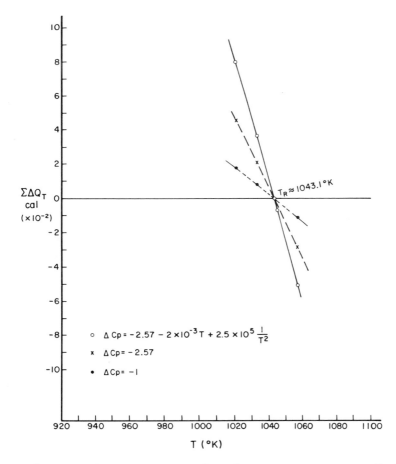

Fig. 4. The determination of reference temperature T_R by graphical solution of equation (8).

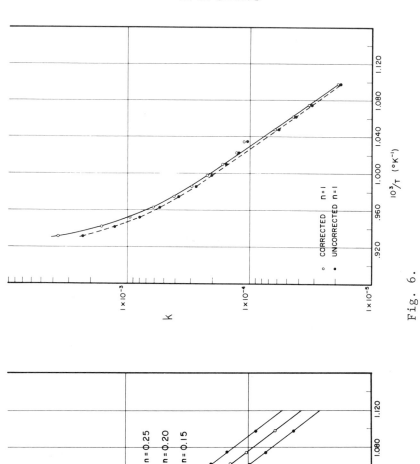

Fig. 6. Arrhenius plot of data obtained from Fig. 2, utilizing equations (11) and (17) for n = 1.0.

Fig. 5. Arrhenius plot of data obtained from Fig. 2, utilizing equations (11) and (17) for n = 0.2.

DECOMPOSITION MECHANISM OF Mg(OH)$_2$ AND Mg(OD)$_2$ I.

Friedemann Freund [+] and Hans Nägerl[++]

Introduction

The dehydration of Mg(OH)$_2$ has been the object of a number of papers published in the past few years. Recent publications are those of GORDON and KINGERY (1,2), who investigated mainly the kinetics of the decomposition, and BRETT and ANDERSON (3). References to earlier work on the subject will be found in these papers. On the basis of their results, BRETT and ANDERSON (3) reject the so-called inhomogeneous dehydration mechanism forwarded earlier by BALL and TAYLOR (4) without, however, adding new aspects to the discussion. FREUND (5) presented the view that the dehydration reaction should actually consist of two subsequent steps, the first being the formation of H$_2$O molecules from the OH$^-$-groups within the lattice, the second being the removal of these H$_2$O molecules from the lattice.

The initial proton transfer necessary to form H$_2$O molecules out of OH$^-$-groups is thought to take place via a tunnelling process:

eq. [1] $[OH^-] + [OH^-] \leftrightharpoons [O^{2-}] + [H_2O]$

The braquets symbolize lattice sites. The subsequent removal of the H$_2$O molecules formed after

[+] Institute of Inorganic Chemistry, University, 34 Göttingen, Hospitalstr. 10 Germany

[++] Fourth Institute of Physics, University, 34 Göttingen, Bunsenstr. 13 Germany

eq.[1] should then be a diffusion process leading at first to unoccupied anionic lattice sites (symbolized by empty braquets):

eq. [2] $[H_2O] \rightarrow [\quad] + H_2O_{gas}$

The empty lattice sites will eventually disappear in the course of recrystallization reactions (6).

The assumption that tunnelling plays a vital role in the complex dehydration reaction leads to an understanding of the nature of the residual OH^--groups, which are found up to high temperatures in all dehydration experiments (7). The same concept may be applicable to the question of thermal stability of any hydroxide compound (8).

Comparison between Mg(OH)$_2$ and Mg(OD)$_2$

Recently MORGAN (9) pointed out that the kinetic data of the dehydration of $Mg(OH)_2$ and $Mg(OD)_2$ show no measurable difference over the temperature range from 250 - 350°C. Fig 1 shows the Arrhenius plot for the dehydration of $Mg(OH)_2$ and $Mg(OD)_2$ after MORGAN (9).

The absence of an isotopic effect seems to be incompatible with the assumption that the initial dehydration step depends upon proton, respectively deuteron, tunnelling. In any tunnelling process involving isotopes of different masses one would expect to find an influence of the mass of the tunnelling particle upon the tunnelling probability, and hence upon the rate constant.

The tunnelling probability $\pi^o_{n_i}$ of a particle of mass m is given by

eq. [3] $\pi^o_{n_i} \sim \exp -(\dfrac{2}{\hbar} \displaystyle\int_{x_1}^{x_2} \sqrt{2m\, \Delta E_i(x)}\ dx)$

where $\Delta E_i(x)$ is the height and (x_2-x_1) the width of the actual potential barrier at the tunnelling level n_i. $\hbar$ is the Planck constant.

Application of the mean value theorem replaces
the actual "rounded-of" barrier by an equivalent
rectangular barrier and thus reduces eq. [3] to:

eq. [4] $\pi_{n_i}^{o} \sim \exp -(\frac{2l_i}{\hbar} \sqrt{2m \, \Delta E_i(red)} \,)$

where $\Delta E_i(red)$ and l_i are the height and the
width of the barrier over the tunnelling level n_i.

Since the mass of the deuteron is twice that of
the proton, wherever tunnelling occurs in the
manner described by eqs. [3] and [4], a marked
isotopic effect is to be expected.

As stated above, the dehydration of a hydroxide
is probably a complex reaction sequence involving
at least two subsequent steps, eq. [1] and eq.[2].
Each step is characterized by its particular
reaction constant. The kinetics of the total process will be governed by the slowest reaction
step, which is said to be "rate-controlling".
In case the second step, eq.[2], is rate-controlling, the anticipated isotopic effect on the
kinetic data may well be too small to be detected,
due to the relatively small difference in masses
between H_2O and D_2O. The diffusion coefficient
for H_2O and D_2O will differ only by a factor 1.05.

We can therefore, tentatively, conclude that the
absence of an isotopic effect in the dehydration
characteristics of $Mg(OH)_2$ and $Mg(OD)_2$ might be
due to the fact that the diffusion of the molecular species, H_2O and D_2O following eq. [2], is
always the rate controlling step.

However, this argument still does not solve the
problem raised by the postulated sequence of two
subsequent reaction steps. Before any H_2O, respectively D_2O, molecule can start to diffuse and
eventually escape from the lattice (which is
what one actually measures in dehydration experiments), it must have been formed by some proton,
respectively deuteron, transfer process. In other
words, the tunnelling process, being the initial
step, should play the rôle of the "triggering"

step of the whole dehydration reaction. But if it were so, the absence of an isotopic effect in the kinetic data is puzzling. Again the question rises whether tunnelling occurs at all.

Yet, we shall try to show that our reasoning so far is not conclusive. It does not suffice to reject tunnelling all together.

Eqs. [3] and [4] describe the tunnelling of a particle under the strict assumption that the filled donator level n_i coincides with the unfilled acceptor level n_i^+ on the energy scale. Only then the wave functions assigned to the mass particle on the filled and the unfilled level, respectively, will overlap, leading to a mass transfer. Evidently, the proton is bonded more strongly in an OH^--group than it is in an H_2O molecule in similar surroundings. The two protons attached to one oxygen ion interact in such a way as to weaken the O-H-bond. Taking, as it is postulated in eq.[1], the OH^--group and the H_2O molecule on crystallographically equivalent positions, the zero-point energy levels, n_0 and n_0^+ will not overlap on the energy scale. Therefore, tunnelling will normally not be possible on the zero-point level. However, in the second part of this paper (to be published later) we shall show that coupling of the OH stretching vibration with lattice modes may lead to an overlap, and hence tunnelling, on the zero-point level(10).

Tunnelling Using Higher Excited Levels

In the present paper we shall extend eqs.[3] and [4] and thus arrive to a possible mechanism which could explain the absence (or smallness) of the isotopic effect and yet involve tunnelling.

In fig. 2 the double potential well is shown schematically for a proton transfer between a pair of OH^--groups as described by eq.[1]. It is assumed that the donator group is on the left

hand side. The zero-energy levels are shown not
to coincide in fig. 2, but the first excited
level n_1 coincides with one of the n_i^+-sublevels.
This is a special assumption, but it can be
justified by the mismatch between the energy
levels on the donator and the acceptor side.

Under these conditions tunnelling will become
possible on the first excited level or any higher
level n_i which happens to coincide with any n_i^+-
sublevel. Since the width of the separating
barrier, (x_2-x_1), and its height ΔE_i decrease
with increasing i , for a particle, being at the
higher level, tunnelling becomes easier. On the
other hand, the chances to reach higher energy
levels decreases with increasing i.

The population density of the i-th excited level,
π_{n_i} of a harmonic oscillator is given by:

eq. [5] $\qquad \pi_{n_i} \sim \exp\left(-\dfrac{i \cdot \hbar \cdot \nu}{2 \cdot k \cdot T}\right)$

where ν denotes in our particular case the OH-
respectively OD-stretching frequencies. $\hbar$, k,
and T have their usual meanings as Planck constant, Boltzmann constant and absolute temperature.

At the starting temperature of the dehydration of
$Mg(OH)_2$ and $Mg(OD)_2$, 250°C corresponding to
approximately 530°K, eq.[5] gives for the population density of the first excited level values
of 0.7 % for the OH- and 2.1 % for the OD-
stretching mode. At 630°K these values increase
to 1.5 and 4.3 % respectively. The occupancy of
higher levels can be neglected.

Multiplying eqs.[4] and [5], we obtain an expression for the total transfer probability π_{n_1}
on the first excited level:

eq. [6] $\quad \pi_{n_1} \sim \exp\left(-\dfrac{2 l_1}{\hbar}\sqrt{m \, \Delta E_1(\text{red})}\right) \cdot \exp\left(-\dfrac{\hbar}{2kT}\right)$

where the first term is a constant.

In fig 3, $\log \pi_{n_1}$ is plotted against $1/T$ for protons and deuterons. This plot exhibits an interesting feature: it shows two intersecting lines for protons and deuterons respectively. The total transfer probability for deuterons is larger at low temperatures than that for protons, and it is smaller at high temperatures. For very high temperatures the temperature-dependent term, eq.[5], goes to unity, so that the intercept with the ordinate is mainly determined by the magnitude of l_i and ΔE_i(red).

The value of l_1 can be estimated roughly from crystallographic data. ΔE_i(red) is the height of the barrier above the tunnelling level n_i. The highest possible value of ΔE_i is given by the dissociation energy of the free OH^--ion. With reasonable assumptions as to the magnitude of l_1 and ΔE_1(red), the two lines in fig. 3 intersect at a rather small angle, and their point of intersection falls within the temperature range between 0 - 500°C.

This leads us to some important conclusions as to the kinetic data. Even if we assume that the tunnelling step is rate controlling over the whole temperature range, no isotopic effect is to expected according to eq.[6]. The temperature range which can be experimentally covered extends only over one hundred degrees, from about 250 - 350°C. If this temperature range is near the point of intersection, as it appears to be on the basis of our estimate, the isotopic effect will be undetectable.

In case the tunnelling step is rate controlling, the total transfer probability, given by eq.[6], can be directly related to the rate constant k shown in fig. 1. Fig 3 would then in fact depict a theoretical Arrhenius plot for the dehydration of $Mg(OH)_2$ and $Mg(OD)_2$, but extended over a much larger temperature range.than the one that can be covered experimentally.

Conclusions

The absence of an isotopic effect in the dehydration kinetics of $Mg(OH)_2$ and $Mg(OD)_2$ does not
rule out the possibility that the dehydration
reaction is a two step process with an initial
proton transfer, operative by tunnelling. If we
assume that tunnelling takes place on the first
excited level of the OH- respectively OD-stretching mode, a temperature-dependent term enters the
expression of the total transfer probability. At
low temperatures, the tunnelling probability for
deuterons is higher than for protons. At high
temperatures, it is the reverse.

In an intermediate temperature range, into which
the actual dehydration temperature of $Mg(OH)_2$
appears to fall, the two curves intersect. In
this temperature range, the total transfer probability for protons and deuterons is nearly the
same, so that no isotopic effect can be observed.

The model suffers from the fact that the actual
shape of the potential barrier between two adjacent OH^--groups is not exactly known. The
temperature at which the two curves, mentioned
above, intersect reacts very sensitively to small
variations in the values of l_i and ΔE_i (red).
Therefore, we would like to emphazise more on the
principle character of this model, rather than on
quantitative results.

An extension of this model, taking into account
coupling between the OH-stretching mode and
lattice vibrations, will be published later (10).

References

1. R. S. Gordon and W. D. Kingery: Thermal Decomposition of Brucite (I) J. Amer. Ceram. Soc. 49, 654, (1966)

2. R. S. Gordon and W. D. Kingery: Thermal Decomposition of Brucite (II) J. Amer. Ceram. Soc. 50, 8, (1967)

3. N. H. Brett and P. J. Anderson: Mechanism of Decomposition of Brucite, Trans. Faraday Soc. 63, 2044, (1967)

4. M. C. Ball and H. F. W. Taylor: Thermal Decomposition of Brucite, Minerol. Mag. 32, 754, (1961)

5. F. Freund: Zum Entwässerungsmechanismus von Hydroxiden, Ber. Dtsch. Keram. Ges. 42, 23, (1965)

6. F. Freund: Kaolinit - Metakaolinit, Modellfall eines Festkörpers mit extrem hohen Störstellenkonzentrationen, Ber. Dtsch. Keram. Ges. 44, 5, (1967)

7. F. Freund: Retention of Hydroxyl Groups on Magnesium Oxide, J. Amer. Ceram. Soc. 50, 494, (1967)

8. F. Freund: Zur thermischen Stabilität von Hydroxiden, Fortschr. chem. Forschg. 10, 347, (1968)

9. personal communication 1968

10. F. Freund and H. Nägerl: Decomposition Mechanism of $Mg(OH)_2$ and $Mg(OD)_2$ II, to be published

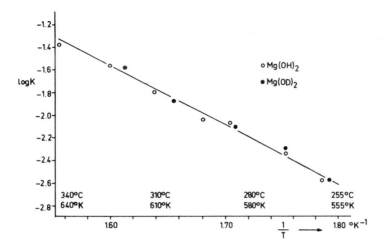

Fig. 1 Arrhenius Plot for the Dehydration of
$Mg(OH)_2$ and $Mg(OD)_2$ after MORGAN (9).

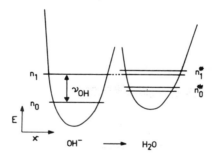

Fig. 2 Double Minimum Potential Curve for the
Proton Transfer According to eq.[1]

1215

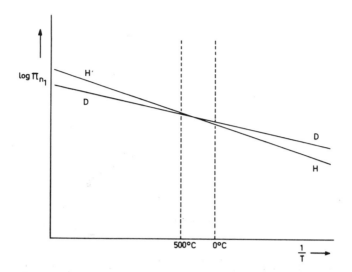

Fig. 3   Total Transfer Probability for Protons
(curve H) and for Deuterons (curve D)
Assuming Tunnelling on the First Excited
Level.

SECTION 5

MINERALS

Chairman:

D. J. Swaine

DIFFERENTIAL-THERMO ANALYSE VON GEMISCHEN AUS FESTEN BRENNSTOFFEN MIT OXIDATIONSMITTELN UND INHIBITOREN

D. Rustschev[+] und K. Jetschewa

chemisch-technologisches Institut

Sofia-56 Bulgarien

Abstract

Even during the last century it was known that solid fuels can undergo self-ignition. The use of a number of chemical substances (inhibitors, etc) is suggested in order to protect the solid fuels from self-ignition.

Differential thermal studies of mixtures of various solid fuels (peat, lignite, brown, coal, bituminous coal and anthracitic coal) with the oxidising agent $NaNO_2$ and inhibitors ($\beta-C_{10}H_7OH$, C_6H_5OH, $NaCl$, Na_2SO_4, Na_2SO_3, Na_2S, $NaHSO_3$ Na_2CO_3, $(NH_4)_2CO_3$, $CaCO_3$ and $MgCO_3$) were carried out. The effects inhibition was estimated by the temperature rise of the marked exothermal effects ($\Delta T = T-T_o$).

ß-Naphthol has a marked inhibiting effect on peat and anthracite (ΔT = 114 and 74 °C respectively). The common Phenol (C_6H_5OH) has proved itself to be a good inhibitor for peat, lignite and weak caking bituminous coal (ΔT = 40, 16 and 11 °C respectively). The inhibiting effect of a dilute solution of Na_2S (0,01 %) on lignite and bituminous coal (ΔT = 46 an 14 °C respectively) is to

---

[+] Presently at Engler-Bunte, Institut, Karlsruhe, Germany

be attributed to its ability to oxidize easily, as
well as to the liberation by hydrolysis of H_2S,
which poisons the active centres of the catalytic
mineral complexes and by this manner retards the
progress of the oxidising chain reaction. The sup-
pression of the oxidation process by the addition
of some inhibitors to peat can be clearly seen
from the differential curves.

Schon im vorigen Jahrhundert war bekannt, daß fe-
ste Brennstoffe sich von selbst entzünden können.
Eine deutsche Statistik (1) zeigt, daß allein vom
Jahre 1889 bis 1896 155 Schiffe untergegangen
sind, die mit Kohle beladen waren, 44 davon brann-
ten infolge Selbstentzündung der Kohle aus. Neuere
Mitteilungen (2) zeigen gleichfalls, daß die meis-
ten Brände in den Kohlengruben auf die Selbstentzünd-
lichkeit der Kohle zurückzuführen sind; von 1950 bis
1960 wurden im niederrheinisch-westfälischen Stein-
kohlenrevier 431 Brände registriert, von welchen 372,
d.h. 86 % durch Selbstentzündung der Kohle verursacht
wurden.

In einer vorangehenden Arbeit (3) wurde gefunden, daß
durch DTA Veränderungen in der Kohle festgestellt
werden konnten, die durch Oxydation während einer
vierjährigen Lagerzeit verursacht worden waren.
Später wurden andere thermische Untersuchungen an
Gemischen verschiedener fester Brennstoffe mit $NaNO_2$
durchgeführt (4), die die Beurteilung ihrer Bestän-
digkeit gegenüber Oxydation und gegen Entzündung ge-
statteten.

Die vorliegenden Untersuchungen von Gemischen fester
Brennstoffe verschiedener Herkunft und Alters mit
dem Oxydationsmittel $NaNO_2$ und Inhibitoren (C_6H_5OH,
Na_2SO_3, Na_2S, $NaHSO_3$, $ß-C_{16}H_7OH$, $NaCl$ u.a.) wurden
durchgeführt um eine neue Methode zur Feststellung
der Stabilität fester Brennstoffe gegenüber Oxydation und Selbstentzündung zu entwickeln und für die
Praxis geeignete Inhibitoren aufzufinden, die mit
Erfolg die festen Brennstoffe vor der Selbstentzündung dieser Prozesse schützen können.

In Zahlentafel 1 sind die Analysendaten angegeben für den Torf und für die Lignit-, Stein- und Anthrazitkohle, mit denen die vorliegenden Untersuchungen durchgeführt wurden. Die für die Differential-thermoanalyse benutzte Apparatur ist in vorangehenden Arbeiten (5 - 7) ausführlich beschrieben worden.

Zahlentafel 1

Charakteristik der festen Ausgangsbrennstoffe

Art der festen Brennstoffe und Herkunft	Feuchtigkeit, %	Asche, % (wf)	Flüchtige Bestandteile, % (waf)	Gesamtschwefel, %
1. Torf aus Vorkommen "Baikal"	11,33	47,00	70,16	0,52
2. Lignitkohle Vorkommen "Mariza–Ost"	14,30	27,80	60,10	4,64
3. Bituminöse Braunkohle a. d. Grube "Schwarzes Meer"	7,29	30,80	63,61	3,86
4. Steinkohle:				
a) Gaskohle	3,32	10,53	37,10	0,93
b) Esskohle	0,76	12,31	17,70	1,86
5. Anthrazit v. d. Grube "Swoge"	3,47	26,18	2,10	1,20

Zuerst wurden die Differential-Thermogramme der festen Ausgangsbrennstoffe im Gemisch mit 2o% $NaNO_2$ bestimmt. Anschließend wurden diese Proben mit wässrigen Lösungen verschiedener Inhibitoren (C_6H_5OH, Na_2SO_4, ß-$C_{10}H_7OH$, NaCl, Na_2SO_3, Na_2CO_3, $(NH_4)_2CO_3$ und $NaHSO_3$), sowie mit 2o %igen Suspensionen von $CaCO_3$ und einem Gemisch von $MgCO_3$ und $CaCO_3$ (1:1) behandelt. Zu diesem Zweck wurden 5 g des gemahlenen Brennstoffs mit 5 ml der Inhibitorlösung bzw. mit lo ml Suspension benetzt und das erhaltene Gemisch 6o Minuten gerührt. Nach dem Filtrieren wurde die Probe mit 25 ml destilliertem Wasser gewaschen und bei Zimmertemperatur getrocknet. Die auf

1221

diese Weise inhibierten festen Brennstoffe wurden mit 2o % $NaNO_2$ vermischt und von neuem der DTA unterworfen. Die Beurteilung der Wirksamkeit der Inhibitoren erfolgte auf Grund der beobachteten Temperaturerhöhung, bei der das Maximum des stark geprägten exothermen Effekts wahrgenommen wird.

In Abb. 1, 2 und 3 sind einige D-Thermogramme der untersuchten Brennstoffe ohne und mit Inhibitoren dargestellt. In Zahlentafel 2 sind die beobachteten Temperaturunterschiede in den Maxima des exothermen Effekts, nach welchem man die Inhibitoren bewerten kann, angeführt.

Eine besonders starke inhibierende Wirkung bei Torf und Anthrazit hat ß-Naphtol ($\Delta T=114$, bzw. $74^{\circ}C$). Es wurde nachgewiesen, daß die antiseptisch wirkenden Stoffe (Phenole u.a.) den anfänglichen Oxydationsprozeß der Selbsterwärmung beim Torf, für den man annimmt, daß er einen bakteriellen Charakter hat, unterdrücken. Außerdem sind die mehrwertigen Phenole die wirkungsvollsten Inhibitoren für Oxydationsreaktionen. Das gewöhnliche Phenol (C_6H_5OH) hat sich als guter Inhibitor für Torf und für die Lignit- Eßkohle erwiesen. ($\Delta T=44,16$ resp. 11 $^{\circ}C$). Seine Wirkung auf die Oxydation der Anthrazitkohle ist jedoch ziemlich schwach ($\Delta T= 3$ $^{\circ}C$).

Die inhibierende Wirkung von NaCl beschränkt sich auf Torf ($\Delta T= 7o$ $^{\circ}C$) und Braunkohle ($\Delta T= 11$ $^{\circ}C$). Eine mögliche Erklärung wäre, daß durch Ionenaustausch Salzsäure entsteht, die die Oxydation behindert. Eine inhibierende Wirkung des NaCl auf Steinkohlen war praktisch nicht festzustellen.

Na_2SO_3 bzw. $NaHSO_3$ hat auf Lignit ($\Delta T = 1o$) Braunkohle ($\Delta T = 5o$), Steinkohle ($\Delta T = 36$ und Anthrazit ($\Delta T = 19$) eine gut inhibierende Wirkung. Die Wirkung der Sulfit- und Bisulfitlösungen basiert auf ihrer Leichten Oxydierbarkeit. Sie können aber nur bei niederschwefligen Kohlen Anwendung finden, weil sie zur Erhöhung des Schwefelgehaltes führen.

Die inhibierende Wirkung von Na_2S (o,o1 %) auf Torf und Steinkohle ($\Delta T= 46$ und 14 $^{\circ}C$) ist sowohl auf die leichte Oxydierbarkeit wie auch auf den bei der

Zahlentafel 2

Wirkung verschiedener Inhibitore auf Torf,
Lignit– Braun– und Steinkohlen

Art des festen Brennstoffs u. des Inhibitors	Maximum des exothermen Effekts, $^{\circ}C$		
	ohne Inbibitor T_o	mit Inhibitor T	Temperaturunterschied ($\triangle T=T-T_o$)
1. Torf a. Vork. "Baikal"	304	–	–
5 %ige Lösung von β-$C_{10}H_7OH$	–	418	114
Suspension v. $MgCO_3$ u. $CaCO_3$	–	408	104
Suspension von $CaCO_3$	–	395	91
1, 0 %ige Lösung v. NaCl	–	347	70
2, 5 %ige Lösung v. Na_2SO_4	–	374	70
0, 01 %ige Lösung v. Na_2S	–	350	46
2,0 %ige Lösung v. C_6H_5OH	–	348	44
2. Lignitkohle von "Mariza–Ost"	387	–	–
Suspension von $MgCO_3$ und $CaCO_3$	–	414	27
2,0 %ige Lösung v. C_6H_5OH	–	403	16
Suspension von $CaCO_3$	–	403	16
2, 5 %ige Lösung v. Na_2SO_3	–	397	10
3. Braunkohle v.d. Grube "Schwarzes Meer"	394	–	–
Suspension v. $MgCO_3$ und $CaCO_3$	–	450	56
2, 5 %ige Lösung v. Na_2SO_3	–	444	50
1,0 %ige Lösung v. NaCl	–	405	11
2, 5 %ige Lösung v. Na_2CO_3	–	400	6
2, 5 %ige Lösung v. $(NH_4)_2CO_3$	–	398	4
4. Gaskohle	456	–	–
5 %ige Lösung v. β-$C_{10}H_7OH$	–	517	61
Suspension v. $CaCO_3$	–	473	17
0, 01 %ige Lösung v. Na_2S	–	470	14
5. Esskohle	496	–	–
2, 5 %ige Lösung v. $NaHSO_3$	–	532	36
2, 5 %ige Lösung v. C_6H_5OH	–	510	14
1, 0 %ige Lösung v NaCl	–	498	2

6. Anthrazit v.d. Grube "Swoge"	497	–	–
5, 0 %ige Lösung von β-$C_{10}H_7OH$	–	571	74
2, 5 %ige Lösung v. $NaHSO_3$	–	516	19
2,0 %ige Lösung v. C_6H_5OH	–	500	3
2, 5 %ige Lösung v. Na_2SO_4	–	500	3
Suspension v. $CaCO_3$	–	496	– 1

Hydrolyse entstehenden H_2S zurückzuführen, der die aktiven Zentren der katalytischen Mineralkomplexe vergiftet und auf diese Weise den Verlauf der Oxydationsreaktionen verzögert. Die Phenole sind gleichfalls als Gifte für diese Katalysatoren anzusehen.

Eine stark inhibierende Wirkung auf Torf haben die Suspensionen von $MgCO_3$ und $CaCO_3$ (ΔT= lo4, resp. 91 ^{O}C). Die Carbonatsuspensionen sind ebenfalls ein effektives Mittel zur Verhinderung der Oxydation von Braun- und Lignitkohle (ΔT= 56, resp. 27 ^{O}C). Sie können auch bei der Gaskohle Verwendung finden (ΔT= 17°C), inkohlten Steinkohle wie Anthrazitkohle tritt ihre schützende Wirkung jedoch nicht auf (ΔT= -1 ^{O}C). Eine verhältnismäßig schwächere inhibierende Wirkung haben die wässrigen Lösungen von Carbonaten (Na_2CO_3 und $(NH_4)_2CO_3$, die bei Braunkohle untersucht wurden (ΔT= 6, resp. 4 ^{O}C)

Die Unterdrückung der Oxydationsprozesse bei Zugabe von Inhibitoren ist aus den Differentialthermogrammen des Torfs besonders klar zu ersehen. Vor dem stark ausgedrückten Exoeffekt infolge der $MaNO_2$-Wirkung sind ein oder zwei Endoeffekte zu beobachten (Abb. 1, Kurven b, c, d), die im Temperaturintervall zwischen 3lo bis 368 ^{O}C registriert wurden. Diese Effekte hängen von der Stärke der ablaufenden endo- und exothermen Prozesse und ihrem Verhältnis zueinander ab. Die Zugabe von Inhibitoren inkohlten Kohlen beeinflußt fast nicht das allgemeine Aussehen ihrer Differentialkurven; sie verschiebt nur das Maximum des exothermen Effekts gegen höhere Temperaturen (Abb. 3).

Schlußfolgerungen

1. Es wurden von Gemischen aus unterschiedlichen festen Brennstoffen (Torf, Lignit-, Braun-, Stein- und Anthrazitkohle) mit dem Oxydationsmittel $NaNO_2$ und Inhibitoren ($\beta-C_{10}H_7OH$, C_6H_5OH, $NaCl$, Na_2SO_4, Na_2SO_3, Na_2S, $NaHSO_3$, Na_2CO_3, $(NH_4)_2CO_3$, $CaCO_3$, $MgCO_3$) durchgeführt. Die inhibierende Wirkung wurde nach dem Ausmaß der Verschiebung des stark ausgeprägten exothermen Effekts nach höheren Temperaturen ($\Delta T= T-T_o$) beurteilt.

2. Es wurde festgestellt, daß das $\beta-C_{10}H_7OH$ eine besonders starke inhibierende Wirkung auf Torf und Anthrazit hat. Die Carbonatsuspensionen ($MgCO_3$ und $CaCO_3$) sind bei Braun-, Lignit- und Gaskohle ziemlich wirkungsvoll wesentlich weniger jedoch beim Anthrazit. Na_2SO_3/NaHSO sind geeignete Inhibitoren für die Braun-,Eß- und Anthrazitkohle. Na_2S kann sowohl beim Torf, als auch bei der Gaskohle und das $NaCl$ - beim Torf und der Braunkohle angewendet werden.

L i t e r a t u r

1. Deutsche Spediteur- und Reederzeiting, 6 (1897)

2. H. Bücher, Glückauf, **98**, 1399 (1962)

3. D. Roustschev, Chimie analytique, **47**, 243 (1965)

4. D. Rustschev und Ph. Philippowa, Jahrbuch des CHTI, **11**, S. 119 (1964)

5. D. Rustschev u.a., Jahrbuch des CHTI, **8**, 1 (1961)

6. D. Roustschev, Chimie analytique, **43**, 325 (1961

7. D. Rustschev und W. Konstantinowa, Jahrbuch des CHTI, **9**, 143 (1962)

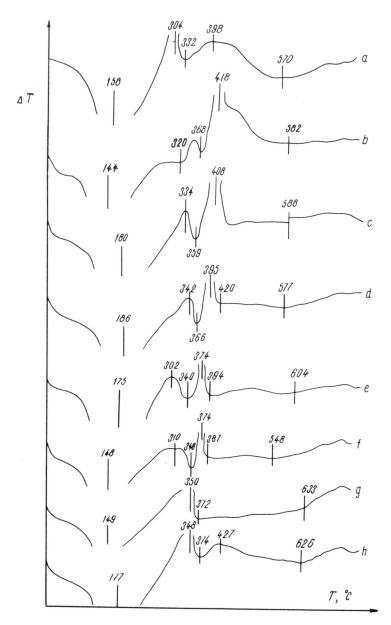

Abb. 1 –Torf–D–Thermogramme:

a – ohne Inhibitore; b – mit 5, 0 % iger Lösung von $\beta\text{-}C_{10}H_7OH$; c – Suspension von $MgCO_3$ und $CaCO_3$; d – Suspension von $CaCO_3$; e – 1, 0 % ige Lösung von NaCl; f – 2, 5 %ige Lösung von Na_2SO_4; g – 0, 01 %ige Lösung von Na_2S; h – 2, 0 % ige Phenollösung

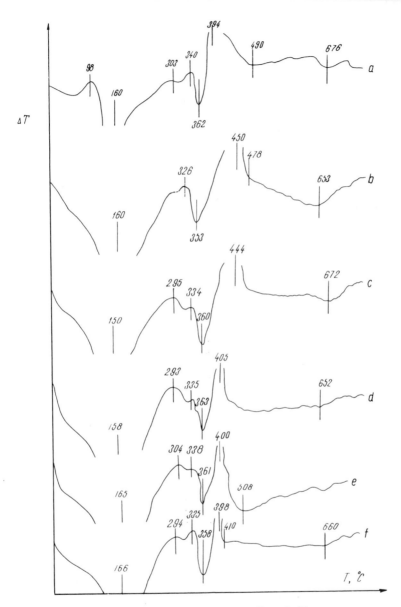

Abb. 2 – Thermogramme von Braunkohle:

a – ohne Inhibitore; b – Suspension von $MgCO_3$ und $CaCO_3$; c – 2, 5 %ige Lösung von Na_2SO_3; d – 1,0 % ige Lösung von NaCl; e – 2, 5 %ige Lösung von Na_2CO_3; f – 2, 5 %ige Lösung von $(NH_4)_2CO_3$

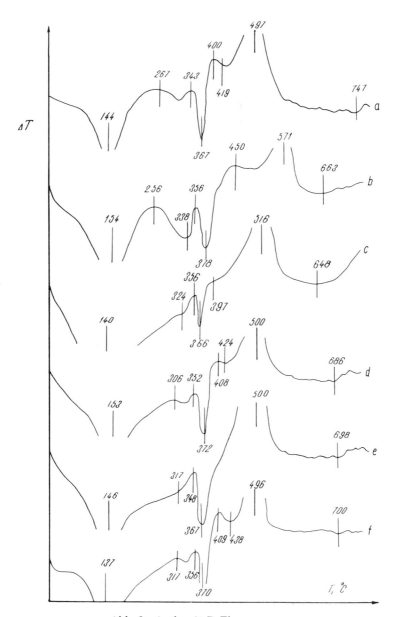

Abb. 3 – Anthrazit–D–Thermogramme:

a – ohne Inhibitore; b – 5, 0 %ige Lösung von β–$C_{10}H_7OH$; c–2,5 %ige Lösung von $NaHSO_3$; d – 2,5 %ige Lösung von Na_2SO_4; e – 2, 0 %ige Lösung von C_6H_5OH; f – Suspension von $CaCO_3$

THERMOANALYTIC-MASS SPECTROMETRICAL INVESTIGATION OF AN OIL SHALE CONTAINING DAWSONITE

M. Müller-Vonmoos* and R. Bach**

Swiss Federal Institute of Technology,
Zurich, Switzerland

Abstract
The content of Dawsonite in an oil shale sample from Colorado (USA) was to be determined. Determination by x-ray analysis was unfeasible because there was no calibration substance. The result of the chemical determination was uncertain because of possible interference by other materials. However the Dawsonite content could be estimated by simultaneous DTA and TG under high vacuum (Mettler Thermoanalyzer), connected with a quadrupol mass spectrometer (Balzers).

Introduction
The content of Dawsonite ($NaAl(OH)_2CO_3$) in an oil shale sample from the Piceance Creek Basin of Northwestern Colorado, Rio Blanco Country, was to be determined. The mineral could be shown clearly by x-ray and infra-red. However neither method was feasible for quantitative determination because a suitable pure Dawsonite was not available for calibration. The Dawsonite could not be isolated from the sample and the synthesized material (1) gave strong diffuse x-ray reflexes. Dawsonite was therefore calculated from chemical

*) Laboratories for Hydraulic Research and Soil Mechanics

**)Laboratory of Agricultural Chemistry

data. But the result seemed to be ambiguous because of the possible interference of other acid-soluble minerals containing Na, Al, water and CO_3 such as Nahcolite ($NaHCO_3$), Dolomite and Analcite ($NaAlSi_2O_6 \cdot H_2O$)(2). Through combination of thermal analysis with mass spectrometry and in connection with x-ray investigations the content of Dawsonite could be determined.

Methods

Determination of the HCl-soluble Al_2O_3 and SiO_2.
The sample was shaken for 5 hours in 0.5 N HCl and then centrifuged. Dissolved Al was determined complexometrically (3) and Si colorimetrically (4).

Thermal analysis. A Mettler "Thermoanalyzer" allowed simultaneous DTA and TG (5). The sample holder ended in two beaker-shaped Pt/PtRh10-thermoelements, containing two platinum beakers of 0.05 cc for sample and reference material. The thermoelement for the measurement of the heating temperature formed a ring around the beakers. Oven dried Zettlitzer kaolin was used as reference material. For the thermoanalyses under normal pressure (Fig.1 and 2) the sample weight was 40 mg and the heating rate 10oC/min. Air flow was 5.72 l/h, nitrogen flow 1.9 l/h. Part of the organic material was extracted with a methanol-benzene mixture (1:1 v/v; soxhlet, 65 hours) at 80-90°C. For the thermoanalysis under high vacuum 10^{-5} to 5.10^{-4}mm Hg) the sample weight was 30 mg and the heating rate 6°C/min.(Fig.4). The thermobalance was connected with a quadrupol mass spectrometer (Balzers, Liechtenstein)(6). It was set for a scanning range of 1 to 50 and a scan speed of 1 second per mass unit. The following masses were evaluated (Fig.3).

water	17,18
CO_2	44
crack-products	2,14,15,26,27,29,39,40, 41, 42, 43.

From the peaks of the mass spectrogram the partial ion currents were calculated. The partial pressure of the masses was calculated from the partial and total ion current and the total pressure during thermoanalysis. The calculation and the graphic presentation of the representative masses were programmed.
X-ray analysis. A Philips diffractometer (CuK$_\alpha$-radiation) and a Guinier-de Wolff-camera (FeK$_\alpha$-radiation) were used.

Results
The Al_2O_3 dissolved in HCl was 4.0 % and the SiO_2 0.4 % of the air dried sample. The acid-soluble SiO_2 was accounted as Analcite and the corresponding Al_2O_3 was subtracted from the 4.0 %. From the remaining Al_2O_3 resulted a Dawsonite content of 10.3 %.
The thermoanalysis under normal pressure in air showed an endothermic reaction at 160°C and a weight loss of 5.6 % (Fig.1). Between 200 and 500°C occurred strong exothermic reactions and, running into each other, two steps of weight loss amounting to a total of 21.5 %. In nitrogen atmosphere the DTA was strongly disturbed above 200 to 250°C. With methanol-benzene mixture 4.2 % (of sample weight) organic material could be extracted. In nitrogen the thermoanalysis of the extracted sample showed the following reactions (Fig.2):

1. endothermic reaction, 149°C, weight loss 0.8 %
2. endothermic reaction, 379°C, weight loss 3.7 %
3. endothermic reaction, 489°C, weight loss 15.8 %
4. endothermic reaction, 779°C, weight loss 16.9 %

The mass spectrometer indicated the following decomposition products (Fig.4):

1. reaction, 180°C: water and CO_2
2. reaction, 395°C: water and CO_2
3. reaction, 490°C: crack-products of the oil, some water and CO_2
4. reaction, 670°C: CO_2 and some water.

The thermoanalysis in nitrogen was repeated and interrupted immediately after each of the four reactions. X-ray analysis showed the decomposition of Dawsonite in the second reaction and of Dolomite in the fourth reaction. X-ray analysis after the first reaction showed no change compared with the original material.

Discussion

0.5 N HCl dissolved 4.0 % Al_2O_3. According to Smith and Milton (2) the oil shale from the Piceance Creek Basin contains also Nahcolite, Dolomite and Analcite, minerals which also dissolve in HCl and influence the calculation of Dawsonite from chemical data. Therefore, the low HCl-soluble SiO_2 was calculated as Analcite and the corresponding amount of aluminium subtracted. From the remaining aluminium a Dawsonite content of 10.3 % was calculated. To ascertain this result we attempted to determine the content of Dawsonite by thermoanalysis.

There is only little information on thermoanalysis of Dawsonite. Beck (7) reported two endothermic reactions, the weaker one at 300°C (peak temperature) and the stronger one at 440°C. The first reaction resulted in no change in crystalline structure detectable by x-ray analysis, and it was interpreted as loss of "non-essential water from the structure". During the second reaction the mineral was destroyed.

Our thermoanalysis in air (Fig.1) showed strong exothermic reactions and two overlapping losses in weight between 200 and 500°C. We assumed that these reactions to be caused by the decomposition of organic material and the mineral-typical reaction of Dawsonite to be masked by the exothermic reactions. We tried, therefore, to suppress the exothermic reactions with nitrogen. However the DTA was strongly disturbed by the cracking. After extraction of a part of the organic material it was possible, to recognize the mineral-typical reactions in nitrogen (Fig.2). However a definite interpretation of the curves was difficult. When the extracted material was used the first reaction was much smaller. We assumed that the cause of the reaction was the loss of water (the "non-essential water from the structure") and that some of this water was lost during extraction. We assumed that the second reaction was caused by the decomposition of Dawsonite. The sample blackened during the third reaction and the endothermic reaction was relatively weak. Both indicated a decomposition of organic material. The fourth reaction was probably the decomposition of Dolomite.

Through the combination of DTA, TG and mass spectrometry in connection with x-ray analysis after each of the reactions, the nature of the reactions could be detected.

During the first reaction water and CO_2 were released. X-ray analysis showed no change. From the work of Smith and Milton (2) and Beck (7) one can conclude that this reaction is caused by the decomposition of Nahcolite. However, Nahcolite could not be detected by x-ray.

Water and CO_2 were also given off in the second reaction and the structure of Dawsonite was destroyed. From the weight loss in the second reaction a Dawsonite content of 10 % was calculated. This result agreed well with the calculation from chemical data.

The mass spectrometer showed that products typical for thermal decomposition of oil were formed during the third reaction. After the third reaction the x-ray reflexes of Dolomite began to disappear and the mass spectrometer showed the release of CO_2.

References

1. E. Bader und U.Esch, Zeitschr. Elektrochem. 50, 266(1944)
2. J.W.Smith and Ch.Milton, Economic Geology 61, 1029(1966)
3. M.Weibel, Zeitschr.Anal.Chem. 184, 322(1961)
4. J.B.Mullin and J.P.Riley, Anal.Chim.Acta 12, 162(1955)
5. H.G.Wiedemann, Chemie-Ing.-Techn. 36, 1105(1964)
6. R.Giovanoli und H.G.Wiedemann, Helv.Chim.Acta 51, 1134(1968)
7. C.W.Beck, Amer.Mineral. 35, 985(1950)

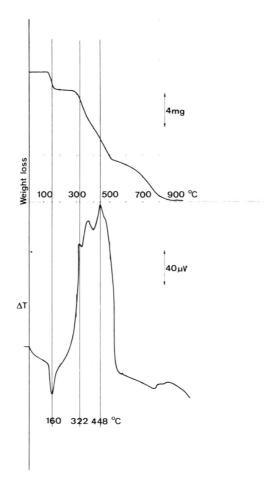

Fig.1   Thermoanalysis of the oil shale under nor-
        mal pressure; air flow 5.72 l/h, heating
        rate 10°C/min., sample weight 40 mg.

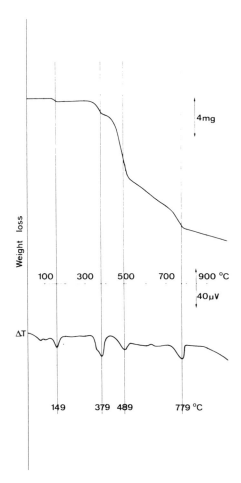

Fig.2   Thermoanalysis of the extracted oil shale
under normal pressure; nitrogen flow
1.9 l/h, heating rate 10°C/min., sample
weight 40 mg.

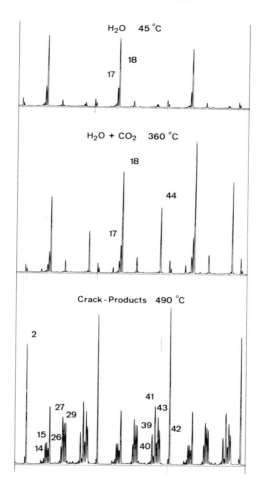

Fig. 3   Sections of the mass spectrogram from the thermoanalysis of the extracted oil shale under high vacuum; scanning range 1 to 50, scan speed 1 sec. per mass unit, ion current 10^{-8} amp. full scale.

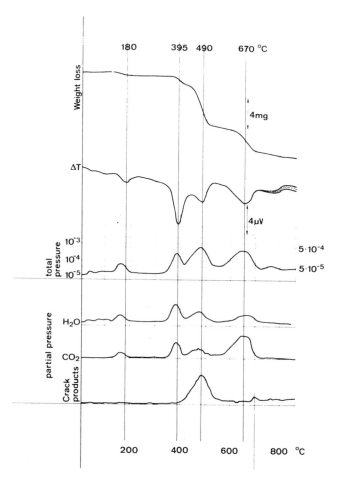

Fig.4 Thermoanalysis of the extracted shale under high vacuum 10^{-5} to 5.10^{-4} mm Hg, heating rate $6^{o}C/min.$, sample weight 30 mg.

THE GIBBSITE DEHYDROXYLATION FORK

William Lodding

Department of Geology
Rutgers-The State University
New Brunswick, New Jersey

Abstract

When heated at a constant rate gibbsite dehydroxylates partly to boehmite (alpha-aluminum monohydroxide) at approximately 250°C; the remaining gibbsite goes directly to transition alumina between 250 and 330°C. This sequence is thought to be due to blocking by boehmite crystallites. The influence of particle size, partial pressure of water vapor and heating rates were investigated. Ratios of boehmite to chi-alumina were computed by DTA peak area measurement and weight loss. They were 0.27 for Brazillian gibbsite and 0.81 for coarse alpha-aluminum trihydrate (Alcoa).

Introduction

The deceptively simple dehydroxylation of gibbsite (alpha-aluminum trihydroxide) has been studied by many investigators; gibbsite is an important mineral in bauxites and its dehydroxylation path is of interest in preparing alumina for the Bayer process. Brown, Clark and Elliott (1) first showed that the dehydroxylation takes place by a dual route, and that both boehmite (alpha-mono-aluminum hydroxide) and an anhydrous alumina form when gibbsite is heated. DeBoer et al (1a) relate it to particle size and the presence of foreign ions. Tertian and Papee (2) and Ginsberg et al (3) reported the formation and structure of the transition aluminas which form in addition to boehmite. Brindley and Nakahira (4) confirmed the dual route by careful isothermal studies and reported activation energies for the two processess. Wayman (5) determined the effect of the partial pressure of water vapor on the rate and extent of the gibbsite-boehmite transformation, and found that at 35°C the R.H. must be smaller than 4×10^{-5} percent to make the reaction go. Rosenquist and Jorgensen (6) reported that the tritium

uptake during the gibbsite-boehmite transformation performed at 300°C and 84.5 atm. was only 40 percent, and
conclude that this indicates a solid-state transformation,
and no breakdown and reconstruction. Paulik, Paulik and
Erdey (7) studied the gibbsite dehydroxylation by simultaneous DTA, TG, and TD.

Methods

In this study a natural crystalline gibbsite from
Brazil (Wards Sci. Estab.) was purified by treatment with
dilute hydrochloric acid and washing, to remove the
hydrous iron oxide coatings. A synthetic coarse-grained
alpha-aluminum trihydroxide (ATH) was obtained from
Aluminum Corp. of America, for comparison.

DTA was performed in a Lodding-Hammel furnace with air
or steam streaming through the sample at approx. 50 ml/
minute. In some runs the air was first passed through
P_2O_5. A dynamic flow of water vapor was produced following the method described previously by Lodding and Ojamaa
(8). The heating rate was 8 degrees per minute. Bare
Platinel thermocouples were used for measurement; the
sample weight was 300 mg. Recently a Mettler Thermoanalyzer became available and analyses were made by
simultaneous DTA, TG with open sample cups, a sample
weight of 5 mg and a heating rate of 8°C/minute.

Experimental

The dehydroxylation path of gibbsite was studied by
DTA under carefully regulated partial pressures of water
vapor. The boehmite/chi-alumina ratios varied very little,
whether DTA was performed in a stream of P_2O_5-dried air,
room air, or steam, as long as the pressure was kept near
atmospheric. A significant difference is found, however,
is one compares the thermograms of chemically precipitated
alpha-aluminum trihydroxide with those of a natural gibbsite from Brazil.

It is useful to compare these thermograms with one of
Brindley and Nakahira representing the first derivative of
the weight loss determined by heating for 12 hours at each
measured temperature. These authors used a coarse Alcoa

alpha-aluminum trihydroxide similar to that in the present
study. FIG. I. The top curve is one of Alcoa ATH, run in
a stream of air previously dried by passing it through
P_2O_5. The first endotherm (A_1) corresponds to the gibbsite-boehmite transformation with a maximum at 210°C; the
second endotherm (A_2) is caused by the gibbsite chi-
alumina dehydroxylation; it partly overlaps the first, and
its peak is at 330°. A third endotherm (A_3) at about
530°C is due to the boehmite-gamma alumina dehydroxylation.
The same three endotherms can be seen in the second thermogram, of natural crystalline gibbsite. Here all endotherms
start and peak at higher temperatures. The first two peaks
are less clearly resolved, and both A_1 and A_3 are visibly
smaller than in the case of the Alcoa ATH. The third
thermogram is that of the first derivative of a weight loss
curve by Brindley and Nakahira (4) obtained of a similar
coarse Alcoa ATH by stepwise heating for periods of 12
hours at each temperature. This curve therefore represents
essentially equilibrium conditions, as distinguished from
the dynamic heating at 8°C per minute used by the author.
Yet the character of this thermogram is essentially the
same as that obtained by DTA, except that, as one would
expect, all peaks occur at considerably lower temperature.

The fact that endotherms A_1 and A_2 overlap only slightly
in Alcoa ATH was convenient to check by X-ray diffraction
the amounts of gibbsite and boehmite present when heating
is stopped at 240°C. Products heated to 425° and 600°C
were likewise examined by X-ray diffraction.

Since the first two endotherms are roughly the same
temperature range, it is possible to compare peak areas,
and to arrive at relative abundance of gibbsite and
boehmite present at this point. The enthalpy ratio of the
gibbsite⟶chi-alumina to gibbsite⟶boehmite is 2.48. If one
multiplies the areas under A_1 by this factor, they become
equivalent to A_2 and may be used to compute the gibbsite/
boehmite ratio. This is the amount of gibbsite which
dehydroxylates to boehmite compared to gibbsite which goes
directly to chi-alumina. Gibbsite/boehmite ratios were
obtained on a number of runs performed under varying atmospheres, from P_2O_5 to high water vapor, and also on the
natural gibbsite from Brazil.

1241

Table 1 summarizes these analyses.

Sample 2/37 Alcoa-ᴕATH

Run	Tc_1	A_1	Tc_2	Tp_2	A_2	Tp_3	A_3	%B
3808D	185	5.6	250	325	32.			32.
3809D	185	4.95	255	330	32.3	530	2.8	29.
3807S	190	5.65	265	340	33.7			31.
3798S	187	4.0	260	325	25.5			29.
3825ST	185	4.3	255	320	26.6	540	3.5	30.0
3826GST	186	5.5	255	330	37.	540	4.2	28.
3823G	195	1.6	228	238	39.3	530	2.7	10.
38246V	195	2.3	228	340	30.6	535	2.85	16.
$3837P_{0.5}$	185	3.4	225	275	18.4	505	2.3	31.
			330*	380*	1.0*			
3838P780	188	6.6	230	300	25.5	520	3.3	42.

*Fourth peak

Sample 2/36 Purif. Brazil Gibbsite

Run	Tc_1	A_1	Tc_2	Tp_2	A_2	Tp_3	A_3	%B
3794A	250	2.2	295	373	34.1	550	1.25	14.
3796P	255	2.3	298	374	28.8			17.
3795S	235	2.2	275	350	33.2			15.

$$\%B = \frac{A_1F}{A_1F + A_2}$$

F=peak area ratio: $\dfrac{\Delta HB}{\Delta H_x Al_2O_3} = \dfrac{67.3}{27.1} = 2.48$

A=Air   ST=Static   P=Pressure
D=P_2O_5 V=Vacuum   Tc=Critical Temp
S=Steam   G=Ground   Tp=Peak Temp
                                    B=Boehmite

$A_{1,2,3}$=Area (cm^2) 1st 2nd 3rd endotherm

In natural gibbsite from Brazil the percentage of boehmite forming is approximately half of that forming in Alcoa-ATH under the same conditions. If 33% of the Alcoa-ATH transforms to boehmite and the remainder directly to xi-alumina, the boehmite to chi-alumina weight ratio is 0.81. For the natural gibbsite from Brazil the ratio is 0.27

The gibbsite/boehmite ratio can be determined more directly from the weight loss. By comparing DTA and TG it is possible to separate the weight loss due to each

step in the dehydroxylation. Alcoa alpha-ATH gave a
weight loss of 7.15% between 180 and 240°C on the Mettler
instrument; this corresponds to 31% boehmite formed. On
the other hand, the boehmite to gamma-alumina dehydroxylation between 500 and 600°C produced a weight loss of 4.2%
which is equivalent to 44% boehmite. These figures suggest
that some boehmite is still forming at temperatures above
240°C, simultaneously with chi-alumina. Weight loss of
the boehmite dehydroxylation step is therefore the more
reliable way to determine the gibbsite/boehmite ratio.
This weightless method cannot be applied in the presence
of clay minerals, which dehydroxylate in the same temperature range as boehmite.

Brindley and Nakahira (4) attribute the slowing of the
boehmite formation to water vapor atmosphere enveloping the
gibbsite core. This is an attractive hypothesis. In our
experiments, however, with carrier gas or water vapor
streaming through the sample material during DTA we did not
detect a measurable change in the gibbsite/boehmite ratio,
no matter what the partial pressure of water vapor was.
At reduced pressure ($P_{0.5mm}$) less boehmite is formed, and
the following interesting changes occur (Figure 2):

1) the gibbsite to boehmite transformation starts at
nearly the same temperature at P_{780mm} and at $P_{0.5mm}$.

2) the rate of the gibbsite to boehmite transformation
is considerably faster at P_{780} than at $P_{0.5}$ (8.4 and
2.6°C/min.). The opposite occurs in the gibbsite to chi-
alumina transformation where the rate is slower at P_{780}
than at $P_{0.5}$ (3.3 and 5.0°C/min.).

3) a fourth broad endotherm is observed with a peak at
approximately 380°C in DTA at reduced pressure.

These effects of reduced pressure on the behavior of the
gibbside dehydroxylation are not easily explained. The
fact that the gibbsite to boehmite transformation always
starts at the same temperature (at a given heating rate),
no matter what the the total and partial pressures does
not fit with the model of water vapor as the controlling
factor. The effect of wet-grinding on the thermal dehydroxylation of Alcoa ATH is shown in figure 3. Notice that the

onset of the gibbsite-boehmite transformation and its critical and peak temperatures are not affected by grinding. On the other hand even light grinding changes the onset of the second trans formation (gibbsite to chi-alumina) to lower temperature. Thirty-minutes grinding makes this effect more pronounced. Erdey and Paulik (9) have shown that after prolonged grinding (24 hours) and centrifuging, the first and second peaks merge; the single peak is still above 300°C. This behavior suggests that the boehmite to chi-alumina ratio depends on particle size and surface area. Boehmite forms at the outset of dehydroxylation. It is conceivable that in this solid-state transformation (Rosenquist, 6) boehmite forms an impervious layer around the unreacted gibbsite, preventing further dehydroxylation until a much higher temperature is reached. This model is somewhat difficult to take; the newly formed boehmite crystallites occupy a smaller volume (weight loss 14.5%, and a specific gravity increase from 2.4 to 3.0) while the gibbsite core is still dilating, although not much 0.8% linear) according to Paulik and Erdey (7). Figure 4 shows schematically how the boehmite crystallites, even with a diminished volume, may produce an impervious layer. The increase in volume of the gibbsite core compensates in part for this shrinkage.

We still have to explain why in the natural gibbsite all dehydroxylation steps require higher temperatures than in the chemically precipitated Alcoa ATH. This phenomenon is found in many other chemically precipitated crystals when compared their analogs grown in nature. Asselmeyer's (10) experiment may help explain it; he found that introduction of a small quantity of europium into the gibbsite lattice reduced all dehydroxylation temperatures of alpha-ATH by as much as much as 100°C, and he related this phenomenon to stresses and dislocations produced in the gibbsite lattice. Stress release during heating tends to facilitate solid-state transformations, and the result may be that they take place at lower temperature. If we apply this reasoning to our experimental results it would indicate that the natural gibbsite contains fewer impurities in the crystal lattice than the chemically precipitated Alcoa gibbsite. Table 2 is a comparison of the elemental composition of the Alcoa and the Brazilian gibbsites. The latter is significantly lower in Ca, Mg, and Na, and probably has fewer lattice substitutions. Silica and iron are surface coatings.

Table 2

Gibbsite	Brazil 2136	Alcoa 2137
SiO_2	0.03	0.02
Fe_2O_3	0.06	0.05
TiO_2		0.003
CaO	0.04	0.14
MgO	0.02	0.05
K_2O	0.06	0.05
Na_2O	0.30	0.60
Ga_2O_3		0.02
L. I.	33.60	33.90

Summary

(1) DTA and X-ray studies indicate that the boehmite to xi-alumina fork is caused by the formation of an impervious layer which prevents the transformation from going to completion.

(2) The onset and peak temperatures of the gibbsite to boehmite step are controlled by the presence or absence of lattice substitutions and by the heating rate; they are largely independent of particle size and surrounding atmosphere.

(3) The second step in the dehydroxylation--gibbsite to chi-alumina-- is dependent on particle size and lattice dislocations.

(4) The weight loss occurring between 450°C and 600°C can be used to determine the boehmite to chi-alumina ratio if clay minerals are absent; in the presence of clay minerals the DTA peak areas of the first two steps can be used to compute approximate ratios.

(5) DTA and steady-state thermograms of the gibbsite dehydroxylation show identical sequence of events, and peak areas of comparable magnitude.

Acknowledgments

Alpha-aluminum trihydroxide and analyses were gratiously supplied by Aluminum Company of America. I want to thank Dr. Robert C. Mackenzie for critical review and helpful suggestions, and Richard W. Ott for analyses on the Mettler Thermoanalyzer.

References

1. Brown, J. F.; Clark, D.; Elliott, W. W.: J. Chem. Soc. Lon. 84-88 (1953).
1a. DeBoer, J. H.; Fortuin, J. M. H.; Steggerda, J. J.; Proc. Acad. Sci. Amst., B57, 170, (1954).
2. Tertian, R.; Papee, D.: J. Chim Phys. 55, 341-353 (1958).
3. Ginsberg, H.; Huttig, W.; Strunk-Lichtenberg, G.: Z. Anorg. Chem. 293 33-46, 204-213 (1957).
4. Brindley, G. W.; Nakahira, M.: Z. Krist. 112 136-149 (1959).
5. Wayman, C. H.: Clays and Clay Min. 11, 84-90, Pergamon Press (1963).
6. Rosenquist, I. Th.; Jorgensen, P.: Proc. Int. Clay Conf. Osborne Press, London, I 63 (1966).
7. Paulik, F.; Paulik, J.; Erdey, L.: Anal. Chim. Acta 41, 170-172 (1968).
8. Lodding, W.; Ojamaa, L.: J. Inorg. Nucl. Chem., 27 1261-1268 (1965).
9. Erdey, L.; Paulik, F.: Acta Chim. Hung. 21, 2, 1-4 (1963).
10. Asselmeyer, F.: Z. Angew. Phys. 1, 26-35, (1947).

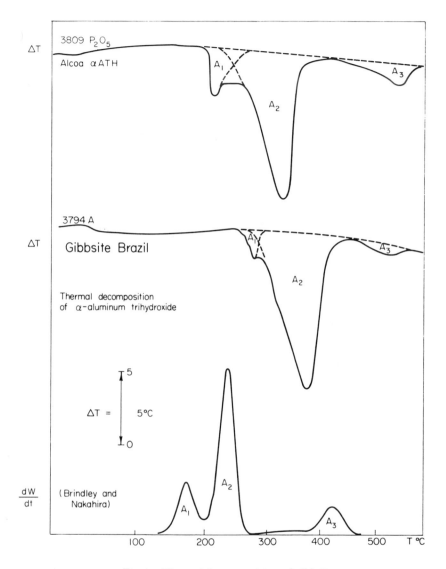

Fig. 1. Thermal decomposition of gibbsite.

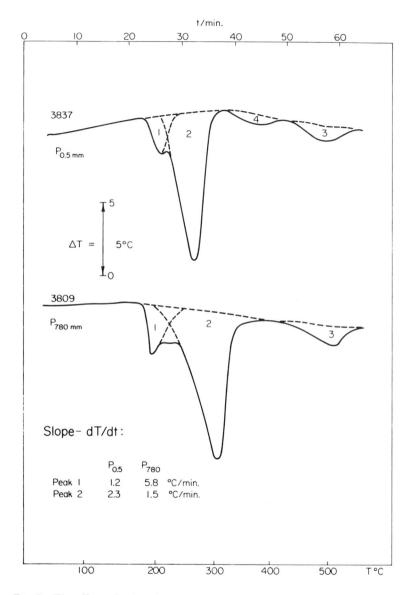

Fig. 2. The effect of reduced pressure on the gibbsite dehydroxilation in DTA.

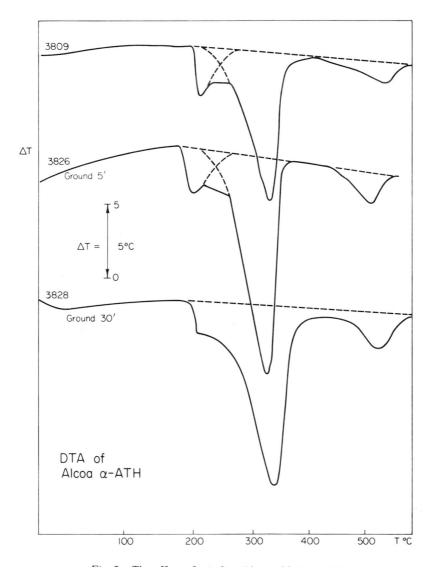

ΔT

3809

3826
Ground 5'

ΔT = | 5°C

3828

Ground 30'

DTA of
Alcoa α-ATH

100   200   300   400   500   T °C

Fig. 3.   The effect of grinding Alcoa gibbsite on DTA.

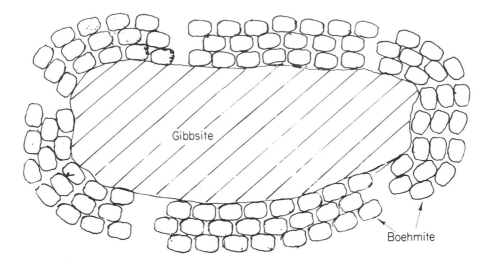

Fig. 4. A tentative model for the gibbsite to boehmite transformation; schematic view of a gibbsite crystallite partially altered to boehmite, and the onset of xi-alumina formation.

SIMULTANEOUS DTA-TG-MSA APPARATUS FOR THERMAL STUDY OF NATURAL FUELS

John Ward Smith and Donald R. Johnson

Laramie Petroleum Research Center
Laramie, Wyo.

Abstract

Quadrupole equipment added to apparatus designed expressly for thermal analysis of natural fuels like oil shale provides continuous mass spectrometric analysis (MSA) of evolving gases, differential thermal analysis (DTA), and thermogravimetry (TG) simultaneously on a single sample. Described is tested apparatus developed specifically to solve problems inherent in thermal analysis of solid fuels. Key to this solution is the use of thin, flat pans as sample holders. Adaptation of the quadrupole equipment to sample and analyze evolving gases in a carrier stream is described. Because gases evolve rapidly from the thin sample layer, the resulting gas analysis corresponds closely with DTA and TG results. Tests run on Green River Formation oil-shale minerals demonstrate the value of the MSA data generated by the quadrupole gas analyzer.

Introduction

The natural solid fuels--oil shales, black shales, and coals--represent tremendous stores of fossil fuel energy. The fuels' thermal properties are an integral part of their value. Coal can supply energy by direct combustion, but thermal treatment of certain coals generates valuable products, coke and coal tar. Thermal degradation is still the only feasible method of producing energy products from oil shales and black shales. Solid fuels all contain mineral components contributing to thermal behavior of the fuels. By evaluating the thermal effects of

1251

minerals in the fuels, thermal analysis characterizes the
fuels both in composition and in processing behavior.
Studying the thermal behavior of fuels and their components by thermoanalytical methods is, therefore, a valuable
approach. Previous thermal studies of natural fuels were
reviewed by Smith and Johnson (1).

Thermal analysis of natural fuels presents problems
not solved by the usual thermal analysis equipment. During
study of Green River Formation oil shales the U.S. Bureau
of Mines developed equipment and techniques to overcome
these particular analytical problems. Key to this development is the heating of a thin layer of sample in a thin
metal sample holder. McAdie (2) and Paulik and others (3)
reported simultaneous DTA-TG on thin-layered samples held
in massive sample holders, but the thin metal holder
arrangement described here is unique. The described
apparatus assembled around these pans solves or minimizes
the natural fuel problems, providing differential thermal
analysis (DTA), thermogravimetry (TG), derivatives of each,
and mass spectrometric effluent gas analysis (MSA) simultaneously on a single sample. Application of this equipment to thermal analysis problems in oil shale is illustrated.

Natural Fuel Problems

Thermal analysis of solid natural fuels presents
difficulties associated with the character of these
materials and with their response to various experimental
conditions. In 1967 Smith and Johnson (1) evaluated these
problems, grouping them under the following five headings:

(1) Combustion, the burning of the fuel's organic
     matter during analysis;
(2) recondensation, the redeposition and revolatil-
     ization of evolving hydrocarbon gases;
(3) property changes, the alteration in physical and
     thermal characteristics of the sample during
     heating;
(4) heterogeneity, the mixture of assorted materials
     composing natural fuels; and
(5) representation, making an analyzed sample repre-
     sent a natural material.

These problems are evaluated and possible means of overcoming them are suggested in the appendix to this paper.
At least partial solution to all of these problems is
necessary to achieve satisfactory thermal analysis of
natural fuels.

Solving these problems inherent in thermal analysis
of natural fuels requires pyrolysis of a macrosample in a
dynamic atmosphere of a selected gas to prevent or control
combustion, to provide an adequately representative sample
of the natural material, and to help control recondensation
effects by removing evolved gases. Because processing
procedures take place at atmospheric pressures, the atmosphere over the thermal reaction should be at atmospheric
pressure. The sample should be heated evenly as a thin
layer on a heat-conducting sheet to minimize effects of
recondensation and property changes. Sensitive DTA measurements obtained simultaneously with TG and continuous
evolved gas evaluation are required to detect and interpret
the multiple heat effects generated by the assortment of
components occurring in the heterogeneous natural fuels.
All of these requirements are additional to the more usual
thermal analysis requirements evaluated in detail by
Garn (4).

Apparatus

Equipment developed and assembled by the U.S. Bureau
of Mines to fulfill these requirements is presented in
block diagram in Figure 1. The components include the
thermal analysis cell, consisting of the sample holder,
the reaction chamber, and the heating system; the DTA
unit; the TG unit; and the MSA unit, consisting of the
quadrupole gas analyzer, the automatic pressure control
valve, and the vacuum system. The important components
are described individually.

Sample Holder

The key to meeting the peculiar problems inherent in
thermal analysis of solid fuels is the unique sample holder
arrangement shown in Figure 2. The sample and reference
pans suspended at the bottom of a pendant quartz rod are
thin 0.003-inch (0.0762-mm) metal discs 0.75 inch (19 mm)

1253

in diameter with a rim raised 1 mm. The discs are made of
a platinum-3.5 percent rhodium alloy to resist corrosive
conditions many fuels generate during heating. The holder
supports the sample in a thin layer (1 mm) distributed
uniformly on a metal sheet. The heat-conducting metal
sheet unifies the heating pattern in the thin sample layer.
Smoothing the sample to the rim insures uniform sample
thickness and guarantees easy replication of sample geometry.

For natural fuels the samples tested are usually
ground to pass a 100-mesh screen. Depending on the bulk
volume of the powdered specimen, the sample holder in
Figure 2 contains 0.2 to 0.3 g of sample, an amount sufficiently large to insure adequate representation. The pan
design permits pyrolysis of a relatively large sample
weight in a layer no thicker than 1 mm, facilitating rapid
escape of evolving gases and preventing recondensation of
heavy oils on unreacted sample.

Reaction Chamber

To provide atmosphere control a platinum reaction
chamber encloses the sample holder. In Figure 2 this
chamber appears as a dark outline. The carefully rate-
controlled stream (flow rate used in this paper was 150
cm^3/min) of selected gas enters the reaction chamber at the
top and is preheated in flowing down over the Pt-gauze
diffusers mounted above the sample pans. In sweeping past
the sample holder the gas stream carries off evolving gases
immediately. These gases travel up the short outlet pipe,
which is heated to prevent condensation, and arrive at the
reaction chamber outlet continuously as they evolve. Vent-
ing the gas stream to the atmosphere controls the pressure
in the reaction chamber to atmospheric.

Completing the isolation of the reaction chamber required enclosing the balance mechanism within it. Figure 3
shows the complete atmosphere control system. A water-
cooled connector couples the platinum tube to the balance
capsule, and a rubber-gasketed bell jar placed over the
balance closes the system. Although the balance mechanism
is actually inside the reaction system, no gas flows through
the balance enclosure, and no product gases enter the balance capsule. Before heating begins, the reaction system

is evacuated, flushed, and filled with the selected carrier gas. The balance capsule remains filled with carrier gas during operation, sealed off by the gas stream.

DTA Measurement

Sensitive DTA and direct temperature measurements are provided by spot welding the two wires of Platinel* thermocouples along the bottom of the sample holder. The method of thermocouple attachment is illustrated in the photograph and the diagram in Figure 2. The temperature sensed and the voltage signal produced are characteristic of the pan's entire sample area as evidenced by moving the wire and weld locations and testing response to quartz inversion. Only insignificant variations in DTA response were detected. By making the entire pan sense the thermal behavior of a sample and by using thin, light-weight (0.5 g) sample pans this system responds sensitively to thermal changes in the sample. Temperature of the reference pan is recorded routinely. Sample temperature could be measured directly by welding the temperature thermocouple to the sample pan.

TG Measurement

Simultaneous TG measurements are obtained by suspending the sample holder on an electrically driven null-point beam balance (Model RA, Cahn Instrument Company). The suspending quartz tubing (Figures 2 and 3) carries the four separate thermocouple wires up to the balance beam. Tiny looped wires carry DTA and temperature signals from the center of the free but nonmoving beam to the recorder system. The electrical balance signal is carried to the same recorder for simultaneous plotting. Commercially available thermal analysis equipment (Deltatherm, Technical Equipment Corporation) records the simultaneous DTA and TG signals, controls the heating rate of the furnace surrounding the reaction chamber, and electronically computes and records a derivative signal from either the DTA or TG signals. A second time derivative computer, Cahn Instrument Company's Mark II, prepares a derivative signal from the TG signal for separate recording.

---

* Reference to trade names is made for identification only and does not imply endorsement by the Bureau of Mines.

MSA Unit

Simultaneous and continuous mass spectrometric analysis (MSA) of evolving gases is provided by a recently added quadrupole gas analysis system. In essence the system continuously extracts a small sample from the carrier gas at atmospheric pressure and admits this sample continuously to the quadrupole gas analyzer for mass analysis at very low pressure. Because we believe the use of a quadrupole instrument for analysis of a dynamic gas stream is novel to thermal analysis, some detail on the nature, the purpose, and the operation of the equipment will be presented. The MSA system consists of the following components: (1) An automatic pressure controller, (2) an ionization gauge controller operating a Bayard Alpert tube, (3) a quadrupole residual gas analyzer, and (4) high-vacuum pumping equipment.

The automatic pressure controller samples the carrier gas. The controller (Granville-Phillips-Model APC) is a servomotor-driven valve responding precisely to pressure signals from the ionization gauge controller. Reacting rapidly to small pressure signal changes, the valve opens when the pressure drops or closes when the pressure goes up. Quite easily the valve can maintain pressure in the high vacuum system constant within $\pm$ 0.1 x 10^{-6} torr, for example. The intake or high-pressure side of the automatic valve samples the carrier gas stream, and the gas analysis system lies on the low-pressure side. The valve maintains about one atmosphere pressure across itself but permits a continuous flow of sample gas to enter the high vacuum system. To make this flow rate relatively high but still to maintain the 10^{-6} torr pressure required for quadrupole operation, the pumping equipment was selected to have high capacity relative to the volume of the system. The evacuated section is relatively small, consisting of the automatic pressure control valve, the quadrupole ionizer, and a Bayard Alpert tube in addition to the pump itself. A commercial diffusion pump (Model TM-4, TM Vacuum Products Company) with a rated pumping speed of 680 liters per second has proven quite satisfactory as part of the gas analysis apparatus. Only a tiny fraction of the total gas flow is extracted for gas analysis, leaving the rest for collection, if desired.

Gas flowing through the sampling valve is directed into the ionizer of the quadrupole gas analyzer (Model QUAD 150 RGA, Ultek Division of Perkin Elmer). The ionized gas is mass-sorted by the quadrupole array, yielding a continuous mass spectrometric analysis of the gas components put out as electrical signals for recording or oscilloscope display. This quadrupole instrument has several features particularly suitable for analysis of the gases evolved from thermal analysis. One is its small physical size, 13 inches long and 6 inches maximum diameter. Another is its simplicity and ease of maintenance, because it can be baked out or can be disassembled and reassembled quickly for cleaning if necessary. Its low ionizing potential generates relatively simple ion fragmentation patterns, making the mass spectrum output simpler to evaluate. Its high sensitivity (5×10^{-14} torr for N_2, output 20 amp/torr) and good resolution make feasible the determination of small amounts of evolved gases in large amounts of carrier gas. Times for sweeping the mass range are continuously variable from 130 milliseconds to 10 minutes, making it possible to follow clearly the rate pattern of any thermal reaction. In addition a single mass number can be continuously monitored.

In thermal analysis of natural fuels the product gases of importance are C_2H_6, C_3H_8, C_4H_{10}, C_5H_{12}, their olefinic counterparts, H_2, CH_4, NH_3, H_2S, CO, CO_2, and H_2O. In general H_2O, CO_2, and H_2S might be considered mineral gases. Organic degradation products of greater molecular weight become too complex to offer mass spectral data meaningful to thermal analysis of natural fuels. An air-cooled condenser traps the heavier organic vapors before the carrier gas is sampled. The mass range of the quadrupole analyzer is particularly suitable to thermal analysis of natural fuels. The instrument covers the mass range from 1 through 150 in a single sweep. The bottom limit is vital in order to include hydrogen, always produced in thermal breakdown of fuels, simultaneously with the other gases. The higher limit needed is usually no greater than 44, although occasionally reaching mass 75 may be necessary to include the pentanes. The sweep range is easily set.

Assembly

The complete apparatus for thermal analysis of natural fuels is shown in block diagram in Figure 1. In the diagram the thermal analysis cell includes the sample holders, the reaction chamber, and the heating system. During the programmed heating of a sample the apparatus can continuously determine and record DTA and its derivative and TG and its derivative, and can analyze the effluent gas for a single component or a group of components as desired. Data output, indicated in Figure 1 by the word (RECORD), includes the following items, shown with the equipment's capability range.

DTA	Sensitivity range from 7.5° to 0.02° C per inch of a 10-inch chart. Peak area reproducible with standard samples within $\pm$ 2 percent.
DDTA	Electronically computed time derivative of DTA, response of 1-inch deflection for a change of 0.075° C/min, useful for picking start points and inflections.
TG	Full scale on 10-inch chart can equal 1, 2, 5, 10, 50, 100, or 500 mg. TG reproducibility better than $\pm$ 2 percent.
DTG	Electronically computed time derivative of TG, response of 1 inch deflection for 2 to 200 mg/min. Derivative shape compares with DTA plot.
MSA	Chart plotted readout equivalent to DTA and DTG plots. Area under component curve proportional to amount of component produced from sample. Calibration with known compounds essential to quantitization.

Applications

Capabilities of the apparatus for simultaneous DTA-TG-MSA determinations on natural fuel problems are illustrated by results obtained on two samples. The first demonstrates

the coordinated function of all the outputs in evaluating
low-temperature decomposition of an oil-shale mineral. The
second demonstrates how an oil-shale characteristic, almost
unapproachable by other analysis techniques, is easily
defined and evaluated by simultaneous DTA-TG-MSA, resolving a long-standing oil-shale mystery.

The mineral nahcolite ($NaHCO_3$) occurs in Colorado's
Green River Formation oil shale as discontinuous crystals
and crystal masses imbedded in the oil shale. Nahcolite
content of shale and the heat it requires to break down
are important to oil-shale processing. Figure 4 displays
output records for a single nahcolite degradation run at
$10°$ C per minute. The records are photographed in keeping
with ICTA wishes for faithful reproduction. At the bottom
are the DTA and TG records together with DDTA. In the
center is the DTG record. At the top is the MSA record of
mass 18 overlying mass 17, both produced by the water
evolved from the sample. Figure 4 demonstrates the direct
comparability of DTA, DTG, and MSA records for the reaction. Each of these plots is a function of the reaction
rate, and their similarity indicates that they are seeing
the same reaction. The plots show truly simultaneous continuous recording of the thermal event in process. No lag
appears in recording the production of water, the least
mobile of the gases. Area under the DTA peak is a function of heat required, area under the DTG peak is a function of weight loss, and area under the MSA peak is a
function of evolved water. Clean crushed nahcolite crystals, sample weight 194 mg, show a 70.5-mg weight loss,
which is 98.5 percent of the theoretical weight loss for
sodium bicarbonate over this temperature range. (TG scale--
10 mg equal 1 chart inch, the primary chart division; DTA
scale--1.5° C per inch.) The close approximation to the
theoretical value indicates that the crystals were nearly
pure $NaHCO_3$. Thermal analysis can efficiently analyze oil
shale for its nahcolite, and for nahcolite's degradation
heat requirements and gaseous products, including water.

The second application concerns illite clay, a
ubiquitous mineral constituent of Green River oil shale
unmeasurable by any previously available procedure. Even
X-ray diffraction can only indicate its presence but not
measure its amount. Illite contains hydroxyl groups in its

lattice. On heating these should consume heat to become water, but heat, weight, and water determinations failed to evaluate the clay degradation. After reporting his unsuccessful attempt to detect illite in oil shale by DTA measurement of this heat, Heady (5) stated:

> Illite clay could have been present in appreciable quantity and yet not have been detected owing to lack of sensitivity of the apparatus. This sensitivity...was sufficient to detect small thermal changes...of short duration...such as the alpha-beta inversion of quartz. However...where the reactions occur gradually, as in illite clay, the sensitivity proved to be insufficient.

Figure 5 demonstrates MSA detection of clay water. Heady's "gradual" comment was quite correct, for the clay water appears gradually over the entire temperature range from 600° to 800° C (10° C per minute heating rate). A weight loss is associated with this, and between the MSA and TG a measure of clay water evolved may be obtained after calibration. This is a direct function of the clay content of the sample, and the clay water has consistently been an uncorrectable error in determination of the hydrogen content of oil shale's organic fraction.

The sample tested here in a helium atmosphere had been treated in Tracerlab's Low Temperature Asher (Model LTA 600), which removed not only the organic matter from the oil shale but also nahcolite and the gibbsite (?) shoulder preceding the dawsonite DTA peak (1). Degradations of dawsonite, "ferroan," and the Mg part of dolomite appear as strong peaks on the CO_2 MSA plot also given in Figure 5 (1).

Conclusions

Thin, flat pan sample holders with thermocouples welded on their bottoms contribute heavily to solving the thermal analysis problems inherent in the study of solid natural fuels. Incorporated in apparatus developed for the purpose, the unique sample holders should make possible simultaneous DTA, TG, and MSA on oil shales, coals, and black shales. The recently added quadrupole MSA has already demonstrated its value in providing significant data in the study of thermal behavior of solid fuels. In particular, a method for measuring illite clay's thermal behavior in oil shale has been developed.

Acknowledgments

The work upon which this report is based was done under a cooperative agreement between the Bureau of Mines, U.S. Department of the Interior, and the University of Wyoming.

References

1. J. W. Smith and D. R. Johnson, Proceedings of the Second Toronto Symposium on Thermal Analysis (Chemical Institute of Canada, Toronto, 1967), 95.
2. H. G. McAdie, Anal. Chem. 35, 1840 (1963).
3. J. Paulik, F. Paulik, and L. Erdey, Anal. Chim. Acta 34, 419 (1966).
4. P. D. Garn, Thermoanalytical Methods of Investigation (Acad. Press, New York, 1964), 606 pp.
5. H. H. Heady, Am. Mineral. 37, 804 (1952).
6. C. M. Gamel, Jr., and W. J. Smothers, Anal. Chim. Acta 6, 442 (1952).
7. M. Weltner, Acta Chim. Hung. Tomus 43, 89 (1965).

Appendix

Thermal analysis of the solid natural fuels--oil shales, coals, and black shales--presents several problems associated with the character of these materials and with their response to experimental conditions. The nature of these problems is outlined below, together with possible means of overcoming them (1).

(1) Combustion. Natural fuels burn during thermal analysis if air or other combustion-supporting gas can reach the sample. This combustion is surprisingly efficient. Gamel and Smothers (6) were able to burn coal in a 1/2-inch-deep pocket 1/4-inch in diameter, with no provision for forcing air in the pocket, as thoroughly as in a combustion bomb designed for efficient combustion. Areas under the DTA curves obtained were proportional to

analytically determined heats of combustion. Weltner (7) used DTA to determine patterns of combustion for coals. Smith and Johnson (1) showed that even tiny amounts of air in a dynamic gas stream over a heating fuel sample generated huge exotherms from combustion.

The energy represented by the DTA exotherm in a fuel's combustion reaction overrides and obliterates all DTA response to other thermal events occurring in the sample over a wide temperature range. Combustion also causes high local heating in the sample and changes the thermal behavior of the rest of the material to that of the ash remaining behind. Selection and thorough control of the atmosphere over and in a sample is vital to the thermal analysis of solid fuels.

(2) Recondensation. Most natural fuels produce oil or tar on thermal treatment. For oil shales and coking coals the thermal process producing this oil generates the fuel's economic value; consequently, this thermal reaction is of particular interest. Usually the oil produced is heavy, viscous, and readily condensible. In many commercial sample holders recondensation generates the unhappy result illustrated in Figure 6 on oil-shale samples. In the sample well, oil shale heats unevenly, initially producing volatile oil only at the bottom. This first oil moves up into the sample, condenses, and forms a gas-proof layer so that oil and gas subsequently produced cannot escape. Pressure builds until the entire sample boils out of the well. Dilution with inert materials is the usual procedure for overcoming this difficulty, but this is objectionable for three reasons: First, interaction or catalytic effects introduced with the diluent may completely alter the pyrolysis pattern; second, multiple recondensations are promoted; and third, many of the significant heat effects are relatively small and may be decreased below detectability.

Recondensation produces several mechanical and thermal processes objectionable to meaningful thermal analysis of natural fuels. Consequently, recondensation must be limited or avoided. Uniform heating of a fuel sample in a thin layer can prevent or minimize recondensation in a sample. Evolving vapors should immediately be carried away from the sample.

(3) Property changes. Physical and thermal properties of oil shales and the other natural solid fuels change significantly during programmed heating. They may shrink or expand as gases leave. Removal of hydrocarbon volatiles and coking of the residual organic matter produces a porous char whose heat-transmitting properties differ from those of the original organic matter and the inert reference material. Only if the sample and its residual degradation products are not required to conduct heat can effects of these property changes on heat transmission be eliminated. A thin sample layer on a heat-conducting sheet minimizes this problem.

(4) Heterogeneity. Natural fuels are complex materials. They contain widely varying amounts of solid, combustible, carbonaceous matter ranging in character from petroleum like in Green River Formation oil shale to graphite like in anthracite coal. They also contain mineral constituents in various amounts. In general these minerals are intimately mixed with the organic material. During pyrolysis of a fuel its minerals contribute thermal effects warranting investigation. For example, the heat required to retort shale oil from the organic matter in Green River oil shale includes that consumed by minerals reacting or decomposing below retorting temperatures. Efficient engineering design of an oil-shale retort requires knowledge of the thermal reactions of oil-shale minerals. DTA can help to evaluate heat requirements individually and quantitatively. Determination of weight loss during thermal reactions would greatly aid this evaluation. Also, continuous identification and quantitization of evolved gases could diagnose and evaluate reactions as they occur. Because the solid fuels are complex interacting systems, separate determinations are difficult to correlate and compare precisely. Consequently, the TG and MSA measurements should be obtained simultaneously with DTA on a single sample.

(5) Representation. Because natural fuels are heterogeneous, adequate representation of the natural material requires samples substantially larger than the 5 to 10 milligrams frequently used in thermal analysis of more homogeneous materials. To represent the average character of the material and to avoid measuring internal variations in a

1263

specimen, the analyzed sample should weigh perhaps 20 times more than the microsample size frequently tested.

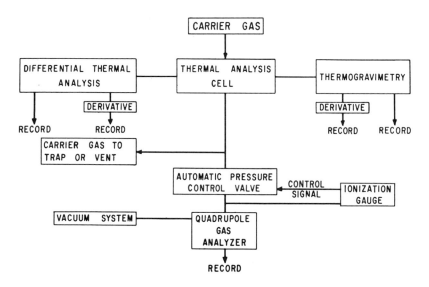

Fig. 1   Thermal analysis system for natural fuels.

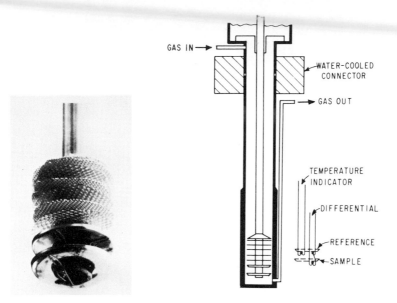

GAS IN →

WATER-COOLED
CONNECTOR

→ GAS OUT

TEMPERATURE
INDICATOR

DIFFERENTIAL

REFERENCE

SAMPLE

Fig. 2   Thin-pan sample holder.

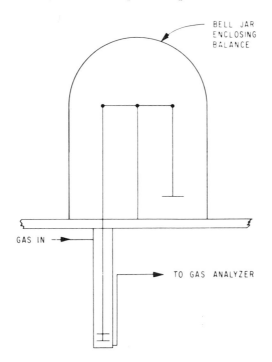

BELL JAR
ENCLOSING
BALANCE

GAS IN →

→ TO GAS ANALYZER

Fig. 3   Atmosphere control system.

1265

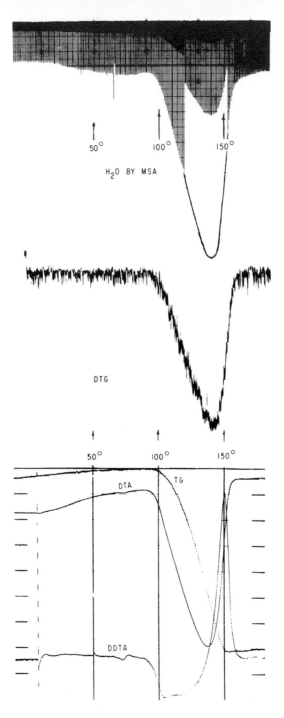

Fig. 4 Thermal analysis of nahcolite.

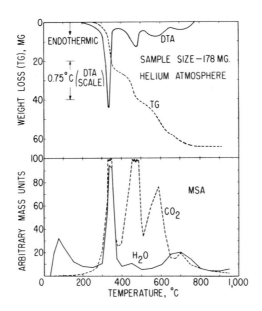

Fig. 5 MSA detects water from clay degradation, 600°-800° C.

Fig. 6 Oil shale climbs out of a sample holder. Note exposed thermocouples at left and shale residue on cover at right.

INVESTIGATIONS ON THE THERMAL CURVES OF ALUNITE

ASSOCIATED WITH OTHER MINERALS

Gianni Lombardi

Istituto di Petrografia - University of Rome, Italy

Introduction

While carrying out a series of investigations and thermal analyses on alunitic rocks of the district of Tolfa, Rome (Lombardi, 1967) some interesting observations were made regarding the influence of other mineralogical components on the decomposition of alunite. The different processes can well be followed by thermal methods. In this work artificial mixtures of alunite with boehmite, kaolinite, calcite and dolomite were analyzed. From the results obtained it was also possible to ascertain the precautions to be taken in the semi-quantitative determination of the sulphate in alunitic rocks by means of DTA[*].

Before beginning these investigations extensive bibliographic research was made on the minerals of the alunite series and on the alunitic rocks in general. Although the literature on these sulphates is very ample, modifications of the thermal curves due to the participation in the paragenesis of other compounds have been the object of relatively few studies. For example a paper of Kerr and Kulp (1959) deals with analyses of artificial mixtures of

---

[*] As regards general characteristics of alunite and its thermal behaviour, we refer to the work of the author (1967) and chiefly to the monography of M.A. Kashkai "The alunites, their natural place in the earth's crust, genesis and their application"(1969), pending publication.

alunite-jarosite and alunite-kaolinite; the authors do not however discuss in detail the effects obtained.

Kashkai and Babaiev (1959) published DTA and TGA of mixtures of alunite-quartz, pointing out that in the presence of large amounts of quartz the $730^{\circ}C$ exothermic peak characteristic of the alunite curve was absent. The same authors, moreover, have carried out analyses of dickite and alunite mixtures, the results of which have not been published as yet, but only announced in the program of the 1st ICTA held at Aberdeen in 1965.

Bayliss and Koch (1955) refer to the effect of NaCl on the desulfurization of alunite. Gad and Barrett (1949) and Gad (1950) studied the reactions occurring between alunite and natural clays when heated, completing their work with several roentgenographic data.

In literature, moreover, there are numerous thermal analyses of alunitic rocks, mostly made by Russian researchers, where the sulphate is found in the most different paragenesis; however, the influence of the single minerals of the associations, normally, is not specifically examined.

Methods and materials

Two thermal analysis apparatus were used in the investigation: a) A Mettler Thermoanalyzer equipped with platinum crucibles with internal shield for protection of the thermocouples (Pt-Pt/Rh 10%), placed in a sample-block. b) A Netzch DTA apparatus with platinum cylindrical crucibles, the thermocouples being immersed in the sample.

All analyses were carried out with linear heating rate of $10^{\circ}C$/min up to $1600^{\circ}C$ with the Mettler. Normally no effects were registered on the DTA at high temperatures and, therefore, only the DTA curves obtained with the Netzch furnaces up to $1200^{\circ}C$ have been reproduced here; when present, transformations above $1200^{\circ}C$ are cited in the text.

The alunite $\underline{/}(K,Na)Al_3(SO_4)_2(OH)_6\underline{/}$ used as standard in these investigations was collected in the quarry of

Cimitero di Allumiere (Tolfa-Rome), where it is associated with highly kaolinized rocks, derived from metasomatism of primary acidic volcanites. The mineral is powdery, very fine grained, with a characteristic pinkish colour and it occurs in small veins and pockets in the kaolinized rock. Practically pure in the natural state, it has only rare inclusions of halloysite and quartz. With a heating rate of 10°C/min, at 1000°C the material shows a loss of weight of 41.7%, corresponding to a 95.2% pure alunite. Chemical tests for sulphur and alkalies gave the following results: SO_3 = 36.02, Na_2O = 3.38, K_2O = 4.02. The sample therefore can be classified as a natroalunite, in the same way as a similar material collected a few meters away from this one and analyzed in a previous work of the author.

Following the same criteria applied in other investigations of alunitic rocks of Tolfa analyses were carried out on material homogenized and ground in a hand mortar to pass a < 75μ sieve. Alumina T61 Alcoa was used as inert material and as sample diluent. It was found to be a very good inert because of its very fine grain size (95% minus 44μ), its virtual complete chemical inertness and its relatively low water absorption capacity. Calcined kaolinite, preferred in other investigations because of properties of thermodiffusivity and thermal conducibility closer to those of alunite, at high temperature reacts with the decomposition products of the sulphate, causing notable modifications on the thermal curves.

In the interest of reproducibility the crucibles were filled to the same depth and this was achieved by appropriate dilutions with alumina. The final weight for the Netzch crucibles was, approximately, 900mg. Since solid state reactions are known to occur as heating alunite, every effort was made to ensure the uniformity of these preparations in the course of the various series of analyses.

Alunite-boehmite mixtures

In nature alunite is frequently found in association with oxides of aluminium, gibbsite, boehmite and diaspore (Pardossy, 1959; Freidrich, 1960; Shomi Iwanoto, 1963; Safdar and Hamad, 1966).

In the present work investigations on the influence of boehmite on the thermal curves of alunite were carried out. As a standard, a sample from lava Castello (Dragoni-Caserta) was used, small amounts of hematite and anatase being found in this boehmite (Burragato, 1964). Boehmite was chosen because its characteristic endothermic reaction is within the same temperature range as that of the dehydroxylation of alunite.

In Fig. 1 are shown DTA curves of alunite-boehmite mixtures in various proportions; the amount of sulphate in the mixtures was constant (alunite 10 = 150mg). From DTA and TGA curves (Fig. 2) it can be concluded that the presence of boehmite leads to modifications on the thermal curves of alunite, although there is no evidence that the two components react. The shape of the dehydroxylation peak of the sulphate is not substantially altered; there is, however, a lowering of the characteristic temperature and an increase in peak area. This increase is merely a summation of the two dehydroxylations and this is confirmed by the close approximation of the calculated (loss of weight of alunite + loss of weight of boehmite heated separately) and experimental weight losses.

The presence of boehmite does not induce substantial modifications of the exothermic peak of alunite at 730°C, except for a slight reduction of its size. However, the desulfurization peak shows a progressive decrease in area as the boehmite contents increase, and a lowering of peak temperature as found with the dehydroxylation peak. These modifications are also reflected by the TGA curves, while the total experimental values of the losses, at temperatures of over 800°C, are slightly higher than the calculated. Above 1200°C the course of the decomposition of the sulphates present is also altered by boehmite, as shown by the divergencies of the curves at high temperatures.

Alunite-kaolinite mixtures

Kaolinite, as well as halloysite, is one of the minerals most frequently associated with alunite in nature and the paragenesis is well documented. Mixtures of standard alunite and the well-ordered kaolinite N.3 of Birch Pit, Macon, Georgia were investigated by DTA (Fig. 3, where alunite 10 = 200mg) and by TGA (Fig. 4). Since calcined kaolinite affects the desulphurization of alunite, alumina was used as the inert and diluent.

From the DTA curves the dehydroxylation of alunite and kaolinite occur within the same temperature range, but above an alunite-kaolinite ratio of 10:5 the peaks begin to resolve, kaolinite being the higher. This shift is also observed on the TGA curves. The dehydroxylation of alunite is more rapid than that of kaolinite, as can be seen from the shape of DTA peaks and DTG of pure samples, and alunite delays the dehydration of kaolinite. As an hypothesis to explain the temperature increase of the peak of the clay mineral it could be assumed that the hydroxyl water released from the alunite and filling the pores represses the dehydroxylation of kaolinite. After the dehydroxylation in all the mixtures analyzed here, calculated and experimental losses of weight coincide again at temperatures of about 650-675°C.

On the DTA curves the position and shape of the characteristic exothermic peak of alunite at 730°C and the temperatures of the desulphurization peak are modified by the presence of kaolinite. The exothermic peak is almost suppressed with alunite-kaolinite ratios of 10:5. For ratios up and including 10:20, however, a small inflection persists to temperatures very close to those characteristic of the peak itself. Similarly desulphurization occurs at lower temperatures and the process is accentuated for higher percentages of kaolinite. It is presumably for this reason that the exothermic reaction at 730°C, due to the crystallization of γ-alumina from alunite, is not fully expressed.

Gad and Barrett (1949) and Gad (1950) investigated the thermal decomposition of natural alunite-clay deposits by X-ray diffraction, noting that the dehydrated clay minerals react with the decomposition products of alunite to give glass, mullite and γ-alumina. All SO_3 is liberated by 1000°C. Moreover, the exothermic peak of kaolinite is suppressed by high alunite concentrations and for slightly lower concentrations the peak is reduced in size and temperature lowered. According to these authors this is due to "the reaction between dehydrated clay and

dehydrated alunite raises the $Al_2O_3:SiO_2$ ratio in the
collapsed clay lattice. Thus, permitting γ-Al_2O_3 to
crystallize over a wide range of temperatures from $780^{\circ}C$,
so that the sharp exothermic peak of clay at $980^{\circ}C$ is
reduced, depending on the amount of alunite present".
This hypothesis is substantiated by the results obtained
with the DTA of these artificial mixtures (Fig. 7).

Gruver et al. (1949) also refer on DTA curves of
kaolinite mixed with Fe_2O_3, Na_2CO_3, NaCl and calcined
kaolin. The presence of some of these components even in
percentages below 10%, can cause, among other effects,
substantial modifications of the areas of the exothermic
peak. In agreement with the results of Gad and Barrett
the authors state that "it appears that effective supp-
ression is caused by fusible impurities in the kaolin".

The experimental weight losses for alunite-kaolinite
mixtures, at temperatures above $820^{\circ}C$ are lower than the
calculated (Fig. 4) and clearly related to the amount of
clay present. This results from the fact that more SO_3
is liberated from these mixtures than from pure alunite and,
as observed in the next sections, from the mixtures of
alunite and carbonates. Presumably, because the dehydroxylation products of kaolinite are not sufficiently alkaline
to fix the SO_3 as alkali sulphates.

Alunite-calcite mixtures

Although they are not frequent in nature, associations
of alunite and calcite have been reported (Karyakin and
Remizov, 1956; Caillere and Maratos, 1958; Vinnichenko-
Uklonskaya, 1966). In addition there are also several
studies, primarily of industrial interest, carried out
mainly by Russian workers (see for example Kutateladze
and Dzhincharadze, 1959), on the modifications caused by
the presence of variable percentages of alunite on the
technical characteristics of cements.

In Fig. 5 is reproduced a series of DTA curves of
alunite-calcite (Merck $CaCO_3$) mixtures in different proportions, the quantity of alunite being constant (alunite
10 = 300mg). The complex reactions which occur at high

temperatures between the two components are reflected in the patterns of the DTA curves, while TGA (Fig. 6) exhibit considerable less resolution.

Following the dehydroxylation of alunite a series of reactions take place: desulphurization of alunite, formation and crystallization of calcium sulphate, crystallization of alumina, decomposition of carbonate; a number of these reactions tend to overlap. From X-ray examination of samples heated to various temperatures the principal reactions were established. Calcium sulphate (ASTM 6-0226) is present in the reaction product from 650°C to over 1400°C and calcium aluminates (as for example ASTM 8-5) were also recognised. Between 600°C and 1400°C, X-ray patterns close to those of complex sulphates and sulphoaluminates of K, Na and Ca were observed and, so far as can be ascertained, data is not available to identify those compounds unambiguously. More complete data could perhaps be obtained using a temperature-controlled X-ray camera, with which it is possible to observe these products at their temperature of formation.

On the DTA curves, modifications of shape, dimension and position of the peaks are interdependent and closely reflect the relative percentages of alunite and calcite. Addition of calcite slightly reduces the area of the dehydroxylation peak of alunite and decreases the characteristic temperature. This is considered to be a flux effect, and is substantiated by the fact that the experimental weight losses in this dehydroxylation range are slightly less than the calculated. It is established that under certain experimental conditions, calcite partially decomposes around 400°C; judging from the intensity of the reactions it is probable that the interactions between sulphate and carbonate commences about these temperatures. Additions of calcite to the mixtures reduces the peak temperature of the 730°C exothermic effect due to the crystallization of γ-alumina (from 730°C with alunite-calcite ratios of 10:1 to 660°C for 10:20 ratios). At the same time the area of this peak increases, attaining a maximum for alunite:calcite ratios of about 10:8. It is interesting to note that, as in other mixtures sharpening accompanies increases in peak area.

With increasing calcite concentration the desulphurization temperature of alunite is also reduced, but, as
the fall in peak temperature with calcite content is more
rapid for this reaction than for the χ-alumina   crystallization, the latter is progressively masked. The exothermic effect reflecting the heat of formation of calcium
sulphate was not detected even with double DTA analyses and
it can only be concluded that this is masked by another
reaction or reactions.

Sulphur trioxide liberated by the decomposition of
alunite reacts with the carbonate and with increasing carbonate concentrations the desulphurization peak decreases
enabling development of the χ-alumina exothermic peak up
to the maximum mentioned above. It is possible that carbonate produces structural modifications in the alunite
lattice, the dehydration temperature is lower markedly, so
that only partially recrystallization of χ-alumina can
take place. This could also account for the reduction in
sharpness of the exothermic peak.

Table 1.

Losses in weight (in mg) for 3 mixtures of alunite and calcite									
	I			II			III		
$T^{o}C$	C	E	Diff	C	E	Diff	C	E	Diff
620°	14.5	15.0	-0.5	14.8	16.3	-1.5	15.5	17.7	-2.2
800°	33.0	27.5	5.5	41.5	32.5	9.0	52.7	36.7	16.0
900°	49.0	33.2	15.8	83.5	55.0	28.5	125.5	84.7	40.8
1000°	50.5	34.2	16.3	85.1	55.3	29.8	127.5	99.6	27.9
1200°	52.0	39.0	13.0	87.2	57.5	29.7	129.7	99.8	29.9
1300°	53.3	44.5	8.8	88.3	63.0	25.3	131.2	100.2	31.0
1400°	56.5	48.8	7.7	91.5	68.5	23.0	133.7	102.3	31.4
1500°	60.5	53.0	7.5	96.5	76.5	20.0	138.1	111.1	27.0
1600°	64.3	61.5	2.8	99.8	96.5	3.3	140.6	128.8	11.8

C = calculated loss of weight (loss of weight of alunite +
    loss of weight of calcite heated separately)
E = experimental values for mixtures alunite-calcite
Diff = C - E
I = 100mg alun + 20mg calc; II = 100mg alun + 100mg calc;
III = 100mg alun + 200mg calc

The calculated and experimentally determined weight loss on heating alunite-calcite mixtures are given in Tab.1. Differences between the calculated and observed weight losses have been mentioned above. For concentrations of calcite in excess of 50% the differences tend to be constant because practically all of the available SO_3 reacts with the carbonate. X-ray analyses showed that the resulting $CaSO_4$ and the other complex sulphate of K,Na and Al decompose only above $1200^{\circ}C$ as also evidenced by a small endothermic effect on the DTA, the peak temperature of which is dependent upon the amount of calcite originally present in the sample.

These results were also confirmed by chemical tests for sulphur on a mixture of alunite-calcite 1:1 heated at $1200^{\circ}C$, which showed that practically all the original SO_3 was still present. On the TGA (Fig. 2 and Tab.1) for mixtures of 1:1, with a total initial weight of 200mg, at $1200^{\circ}C$ there is a weight loss of 57.5mg. Of this 44mg are due to CO_2 and the remainder, the water of crystallization of the sulphate. It is to be noted that, although the analyses were carried out in open crucibles, no appreciable loss of SO_3 occurred.

The characteristics of the calcite decomposition peak are markedly affected by the amount of alunite present. The endothermic decomposition of the carbonate is only well developed on the curves of mixtures of alunite-calcite with ratios higher than 10:5 and always has a reduced area. This carbonate decomposition peak reflects the excess of carbonate following the SO_3-carbonate reaction and it shows a double endothermic peak system similar to that of dolomite. It could result from the fact that, under the experimental conditions employed, the CO_2 produced in the initial stages of decomposition does not diffuse rapidly enough from the site of the reaction and hence tends to elevate the decomposition temperatures of the bulk of the carbonate. However, this is not evident on the curve for calcite alone and must therefore be associated with some change induced by the presence of the sulphate. It has been noted, moreover, in other series of analyses, that changes in the shape and temperatures of this peak system are related to the degree of compaction.

Alunite-dolomite mixtures

Naturally occurring alunite-dolomite mixtures are not reported, but the properties of artificial mixtures of these minerals are well documented since they are used in the manufacture of particular mortars and cements. X-ray examination of the thermal products of such mixtures (Kutateladze and Dzhincharadze, 1959; 1957) indicate that solid state reactions occur in which calcium sulphate is formed, but there is no evidence of SO_3 liberation. Also Kasai Junichi <u>et al.</u> (1964) examined the characteristics of a self-hardening mortar, produced by the combination of alunitic and dolomitic mortars. According to their findings, three types of reactions occur during the hardening process of this mortar: 1) Al_2O_3 of alunite reacts with $Ca(OH)_2$ and gives calcium aluminates; 2) SO_3 of alunite reacts with $Ca(OH)_2$ and gives $CaSO_4.2H_2O$; 3) the Ca-aluminates react with $CaSO_4.2H_2O$ and give $3CaO.Al_2O_3.CaSO_4.31-32H_2O$.

In this investigation mixtures of alunite with a sample of Liassic dolomite from Portello, Caserta, were used. The sample contained 91% dolomite, impurities being principally clay minerals and calcite and was employed in its natural state, without submitting it to enrichment processes. The DTA (where alunite 10 = 300mg) and TGA curves of mixtures of alunite and dolomite are given in Fig.7 and 8 respectively.

The effect of increasing amounts of dolomite is similar to that noted for calcite. However, the reduction in area and the decrease in temperature of the alunite dehydroxylation peak are more pronounced. The γ-alumina crystallization ($730^\circ C$) shows a progressive decrease in peak temperature and an increase in size up to an alunite-dolomite ratio of 10:2.5. Higher concentrations of dolomite produce a marked reduction in the size of this peak and for an alunite-dolomite mixture of 10:10 it is virtually absent. The desulphurization peak is reduced in size with higher dolomite contents and is eventually replaced by the first dolomite decomposition peak. It has been considered that the double peak on the DTA of dolomite corresponds to
$$CaCO_3.MgCO_3 \rightarrow CaCO_3 + MgO + CO_2$$
then there is the possibility that the $CaCO_3$ and the SO_3

from alunite react together. X-ray analyses of a alunite-dolomite mixture 1:1 heated at $800^{\circ}C$ showed that, among the principal components, $CaSO_4$, MgO, complex sulphate of K, Na, Al and Ca-aluminates are present.

From TGA evidence, even before the dehydroxylation of alunite is completed, there is an appreciable difference between the calculated and experimental weight losses of alunite-dolomite mixtures greater than the divergence noted with corresponding amounts of calcite. A chemical test for sulphur of an alunite-dolomite mixture 1:1, heated at $1200^{\circ}C$, showed that, as with calcite, practically all SO_3 here is still present at that temperature. This suggests that weight losses above $600^{\circ}C$ can be attributed mainly to the loss of CO_2 from the dolomite. When sulphate is present the carbonate structure is broken down at a lower temperature, a phenomenon noted also with alunite-calcite mixtures. However, for mixtures with a high content in dolomite, the second dolomite peak shows evidence of doubling but not so marked as on the curves of high calcite-alunite mixtures. Above $950^{\circ}C$ the courses of the losses of weight follow more or less the same general pattern as those observed in the alunite-calcite mixtures.

Conclusions

Thermal analyses has proved an attractive method to study the reactions occurring between alunite and certain commonly associated mineralogical components. From the investigations detailed in this paper, it can be concluded that while the interactions of alunite with boehmite and kaolinite do not produce marked effects on the alunite curves, reactions between alunite and carbonates result in significant changes in the stages of the decomposition of alunite. The principal cause is attributed to the fact that SO_3 is fixed as calcium sulphates stable up to temperatures above $1200^{\circ}C$. The thermal methods, particularly DTA, gave an authentic record of the numerous solid state reactions occurring between alunite and other minerals and, in conjunction with X-ray analyses, can obviously be developed to provide a valuable method of constructing phase diagrams of the products at each stage of the heating cycle.

A number of observations can be drawn concerning the use of DTA and TGA for the semi-quantitative determination of alunite in naturally occurring deposits.

Because of the abundance of rocks containing minerals which undergo thermal transformations in the region of $550°C$ (for example kaolinite, quartz, boehmite etc.), the dehydroxylation peak of the sulphate at $555°C$ cannot normally be used in quantitative work. The desulfurization peak can be utilized, but only when the parageneses are known.

Concerning the artificial mixtures examined, the presence of boehmite reduces the size of the desulphurization peak slightly, but only when the boehmite content is very high. Consequently, for many samples the effect can be neglected. For alunitic rocks with an appreciable kaolinite content the endothermic effect reflecting the loss of SO_3 may be used, within limits, to assess the alunite concentration. Because of the rapidly successive and simultaneous solid state reactions occurring between alunite and carbonates when heated, DTA can only be used for analyses of alunitic materials contaminated to a low degree with carbonate.

The experimental thermobalance curves agree only over a limited range of temperatures with theoretical weight loss values. Consequently, its quantitative role is limited to reasonably pure alunitic samples.

Acknowledgements

The author is indebted to Prof. C. Lauro of the University of Rome and to B. D. Mitchell of the Macaulay Institute for Soil Research, Aberdeen, Scotland, for the helpful discussions during the course of this work.

References

1. G. Lombardi, Periodico Mineral. (Rome) 36, 399 (1967)
2. P.F. Kerr and J. L. Kulp, Am. Mineralogist 33, 387, (1948)
3. M.A. Kashkai and I.A. Babaiev, Izv. Akad. Nauk Azerb. SSR, Ser. Geol.-Geogr. Nauk, no.6 (1959)

4. N.S. Bayliss and D.F.A. Koch, Australian J. Appl. Sci. 6, 298, (1955)
5. G.M. Gad and L.R. Barrett, Trans. Brit. Ceram. Soc. 48, 352, (1949)
6. G.M. Gad, J. Am. Ceram. Soc. 33, 208, (1950)
7. Gy. Bardossy, Acta Geol. Acad. Sci. Hung. 6, 1, (1959)
8. G. Friedrich, Neues Jahrb. Mineral. Abhandl., 94, 208 (1960)
9. Shomi Iwamoto, Hiroshima Daigaku Chigaku Kenkyu Hokoku 12, 73, (1963)
10. M. Safdar, Anwar Hamid and Mushtaq Ahmad Naz, Pakistan J. Sci. Ind. Res. 9, 224, (1966)
11. F. Burragato, Periodico Mineral (Rome) 33, 501, (1964)
12. R. M. Gruver, E.C. Henry and H. Heystek, Am. Mineralogist 34, 869, (1949)
13. L.I. Karyakin and I.N. Remizov, Vopr. Mineralog. Osad. Obrazov. L'vovsk. Gos. Univ. 3-4, 398, (1956).
14. S. Caillere and G. Maratos, Bull. Soc. Franc. Mineral. Crist. 81, 16, (1958)
15. N.T. Vinnichenko-Uklonskaya, Nauchn. Tr., Tashkent. Gos. Univ. 273, 30, (1966)
16. K.S. Kutateladze and N. G. Dzhinsharadze, Stroi, Materialy 5, no.7, 35, (1959)
17. N.G. Dzhincharadze and K.S. Kutateladze, Tr. Gruzinsk. Politekhn. Inst. 2, 82, (1957)
18. Junichi Kasai, Hironobu Inoue and Manjiro Nakahara, Sekko To Sekkai 70, 108, (1964)

Rome, August 1968

  Istituto di Petrografia of the University of Rome
  Centro di Studio del C.N.R. per la Mineralogia e la
  Petrografia.   Sez. II Petrografia

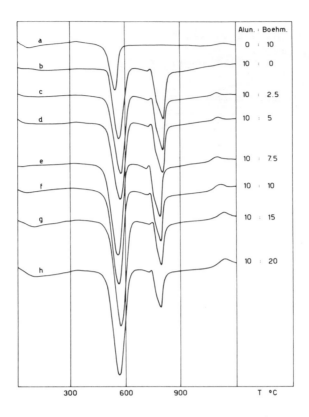

Fig. 1 - DTA curves for mixtures alunite-boehmite Netzch-L.N. apparatus. Sensit. 50 μV/in

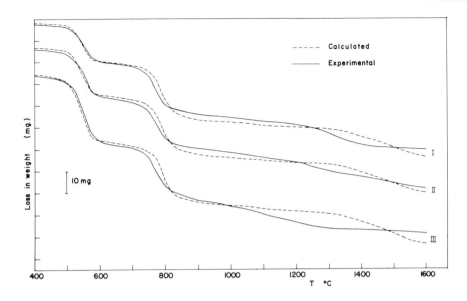

Fig. 2 - Thermobalance curves for mixtures
alunite-boehmite
I   = 100 mg alun + 50 mg boehm
II = 100 mg alun + 100 mg boehm
III = 100 mg alun + 200 mg boehm

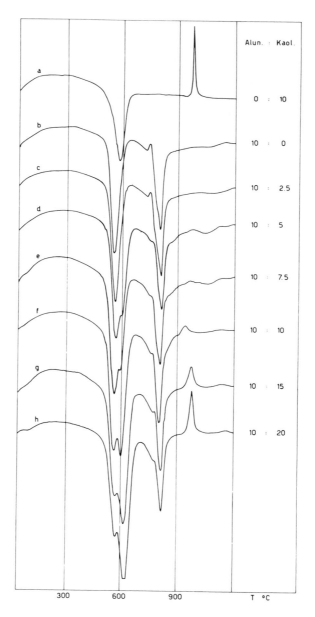

Fig. 3 - DTA curves for mixtures alunite-kaolinite
Netzch-L.N. apparatus. Sensit. 50 μV/in

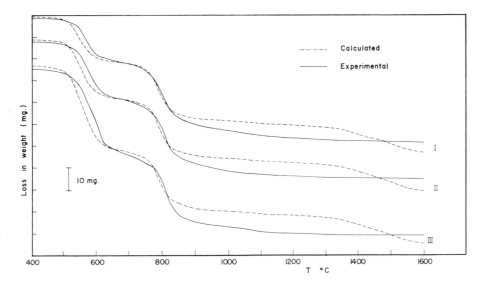

<u>Fig. 4</u> - Thermobalance curves for mixtures
alunite-kaolinite
I   = 100 mg alun + 50 mg kaol
II = 100 mg alun + 100 mg kaol
III = 100 mg alun + 200 mg kaol

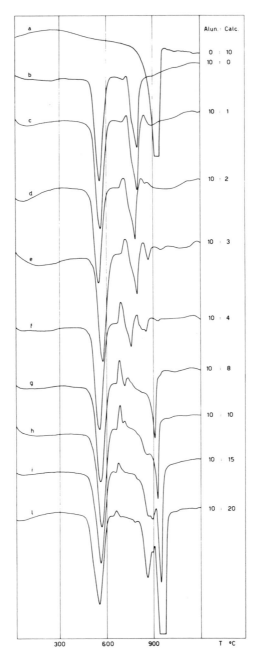

Fig. 5 - DTA curves for mixtures alunite-calcite
Netzch-L.N. apparatus. Sensit. 50 μV/in

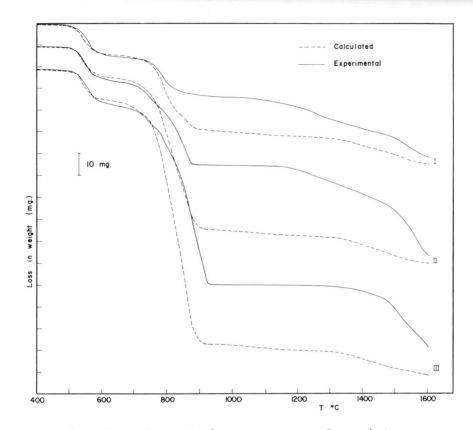

<u>Fig. 6</u> - Thermobalance curves for mistures
       alunite-calcite
       I   = 100 mg alun + 20 mg calc
       II = 100 mg alun + 100 mg calc
       III = 100 mg alun + 200 mg calc

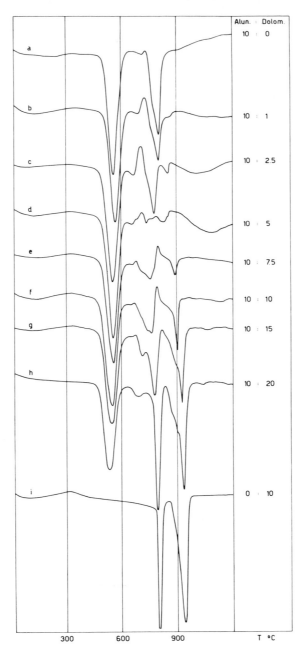

Fig. 7 - DTA curves for mixtures alunite-dolomite
        Netzch-L.N. apparatus. Sensit. 50 μV/in

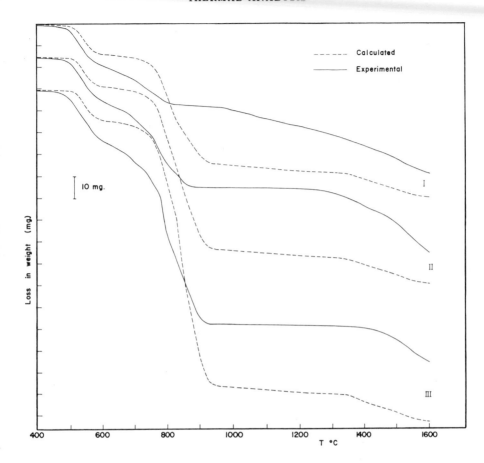

Fig. 8 - Thermobalance curves for mixtures
                    alunite-dolomite
                    I   = 100 mg alun + 50 mg dolom
                    II = 100 mg alun + 100 mg dolom
                    III = 100 mg alun + 200 mg dolom

THERMAL DECOMPOSITION RATE
OF MOLYBDENITE IN VACUUM

Yoichi Maru,* Koichi Ito** and Yoshio Kondo***

* Research Assistant, Department of Metallurgy, Kyoto University, Kyoto, Japan

** Former graduate student, Kyoto University,
   now with Kambara plant, Nippon Light Metal
   Co. Ltd., Shizuoka Pref., Japan

*** Professor, Department of Metallurgy, Kyoto
    University, Kyoto, Japan

The decomposition of molybdenite
(molybdenum disulfide) to Molybdenum
metal was studied using a vacuum thermobalance. Mo_2S_3 is formed as an intermediate product although the steps were
not isolated. While the fraction
decomposed is less than 0.7, the
reaction follows a parabolic rate law.
The data suggest that the limiting step
is the diffusion of sulfur from the
reaction interface to the partial
surface.

Although some sulphide minerals decompose at higher temperature, thermal decomposition technique for extracting metals is an unexplored field in extractive metallurgy. In 1961, Climax Molybdenum Company (1) developed a process of vacuum thermal decomposition of molybdenite (MoS_2) into metallic molybdenum and revealed a possibility of applying this technique in extractive metallurgy.

It is known in the thermal decomposition of MoS_2 that Mo_2S_3 is formed as an intermediate product during the course of decomposition (2). The decomposition equations are written as

$$4 \ MoS_2 = 2 \ Mo_2S_3 + S_2 \qquad (1)$$

$$2/3 \ Mo_2S_3 = 4/3 \ Mo + S_2 \qquad (2)$$

The thermodynamics of these reactions were studied by McCabe (2) and by Stubbles and Richardson (3). The standard free energy changes in cal/mole S_2 are given by Stubbles and Richardson as,

$$\text{for reaction (1); } \Delta G^\circ_o = 86,380 - 40.09T \qquad (3)$$
$$\text{for reaction (2); } \Delta G^\circ = 85,700 - 36.41T \qquad (4)$$

Fig. 1 demonstrates the equilibrium pressure. It is seen in this figure that MoS_2 and Mo_2S_3 equilibrate with each other at $860^\circ C$ at 10^{-5} mmHg and that Mo_2S_3 is in equilibrium with Mo at $910^\circ C$ at the same pressure. On the other hand, however, the kinetics of the decomposition still remains unclarified.

Generally, the thermal decomposition of sulphide mineral is an endothermic reaction. The overall process of thermal decomposition of solid particles is said to be composed of the following three sequential steps (4):

(1) transfer of heat from environment to the reaction interface within the particle through the shell of decomposed product,

(2) decomposition at the reaction interface and

(3) transfer of the evolving gas towards the environment through the decomposed shell.

And the rate-determining step of the reaction is different according to the properties of material and the decomposing conditions. Maru, Yoshida and Kondo (5) examined the kinetics of decomposition of Mo_2S_3 in a pelletized form and suggested that step (3) plays the most important role; the transfer rate of sulphur gas through the metallic Mo shell determines the overall rate.

Based upon this result, it is intended in this work to establish the kinetic expression of overall thermal decomposition of MoS_2 pellet into metallic Mo during which the formation and the decomposition of Mo_2S_3 are included.

1.   Material

In the thermal decomposition study of MoS_2 pellet performed by Scholz, Doane and Timmons (1), "Lubricant Grade MoS_2" was used.   This material was a product from a new milling process at the Climax mine and is contaminated with flotation oil.   Our preliminary experiments on the pelletized MoS_2 powder of "Technical Fine Grade" revealed the formation of Mo_2C during the decomposition.   It is supposed to be caused by the contaminating flotation oil.

For the kinetic evaluation of thermal decomposition of MoS_2, possible interferences by Mo_2C should be eliminated.   For this reason, MoS_2 crystal was used instead of flotation concentrate.   Molybdenite crystals mined in China were sent to this laboratory through the courtesy of Climax Molybdenum Company in New York.   The powder was scraped from the crystal with a stainless steel knife and was ground in an agate mortar into a size under 300 mesh.   This powder was pressed into a disc-shaped pellet of 11.7 mm diameter and about 1 mm high.   The pressure used was 470 and 94 kg/cm^2 and the void fraction of the pellet was estimated at 0.30 ±0.01 and 0.45 ±0.01, respectively.

2. Experimental Apparatus and Procedure

Weight loss of the MoS_2 pellet during the thermal decomposition was measured by thermogravimetric analysis.

The experimental apparatus is illustrated schematically in Fig. 2.   It consists of a vacuum furnace of molybdenum resistance wire heating provided with a quartz spring balance.   Its sensitivity is 0.039 mg per micron.   The outer and inner parts of Sinter-Korund reaction tube within the furnace are separately evacuated down to below 5 x 10^{-5} mmHg.   The sample dish of 20 mm diameter hung from the quartz spring is made of tantalum plate.   It is coated with molten

alumina in order to protect it from corrosive sulphur
gas.   Tantalum wire which is used to hang the dish
is also attacked by sulphur gas.   Since it is difficult to coat it with molten alumina, it is replaced by
a new one after several runs.   The weight gain of
this wire was found to be trivial and can be omitted.
Uniform temperature zone in vertical direction within
the reaction tube was found to be about 4 cm long and
the sample dish was kept within this zone during the
measurement.   Upper flange of the furnace is equipped
with a water cooling tube to prevent the displacement
of quartz spring caused by thermal expansion of the
glass tube.
      Isothermal measurement of the weight loss of MoS_2
pellet was carried out at the temperature of 1190, 1240,
1290, 1340, 1390 and $1440^\circ C$, respectively.   The
decomposed products were analysed by X-ray.

3.   Experimental Results

      The weight loss of MoS_2 pellet was transformed into
the fraction decomposed, x, by

$$x = \left(\frac{W_0 - W}{W_0}\right)\left(\frac{M_{MoS_2}}{M_{S_2}}\right) = \left(\frac{W_0 - W}{W_0}\right)\left(\frac{1}{4f_1 M_{S_2}}\right) \tag{5}$$

The results of isothermal decomposition are illustrated
in Fig. 3.   No curve break was found in this figure
and the decomposing rate increases by raising temperature.
From a logarithmic expression of x vs. θ , it was found
that logx is proportional to $\log\theta$ below about 0.7 of x.
Since its slope was estimated at about 0.5, we have,

$$x^2 = k\theta \tag{6}$$

where $x < 0.7$

x^2 was plotted against θ in Fig. 4.   It was also
observed in the partially decomposed pellets that the
appearance of sections of outer shell and of inner core
is different; MoS_2 particles seemed to remain undecomposed in the core.   Parabolic law of equation (6)
and the different appearance lead us to presume that
there is a decomposing interface within the pellet which
moves inwards during decomposition starting from the
surface.
      From the slopes of x^2 vs. θ plot of Fig. 4, the
apparent activation energy of decomposition was estimated

1294

at 86.4 kcal/mole by using the least squares method. Arrhenius expression of this rate constant k is,

$$k = A_1 e^{-\frac{86,400}{RT}} \qquad (7)$$

On the other hand, from equations (3) and (4), the equilibrium pressure of S_2 of equations (1) and (2) are,

$$p_1 = A_2 e^{-\frac{86,400}{RT}} \qquad (8)$$

$$p_2 = A_3 e^{-\frac{85,700}{RT}} \qquad (9)$$

From these equations, it is seen that the temperature dependent exponential term of rate constant k is very close to that of equilibrium pressure of S_2 gas.

4. Discussion

4.1 Mass transfer model

Among the three sequential steps of decomposition mentioned above, Maru (5) proposed regarding the decomposition of Mo_2S_3 pellet that the transfer rate of sulphur gas through the outer shell of metallic Mo determines the overall decomposition rate. With this model of mass transfer in mind, three- and two-phase models shown in Fig. 5 are examined. The former is intended to be applied to the earlier stage of decomposition and the latter to the later stage where MoS_2 is already decomposed. The assumptions on these models are as follows.

1) Decomposition of MoS_2 proceeds through the intermediate product of Mo_2S_3 into metallic Mo; a layer of Mo_2S_3 is formed between the inner core of MoS_2 and the outer shell of Mo and their interfaces move inwards during the decomposition. At the interface of MoS_2/Mo_2S_3, both components equilibrate each other and the pressure of S_2, p_1, can be calculated by equation (8), and the pressure of S_2 at the interface of Mo_2S_3/Mo, p_2, is calculated by equation (9).

2) Resistance of mass transfer within particles is omitted.

3) The area of upper and lower basal planes of the pellet is more than five times larger than that of the lateral surface. And it is assumed that the greater

1295

part of outward flux of sulphur gas passes through the basal planes of the pellet, and that the flux through the lateral surface is omitted.

4) Change of the dimension of the pellet during the decomposition is neglected.

Three-phase model of MoS_2-Mo_2S_3-Mo

In the earlier stage of decomposition, MoS_2 remains in the core. The model is illustrated in Fig. 5(a). In this figure, it is shown that the pressure of S_2 gas is equal to its equilibrated value of p_1 at the interface I and that it is equal to p_2 at the interface II.

The flux of S_2 gas passing through the Mo_2S_3 shell, N_2, is expressed by

$$N_2 = - D_2 \frac{\partial c}{\partial y} = \frac{D_2}{RT} \frac{p_1 - p_2}{y_2 - y_1} \qquad (10)$$

Similarly, the flux of S_2 gas through the Mo shell, N_3, is

$$N_3 = - D_3 \frac{\partial c}{\partial y} = \frac{D_3}{RT} \frac{p_2 - p_3}{\ell - y_2} \qquad (11)$$

where D_2 and D_3 denote the effective diffusivities of sulphur gas in each layer. They are expressed by the following equations (6) because of dominant Knudsen diffusion in the vacuum of about 10^{-5} mmHg.

$$D_2 = f(\varepsilon_2) D_{K_2} = \frac{2}{3} f(\varepsilon_2) \bar{r}_2 \bar{v} \qquad (12)$$

$$D_3 = f(\varepsilon_3) D_{K_3} = \frac{2}{3} f(\varepsilon_3) \bar{r}_3 \bar{v} \qquad (13)$$

On the other hand, evolving rate of S_2 gas at the interfaces I and II, G_1 and G_2, respectively, are given by

$$G_1 = - \frac{dy_1}{d\theta} \rho_1 \frac{1}{4 M_{MoS_2}} = - \rho_1 f_1 \frac{dy_1}{d\theta} \qquad (14)$$

and

$$G_2 = - \frac{dy_2}{d\theta} \rho_2 \frac{3}{2 M_{Mo_2S_3}} = - \rho_2 f_2 \frac{dy_2}{d\theta} \qquad (15)$$

To combine the equations (10), (11), (14) and (15), the

material balance expressions concerning sulphur gas at
the interfaces I and II,

$$G_1 = N_2 \qquad (16)$$

$$N_2 + G_2 = N_3 \qquad (17)$$

are used.   Thus,

$$-\rho_1 f_1 \frac{dy_1}{d\theta} = \frac{D_2}{RT} \frac{p_1 - p_2}{y_2 - y_1} \qquad (18)$$

and

$$\frac{D_2}{RT} \frac{p_1 - p_2}{y_2 - y_1} - \rho_2 f_2 \frac{dy_2}{d\theta} = \frac{D_3}{RT} \frac{p_2 - p_3}{\ell - y_2} \qquad (19)$$

From these two equations, we have

$$\rho_1 f_1 (\ell - y_1) dy_1 + \rho_2 f_2 (\ell - y_2) dy_2$$

$$= -\frac{1}{RT} \left\{ D_2 (p_1 - p_2) + D_3 (p_2 - p_3) \right\} d\theta \qquad (20)$$

Intergration of this equation (20) with an initial
condition of $y_1 = y_2 = \ell$ at $\theta = 0$ yields the
relationship between y_1 and y_2 in the form of

$$y_2 = \left[1 - \sqrt{\left\{ \frac{2K\theta}{\ell^2} - \rho_1 f_1 \left(1 - \frac{y_1}{\ell} \right)^2 \right\} \frac{1}{\rho_2 f_2}} \right] \ell \qquad (21)$$

where

$$K = \frac{D_2 (p_1 - p_2) + D_3 (p_2 - p_3)}{RT} \qquad (22)$$

To eliminate y_2 from equation (18), equation (21) is
inserted and we have

$$\left[\sqrt{\left\{ \frac{2K\theta}{\ell^2} - \rho_1 f_1 \alpha^2 \right\} \frac{1}{\rho_2 f_2}} - \alpha \right] d\alpha = -\frac{D_2}{RT} \frac{(p_1 - p_2)}{\ell^2 \rho_1 f_1} d\theta \qquad (23)$$

where

$$\alpha = 1 - \left(\frac{y_1}{\ell} \right) \qquad (24)$$

This α is nondimensional volume of decomposed MoS_2 into
Mo_2S_3.   A solution of equation (23) is expressed by

$$\alpha^2 = k_1 \theta \qquad (25)$$

where

$$k_1 = \frac{1}{RT\ell^2(\rho_1 f_1 + \rho_2 f_2)}\left[D_2(\rho_1 - \rho_2)\left(1 + \frac{2\rho_2 f_2}{\rho_1 f_1}\right) + D_3(\rho_2 - \rho_3)\right.$$
$$\left. + \sqrt{\{D_2(\rho_1 - \rho_2) + D_3(\rho_2 - \rho_3)\}^2 + 4D_2 D_3(\rho_1 - \rho_2)(\rho_2 - \rho_3)\frac{\rho_2 f_2}{\rho_1 f_1}}\right] \quad (26)$$

On the other hand, the rate of weight loss of the pellet is correlated with the moving rates of the two interfaces by,

$$-\frac{dW}{d\theta} = 2\pi r^2\left(\rho_1 f_1 \frac{dy_1}{d\theta} + \rho_2 f_2 \frac{dy_2}{d\theta}\right)M_{S_2} \quad (27)$$

By integrating equation (27) with the initial conditions of $W = W_0$ and $y_1 = y_2 = \ell$ at $\theta = 0$, fraction decomposed x defined by equation (5) becomes,

$$x = \frac{1}{4}\left\{\left(1 - \frac{y_1}{\ell}\right) + \frac{\rho_2 f_2}{\rho_1 f_1}\left(1 - \frac{y_2}{\ell}\right)\right\} \quad (28)$$

and with equations (21), (24) and (25), it is transformed into

$$x = \frac{1}{4}\left[\left(1 - \frac{y_1}{\ell}\right) + \frac{\rho_2 f_2}{\rho_1 f_1}\sqrt{\left\{\frac{2K\theta}{\ell^2} - \rho_1 f_1\left(1 - \frac{y_1}{\ell}\right)^2\right\}\frac{1}{\rho_2 f_2}}\right]$$
$$= \frac{1}{4}\left\{1 + \frac{1}{\rho_1 f_1}\sqrt{\rho_2 f_2\left(\frac{2K}{k_1\ell^2} - \rho_1 f_1\right)}\right\}(k_1\theta)^{\frac{1}{2}} \quad (29)$$

And the final rate equation is,

$$x^2 = \frac{k_1}{16}\left\{1 + \frac{1}{\rho_1 f_1}\sqrt{\rho_2 f_2\left(\frac{2K}{k_1\ell^2} - \rho_1 f_1\right)}\right\}^2 \theta = k\theta \quad (30)$$

where

$$k = \frac{k_1}{16}\left\{1 + \frac{1}{\rho_1 f_1}\sqrt{\rho_2 f_2\left(\frac{2K}{k_1\ell^2} - \rho_1 f_1\right)}\right\}^2 \quad (31)$$

This is a parabolic expression similar to equation (6). Equation (30) holds when $y_1 > 0$, or, from equations (24) and (25)

$$\theta < \frac{1}{k_1}$$

Two-phase model of Mo_2S_3–Mo
_____

When $\theta \geq 1/k_1$, MoS_2 disappears in the core of the pellet and it is composed of Mo_2S_3 and Mo. Fig. 5(b) demonstrates the model. The value of y_2 at $\theta = 1/k_1$, denoted by y_2^0, is calculated from equation (21) as,

$$y_2^0 = \left\{ 1 - \sqrt{\left(\frac{2K}{k_1 l^2} - p_1 f_1 \right) \frac{1}{p_2 f_2}} \right\} l \qquad \text{at} \ \theta = \frac{1}{k_1} \qquad (32)$$

Concerning the fraction decomposed at $\theta = 1/k_1$, x^0, equation (29) yields,

$$x^0 = \frac{1}{4} \left\{ 1 + \frac{1}{p_1 f_1} \sqrt{p_2 f_2 \left(\frac{2K}{k_1 l^2} - p_1 f_1 \right)} \right\} \qquad \text{at} \ \theta = \frac{1}{k_1} \qquad (33)$$

With this initial value of x^0, x can be obtained in the similar way as equation (28). It is

$$x = x^0 + \frac{p_2 f_2}{4 p_1 f_1} \left(\frac{y_2^0 - y_2}{l} \right) \qquad (34)$$

From this equation,

$$y_2 = y_2^0 - \frac{4 p_1 f_1 l}{p_2 f_2} (x - x^0) \qquad (35)$$

Substituting equations (32) and (33) in this equation, it becomes

$$y_2 = l - \frac{4 p_1 f_1 l}{p_2 f_2} \left(x - \frac{1}{4} \right) \qquad (36)$$

This is the relationship between y_2 and x in this model.

Mass transfer equations (11) and (15) can be applied to this model, and the material balance expression at the interface is,

$$N_3 = G_2 \qquad (37)$$

Thus, equations (11), (15) and (37) yield,

$$-(l - y_2) dy_2 = \frac{D_3}{RT} \frac{(p_2 - p_3)}{p_2 f_2} d\theta \qquad (38)$$

To obtain the rate equation, it is thought better to replace the variable y_2 by x. Equation (36) and its differentiated form of

$$dy_2 = - \frac{4 p_1 f_1 l}{p_2 f_2} dx \qquad (39)$$

is used and equation (38) is rewritten as,

$$\left(x-\frac{1}{4}\right)dx = \frac{D_3(p_2-p_3)}{RT}\frac{p_2 f_2}{(4 p_1 f_1 \ell)^2} d\theta \tag{40}$$

With the initial condition of equation (33), its integrated form is,

$$\left(x-\frac{1}{4}\right)^2 = \frac{D_3(p_2-p_3)p_2 f_2}{8RT\ell^2(p_1 f_1)^2}\theta + \frac{p_2 f_2}{8 p_1 f_1}\left\{\frac{D_2(p_1-p_2)}{RT k_1 \ell^2 p_1 f_1} - \frac{1}{2}\right\} \tag{41}$$

With conventional constants,

$$k' = \frac{D_3(p_2-p_3)p_2 f_2}{8RT\ell^2(p_1 f_1)^2} \tag{42}$$

and

$$C = \frac{p_2 f_2}{8 p_1 f_1}\left\{\frac{D_2(p_1-p_2)}{RT k_1 \ell^2 p_1 f_1} - \frac{1}{2}\right\} \tag{43}$$

the final rate equation is expressed by

$$\left(x-\frac{1}{4}\right)^2 = k'\theta + C \tag{44}$$

Rate equations (30) of three-phase model and (44) of two-phase model are demonstrated schematically in Fig. 6.

4.2   Examination of the mass transfer model
   Based upon the mass transfer models illustrated in Fig. 5, rate equations (30) and (44) were derived. It is intended to examine the validity of these rate equations.

Fitness of rate equations for the results of thermo-gravimetric analysis
   To verify the equation (30) of three-phase model and the equation (44) of two-phase model, linear relationships are to be approved between x^2 and θ and between $(x-1/4)^2$ and θ, respectively. It was already shown in Fig. 4 that the measured x^2 is proportional to θ when x is below 0.7 and that it deviates from the straight line in the later stage of decomposition. In this stage of deviation, $(x-1/4)^2$ instead of x^2 was plotted against θ. It is clarified in Fig. 7 that $(x-1/4)^2$ is proportional to θ when x is between 0.7 and 0.9. When x exceeds 0.9, the proportionality can not be seen, probably due to some other effect such as sintering occurring in the final

stage.   Apparent activation energy in this stage was
estimated at 86.07 kcal/mole from the slope in Fig. 7.
It is also very close to the temperature dependent
exponential term of equilibrium pressure of S_2 given by
equation (9).   Together with equations (22), (26),
(31) and (42), it is supposed that the closeness of
temperature dependent exponential term of rate constants
to those of equilibrium pressure of S_2 reveals that the
effective diffusivities D_2 and D_3 do not change exponentially with temperature.

X-ray diffraction patterns of partially decomposed pellet

It was mentioned above that the three-phase model
can be applied to the decomposition when x is below 0.7
and that the two-phase model replaces the former in the
later stage of $0.7 < x < 0.9$.   This means that MoS_2
disappears at $x^0 \approx 0.7$.   To confirm this, we tried
to investigate the X-ray diffraction patterns of pellets
partially decomposed at 1240°C.   The outer shell of
the pellet was scraped with a knife from the inner core
and they were examined separately.   The diffraction
patterns are demonstrated in Fig. 8.   The diagram
reveals that MoS_2 remains in the core at x = 0.65 and
0.75 and disappears at x = 0.80.   This suggests that
the critical value x^0 lies between 0.75 and 0.80.
It may be presumed that this result coincides fairly
well with the result of thermogravimetric analysis.
It is also seen in Fig. 8 that the intensity of diffraction peaks of MoS_2, Mo_2S_3 and Mo are quite different
between the inner core and the outer shell.   This
may also indicate the inward progress of decomposing
interface during the reaction and it is consistent with
the mass transfer model so far mentioned.

Examining proportionality of rate constants k and k' to the reciprocal square height of pellet, $1/(4\ell^2)$

The rate constants k and k' of equations (31) and
(42) are seen to be proportional to $1/(4\ell^2)$.   In
order to investigate this relationship, isothermal
decomposition was carried out with pellets of different
heights.   The amounts of 0.3, 0.4 and 0.5 g MoS_2
powder were chosen and pellets were prepared with a
pressure of 470 and 94 kg/cm^2.   They were decomposed
at 1240 and 1290°C.   Rate constants k and k' in ear-

lier and later stages of the decomposition were plotted against $1/(4\ell^2)$ in Fig. 9. From this, proportionality of the rate constnats to $1/(4\ell^2)$ was observed.

Estimation of effective diffusivities D_2 and D_3 and the critical value of fraction decomposed x^0

It was shown in the preceeding sections that the rate equations based on the mass transfer model can be applied to the decomposition of MoS_2 pellet, that the X-ray diffraction patterns of partially decomposed pellet was presumed to support the model and that the rate constants measured are proportional to the reciprocal square height of the pellet; it is also a proof of this model.

With these results in mind, we pursued further to estimate the effective diffusivities of sulphur gas, D_2 and D_3, through the shells of Mo_2S_3 and Mo, respectively. It becomes also possible, with D_2 and D_3 obtained, to calculate x^0, the critical value of fraction decomposed where MoS_2 disappears.

The rate constant k' defined by equation (42) contains only D_3 and it can be estimated from given values of p_2, p_3, ρ_1 and ρ_2. Of these values, p_2 is presumed to be calculated by equation (9) because of equilibrium established at the interface of Mo_2S_3/Mo. The pressure of sulphur gas at the outer surface of pellet, p_3, is assumed at around 5×10^{-5} mmHg in the reaction tube and it is much lower than p_2. Apparent density of MoS_2, ρ_1, can be calculated from the weight and size of the pellet. However, the apparent density of Mo_2S_3 layer, ρ_2, can not be calculated in this way because of its unknown void fraction within the pellet. And the following expression was presumed.

$$\rho_2 = 5.81 \left(1 - \frac{\varepsilon_1 + \varepsilon_3}{2} \right) \tag{45}$$

where 5.81 (g/cm^3) is the net density of Mo_2S_3 (7) and ε_3 is the void fraction of Mo measured on the decomposed pellet. The void fraction of the pellet, ε_1, was estimated by the following equation,

$$\varepsilon_1 = 1 - \frac{\rho_1}{5.06} \tag{46}$$

where 5.06 (g/cm^3) is the net density of MoS_2 given by

de Schulten (8).   With these values of pressure and
density and with the rate constant k' obtained by the
least squares method from the thermogravimetric analysis, D_3 was calculated and listed in Table 1.
    Maru (5) studied the thermal decomposition rate of
synthetized Mo_2S_3 pellet and estimated the effective
diffusivity of sulphur gas through the metallic Mo shell
formed.   It is also illustrated in the table.
By comparing them, it is seen that both values coincide
fairly well, though the latter is a little higher than
the former.   This is probably because of the difference in the way of estimating ρ_2.
    The effective diffusivity of sulphur gas through
Mo_2S_3 shell, D_2, can be calculated with D_3 and the rate
constant k at the earlier stage of decomposition.
Equations (22), (26) and (31) were used.   In addition
to p_2, p_3, ρ_1 and ρ_2 presumed above, p_1 is assumed
to take its equilibrium value calculated by equation (8)
which concerns the equilibrium at the interface of
MoS_2/Mo_2S_3. D_2 is also summarized in Table 1.
    And finally, it becomes possible with D_2 and D_3 to
calculate the critical value of fraction decomposed,
x^0.   Equation (33) together with equations (22) and
(26) was used and the calculated values of x^0 are
illustrated in Table 1.   This table also contains
the values of x^0 measured by thermogravimetric analysis
which is the deflecting point from parabolic law observed
in Fig. 5.   Calculated x^0 values are seen to be lower
than the observed values probably due to the higher
values of diffusivities estimated above.

Effective diffusivity and void fraction
    In the mass transfer model proposed, diffusion of
sulphur gas through porous shells of Mo_2S_3 and Mo is
supposed to be of Knudsen type.   As shown in
equations (12) and (13), the effective diffusivity is
expressed by

$$D_e = f(\varepsilon)D_k \qquad (47)$$

where $f(\varepsilon)$ is a function of void fraction and D_k
denotes Knudsen diffusivity.   According to kinetic
theory of gas (6),

$$D_K = \frac{2}{3}\,\bar{r}\,\bar{v} \tag{48}$$

where $\bar{r}$ is mean pore radius of void and $\bar{v}$ is mean
molecular velocity of gas, which is

$$\bar{v} = \sqrt{8RT/\pi M_{S_2}} \tag{49}$$

From these equations, the Knudsen diffusivity is to be
proportional to $T^{1/2}$. The dependency of effective
diffusivities upon temperature is, however, not clear
from Table 1, owing to the possible error in the
measurement and to the unknown function of $f(\varepsilon)$.

The relationship between effective diffusivity D_3
and the void fraction of the pellet is investigated
further in this section. D_3 was chosen because of
its better precision than that of D_2. By changing the
amount of MoS_2 powder and the pressure, four pellets
were prepared and they were decomposed at $1290^{\circ}C$.
The effective diffusivity D_3 obtained are summarized
in Table 2. D_3 is seen to increase when the void
fractions ε_1 and ε_3 are raised. This may suggest
that the mechanism of mass transfer through the decom-
posed shell is not of ionic character but of gaseous
diffusion; if the sulphur is transported through the
shell in the form of anion, the effective diffusivity
decreases in a pellet of higher void fraction which
may cause poorer contact between particles.

5.   Summary
Thermal decomposition rate of disc-shaped MoS_2
pellet was pursued in vacuum at the temperature of 1190
to $1440^{\circ}C$. The decomposition proceeds through the
intermediate product of Mo_2S_3 into metallic Mo.
Molybdenite crystal was used as the material in order
to avoid possible interferences caused by flotation oil
contamination.

Isothermal measurement of thermogravimetric analysis revealed that a parabolic equation in the form of
$x^2 = k\theta$ can explain the experimental results when x is
below 0.7. Above this critical value of x^0, the
decomposing rate is depressed.

Based on Maru's results (5) on the thermal decomposition of synthetized Mo_2S_3 pellet, a mass transfer

model was proposed.   In this model, it is assumed
that the transfer rate of sulphur gas evolving at the
decomposing interfaces through the shell of decomposed
products determines the overall rate.   The shells
are composed of Mo and of Mo_2S_3.   Equilibria of
interfacial reactions were presumed at the interfaces
of MoS_2/Mo_2S_3 and Mo_2S_3/Mo.   Moreover, outward flux
of sulphur gas transfer is assumed to pass through the
basal planes of the pellet and the flux through its
lateral surface is omitted.

On these assumptions mentioned above, the following two rate equations were derived.

$$x^2 = k\theta \qquad \text{when } x < x^0$$
$$(x - \tfrac{1}{4})^2 = k'\theta \qquad \text{when } x \geqq x^0$$

The rate constants k and k' in these equations were
expressed by equations (31) and (42) in 4.1.   These
rate equations satisfied the experimental results, and
MoS_2 is presumed to disappear at the critical value of
$x^0 \doteqdot 0.7$.

X-ray diffraction patterns of partially decomposed
pellet also seems to support this model.   According
to the equations (31) and (42), the rate constants k
and k' are to be proportional to the reciprocal square
height of pellet, and this proportionality was also
confirmed.

The diffusion of sulphur gas through the shells of
Mo_2S_3 and of Mo is supposed to be of Knudsen type and
the effective diffusivities were estimated by using the
values of pressure of sulphur gas and of apparent
densities of the components concerned.   The magnitude
of these effective diffusivities were estimated at about
1 cm^2/sec or less and they increased by raising void
fraction.   This may suggest that the mechanism of
mass transfer through the decomposed shell is not of
ionic character but of gaseous diffusion.

Nomenclature

D_2 = effective diffusivity of S_2 through
    Mo_2S_3 shell cm^2/sec
D_3 = effective diffusivity of S_2 through
    Mo shell cm^2/sec

D_k = Knudsen diffusivity $\qquad$ cm^2/sec

f_1 = $1/(4M_{MoS_2})$ $\qquad$ mole/g

f_2 = $3/(2M_{Mo_2S_3})$ $\qquad$ mole/g

G_1 = evolving rate of S_2 at MoS_2/Mo_2S_3
 $\quad$ interface $\qquad$ mole $S_2/sec \cdot cm^2$

G_2 = evolving rate of S_2 at Mo_2S_3/Mo
 $\quad$ interface $\qquad$ mole $S_2/sec \cdot cm^2$

k = rate constant at earlier stage
 $\quad$ ($\theta < 1/k_1$) $\qquad$ 1/sec

k' = rate constant at later stage
 $\quad$ ($\theta \geqq 1/k_1$) $\qquad$ 1/sec

k_1 = see Eq. (26) $\qquad$ 1/sec

K = see Eq. (22) $\qquad$ mole $S_2/sec \cdot cm$

ℓ = half thickness of pellet $\qquad$ cm

M = molecular weight $\qquad$ g/mole

N_2 = flux of S_2 through Mo_2S_3 shell $\qquad$ mole $S_2/sec \cdot cm^2$

N_3 = flux of S_2 through Mo shell $\qquad$ mole $S_2/sec \cdot cm^2$

p_1 = equilibrium pressure of S_2 at
 $\quad$ MoS_2/Mo_2S_3 interface $\qquad$ atm

p_2 = equilibrium pressure of S_2 at
 $\quad$ Mo_2S_3/Mo interface $\qquad$ atm

P_3 = pressure in the reaction tube $\qquad$ atm

r = radius of pellet $\qquad$ cm

$\bar{r}$ = mean pore radius $\qquad$ cm

$\bar{v}$ = mean molecular velocity of gas $\qquad$ cm/sec

W = weight of pellet $\qquad$ g

W_0 = initial weight of pellet $\qquad$ g

x = fraction decomposed $\qquad$ ____

x^0 = critical value of x where MoS_2
 $\quad$ disappears $\qquad$ ____

y_1 = half thickness of MoS_2 core $\qquad$ cm

y_2 = half thickness of Mo_2S_3 shell + MoS_2
 $\quad$ core $\qquad$ cm

y_2^0 = critical value of y_2 where MoS_2
 $\quad$ disappears $\qquad$ cm

α = nondimensional volume of decomposed
 $\quad$ MoS_2 into Mo_2S_3 ($= 1-(y_1/\ell)$) $\qquad$ ____

ε_1 = void fraction of MoS_2 pellet $\qquad$ ____

ε_3 = void fraction of Mo shell $\qquad$ ____

θ = reaction time $\qquad$ sec

ρ_1 = apparent density of MoS_2 pellet $\qquad$ g/cm^3

ρ_2 = apparent density of Mo_2S_3 shell $\qquad$ g/cm^3

References

1. W. G. Scholz, D. V. Doane and G. A. Timmons, AIME Trans. TMS-AIME, 221, 356, (1961)
2. C. L. McCabe, J. Metals, 7, 61, (1955)
3. J. R. Stubbles and F. D. Richardson, Trans. Faraday Soc. 56, 1460, (1960)
4. C. N. Sattersfield and F. Feakes, AIChE Journ. 5, 115, (1959)
5. Y. Maru, H. Yoshida and Y. Kondo, Trans. JIM. in press
6. N. Wakao and J. M. Smith, Chem. Eng. Sci. 17, 825, (1962)
7. F. Jellinek, Nature, 185, 1065, (1961)
8. A. De Schulten, Bull. Soc. Min. 12, 545, (1889)

Table 1   Rate Constants and Effective Diffusivities

Temperature (°C)	1240	1290	1340	1390	1440
$k \times 10^4$ (l/min)	7.09	23.6	43.5	149.5	174.3
$k' \times 10^4$ (l/min)	3.87	11.4	20.5	55.5	114.0
D_3 calc. (cm^2/sec)	1.55	1.72	1.37	1.57	1.72
D_3 (cm^2/sec) (obtained by Maru[5])	1.68	1.83	1.62	1.88	2.18
D_2 calc. (cm^2/sec)	0.226	0.411	0.366	0.860	0.059
x^0 calc. (—)	0.55	0.48	0.47	0.40	0.72
x^0 obs. (—)	0.70	0.71	0.71	0.74	0.72

Table 2   Effective Diffusivity, D_2

Pressing conditions of pellet	ϵ_1	ϵ_3	D_3 (cm^2/sec)
0.5g, 470 kg/cm^2	0.289	0.719	1.62
94 kg/cm^2	0.443	0.827	3.52
0.3g, 470 kg/cm^2	0.299	0.713	1.15
94 kg/cm^2	0.442	0.805	2.77

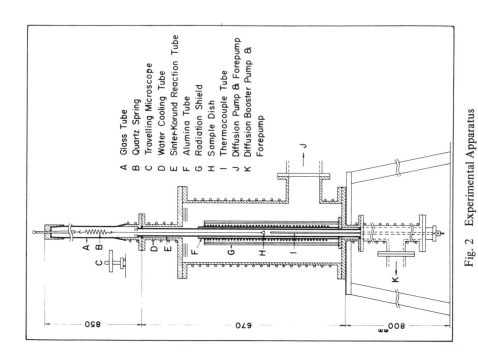

Fig. 2 Experimental Apparatus

A Glass Tube
B Quartz Spring
C Travelling Microscope
D Water Cooling Tube
E Sinter-Korund Reaction Tube
F Alumina Tube
G Radiation Shield
H Sample Dish
I Thermocouple Tube
J Diffusion Pump & Forepump
K Diffusion Booster Pump &
Forepump

Fig. 1 Equilibrium Decomposition Pressure

Eq.(1): $4MoS_2 = 2Mo_2S_3 + S_2$
Eq.(2): $\frac{2}{3}Mo_2S_3 = \frac{4}{3}Mo + S_2$

—— Richardson and Stubbles
- - - McCabe

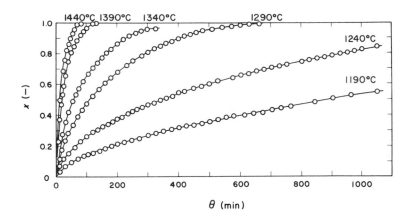

Fig. 3   Experimental Results of Isothermal Decomposition

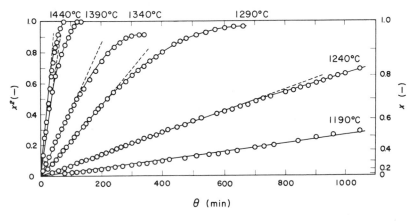

Fig. 4 $x^2 - \theta$ Plot

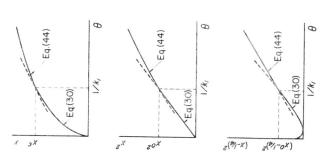

Fig. 6   Illustration of Rate Equations

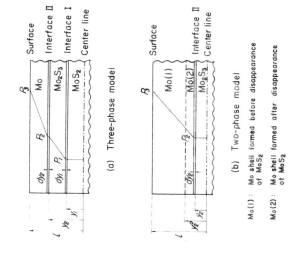

(a) Three-phase model

(b) Two-phase model

Mo(1): Mo shell formed before disappearance of MoS$_2$

Mo(2): Mo shell formed after disappearance of MoS$_2$

Fig. 5   Mass Transfer Model

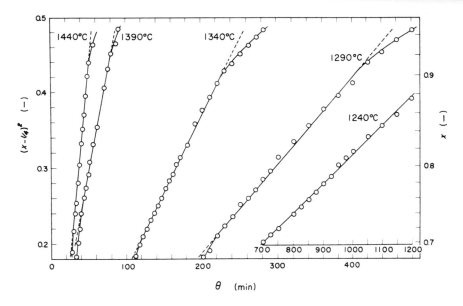

Fig. 7 $(x-\frac{1}{4})^2 - \theta$ Plot

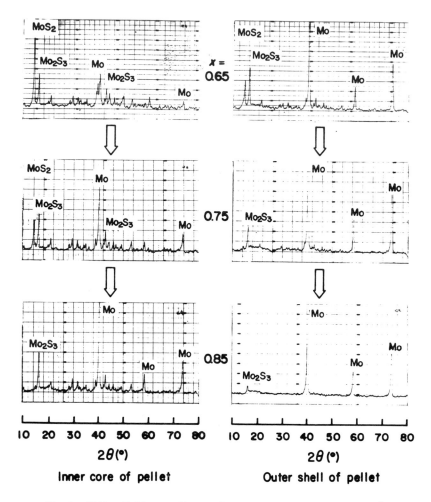

Fig. 8　X–Ray Diffraction Pattern (0.3g pellet pressed at 470 kg/tm^2, and decomposed at 1240°C)

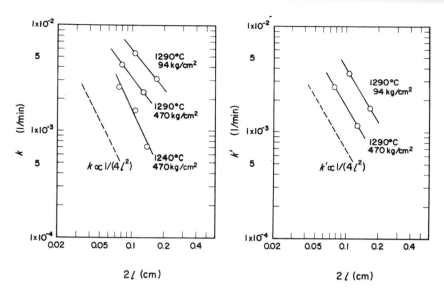

Fig. 9   Relationship Between Rate Constants and Receprocal Square Height of Pellet

SECTION 6

APPLIED SCIENCES

Chairmen:

E. M. Bollin
D. M. Speros

THE RAPID DETERMINATION OF SOLID FAT INDEX
WITH A SCANNING CALORIMETER

J. A. Prendergast

Instrument Products Division
E. I. du Pont de Nemours & Co.
Wilmington, Delaware 19898

A great deal of effort has been devoted to the development of techniques required to measure the various physical and chemical phenomena involved in the study of fats and oils. An inordinate share of this effort has been spent on the determination of "hardness" or degree of crystallization. Since it critically affects the taste and texture of a fat and its subsequent by-products, this determination is of great concern to manufacturers and users of these materials. Consequently, an extensive effort has been put forth to standardize the determination. The method which has emerged has become known as Solid Fat Index (SFI) (1). Essentially it consists of the dilatometric measurement of the expansion of a fat sample which has been partially melted and equilibrated for 15-30 minutes in a series of isothermal baths. The difference between the observed dilations and the thermal expansion of the liquefied fat, along with a volume correction for the glass dilatometer and the aqueous indicator solution, are used to calculate the SFI at each temperature. The determination is usually made at five standard temperatures, 10°C, 21.1°C, 26.7°C, 33.3°C and 37.8°C.

Fats are complex mixtures of triglycerides and fatty acids, with various polymorphic forms exhibiting a wide range of crystallite types and sizes. The dilation observed in this method is the effect on specific volume due to the melting of these crystal species. This change in volume is expressed in units of ml/kg of fat and is plotted vs. temperature to construct an SFI curve. Including the elaborate procedure required for sample preparation, and the lengthy period of equilibration at each temperature, the entire determination consumes several hours. It is an empirical measurement arbitrarily chosen to be the standard for the industry. As such, it has little absolute correlation with other methods of qualitatively and quantitatively determining degree of crystallization. Analysts have attempted to apply other techniques, including X-ray diffraction and NMR (2) spectroscopy, with varying degrees of success. None have been able to replace the AOCS method described above.

Since the determination of Solid Fat Index involves the thermal phenomena of forming and melting of crystals, thermal analysis would appear to be the logical analytical technique for the measurement. Recent instrumental advances in scanning calorimetry have provided a rapid, accurate and precise means of measuring the enthalpic energies inherent in these phenomena. This study was undertaken in order to evaluate Scanning Calorimetry as a technique to simplify the SFI determination; to reduce the time required to 30-40 minutes; to develop a method based on the calorimetric measurement of ΔH_f that could be correlated with commonly accepted SFI values.

All experimental work was performed with the Du Pont 900 Thermal Analyzer unit complete with a Differential Scanning Calorimeter Cell. This cell is shown schematically in Figure I. It has a constantan disc brazed into a silver heating block. The disc has two raised platforms on the underside of which are welded a pair of thermocouples. These are the transducers for the detection and monitoring of the differential signal developed between a sample and reference materials as the former undergoes a thermal transition. The reference thermocouple is made at the junction of the constantan disc and the single chromel wire at the left, while the sample thermocouple is the chromel-alumel junction at the right. The output of the latter drives the X-axis of an X-Y recorder, while the differential signal between sample and reference drives the Y-axis. Thus, the coordinates of the thermogram obtained with this device are ΔT vs. T (sample).

This readout system has an inherent deficiency when a quantitative calorimetric determination is attempted. As a sample begins to melt, its temperature slows to a virtual halt as it absorbs enough heat to complete the transition. Consequently, the X-axis pen speed also slows to a near stop. The actual pen speed and the resultant area recorded then become partially dependent on thermal characteristics of the sample, other than ΔH_f, such as thermal conductivity, heat capacity, particle size, etc. All of these factors can vary from sample to sample. Optimum quantitative work with the cell requires a time-based readout system. The apparatus can be readily converted to the proper readout simply by reversing the usual placement of sample and reference pans and allowing the X-axis to record the temperature of the reference. During a programmed run, the reference undergoes no transitions and thus proceeds at a linear heating rate. Consequently, the X-axis will also plot linearly because it is being driven by the output of the thermocouple monitoring the reference. The thermogram obtained during a programmed run with this arrangement is equivalent to ΔT vs. time. Data obtained with this system were compared to those obtained using an ordinary time-base Mosely recorder plotting the Y-axis deflection vs. time. The results were equivalent within the limits of experimental error.

The sample pan normally used with this cell is a cylindrically shaped flat-bottomed aluminum pan 0.003 in. thick. While using this pan with fat samples, two minor difficulties were encountered. Upon cooling, the molten fat recrystallized around the sides of the pan and was not in optimum thermal contact with the thermocouples. In addition, if the sides of the pan were slightly creased, the sample would occasionally wick up over the top and spill on to the disc.

To eliminate these problems, a special pan was employed as shown in Figure II. It had a stamped indentation which fit over the raised platform on the constantan disc. Due to the surface tension effect around the edge of the indentation, the fat sample, when placed in the pan, formed a neat globule that remained in place throughout the entire procedure. This prevented any flow of sample away from the center and kept it in good contact with the thermocouple. The pan proved to be an additional aid to the operator who could "eyeball" the size of the globule and readily reproduce a 7-9 mg sample.

Accurate determination of the degree of crystallization of these fats required very precise temperature
measurement and careful control of the thermal history of
the sample. Just as the dilatometric technique takes great
caution with these parameters, so must the thermal method.
The instrument employed in the study had a starting temperature control with 5X scale expansion and a maximum temperature (X-axis) sensitivity of 5°C/inch. The temperature
of the sample could thus be set, read, and reproduced to
within ±0.1°C. The temperature programmer maintained heating and cooling rate accuracy and reproducibility to within
±0.1°C/min.

The instrument is designed to give a continuous thermal profile of materials for qualitative and quantitative
analysis. A typical scan is shown in Fig. III. It is the
thermogram of a sample of frying fat which was cooled from
60° to -120°C, then programmed at 10°C/min. through its
melting range in the scanning calorimeter cell. At approximately -90°C a change in heat capacity occurs. Melting
commences at approximately -20°C, and continues until 50°C
where the sample becomes totally liquefied. The area under
the curve is directly proportional to the energy absorbed
by the melting sample. The amount of area measured from
any given temperature through complete melting is a measure
of the degree of crystallinity or hardness of the sample at
that temperature. The correlation of data from this type
of device with conventional SFI data is a relatively simple
procedure. For vegetable stock, the following technique
has been developed and used successfully:

A weighed sample of 7-10 mg of fat is placed in the
cell which is held isothermally at 60°C. The sample is
melted and all previous thermal history is erased. It is
then cooled to approximately 10-20°C below the lowest SFI
temperature of interest and held until crystallization is
completed. This is indicated by the movement of the ΔT
axis on the X-Y recorder coming to a halt at maximum sensitivity. The fat is then heated through its melting range
at a rate of 10°C/min. The trace is allowed to run 10 or
15°C past the end of the melt to establish the baseline
which is then extrapolated back across the entire chart.
Perpendicular lines are dropped to the baseline at each of
the standard SFI temperatures, as shown in Figure IV. The
area under the curve from each of these temperatures

through the melt is a direct measure of the solid fat
crystals and the energy required to melt them. These areas
are measured with a polar planimeter, normalized for weight
and related to commonly accepted SFI values with a calibration curve constructed with data from samples of known SFI
values run in an identical manner.

The extrapolation of the baseline in the above described manner approximates the actual heat capacity of the
liquid fat. To illustrate this, the temperature programmer
was switched to HOLD at 50°C and the recorder was back-
shifted 10 inches. The program was resumed and the specific heat profile was plotted on the same chart. The scan
shows that the extrapolation is a very close approximation
to the actual thermal behavior of the liquid sample.

The perpendicular lines at the specific temperatures
are an over-simplification of the actual melting phenomena.
However, when the calibration curve is obtained with
standard samples run in this manner, data with 3% precision
is obtained. This procedure has been demonstrated satisfactorily for over a dozen different stocks currently employed by manufacturers. Figure V is a calibration curve
constructed with data from 40 samples with SFI values
ranging from 1.0 to 42.0. It illustrates the relationship
between the DSC and dilatometric methods and shows the
spread of the data.

This method can readily cope with the three basic
types of fat materials described by Hannewijk et. al. (3):
the "pure", "plastic", and meta-stable forms. The so-
called "pure" fats are those which have a relatively narrow
melting range. Plastic fats are those with a large array
of crystallites and thus have a broad melting profile.
Fats that exist in meta-stable forms are most frequently
encountered when dealing with animal fats and blends which
have been rapidly cooled. The dilation curves for these
materials are shown in Figure VI. The expansion characteristics of the pure and plastic substances are simply re-
flective of the molecular weight distributions. The solid
sample expands only slightly as the temperature is raised
from A to B. At B, melting begins and the expansion increases at a rate directly proportional to the amount of
crystals melting at that temperature. In the meta-stable
form, expansion begins to accelerate at B, but suddenly

reverses itself at C. This contraction is explained by Hannewijk as the conversion of the fat to a more stable form with a lower specific volume.

The thermal equivalent of this behavior is shown in Figure VII. It is a blended sample that had been cooled at 10°C/min. from 60°C to -120°C then re-heated at the same rate. A large "cold crystallization" exotherm was observed at 26°C. This is due to the kinetics of the tri-glyceride crystallites. When the sample is cooled at a rate of 10°C/min. there is insufficient time for some of the species to crystallize. They become trapped in the solidification of the surrounding medium before they can nucleate and form stable crystals. Then, as the sample is re-heated, the surrounding medium softens and releases the trapped species which undergo rapid re-crystallization, followed by melting. This re-crystallization exotherm on the scan prohibits use of the graphical treatment described in this method.

For samples exhibiting this behavior, an additional step in the pretreatment of the thermal history is required. As the sample is cooled down from 60°C, it must be held isothermally at 26°C for several minutes to allow suf-ficient time for nucleation of the slower forming crystal-lites. The results of this tempering procedure can be seen in Figure VIII. A completely endothermic scan is obtained and the technique is easily applied. For samples with this characteristic behavior, a separate calibration curve is required. It must be constructed with data from fat standards of similar behavior run in an identical manner.

In summary, a thermoanalytical technique has been developed as a substitute for the dilatometric SFI determi-nation. It consists of a graphical treatment of data from a scanning calorimeter. The time required to obtain the five SFI values has been reduced from several hours to less than 40 minutes. The continuous readout available with this method allows the investigator to easily detect samples with meta-stable forms. Subsequently, he can determine when and how to alter the thermal treatment of the sample for optimum results. The method may be applied to virtually all types of fat products, with appropriate modifications of their thermal history, and suitable standards for calibration.

Acknowledgements

The author would like to thank Messrs. William Koester, William Miller and Paul Steele of the Proctor and Gamble Company for their generous donation of standard samples, without which this study could not have been completed.

References

1. Official and Tentative Methods of the AOCS Solid Fat Index Method Cd 10-57.
2. Pohle, W. D.; Taylor, J. R. and Gregory, R. L., JAOCS, 42, 1075-1078 (1965).
3. Hannewijk, J.; Haighton, A. J. and Hendrikse, P. W., "Analysis and Characterization of Oils, Fats and Fat Products", Ed. by H. A. Boekenoogen, Interscience Publishers, London (1964).

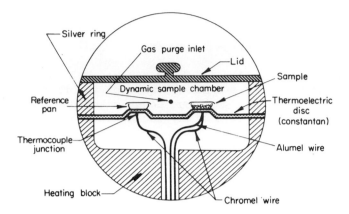

Silver ring

Gas purge inlet

Lid

Sample

Dynamic sample chamber

Reference pan

Thermoelectric disc (constantan)

Thermocouple junction

Alumel wire

Heating block

Chromel wire

Fig. 1 - DSC Cell Cross Section

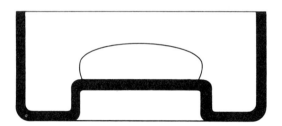

Fig. 2 - SFI Sample Pan

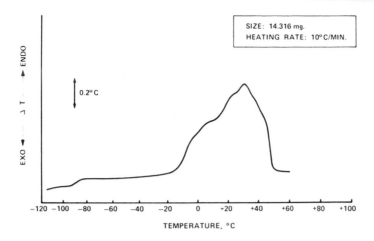

Fig. 3 - Fat - Complete Thermal Profile by DSC

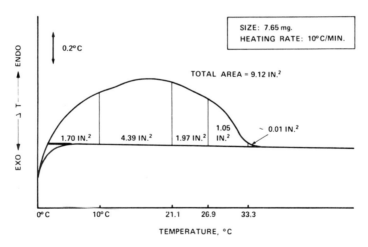

Fig. 4 - SFI Determination

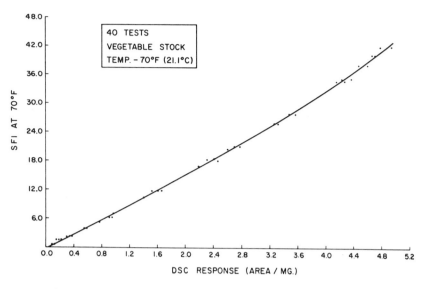

Fig. 5 - DSC Response (Area/mg) vs. SFI

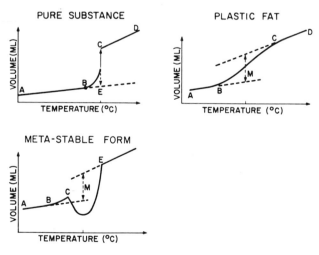

Fig. 6 - Dilatation Curves

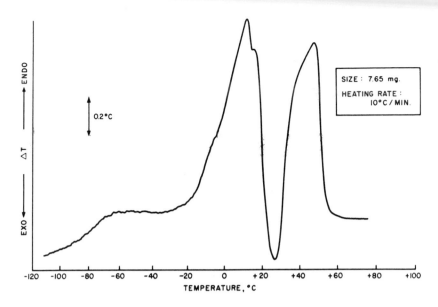

Fig. 7 - Fat - Animal - Vegetable Blend

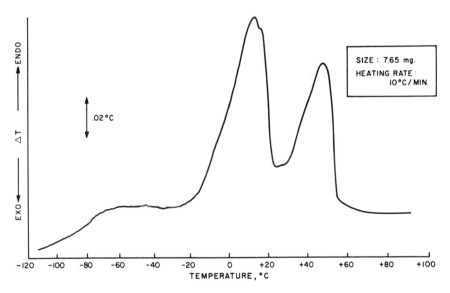

Fig. 8 - Fat - Animal - Vegetable Blend
(Tempered 5 min. at 26°C)

DTA/TGA INVESTIGATION OF REACTIONS IN SODIUM-LEAD-SILICATE GLASS BATCH

W. Richard Ott and Malcolm G. McLaren

Rutgers, The State University
New Brunswick, N. J.

Abstract

The melting of a sodium-lead-silicate glass batch was investigated. It was found that new compounds are formed which subsequently react with the remaining raw materials to produce a liquid phase through eutectic melting. This liquid phase then dissolves the remaining silica as the temperature is increased until the glass is batch free. Differential thermal analysis performed simultaneously with thermogravimetric measurements, in conjunction with x-ray diffraction, have been utilized to determine the nature and sequence of reactions which have occurred.

The effect of different types of lead additions and different particle sizes of lead silicates on the reactions which occur in the glass batch was determined.

This study was undertaken to clarify the role of lead-oxide and lead-silicates in the melting of a sodium-lead-silicate glass batch.

Introduction

The reactions which occur in glass tanks and pots as the raw materials are heated have received only limited attention.[1-6] The choice of raw materials in the commercial glass making process has largely been on the basis of short-run economic considerations. Some of the effects of this on batch melting in a continuous glass tank have been described by Platt:[7] "Batch is seen running straight down the slope (of the batch pile) into the glass as it is filled; piles of batch may be seen lying stationary, snaking down the tank, or even floating in circles like icebergs for hours at a time." These conditions lead to inhomogeneity in the glass, increased fining time, increased lead loss, and decreased tank life. Problems such as these have forced an examination of the reactions which precede the formation of the final glass composition.

This work was performed in an effort to clearly define the role of litharge and lead-silicates in the glass melting process. This knowledge will then allow the glass technologist to choose the best combination of pre-reacted raw materials for a particular glass batch.

Experimental Procedure

A Mettler Thermoanalyzer was used to obtain the simultaneous plot of temperature, weight change, DTG, and DTA. The sample holder is shown in Fig. 1. The furnace control thermocouple is located directly adjacent to the reference thermocouple. All samples were run in a flowing air atmosphere which had been passed through molecular sieves to remove any moisture. Platinum crucibles were used and were in direct contact with the Pt/Pt-10Rh thermocouples utilized in this apparatus. An automatic derivative computer was used to determine dw/dt. Five hundred mg. of granular alumina served as the reference material. The samples were heated at $8^{\circ}C/min$.

X-ray diffraction was used to identify the reaction products by quenching the samples both before and after reactions occurred.

The study was carried out on the raw materials, combinations of two raw materials and finally, on combinations of three raw materials; the three component system yielding a glass of 61 weight % SiO_2, 33.6 weight % PbO, and 6.4 weight % Na_2CO_3.

The two component systems raw materials are in the same ratio to each other as they are in the final glass.

Discussion of Results

A. One Component Systems

1. Powdered Flint - Ottawa powdered flint is 99.75% SiO_2. This material is pulverized and thus has angular grains of which 91% is less than 74 microns and 72% is less than 44 microns. Fig. 2(a) shows the DTA trace for flint. The endothermic peak at $575^{\circ}C$ is the result of the inversion of α-quartz to β-quartz. There is no weight loss observed on heating.

2. Soda Ash - Plant grade soda ash is 99.7% Na_2CO_3. Only 1% passes through a 200 mesh sieve, while 97% passes through a 30 mesh sieve. Fig. 2(b) shows the DTA trace for this material. The endothermic peak at $857^{\circ}C$ is the result of melting.

3. Litharge - Electronic grade litharge is 99.8% PbO and 99.0% minus 325 mesh. Fig. 2(d) shows the weight trace up to 1100°C. A weight gain occurs over the region 475-540°C and then a weight loss occurs from 540-580°. This is attributable to the oxidation of litharge to red lead and then its subsequent decomposition back to litharge.

$$6PbO + O_2 \xrightarrow{475 - 540°C} 2Pb_3O_4 \xrightarrow{540 - 580°C} 6PbO + O_2$$

A DTA peak (Fig. 2(c)) at 565°C occurs during decomposition. The endothermic peak at 892°C is the result of the melting of the litharge. The weight loss above 950°C is the result of volatilization of the PbO.

4. Tribasic Lead Silicate - 92.0% PbO - 8.0% SiO_2 is a eutectic mixture of $4PbO \cdot SiO_2$ and $2PbO \cdot SiO_2$. This lead silica mixture ($PbO \cdot 0.33 SiO_2$) has been melted and water quenched, giving a glass which is 93% -10,+80 mesh. Ground material is 98.6% -325 mesh. The exothermic doublet in the DTA trace of the ground material (Fig. 3 (a)) at 347°C and 378°C is the result of devitrification of the glass into a crystalline phase. The endothermic peak at 726°C is the result of eutectic melting. The DTA trace of the granular material (Fig. 3(b)) is essentially the same as that of the ground material.

5. Lead Monosilicate - 85.0% PbO - 15.0% SiO_2 is a eutectic mixture of $2PbO \cdot SiO_2$ and $PbO \cdot SiO_2$. This lead silica mixture ($PbO \cdot 0.67 SiO_2$) has been melted and water quenched, giving a glass which is 95% (-10,+80) mesh. Ground lead monosilicate is 98.6% minus 325 mesh. The exothermic peak at 490°C in the DTA trace (Fig.3 (c)) is devitrification of the glass into a crystalline

phase. The endotherm at 720°C is eutectic melting of the material. Devitrification in the granular material occurs at a higher temperature
(517°C) and melting is not as well defined.

B. Two Component Systems

1. Soda Ash - Silica (Fig. 4). A mixture of
10 weight percent soda ash and 90 weight percent
silica was heated to 1000°C. This is the same
Na_2CO_3 to SiO_2 ratio which is present in the final
three component glass. Over the range 500 - 700°C
there is a gradual weight loss, indicating some
formation of a sodium silicate. The weight loss
becomes more pronounced over the region 700 -
800°C and reaches a maximum at 845°C. This indicates that the main portion of this reaction
does not occur until the Na_2CO_3 melts. X-ray
identification of the reaction products showed
the presence of sodium metasilicate $Na_2O \cdot SiO_2$.
Once sodium metasilicate is formed further reaction with silica will give sodium disilicate.[8]
The sodium disilicate can then form a liquid by
melting eutectically with either silica or sodium
metasilicate. These results are in good agreement with the work of Wilburn and Thomasson.[1]

2. Lead Monosilicate - Soda Ash (Fig. 5).
A mixture of 85% ground lead monosilicate and 15%
Na_2CO_3 was heated to 1000°C. After devitrification of the lead monosilicate (490°C) a reaction
between the soda ash and lead monosilicate occurs
at 650°C. The initial reaction results in the
formation of a sodium-lead-silicate, the quantity of which is governed by the limited amount
of SiO_2 available for reaction. As the temperature is increased, more Na_2O is taken into the
sodium-lead-silicate until the reaction is completed at 900°C.

3. Tribasic Lead Silicate - Soda Ash (Fig.5). A mixture of 84% ground tribasic lead silicate and 16% soda ash was heated to 1000°C. The doublet at 347°C and 378°C is the result of devitrification of the glassy phase. The endotherm at 680°C accompanied by a DTG peak is indicative of a reaction to form a sodium-lead-silicate. With less silica available than with lead monosilicate the result is less soda ash being converted into the sodium-lead-silicate. If additional silica is added, as in the case in Fig. 8(a), then the reaction occurs at 600°C which is lower than with lead monosilicate. The results in Fig. 8(a) were achieved with a quantity of silica greatly in excess of that available in lead monosilicate. An endotherm is present at 839°C and again a DTG peak is also present. This is an indication that a further sodium-lead-silica reaction is occurring. However, the insufficient quantity of silica makes completion of this reaction by 900°C impossible.

4. Lead Silicate - Silica (Fig. 6). A mixture of 61% SiO_2 and 39% tribasic lead silicate was heated to 1000°C. The devitrification peaks of tribasic lead silicate and the inversion of $\alpha \rightarrow \beta$ quartz can be observed on heating. A reaction begins at 650°C and progresses rapidly toward a maximum of 700°C and is completed by 715°C. The reactions are similar to those seen in the soda ash - silica system, in that several forms of silicates are present and melt eutectically with each other to form a liquid phase into which the remaining silica is taken as the temperature is increased. Tammann[9] and Hedvall & Eldh[10] reported significant $PbO-SiO_2$ reactions at 600°C. In this present investigation it was found that using a lead silicate with 8% SiO_2 there is no

evidence of reaction prior to 642°C.

When ground lead monosilicate is used in place of tribasic lead silicate, no reaction is seen until 670°C. The endothermic peak at 728°C is the result of the melting of the lead mono-silicate and subsequent reaction with the silica to form lead metasilicate (PbO·SiO2). The use of granular lead monosilicate gives the same general results. No significant reaction occurs until the melting of the lead monosilicate, at which time lead metasilicate is formed and this melts at 770°C giving an endotherm.

The soda ash - lead silicate system showed increased reactivity of the lead silicate as the % SiO2 increased. The higher SiO2 level allowed formation of a sodium-lead-silicate to occur more rapidly.

In the silica-lead silicate system the reac-tivity of the lead silicate decreased as the % SiO2 increased. The solid-state reaction temper-ature increased as the percent silica in the lead silicate increased. When there was 15% SiO2, as in the case of lead monosilicate, there was no substantial reaction prior to melting of the lead monosilicate. It is evident that the choice of raw materials plays a large part in the solid-state reaction which occurs and hence the path by which the glass is melted.

C. Three Component Systems

1. Silica-Litharge-Soda Ash (Fig. 7). A mix-ture of 61% SiO2, 33.6% litharge, 6.4% soda ash was heated to 1000°C. At 605°C a DTG peak is ob-served which is the result of the formation of a sodium lead silicate. The decomposition reaction proceeds at a slower rate over the range 650 - 750°C and then proceeds rapidly to conclusion by 853°C.

With formation of a sodium-lead-silicate at 605°C and lead silicates by 700°C, eutectic melting of these newly formed compounds results in a substantial liquid phase present at 750°C and allows the reaction to move rapidly to conclusion by 850°C. After 850°C a liquid phase exists which gradually assimilates the remaining SiO_2 (the only crystalline phase still present) as the temperature increases.

The degradation of the silicon-oxygen bond is necessary to form a glass. Near the liquidus temperature the SiO_2 is assimilated into the glass melt very slowly. As the temperature is increased above the liquidus temperature the frequency of rupture of Si-O bonds increases and the silica is taken into the melt at an increased rate.

C. McKinnis and J. W. Sutton[9] have listed the steps by which the quartz structure is finally assimilated into the melt:

1) Diffusion of a highly mobile modifying cation such as Na into an interstitial position within the SiO_2 lattice.
2) Rupture of a Si-O bond of the lattice near this entrapped ion.
3) Coupling of this resultant triply coordinated Si of the lattice with a previously non-bridging oxygen of a unit in the melt.
4) Repetition of this sequence at a number of neighboring sites, yielding a silicate unit from the lattice which is assimilated into the melt.

The practical glass melting temperature usually exceeds the liquidus temperature of the respective finished glass by at least 300 - 500°C;[10] this higher temperature being necessary to provide sufficient energy to assimilate the SiO_2.

2. Tribasic Lead Silicate-Silica-Soda Ash (Fig. 8). A mixture of 57.5% SiO_2, 36.1% tribasic lead silicate and 6.4% soda ash was heated to 1050°C. Tribasic lead silicate, silica, and soda ash react to form a sodium lead silicate as is indicated by the DTG peak at 600°C (similar to that observed with use of litharge). The broad endotherm at 680°C is the result of a reaction between tribasic lead silicate and silica to form a higher % silica lead silicate. These new compounds melt eutectically and the remaining Na_2CO_3 is reacted. The decomposition is completed by 843°C. X-ray diffraction again showed that the only crystalline phase remaining after 850°C is silica.

If granular tribasic-lead-silicate is used in place of the ground material, the lower temperature solid state reactions do not occur. The first major reaction occurs with the melting of the tribasic lead silicate (DTA endotherm 723°C). This starts the reaction with the soda ash and silica. However, the decomposition reaction is not completed until some 40°C later than with the ground material at 890°C.

3. Lead Monosilicate-Silica-Soda Ash (Fig. 9). A mixture of 54.4% SiO_2, 39.2% lead monosilicate, and 6.4% soda ash was heated to 1050°C. The reaction of lead monosilicate-soda ash seen previously in Fig. 5(b) is evidenced by a DTG peak at 610°C. The endothermic peak at 720°C indicates the melting of lead monosilicate. This liquid and the newly formed compounds then react, accelerating the decomposition of the soda ash which is completed by 845°C.

If granular lead monosilicate is used in place of ground lead monosilicate, little reaction occurs until the melting of lead monosilicate. The decomposition reaction then proceeds with a DTG peak at 740°C and a second DTG peak at 850°C, the second being the result of the melting of the remaining soda ash and its reaction with silica. Lead monosilicate has a high viscosity after melting and the fine silica serves to isolate some soda ash grains and prevent reaction with the more reactive lead-silicate. As a result, the decomposition cannot be completed until the remaining soda ash melts and reacts with the silica to form sodium metasilicate. The completion of decomposition is 60°C higher than when ground lead monosilicate was used and 15°C higher than when granular tribasic lead-silicate was used as a batch material.

Summary and Conclusions

With the use of ground tribasic lead silicate, ground lead monosilicate or -325 mesh litharge, solid state reactions occur in the region 600 - 700°C to form new compounds. Through eutectic melting a liquid is formed which incorporates all batch materials by 850°C with the exception of a portion of the SiO_2. The remaining silica is then dissolved as the temperature is increased. When granular lead-silicate materials are used no reaction occurs prior to the melting of the lead silicate. Since the silica becomes the continuous phase, some soda ash is isolated from the more reactive lead silicate and does not react until it melts. When the Na_2CO_3 melts, it reacts with the surrounding silica to form sodium metasilicate and subsequently sodium disilicate. Eutectic melting of these compounds is then possible. This problem is made more dif-

ficult by the high viscosity of lead monosilicate
when it melts as compared with the lower viscosity of tribasic lead silicate. As a result, the
formation of the complete liquid phase minus silica, or the reactive liquid phase, is delayed
until after the melting point of the soda ash and
its subsequent reaction with the silica. The
completed reactive liquid phase is formed 50°C
lower when fine lead-silicate materials are utilized rather than coarse granular materials. The
homogeneity of the glass will probably also be
adversely effected by the use of granular raw
materials, since these require dual reactions to
obtain the reactive liquid phase.

It would be ideal to use all finely ground
raw materials as glass batch mix materials. Serious problems occur, however, due to lead and
soda ash dust being blown into the refractory of
the checker system (a part of the heat regenera-
tion system of the glass tank). As a consequence,
granular raw materials have been used in practice
with the subsequent problems described earlier in
obtaining a homogeneous reactive phase.

This work indicates that a fritted, pre-
reacted material, containing all the necessary
ingredients except the major portion of silica,
would be the best form to make the lead and soda
additions.

Acknowledgements

The authors wish to thank Hammond Lead Products and Mr. William Wilke for sponsoring the
research and to express their gratitude to Mr.
J. S. Nordyke for his helpful suggestions and
original initiation of this project. The authors
are also indebted to the Mettler Instrument Cor-

poration and Mr. Hugh P. Vaughan and Mr. Hans J. Hoehn, for their assistance.

References

1. F. W. Wilburn and C. V. Thomasson, Phys. Chem. Glasses 1, 2, 52-69, 1960.
2. F. W. Wilburn and C. V. Thomasson, J. Soc. Glass Tech. 42, 158-175, 1958.
3. F. W. Wilburn and C. V. Thomasson, Phys. Chem. Glasses 2, 4, 126-131, 1961.
4. R. S. Warburton and F. W. Wilburn, Phys. Chem. Glasses 4,3, 1963.
5. F. W. Wilburn, S. A. Metcalfe, and R. S. Warburton, Phys. Chem. Glasses 6, 4, 107-114, 1965.
6. B. Rosenkrands and B. Simmingsköld, Phys. Chem. Glasses 3, 2, 46-51, 1962.
7. D. M. Platt, Glass Ind., 8, 428-429, 1968.
8. J. Williamson & F. P. Glasser, Phys. Chem. Glasses 7, 4, 127-138, 1966.
9. G. Tammann, Z. Anorg. Chem. 149, 21, 1925.
10. J. A. Hedvall and A. Eldh, Z. Anorg. Chem. 226, 192, 1936.
11. C. McKinnis and J. W. Sutton, J. A. Ceram. S. 42, 4, 194, 1959.
12. R. J. Seider, Progress Report No. 2, LC-21 Rutgers University, 1964.

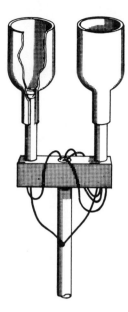

Figure 1.

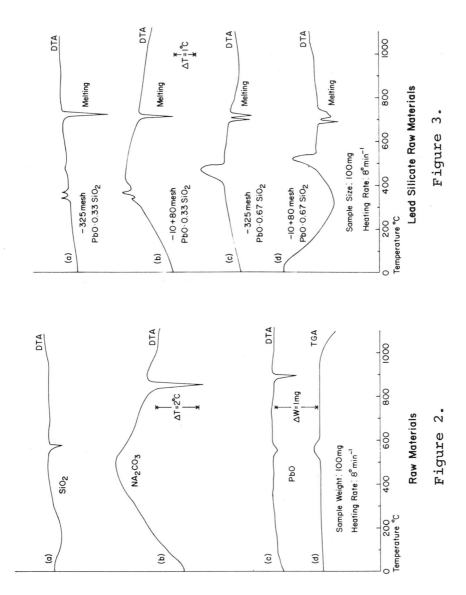

Raw Materials

Figure 2.

Lead Silicate Raw Materials

Figure 3.

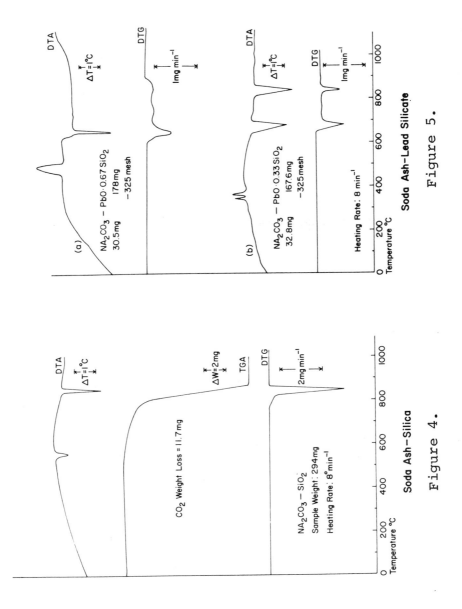

Soda Ash–Lead Silicate

Figure 5.

Soda Ash–Silica

Figure 4.

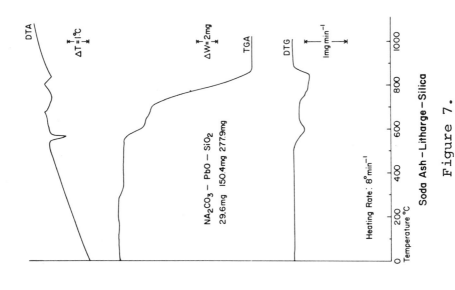

Soda Ash–Litharge–Silica

Figure 7.

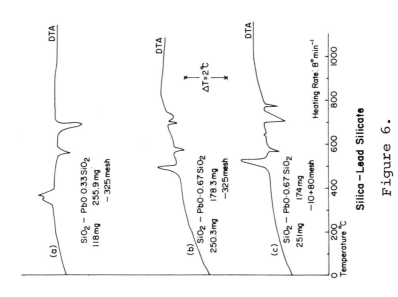

Silica–Lead Silicate

Figure 6.

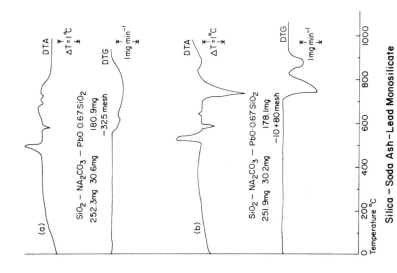

Silica – Soda Ash – Lead Monosilicate

Figure 9.

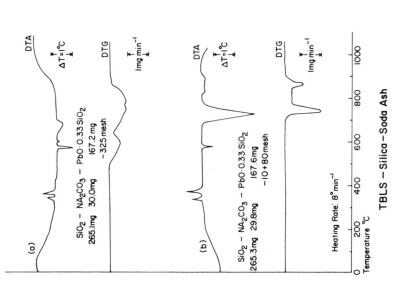

TBLS – Silica – Soda Ash

Figure 8.

HEAT TRANSFER AND COAL PYROLYSIS

William B. Davies and Dennis J. Brown

Department of Fuel Technology and Chemical Engineering
University of Sheffield
England.

Summary

For experiments in which coal spheres were heated in a stream of hot nitrogen, the initial rate of weight loss was constant and was found to be directly proportional to the heat flux, being zero at a gas temperature of about $400^{\circ}C$. In the experiments, the gas temperature was varied from $380^{\circ}C$ to $550^{\circ}C$, the gas flow rate was varied from 20 to 350 $ft^3.hr^{-1}$ and the particle diameter was varied from 1/4 in. to 1 in. The heat equivalent to the loss of unit weight of particle, λ, was 1,770 C.H.U.lb.$^{-1}$. The greater part of this heat absorption was attributed to endothermic coal degradation reactions.

Introduction

During the last decade there has been a renewal of interest in the kinetics of coal pyrolysis and several new theories have been produced to explain the kinetic data obtained. Chukanov, van Krevelen, Pitt and others[1-5] have assumed that the rate-controlling process in devolatilisation is that of chemical reaction and have proceeded to analyse their results on this basis. Using a heated refractory tube through which the fine coal particles were dropped, Chukanov[1] explained his results by postulating five reactions with "activation energies" which varied from 2 to 15 K cal mole^{-1}. These values are low for a chemically-controlled process, an activation energy of 50 K cal mole^{-1} being required for the breaking of a bond to a carbon atom, for example[5]. Very low values are evidence for a physically controlled process.

It is more difficult to discuss the work of Chermin and van Krevelen[2b] as they used programmed heating rates, $0.6 - 6.6^{\circ}C$ min^{-1}, for the furnace in which a quartz capsule containing the coal sample was suspended. This method is more useful for substances which have a sharp decomposition temperature and only one possible set of products, definitely not the case for coal: what one may be measuring for coal, then, as the temperature slowly rises, is the cumulative rate of a fractional distillation process.

Contrasted with this is the finding for isothermal decomposition at temperatures above $400^{\circ}C$ when all the products come off together and have a constant composition during most of the weight loss period[6].

Pitt[3] fitted an empirical equation to measurements of the rate of volatile emission, using a fluidised bed of sand to heat the coal particles. He suggested that this equation represented a large number of first order reactions with a distribution of activation energies. However, a fundamental criticism has been made recently of the application of the Arrhenius equation to devolatilisation rates[7]. For gas and solution reactions it is assumed that there is an equilibrium between activated and non-activated molecules according to the Maxwell-Boltzmann distribution and the use of the exponential rate law then follows. Such an assumption is not valid for solid reactions and rate constant and activation energy can be clearly defined only when there is a suitable hypothesis for a reaction mechanism[8,9]. If the rate constant is defined from the experimental relationship between the quantity of product formed and time, it is difficult to predict whether it will show an exponential dependence on temperature and even if there is such a dependence, approximately, the interpretation of the activation energy remains dubious.

Berkowitz developed a diffusion theory to explain the weight loss curves he obtained using a thermo-balance[10]. This theory is not very well substantiated since parameters were chosen which would best fit the experimental curve. Perhaps more important, Berkowitz did not take any weight loss readings until a considerable time, 5 minutes, had elapsed and 80% of the available volatile matter had already been evolved at $524^{\circ}C$. The early stages of devolatilisation have been neglected by other investigators, also[3,4,5]. Pitt pointed out that for the first order reaction assumed by Berkowitz there was little change of rate constant with temperature, corresponding to a small activation energy; this, again, suggests that some physical factor might be controlling the rate of coal decomposition.

Peters[6], who used a stirred bed reactor to obtain high heating rates, postulated that the controlling factor was the heat transfer required for evaporation of liquid "metaplast" from the coal particles. The activation energy he obtained from the results was 2 K cal mole^{-1}.

The bulk of the evidence points to a low activation energy for devolatilisation. This suggests that a physical process is rate-controlling, the most likely one being heat transfer rather than diffusion. To test this heat transfer hypothesis, weight loss studies were made on individual coal particles suspended from a thermobalance in a stream of hot nitrogen of known temperature and flow rate. For this system, heat transfer by forced convection is the most important, the contribution from radiation being kept at a minimum by choosing a wall temperature of 400°C. Where this was not possible, correction was made for radiant heat transfer as shown in the Appendix.

Apparatus and Experimental

For convective heat transfer, adequate correlations between heat transfer coefficient and flow parameters exist for particles which are spheres, cylinders or rectangular plates. Spheres were chosen for the present study, an advantage of their use being that a slight rotation of the suspension wire did not change the particle profile presented to the gas stream. In order to maintain the same shape during the experiments, the coal spheres were made from a non-swelling, dull, coal from the Shallow Seam at West Cannock No.5 Colliery. This has the analysis shown in Table 1.

The spheres were made as follows: coal cubes were cut from large lumps using a hacksaw and the cubes were shaped into rough spheres using a grinding wheel. Finally, smooth spheres were produced by placing the rough spheres between one static and one rotating silicon carbide grinders, each of which had a hemispherical hole cut into its surface. Sphere diameters were chosen to give a suitable range of

Reynolds Numbers and to suit the range of the thermo-balance.

A flow diagram of the apparatus is shown in Fig.1. The nitrogen (oxygen-free) was supplied to the system from a cylinder via a regulating valve and entered the apparatus on the inlet side of the two rotary vacuum pumps. From the outlet of the pumps the nitrogen was passed to the bank of flowmeters through a glass wool filter. The nitrogen then travelled through a heat exchanger containing four concentric copper tubes to the two main heaters arranged in parallel, each heater containing an 1800 watt **heating** element. The heater was insulated by preformed magnesite surrounded by vermiculite and enclosed in a mild steel casing. The reactor was a 2in. i.d. mild steel tube with a $1\frac{1}{2}$ in.i.d. tube running into it at right angles to admit the coal particles. The reactor side-arm was fitted with sliding shutters so that after insertion of the particle the reactor could be sealed, apart from the small hole required for the suspension wire. The incoming gas passed through an adjustable flow distributor, a solid cylinder through which many small holes had been drilled, to give it a reasonably flat velocity profile. The outgoing gas left the reactor about 6 in. downstream of the coal particle, passing through holes drilled in the reactor wall into a 4 in. i.d. manifold. The reactor was lagged after being wrapped with heating tape connected to a variable transformer so that reactor wall temperature could be varied independently of gas stream temperature and flow rate. In the reactor, three gas temperatures and the wall temperature were measured by thermocouple. Gas pressure in the reactor was very slightly above atmospheric so that there was no risk of air being drawn in and subsequent particle ignition. For the weight loss measurements, a Stanton thermo-balance was used which had a full-scale deflection of 1g. Each coal particle was cemented to a thin metal rod pushed into a small hole on the particle surface; the other end of the metal rod was then suspended from the balance. When the apparatus had reached the required temperature for a particular experiment the particle was introduced into the reactor and a record of change of particle weight with time was obtained.

Several measurements were made of coal particle surface temperature during pyrolysis. A rectangular slab of coal was used in which holes were drilled so that fine insulated thermocouples (0.021 in.dia) could be placed at different distances from the surface being heated, the other surfaces being insulated; the surface temperature was obtained by extrapolation. With nitrogen at 500°C flowing over the slab there was a surface temperature "plateau" from 400° - 420°C during the constant rate period, the temperature rising before and after this stage.

In the experiments performed, the heat transfer to the spheres was changed by variation of the gas temperature in the range 350-550°C, by variation of the gas flow rate in the range 40-400 ft^3.hr.$^{-1}$ and by variation of the particle diameter in the range $1/4$ to 1 in. The range of heat flux covered was from 5×10^{-2} to 50 C.H.U. sec.$^{-1}$ or, expressed in different units, from 40 to 2350 C.H.U.(ft^2)$^{-1}$ sec^{-1}.

Theory

For a system in which heat is transferred to a particle by forced convection, the heat flux is given by:

$$Q = h.A. \quad (T_g - T_s) \tag{1}$$

where Q = heat flux
    h = heat transfer coefficient.
    A = surface area of particle.
    T_g = temperature of gas.
    T_s = temperature of particle surface.

The heat transfer coefficient, h, for the case of a sphere heated or cooled by a fluid stream may be obtained from the following correlation[11]:

$$\frac{hD}{k} = 2.0 + 0.6 \, (Re)^{\frac{1}{2}}(Pr)^{1/3} \tag{2}$$

where D = diameter of spherical particle
    k = thermal conductivity of gas.
    Re = Reynolds Number = $\frac{VD\rho}{\mu}$ V = gas velocity
    ρ = gas density
    μ = gas dynamic viscosity.

Pr = Prandtl Number = $\dfrac{C\mu}{k}$, C = gas specific heat at constant pressure.

The Prandtl Number varied only slightly in the present experiments, the effect of change of Reynolds Number on h being dominant.

From the correlation, h may be calculated for known values of gas temperature, flow rate and particle diameter. For spherical particles, equation (1) becomes:

$$Q = h.\pi D^2 \ (T_g - T_s) \tag{1a}$$

This may then be combined with equation (2) to give

$$Q = \frac{k}{D} \ (2.0 + 0.6 \ (Re)^{\frac{1}{2}} \ (Pr)^{1/3}) \ \pi D^2 \ (T_g - T_s)$$

$$= k \ . (2.0 + 0.6 \ (Re)^{\frac{1}{2}} \ (Pr)^{1/3}) \pi D \ (T_g - T_s) \tag{3}$$

Having calculated h and measured D and T_g, Q may be obtained once the particle surface temperature, T_s, is known.

Based on the results presented previously, it is suggested that the surface temperature might be constant at about $400^\circ C$ during the period of constant rate of weight loss. A surface temperature of approximately $400^\circ C$ has been reported for coal particles during the initial "volatile" combustion period[12].

Once T_s is known, evaluation of Q makes possible a test of the hypothesis that the measured rate of particle weight loss, $\dfrac{dw}{dt}$, is directly proportional to Q. If this is so, then with D and Re constant, a plot of $\dfrac{dw}{dt}$ against T_g should give a straight line with intercept T_s on the temperature axis, provided that T_s is constant and independent of T_g. Also, with T_s and Re constant, a plot of $\dfrac{dw}{dt}$ against D or $w^{1/3}$ should be linear and with T_g and D constant a plot of $\dfrac{dw}{dt}$ against $Re^{\frac{1}{2}}$ should be linear.

Results and Discussion.

Typical weight loss curves are shown in Fig.2. The portion OA of the curve represents the weight loss as water leaves the particle and the surface temperature rises to the temperature of onset of decomposition. The linear portion AB represents a constant rate of weight loss and it is this rate which is used to test the hypothesis of a relationship between rate of weight loss and heat flux. For the portion BC of the curve, the rate of weight loss falls with time; its dependence on temperature and other parameters will not be discussed in the present paper but will be the subject of a further communication.

The Effect of Temperature.

To find the effect of change in gas temperature on the rate of particle weight loss for the constant rate period, $\frac{dw}{dt}$ was plotted against T_g for constant D and Re as shown in Fig.3. The straight line obtained for the gas temperature range from $420^\circ - 510^\circ C$ has an intercept on the temperature axis at about $400^\circ C$. This suggests that T_s is constant at about $400^\circ C$ and independent of T_g for the conditions used in these experiments.

The Effect of Particle Size.

Several experiments were performed in which the particle size was varied whilst T_g and Re were kept constant. The plot of $\frac{dw}{dt}$ against D or $w^{1/3}$, Fig.4, was then again a straight line.

The Effect of Gas Flow Rate.

Further experiments were performed in which T_g and D were held constant whilst gas flow rate, and therefore Reynolds Number, was varied. The plot of $\frac{dw}{dt}$ against $Re^{\frac{1}{2}}$ was again linear, as shown in Fig.5.

It was concluded from the results obtained that $\frac{dw}{dt}$ showed the variation with experimental conditions which was to be expected if it was directly proportional to heat flux, Q. The exact proportionality was obtained by plotting the experimental data in the form

1353

$\dfrac{\dfrac{dw}{dt}}{h.A}$ against T_g, as shown in Fig.6. For some of the experimental points a correction was made to h to allow for radiant heat transfer, as shown in the Appendix.

In Fig.6, the intercept of the straight line on the (gas) temperature axis is about $400°C$, taken to be the mean surface temperature of the coal particles during the constant rate period of decomposition only, for the experimental conditions used.

The gradient of the line represents the heat equivalent to the loss of unit weight of particle and is 1770 C.H.U.lb.$^{-1}$ (or cal.g^{-1}).

$$\frac{dw}{dt} = \frac{Q}{\lambda} \qquad (4)$$

where λ = 1,770 C.H.U.lb^{-1} (or cal.g^{-1}).

It must be emphasised that this value is 1770 C.H.U.lb.$^{-1}$ weight lost, and not initial weight, and applies for the constant rate of weight loss period only.

It is of interest to compare this value of λ with an estimated value for the heat carried away from the particle by volatile products[13]. Such an estimate may be made using the data of Peters[13], since no analyses of volatile products were made in the present experiments.

For a high-volatile coal carbonised by rapid heating, the product yields recorded by Peters are shown in Table 2.

The latent heat of vaporisation of water at $400°C$ and 1 atmosphere pressure was estimated to be 382 C.H.U.lb^{-1} from tabulated enthalpy data[14]. For the tar plus benzene, an estimate of the latent heat of vaporisation was 80 C.H.U.lb.$^{-1}$. Thus the heat leaving the particle at $400°C$ (latent heat only) is 3678 C.H.U. for 37.75 lb. of volatile material or 97 C.H.U.lb.$^{-1}$ volatile material.

Some allowance should also be made for an increase in the temperature of the coal residue during devolatilisation. For the temperature measurements referred to previously, whilst the particle surface temperature remained at or near $400°$ for five minutes, the temperature recorded by thermocouples 0.1in.and 0.2in, below the surface increased by about $100°C$. Taking the specific heat of the coal to be 0.25 C.H.U.lb.$^{-1}$°C.$^{-1}$, this temperature rise corresponds to an increase in residue heat capacity of 25 C.H.U.lb.$^{-1}$. For a residue 80% of the original weight, this amounts to 100 C.H.U.lb^{-1} weight lost.

These two terms add up to approximately 200 C.H.U.lb^{-1} volatile matter and the difference between this figure and that of 1770 C.H.U.lb.$^{-1}$ for λ, that is 1570 C.H.U.lb.$^{-1}$, must be attributed to heat absorption in the endothermic degradation reactions of coal.

Over the full temperature range up to 1000°C or higher, carbonisation is slightly exothermic, values between 30 and 170 C.H.U.lb.$^{-1}$ moist coal being cited for coke-ovens[15]. The laboratory experiments of Terres and Davis showed carbonisation to be slightly endothermic under some conditions, slightly exothermic under others[16]. The difference between the plant and laboratory results is thought to be due to the greater opportunity for exothermic cracking reactions on the plant[16].

For lower temperatures, the majority of the differential thermal analysis data points to carbonisation being endothermic although some of the evidence is conflicting[17]. There is, however, more recent evidence[18,19] that up to about 700°C carbonisation is endothermic and above 700°C becomes exothermic.

Millard[18] made his estimate of endothermic heat of carbonisation on the basis of temperature measurements in a 10 cwt (500 kg) coke oven, 16in.(40cm) wide. Idris Jones and Owen[19] studied an 8in. diameter, fluidised-bed, carboniser and from measurements of total heat input deduced the total heat of carbonisation which included both the heat required to raise the coal temperature and the endothermic heat of carbonisation. When the heat of carbonisation is calculated on the basis of initial weight of coal, the results for the present work are seen to compare well with those of the previous investigators. (Table 4).

More detailed comparison is difficult because only in the present work was a record kept of loss in weight with time. In the other two studies the heat of carbonisation rises with temperature to the maxima shown in the Table. This is consistent with a link between heat of carbonisation and weight loss, the weight loss being higher at higher temperature.

We thank the National Coal Board for a grant in aid of this research.

References

1. Z.F. Chukanov, (a) Dokl.Akad.Nauk.S.S.S.R. 72, No.4. (1950)
    (b) Izv.Akad.Nauk.S.S.S.R., Otd.Tekh. Nauk. No.8. (1954).
    (c) Brennst.Chemie, 37, 234,(1956).
2. (a) D.W. van Krevelen, F.J.Huntjens and H.N.M. Dormans. Fuel, 35, 462 (1956).
    (b) H.A.G. Chermin and D.W. van Krevelen, Fuel, 36, 85, (1957).
3. G.J. Pitt, Fuel, 41, 267, (1962).
4. H.N. Stone, J. Batchelor, and H. Johnstone. Ind.Eng. Chem., 46, 274, (1954).
5. W.Fuchs and A.F. Sandhoff, Ind.Eng.Chem.,44,567,(1942).
6. W.Peters, Gas-u Wasserfach, 98, No.21, 517,(1957).
7. P.C. Yellow, B.C.U.R.A. Monthly Bulletin, 29,No.9, 286, (1965).
8. W. Gomes, Nature, 192, 865, (1961).
9. J.A. Taplin, Nature, 194, 471, (1962).
10. N. Berkowitz, Fuel, 39, 43, (1960).
11. P.N. Rowe, K.T. Claxton, and J.B. Lewis, Trans.Inst. Chem. Eng.,43, T14, (1965).
12. A.S. Kallend and M.A. Nettleton, Erdöl und Kohle, 5, 354, (1966).
13. W. Peters, Gas-u Wasserfach, 99,No.41, 3,(1958); Fuel, 44, 317, (1965).
14. H.M. Spiers, "Technical Data on Fuel", 6th Edition, British National Committee, World Power Conference, (1962).
15. (a) W.Simonis, W.Weskamp and W. Dressler, Brennst. Chemie, 43, 289, (1962).
    (b) C. Meltzheim, J. Lahouste and A.F. Boyer, Chim.et Industr.,87, 603, (1962).
    (c) P.Foch, G. Meimarakis and S. Delessard.,Paper 14, World Power Conf.Sectional Meeting, Switzerland, (1964).
16. F.Denig, in "Chemistry of Coal Utilisation", Edited by H.H. Lowry, Vol.1, J.Wiley & Sons, New York and London, (1945).

17. H.C. Howard, in "Chemistry of Coal Utilisation", Edited by H.H. Lowry, Supplementary Vol., J.Wiley and Sons, New York and London, (1963).
18. D.J. Millard, J.Inst.Fuel, 28, 345, (1955).
19. W.Idris Jones and J. Owen, J.Inst.Fuel, 35, 404,(1962).
20. C.R. Howarth, Ph.D. Thesis, University of Sheffield, (1966).
21. W.H. McAdams, "Heat Transmission", 3rd Edition, McGraw-Hill, New York and London, (1954).

Table 1.

Analysis of non-swelling, dull, coal.

Air-dried basis

Water,	%	8.0
Ash,	%	7.5
Calorific Value, Btu.lb.$^{-1}$		12,170(6,760 C.H.U.lb.$^{-1}$).
B.S. Swelling No.		1a
Gray-King Coke Type		D.E.
Coal Rank Code No.		8/702

Dry,mineral-matter free, basis.

Carbon	%	83
Hydrogen	%	5.2
Volatile Matter	%	45

Table 2.

Product yields, % by weight of pure coal.

Product	%
Gas	7.25
Carbonisation Water	4.10
Tar + Carbonisation Benzene	26.40
Carbonisation Coke	62.25

Table 3.

Comparison of endothermic heats of carbonisation

Coal.	Heat of carbonisation C.H.U.lb.$^{-1}$	Total heat of carbonisation. C.H.U.lb.$^{-1}$	Reference
West Cannock 45% V.M.	531(30%wt loss)		Present work.
Dinnington, 32.6% V.M.	170		Millard
Parkgate, 34.5% V.M.	320		
Waterloo, 32.2% V.M.	780		
Parkgate, 34.5% V.M.		460	Idris Jones
Waterloo, 34.2% V.M.		850	and Owen
Binley, 42.0% V.M.		560	

Table 4.

Correction for radiant heat flux

Particle dia.in.	Reynolds No.	Gas Temp. °C.	Wall Temp. °C.	h_c	h_r
0.5	200	476	414	6.9	1.5
0.5	200	442	416	6.9	3.1
0.76	200	452	409	4.5	1.7
0.76	400	454	430	6.0	5.5
0.76	600	445	430	7.2	6.7
0.76	700	529	480	7.7	7.45
1.00	200	408	462	3.5	14.4

Appendix
Correction for radiant heat flux from reactor walls

When the walls of the reactor are hotter than the coal particle surface, and radiate heat to it, it is necessary to add a radiant heat term to the convective heat flux.
This is given by:

$$Q = \sigma \cdot A \cdot \varepsilon \cdot F \cdot (T_w^4 - T_s^4) \tag{5}$$

where σ = Stefan-Boltzmann constant, 1×10^{-8} C.H.U.ft.$^{-2}$hr^{-1} $^{\circ}$K^{-4}.

A = surface area of particle.
ε = overall emissivity.
F = view factor.
T_w = reactor wall temperature, $^{\circ}$K.
T_s = particle surface temperature, $^{\circ}$K.

The emissivity of bituminous coal is taken to be 0.96[20] and the emissivity of the reactor wall (Mild steel, rough) is 0.95[21]. The overall emissivity is given by:

$$\frac{1}{\dfrac{1}{\varepsilon_1} + \dfrac{1}{\varepsilon_2} - 1} = 0.91$$

The view factor, F, is evaluated by noting that the coal particle can 'see' hot reactor walls except over the areas where there are, first, the side tube A used to admit the particles ($1\frac{1}{2}$ in. diameter, 1 in. from particle centre) and, second, the observation window B at the end of the apparatus (2 in. diameter, 10 in. from particle centre). The solid angles for A and B are:

$$\partial W_A = \frac{\pi \cdot 9}{4 \times 4 \times 1} = \frac{9\pi}{16}$$

$$\partial W_B = \frac{\pi \cdot 2^2}{4 \times 10^2} = \frac{\pi}{100}$$

$$\text{View factor, } F = 1 - \frac{\frac{9\pi}{16} + \frac{\pi}{100}}{4\pi}$$

$$= 0.86$$

$$Q = \sigma .A.0.91 \times 0.86\ (T_w^4 - T_s^4)$$

$$= h_r .A.\ (T_w - T_s)$$

$$\therefore \quad h_r = \sigma \times 0.91 \times 0.86\ \frac{T_w^4 - T_s^4}{T_w - T_s}$$

and since $\sigma = 1 \times 10^{-8}$

$$h_r = 0.783\ \frac{\left(\frac{T_w}{100}\right)^4 - \left(\frac{T_s}{100}\right)^4}{T_w - T_s}$$

Corrections were made, and are shown in Table 4, for seven of the thirty points shown in Fig.6; these points are marked with a cross.

In Table 4

h_c = convective heat transfer coefficient.

h_r = radiative heat transfer coefficient.

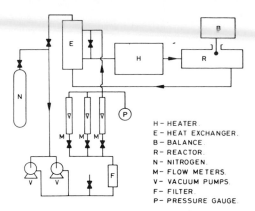

H – HEATER.
E – HEAT EXCHANGER.
B – BALANCE.
R – REACTOR.
N – NITROGEN.
M – FLOW METERS.
V – VACUUM PUMPS.
F – FILTER.
P – PRESSURE GAUGE.

Fig.1.   Flow diagram of the Apparatus.

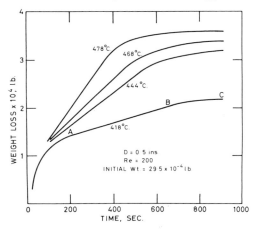

Fig.2.   Typical weight loss curves.

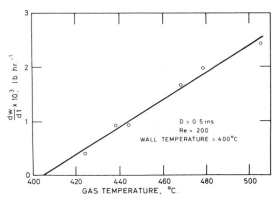

Fig.3.   Plot of $\dfrac{dw}{dt}$ against T_g.

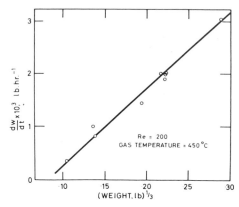

Fig.4.   Plot of $\dfrac{dw}{dt}$ against $w^{1/3}$.

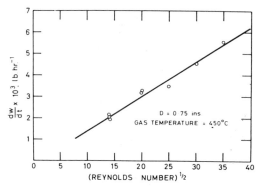

Fig.5.   Plot of $\dfrac{dw}{dt}$ against $Re^{\frac{1}{2}}$.

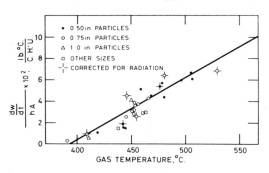

Fig.6.   Plot of $\dfrac{\dfrac{dw}{dt}}{h.A}$ against Tg.

THE USE OF DIFFERENTIAL THERMAL ANALYSIS-EFFLUENT GAS ANALYSIS IN METALLURGICAL RESEARCH INVESTIGATIONS

W. R. Bandi, E. G. Buyok, G. Krapf, and L. M. Melnick

United States Steel Corporation
Applied Research Laboratory
Monroeville, Pa.

For the past four years, we have been using differential thermal analysis (DTA) - effluent gas analysis (EGA) to identify and quantitatively determine small amounts of metal nitrides and carbides in residues chemically extracted from steel (1-6). Such analyses are important because these compounds may affect the mechanical properties of steel. Quantitative analysis for these compounds is accomplished by monitoring the effluent gas from the programmed combustion or decomposition of an aliquot weight (milligram amounts) of the residue heated in a dynamic atmosphere of oxygen. From the composition of the gas, it is possible to calculate the amount of nitride or carbide in the steel. Although DTA-EGA is not a universal solution to the problems inherent in this type of analysis, we have successfully identified and determined compounds which could not be identified or determined by other techniques.

Our application of DTA-EGA is based on the assumption that each metal carbide and nitride has a characteristic combustion or decomposition temperature range in a dynamic atmosphere of oxygen or other gas. We have determined that this assumption is nearly always valid. The DTA-EGA peak temperatures do vary to some extent with the particle size of the compounds.

The usefulness of the DTA-EGA technique is limited by the difficulty in finding chemical reagents that will attack the steel matrix without destroying the compound to be determined. Also, the particle size of the nitrides and carbides may be so small that it becomes difficult to·

retain them on the finest pore-size organic membrane (100A).

The modified R. L. Stone instrument that we have been using has been described previously, (3,4) but the thermograms presented here were obtained with a slightly different sample-heating block (Figure 1). Because some of the welds in previous blocks separated and gas leaks developed after two years of use, the new sample-heating block has no welded joints. (It takes a long time to remove the carbon from the Inconel block material so as to obtain low carbon blanks; therefore, we want the sample-heating block to last as long as possible.) In the new sample holder, we have retained the stacked thermocouple arrangement to ensure a small gas volume and the ability to detect microgram quantities of carbon dioxide in the effluent gas. To balance this thermocouple arrangement, it is necessary to have the same length of platinel wire between each thermocouple and the upper edge of the hot zone; otherwise a large thermal unbalance occurs as the result of conduction of heat by the thermocouple wire itself. In the new sample-heating block the reference gas is not passed through the hot zone. Instead, the sample and reference gases are equilibrated in a constant-temperature cell (Gow-Mac Model Tr III A) containing the thermal conductivity cell. As a result, the time for temperature equilibration causes more lag in recording the thermal conductivity change for CO_2 in the effluent gas than we previously showed. However, Figure 2 shows that the sharpness of both the DTA and EGA peaks has been improved with this sample holder. The DTA (lower) and EGA (upper) responses shown in this figure were obtained for 0.200 mg of cubic NbC and for 0.932 mg of cubic TaC heated at 10 C/min in a dynamic oxygen atmosphere flowing at 3 ml/min. This and subsequent DTA thermograms shown were recorded using a sensitivity setting of 150 microvolts with a 10 mv recorder, whereas the EGA responses were obtained using a 1 mv recorder and a sensitivity setting of 16 with a bridge current of 6 ma on a Gow-Mac Model 9999 power supply.

Even with the improvements in the sample-holder assembly, it is not possible to obtain quantitative data when several carbides and nitrides having nearly the same decomposition temperatures are present in the residue extracted from a steel. When such mixtures are analyzed,

good resolution of the EGA peaks is rarely obtained. Therefore, we have employed a duPont 310 Curve Resolver to produce quantitative information from some EGA responses. The
curve resolver is similar to an analog computer and is
capable of producing skewed and normal Gaussian curves of
various shapes on an oscilloscope screen. With some knowledge of the EGA peak temperature of the compounds that
might be present in the residues, several curves can be
devised such that their sum corresponds to the shape of the
experimental curve that is also projected on the screen. A
quantitative answer for the individual compounds can then
be obtained by integration of each peak area. (However, it
is possible that the EGA response can be represented by
more than one set of simulated curves. What we do is to
get a best fit based on our knowledge of the steel composition and the compounds we expect to find in the residue.)

Some results from two recent investigations will serve
to illustrate our work. The first investigation was concerned with some heat-treated samples of 5 percent nickel
steels containing 0.5 percent Cr and 0.5 percent Mo. All
but the control steel had a carbide or nitride forming
element added to the standard composition. Figure 3 shows
a DTA-EGA recording for a residue extracted from the control sample. This residue was obtained after dissolution
of the matrix in 1-1 HCl at room temperature. The first
EGA peak is caused by the combustion of Fe_2C; this carbide
is never quantitatively isolated in HCl. The second EGA
peak is caused by the combustion of amorphous elemental
carbon which is present in the residue as the result of the
decomposition of Fe_3C and other unstable carbides during
dissolution of the matrix.

Figure 4 shows the DTA-EGA recording of another residue from the same control steel. This residue was also
obtained by dissolution of the steel matrix in 1-1 HCl,
but the dissolution, filtration, washing, and desiccation
were all done under an argon atmosphere instead of in air.
At least 4 times more residue was isolated by using argon.
Both the Fe_3C and the elemental carbon peaks are present,
but a third carbide with a DTA peak at 435 C and EGA peak
at 500 C is also present. A partial analysis of the
residue is shown and indicates that the third carbon
dioxide response is from the combustion of a molybdenum

carbide, possibly cubic Mo_2C, but we have not been able to obtain a diffraction pattern to prove this. Comparing Figures 3 and 4 demonstrates that care must be taken when isolating the compounds from steel if reliable DTA-EGA data are to be obtained.

Figure 5 shows the thermal response for the same type of steel with titanium added. In addition to the Fe_3C and amorphous carbon DTA peaks, there is a double DTA peak at 445 C and 465 C, and still another peak at 710 C. Several unresolved carbon dioxide EGA responses are present around 500 C. A partial analysis of the residue shows that both molybdenum and titanium are present. The DTA peaks at 445 C and 465 C are due, respectively, to molybdenum carbide and to titanium carbide or carbonitride.

The exotherm at 710 C is due to the decomposition of titanium nitride, whereas the endotherm at 760 C is due to the volatilization of MoO_3 formed from the combustion of the molybdenum carbide. The EGA carbon dioxide response was resolved on the duPont Curve Resolver (Figure 6); the carbon dioxide peaks for molybdenum carbide and titanium carbonitride at 520 and 560 C, respectively, corresponding to the DTA peaks at 445 and 465 C are shown.

In previous publications (3,5,6) we showed an EGA nitrogen response for a mixture of titanium carbonitride and titanium nitride isolated from different titanium-bearing steels. These EGA patterns were obtained by using a chromatograph to separate the oxygen from the nitrogen, with helium as the carrier gas (3). There is a 70 or 80 degree lag between decomposition of the nitride and recording of the nitrogen. The EGA nitrogen maxima for the residue isolated from the titanium-bearing 5% Ni steel in the latest work (Figure 7) are very similar to the earlier responses. The DTA peak at 465 C for titanium carbonitride is shown here as an EGA nitrogen peak at 540 C, and the DTA peak at 710 C for titanium nitride is shown here as an EGA nitrogen peak at 780 C.

A greater complication in this study of 5% Ni steels occurred with a heat-treated specimen containing tantalum. Figure 8 shows the DTA-EGA recording obtained on an aliquot weight of the residue isolated from this steel. The EGA peaks for Fe_3C and molybdenum carbide are evident. The EGA response for TaC can also be recognized. But the resolution of the EGA carbon dioxide response (Figure 9) shows that at least two other carbides are present. Partial analysis of the residue showed a large increase in the molybdenum content as compared with that shown before (Figures 4 and 5), and the EGA peak at 650 C was found to be due to the combustion of hexagonal Mo_2C. The response for pure hexagonal Mo_2C is shown in Figure 10. (The endotherm at 800 C is due to the volatilization of MoO_3.) The EGA carbon dioxide peak at 570 C compared favorably with that which we had previously obtained for niobium carbide in other work. Subsequent analysis showed that niobium was present in the steel, probably added as a contaminant in the tantalum. So in this instance, we were able to identify responses for five carbides and carbon, and quantitatively determine three of the carbides. We could also have calculated the concentration of another of the molybdenum carbides (EGA peak at about 475 C) if we had known the formula of this compound.

The second investigation used to illustrate our work was concerned with the quantitative determination of three compounds with the same chemical formula but with two different crystal structures. This occurred in a recent study in which we were attempting to establish the temperature and time necessary for complete precipitation of niobium nitride in an iron-niobium-nitrogen system. In this work we first examined the residue isolated in 10 percent HCl from the hot-rolled specimen, and obtained the EGA responses shown in Figure 11. There are three nitrogen peaks. The response at 510 C compares favorably with that for the pure cubic NbN which we had previously examined. X-ray diffraction examination of the residue showed that it contained hexagonal NbN, and it was concluded by X-ray and EGA examination of other samples that the nitrogen peak at 660 C was caused by decomposition of this compound. However, the peak at 380 C was very perplexing.

The residue was then examined by thermogravimetric analysis (TGA) in the hope that three weight changes would be observed which would correspond to the decomposition

temperatures and be helpful in identifying the EGA peak at
380 C and also in verifying the formulas for hexagonal and
cubic NbN. However, the TGA data showed not three weight
changes, but one weight gain between 270 and 400 C. This
weight gain started at the temperature at which nitrogen
was first evolved, but was complete at a temperature lower
than the EGA nitrogen peaks for cubic and hexagonal NbN.
Examination of pure cubic NbN also showed that the temperature for the weight gain was not consistent with the evolution temperatures for nitrogen. It was, therefore, concluded that the main weight change was due to oxidation of
niobium nitride to niobium oxynitride, and that no Nb_2N or
NbN_2 was present in the residue.

Mori (7) in Japan has referred to a form of NbN other
than the cubic and hexagonal forms. He obtained a partial
X-ray diffraction pattern and said it was due to another
hexagonal NbN and called it epsilon nitride. He also
stated that this compound formed during the decomposition
of the usual hexagonal NbN to give cubic NbN. Epsilon
nitride presumably was formed when a steel was heat-treated
at 800 C; it was not present after the steel was heat-
treated to 1200 C. Figure 12 shows that in our work the
third nitride response disappeared when the Fe-Nb-N alloy
was heat-treated at 950 C for 1/2 hour.

Guard and co-workers (8) also described a NbN, which
they called Δ', that transforms to cubic NbN on heat
treatment. It is our opinion that both Mori and Guard,
et al, are talking about the same intermediate form of
NbN, and we believe that the nitrogen evolution peak
observed at 380 C was caused by this compound. However, we
have no firm basis for this conclusion since an X-ray diffraction pattern was not obtainable.

Table I summarizes the data obtained in this last
study. It also indicates that quantitative results were
obtained since this alloy contains 0.18 percent nitrogen,
and in at least two of the EGA patterns the sum of the
nitrogen responses equalled 0.18 percent.

In conclusion we have found that DTA-EGA can be used
to identify and quantitatively determine individual metal
carbides and nitrides in a complex mixture of compounds

isolated from steels. Although some DTA patterns may be very complex, the technique is practical and informative.

Acknowledgements

The authors wish to acknowledge the help of other members of the U. S. Steel Corporation Applied Research Laboratory; P. A. Stoll, of the Physics and Analytical Chemistry Division who supervised the X-ray diffraction analyses, and D. Dabkowski and J. M. Gray of the Ordance Products and Bar, Plate, and Forged Products Divisions, respectively, who furnished the heat-treated steel specimens used in these studies.

References

1. W. R. Bandi, H. S. Karp, W. A. Straub, and L. M. Melnick, Talanta, 11, 1327, (1964).
2. W. R. Bandi, W. A. Straub, H. S. Karp, and L. M. Melnick, ASTM Spec. Tech. Publ. #393, Am. Soc. Testing and Materials, Phila., Pa., (1966).
3. W. R. Bandi, W. A. Straub, E. G. Buyok, and L. M. Melnick, Anal. Chem., 38, 1336, (1966).
4. H. S. Karp, W. R. Bandi, and L. M. Melnick, Talanta, 13, 1679, (1966).
5. H. S. Karp, E. G. Buyok, W. R. Bandi, and L. M. Melnick, Mat. Res. Bull., 311, (1967).
6. W. R. Bandi, J. L. Lutz, and L. M. Melnick, Journal Iron and Steel Institute (in press).
7. T. Mori, K. Fujita, M. Tokizane, and K. Yamaguchi, Tetsu-to-Hagane, 50, 911, (1964).
8. R. W. Guard, J. W. Savage, and D. G. Swarthout, Trans. AIME, 239, 643, (1967).

TABLE 1

Effect of Temperature on Precipitation of NbN

Heat treatment (°C - time,hr)	%N precipitated	Type of precipitate	Remarks
As-rolled	0.14	cubic, hex. intermediate	
900 - 0.5	0.18	cubic, hex. intermediate	complete precipitation--intermediate form goes to cubic
950 - 0.5	0.17	cubic, hex.	intermediate form disappears
1000 - 0.5	0.18	cubic, hex.	
1050 - 0.5	0.17	cubic, hex.	
1100 - 0.5	0.14	cubic, hex.	partial dissolution of NbN
1150 - 0.5	0.12	cubic, hex.	partial dissolution of NbN
1200 - 0.5	0.11	cubic, hex.	partial dissolution of NbN
1250 - 0.5	0.07	cubic, hex.	partial dissolution of NbN
1300 - 0.5	0.02	cubic, hex.	partial dissolution of NbN
1350 - 0.5	0.008	cubic, hex.	partial dissolution of NbN

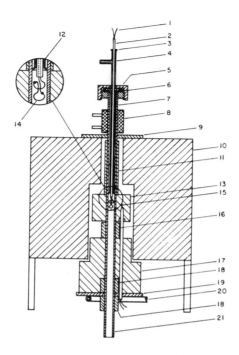

Fig. 1 Sample holder assembly; 1. DTA thermocouple leads, 2. thermocouple insulator, 3. epoxy cement seal, 4. gas exit, 5. hexagonal screw cap, 6. o-ring seal, 7. outer gas outlet tube (Inconel), 8. split water jacket (copper) 9. asbestos, 10. furnace, 11. asbestos, 12. inner gas tube, 13. one piece sample block (Inconel) 14. platinel thermocouple and sample holding wire, 15. control thermocouple, 16. asbestos, 17. fire brick, 18. sleeve nuts, 19. water-cooled flange, 20. cooling coil (copper), 21. gas inlet tube.

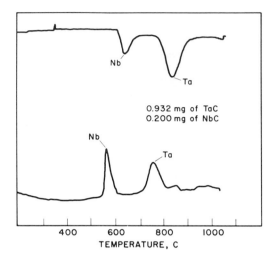

Fig. 2 DTA-EGA recordings for combustion of NbC and TaC (all DTA thermograms recorded at sensitivity of 0.66 inch deflection/C on 10-inch strip chart recorder).

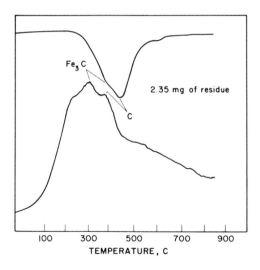

Fig. 3 DTA-EGA recording for combustion of residue extracted in ambient 1-1 HCl from 5% Ni 0.5% Mo steel (extracted in air).

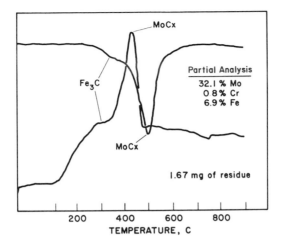

Fig. 4 DTA-EGA recording for combustion of residue extracted in ambient 1-1 HCl from 5% Ni 0.5% Mo steel (extracted in argon).

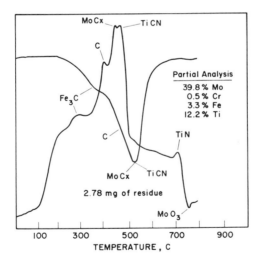

Fig. 5 DTA-EGA recording for combustion of residue from 5% Ni, 0.5% Mo steel containing Ti.

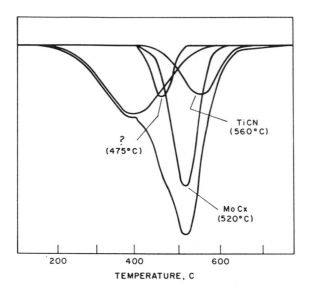

Fig. 6 Resolution of CO_2 responses from combustion of residue from 5% Ni, 0.5% Mo steel containing Ti.

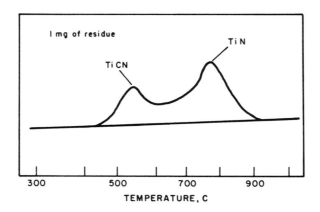

Fig. 7 EGA recording of N_2 evolved from decomposition of TiCN and TiN isolated from a Ti-bearing steel.

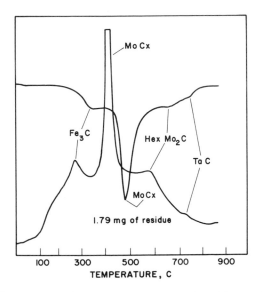

Fig. 8 DTA-EGA recording for combustion of residue from 5% Ni, 0.5% Mo steel containing Nb and Ta.

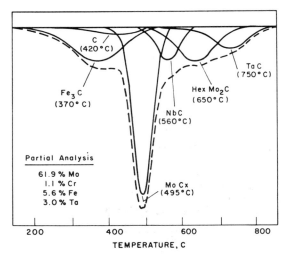

Fig. 9 Resolution of CO₂ responses from combustion of residue from 5% Ni, 0.5% Mo steel containing Nb and Ta.

1375

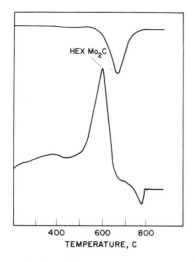

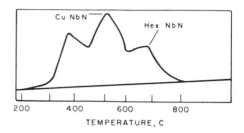

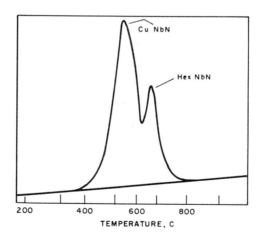

Fig. 10 DTA-EGA record-
ing for combustion of hexagonal Mo_2C.

Fig. 11 EGA-N_2 respones for
decomposition of residue from
as-rolled Fe-Nb-N alloy.

Fig. 12 EGA-N_2 responses for decomposition of residue
from Fe-Nb-N alloy heat-treated at 950 C for 0.5 hour.

THE IDENTIFICATION AND ESTIMATION OF
CARBONACEOUS MATERIALS BY DTA

D.J. Swaine*

CSIRO   Division of Mineral Chemistry
Australia

Abstract

Details are given of a DTA method for carbon, based on
the heat evolved during oxidation. This method has been
used for fly-ash, coke, char, coals, peat, natural graphites, and various artificial carbons. In some cases the
components of binary mixtures may be differentiated.
Quantitative analysis of carbon in fly-ash is outlined.
Carbon separated from shales and other sediments by a demineralization procedure is suitable for this method. DTA
curves are shown for the above applications.

Introduction

The oxidation of carbon is an exothermic reaction
which is readily detectable by DTA. Durirg an investigation
of the possible significance of carbon in fly-ash (the solid
residue in the gas stream from the combustion of pulverized
coal) it was observed that the shapes and peak positions of
the DTA curves produced by oxidation (the carbon exotherms)
were slightly different for two coke-like materials. Further
investigation of a wide range of carbon types has shown the
range of the variations of the peak position and to a less
extent variations of the shape of the carbon exotherms.

This paper discusses the experimental conditions used
to identify carbonaceous materials by DTA, and presents
curves obtained from fly-ash, coke, char, coals, various

---

* Principal Research Scientist.

natural graphites and artificial carbons. The estimation of carbon in fly-ash is cited as an example of the use of the method for quantitative analysis, and examples are given of the identification of mixtures of two types of carbon. The method is also useful for carbonaceous material in sediments, following a separation procedure. Published curves for peat, coal and graphite are not particularly relevant to the present study, and have therefore not been cited.

Details of Method

The DTA apparatus used is essentially that described by Schulz (1), the main differences being the use of (i) a ceramic block with relatively wide wells (6.4 mm diameter, 4.0 mm deep) and (ii) a slow stream of purified air (225 ml/min), introduced at the base of the furnace through a copper ring with equally spaced holes. There was no cover on the block, so that the air passed up and around the top of the sample wells. Calcined alumina (minus 100 B.S.mesh) was used both as reference material and as diluent; the thermocouples were of chromel-alumel and an average rate of temperature-change of 10 ± 0.5 deg C/min was maintained. The extent of the differential temperature change can be estimated from the scale (for 1°C) on the DTA curves. In some of the early work, calcined fly-ash (61% SiO_2, 25% Al_2O_3, 5% Fe_2O_3, 1% TiO_2, 1% CaO, 1.5% MgO, 1% Na_2O, 2% K_2O) was the reference and diluent material; it had been heated at 1100°C to oxidize carbon. Dilution of a sample containing more than a few per cent carbon was carried out by gentle mixing with calcined alumina, using a pestle and mortar. The diluent and the reference material were always the same for a particular test. Experiments showed that loose packing in the relatively shallow wells was necessary to allow ready access of air and egress of volatile combustion products; this was achieved by pouring the sample into the well. Samples containing up to about 2% (i.e. about 10 mg) carbon, did not require dilution, but the smooth complete combustion, which is a feature of the method, was not so readily attainable with higher concentrations of carbon.

Fly-ash, Coke, and Char

The method was developed initially to investigate fly-ash. In general, fly-ash from Australian bituminous coals is high in silicon, aluminium, and iron, with small amounts of titanium, calcium, magnesium, sodium, and potassium, together with a variable amount of carbon, usually of the order of a few per cent. Calcined fly-ash was clearly the best reference material.

Fig. 1 shows a typical DTA curve for a fly-ash from a New South Wales coal compared with those for the relevant coal, a coke and a char. Each sample contained the same amount of carbon as the fly-ash, namely 3-mg, diluted to 300 mg with calcined fly-ash. The curves for the fly-ash, coke, and char are similar, although the carbon in the fly-ash started to oxidize earlier than the char.

Coals and Peat

For coals, the DTA curves differ according to rank. In Fig. 2, examples are given of DTA curves for a Welsh anthracite, a Queensland semi-anthracite, a New South Wales bituminous coal, a South Australian sub-bituminous coal, and a Victorian soft brown coal, together with an American peat for comparison. In each case air-dried coal was used, the sample weight being calculated to an equivalent of 10 mg carbon which was diluted to 500 mg with calcined alumina. The ease of oxidation decreases with increase in rank. These curves are simpler in shape than some other published curves for coals, mainly because of the small weight of sample and the high dilution.

Natural Graphites

Five natural graphites were examined – from Ceylon, Cumberland, Madagascar, Passau, and Ticonderoga – using 3 mg samples diluted to 500 mg with calcined alumina. All gave different curve shapes and peak temperatures (Fig. 3). The wide range of temperature over which oxidation occurs appears to be a feature of the Ceylon and Madagascar graphites.

Artificial Carbons

Several artificial carbons were examined, namely a
spectroscopic graphite (ultra pure), Sterling MT, Sterling
FT, Graphon, acetylene black, ACARB-SRF (an oil furnace
black), and carbon black. 3-mg samples were diluted to
300 mg with calcined fly-ash. Again, differences were observed in curve shape and peak temperature (Fig. 4).

Mixtures of Two Types of Carbon

Fig. 5 shows curves for a mixture of 3 mg of spectroscopic graphite and 3 mg of acetylene black, and for a mixture of 3 mg of spectroscopic graphite and 3 mg of char.
Calcined fly-ash was used as diluent. The components of
the mixtures were detectable, but for two materials having
fairly close peak temperatures the differentiation is either
less definite or impossible. With a mixture of acetylene
black and Graphon (separate curves in Fig. 3) only one curve
was obtained, with a peak temperature midway between those
for acetylene black and Graphon.

Determination of Carbon

In favourable cases it is possible to determine from
the DTA curve the amount of carbon in a sample. This technique was investigated and used successfully for determining the carbon contents of fly-ashes. After trying various
approaches, for example, peak height, peak width at half
peak height, and area under the peak, the latter was selected as the most useful method. Conditions were standardized.
The areas were delineated assuming a straight baseline and
were measured by placing a special transparent weighing
paper over the curve, tracing the relevant outline, cutting
out the appropriate area and weighing the paper. Fig. 6
gives the results of six replicate tests using a fly-ash
containing 2.2%C (determined chemically), to ascertain the
precision of the method. Also shown are the weights of
paper equivalent to the areas under the curves (62.0 ± 5.7mg);
in terms of carbon this result is 2.2 ± 0.2%C, and the peak
temperature is 523 ± 6°C. In practice this chemically analysed standard fly-ash was diluted to give a series of sub-
standards in the range down to 0.1%C and a standard curve
was drawn for area-under-exotherm versus concentration of
carbon.

It should be stressed that the determination of carbon by this DTA method requires a standard curve prepared from samples of known carbon content, with the carbon in a similar form to that in the samples to be analysed.

Geochemical Applications

Carbon in various forms is associated with most shales and other sediments. If the mineral matter is removed, the carbonaceous residue can be readily examined by the DTA method, using calcined alumina as diluent, and graphite, coal, peat and related forms of carbon can be identified.

Demineralization is carried out by treating the sample, ground to about minus 100 B.S. mesh with hydrochloric acid and with hydrofluoric acid. As far as can be seen from DTA curves, graphites are not affected by this treatment. Higher-rank coals are similarly unaffected, but lower-rank coals are altered by this treatment (see Fig. 7). However, the DTA curve of, say, soft brown coal after demineraliz-ation can still be used for identification as it differs from the curves for other coals.

Discussion and Conclusions

The differences in the DTA curves for the various forms of carbon have not been fully explained but no doubt surface properties and adsorbed oxygen are among the relevant fact-ors. Although the catalytic effect of certain cations – for example, lead and silver - is known to enhance the oxid-ation of carbon, there has been no evidence of catalytic effects by minerals or cations known to be associated with the carbons examined so far. The effect of cations on the carbon exotherm under the conditions of the DTA tests out-lined in this paper is being investigated. The complexity of the carbon-oxygen reaction still challenges chemists, and perhaps results of basic studies being undertaken by others may provide a basis for understanding these DTA results.

The experimental work described shows that different types of carbon can be distinguished by a simple DTA test. This can be carried out either on the original sample or, when the carbon is at a very low concentration, on material separated from associated mineral matter. The method has applications to natural carbon-containing substances and to industrial products, where identification and (in some cases) determination of carbon are required.

References

1. R.A. Schulz, Clay Minerals Bull. 5, 279 (1963).

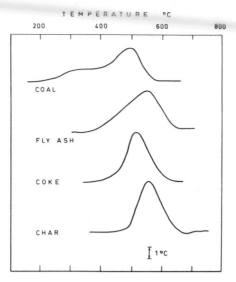

Fig. 1. DTA curves for a New South Wales bituminous coal,
the resulting fly-ash, a coke, and a char.

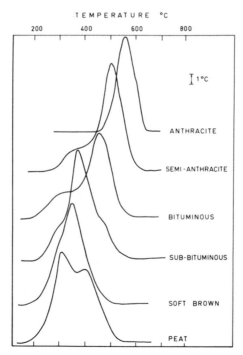

Fig. 2. DTA curve for various Australian coals, a Welsh
anthracite, and an American peat.

TEMPERATURE °C

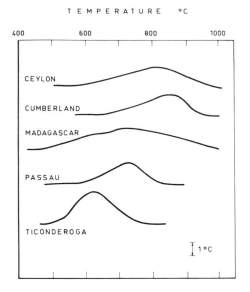

Fig. 3. DTA curve for graphites.

TEMPERATURE °C

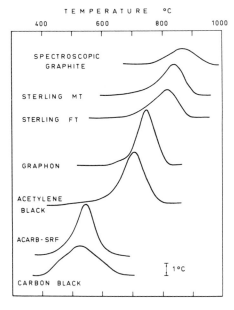

Fig. 4. DTA curves for various artificial carbons.

1384

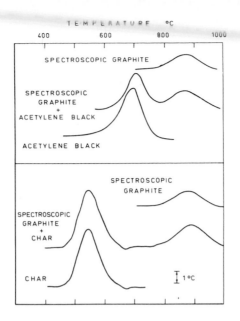

TEMPERATURE °C

SPECTROSCOPIC GRAPHITE

SPECTROSCOPIC
GRAPHITE
+
ACETYLENE BLACK

ACETYLENE BLACK

SPECTROSCOPIC
GRAPHITE

SPECTROSCOPIC
GRAPHITE
+
CHAR

CHAR

Fig. 5. DTA curves for mixtures of two types of carbon.

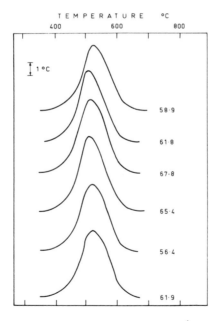

TEMPERATURE °C

58·9

61·8

67·8

65·4

56·4

61·9

Fig. 6. Replicate DTA curves for fly-ash (values against
curves are weights (mg) of paper equivalent to areas).

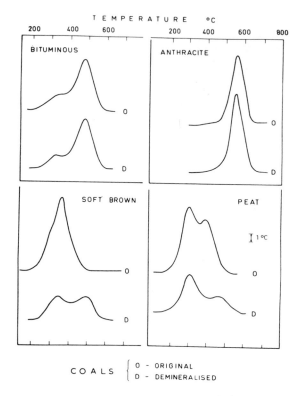

Fig. 7. DTA curves for coals before (O) and after (D) demineralization.

A STUDY OF DIFFERENTIAL THERMAL ANALYSIS (DTA) — EFFLUENT GAS ANALYSIS (EGA) FOR THE DETERMINATION OF PLANETARY ENVIRONMENTAL PARAMETERS*

Edgar M. Bollin

Jet Propulsion Laboratory,
California Institute of Technology

Abstract

The scientific rationale of a thermal analysis experiment for planetary exploration is developed. The ability of the experiment to determine the present state and past evolution of certain planetary environmental parameters that have significance for biological processes is discussed. The capability of the experiment to identify specific mineralogy or geochemical relationships produced by sustained biological action is examined.

Introduction

Two important questions to biologists to be answered in an exploration of Mars are: (a) is life now present or has it been present in the past; and (b) is the environment now capable of supporting life or has it been capable of supporting life at some stage in planetary history? While thermal analysis has a limited capability for total mineral identification, it is highly sensitive for the detection of organics and a number of specific mineral types which are known to have a widespread development on earth under the influence of water or organic activity. Therefore, such an

---

*This paper presents the results of one phase of research carried out at the Jet Propulsion Laboratory, California Institute of Technology, under Contract No. NAS 7-100, sponsored by the National Aeronautics and Space Administration.

experiment has a distinct capability to answer these questions by the determination of the presence or absence of minerals or chemical reactions of biological or environmental significance.

While DTA has not been widely considered as a prime experiment for planetary exploration due to the somewhat large size of laboratory instrumentation and its inability to identify mineralogy as specifically as the X-ray diffractometer or the petrographic microscope under laboratory conditions, studies concerning experiments suitable for lunar and planetary exploration have recommended the use of DTA (1-3). Feasibility studies have been carried out in which an experimental breadboard instrument with a total transducer weight of 10 g has been developed and evaluated (4). Furnace dissipation is approximately 15 W at 1000°C, and sample weight is 15 mg. Analytical capability is nearly equivalent to laboratory instrumentation with high-speed programming. Baseline stability is sufficient for programming at 2400°C/min, but analytical considerations indicate that the most probable upper limit is approximately 50 to 100°C/min.

Lovelock (5) has proposed an experiment in which: ". . . two equal samples of the planetary surface would be heated in a DTA apparatus; one sample in the atmosphere of the planet, the other in an inert gas, such as, argon. An exotherm on the differential signal between the two samples would indicate a reaction between the surface and its atmosphere, a condition most unlikely to be encountered where there is chemical equilibrium as in the absence of life."

DTA experiments have been conceived (6) which would: (a) determine total water in mineral samples; (b) determine total organics in surface samples; (c) identify minerals; (d) determine whether the sample is in thermodynamic equilibrium; and (e) seek evidence of aqueous weathering or organogenic deposits.

A discussion of the use of DTA in the biological exploration of Mars is contained in a study prepared by the staff of the Space Sciences Division of the Jet Propulsion Laboratory (7).

Application of DTA to Extraterrestrial
Mineral Identification

Comparison of DTA With Other Techniques of Mineral Identification

There are only three analytical laboratory techniques that have any established background of capability in mineral identification. They are X-ray diffraction, the petrographic microscope, and DTA. Of these, only X-ray diffraction is rigorously acceptable for unequivocal identification. The petrographic microscope is generally considered adequate for establishing routine textural relationships and identification of the commonly occurring minerals, and is capable of furnishing more interpretative petrographic information that even the X-ray diffractometer. DTA ranks considerably below these instruments in its ability to identify total mineralogy, and is generally used in conjunction with the above techniques, especially when trouble is encountered with the other techniques.

The X-ray diffractometer and the differential thermal analysis instrumentation can be reduced to spacecraft instrumentation without serious loss of laboratory resolution. Such is not the case with the petrographic microscope for some classes of mineralogy. The data obtained are subjective and dependent upon the skill and judgment of the observer, and require extensive sample preparation, exorbitant manipulation, and color fidelity requirements far beyond any presently conceived spacecraft to approach its laboratory performance.

DTA is not a general analytical tool in that it can identify all mineralogic phases uniquely. X-ray diffraction is the only technique that can approach such a definition. Unfortunately, power, weight, sample preparation, and other more serious technological problems prevent consideration of this instrument on all but the most sophisticated spacecraft designs.

Therefore, the problem of which analytical mineralogical technique, based upon laboratory performance, is best suited for planetary spacecraft has very little meaning. A more realistic question is which of these techniques can be used at all for first or second generation restricted payload requirements. Using such a definition places DTA in an unequivocal position for serious consideration as a prime experiment.

1389

Capability of DTA in Total Mineralogic Analysis

DTA does not distinguish between the various types of thermal reactions that may occur in the sample. The information obtained is whether a reaction has occurred which is endothermic or exothermic, the size and characteristic shape of the curve, number of reactions, and the temperature at which the reactions occur. The magnitude of the shift of these parameters with a change of heating rate, or the change of the composition or pressure of the environmental atmosphere surrounding the sample, provides considerable further interpretative data. The addition of a simple nonspecific gas effluent detector allows the discrimination between solid-state or gaseous decomposition reactions. The further addition of a specific detector, such as, a water detector, would narrowly limit the number of possible candidates that could be responsible for a specific reaction. The total evaluation and interpretation of these data with the known thermodynamic relationships of possible or probable mineralogy is beyond the scope of this paper. However, an experiment required to search for only specific mineralogy known to have a widespread development under the influence of high water content or organic activity on earth (such as, hydroxyl and hydrated phases, clay minerals, carbonates, silica and laterites, sedimentary minerals, soil minerals, and evaporites) would provide a very high probability of identification of the majority of minerals that have significant importance to life-related processes.

In cases where identification may be in doubt as to the specific mineral causing a reaction, there is a distinctly limited number of alternative minerals having identical reactions and, in many cases, the resulting geologic interpretation would not suffer considerably, as such a grouping of alternatives have similar environmental relationships. In any event, alternative hypotheses may be examined in the light of total data available and the geologic probability assessed rather closely.

Specific figures as to what percentage of possible mineralogy can be identified from such data are not at present definable, as DTA is not primarily used as an isolated method to identify completely unknown mixtures of materials. Depending upon the assumed planetary model, the figure could range from zero identification for high-temperature anhydrous assemblages, such as, basalt or peridotite, to nearly 100 percent identifiable assuming a mixture of quartz and limonite. However, even in the case of zero identification, it would be known that a high-temperature stable assemblage was present from the lack of thermal reactions.

A more realistic evaluation of the percentage of identifiable biological significant minerals, which occur in sufficient quantity to have a high probability of being sampled by a random probe and which are paragenetically probable on a planet that has at one time supported life processes, results in a high probability of total identification.

The value of DTA-EGA as an experiment does not rest upon its ability to identify specific mineralogy alone, but rather on the ability of the experiment to test hypothetical models that may contain certain mineralogy or thermal characteristics. The determination of the absence of certain phases is as diagnostic for model testing as the presence of certain characteristics; for instance, the absence of water in any form, quartz, or limonite, or the absence of chemical equilibrium. The determination of the presence of a specific hydrate is not nearly as important at present as the determination of whether hydrate or hydroxyl formation has occurred. The ability of DTA to discern the absence of a specific mineral or group of minerals in many cases is very good, and is as sensitive as the ability to identify the presence of a mineral. Such would be the case for hydrates or hydroxyl minerals or limonite in the test of a Martian model.

One of the most attractive features of DTA-EGA instrumentation is the very wide latitude in the adaptability to modification by addition or deletion of specific features with various demands required by a specific flight program. For instance, an extremely lightweight instrument of degraded analytical capability designed to be injected directly onto a planetary surface during, or as the terminal phase of, a hard landing could yield highly significant data. On the other hand, the ability to use facilities and analytical instrumentation that would be included on a rather sophisticated spacecraft, such as, a gas chromatograph or mass spectrometer, would allow the development of a highly flexible instrument capable of a wide range of thermal experiments without a large weight penalty.

1391

While the instrumentation is amenable to being used as an adjunct to or a complement to other instrumentation, the data provided by a thermal analysis experiment should in no way be considered as secondary in importance to other experiments, and the scientific justifications underlying the philosophy of the experiment place it in a highly competitive position in its own right. For instance, the EGA portion of the experiment alone, consisting only of a furnace and a photoionization detector, can readily compete as the most sensitive method available for the detection of the presence of organic material and it can provide a general indication of the nature of such a material by the complexity of its degradation pattern.

Basis of Mineralogic Analysis in Reconstruction of Environment

Since a mineral represents the recorded response of the constituent elements of a system to the energy impressed upon the system, it may be inferred that the factors contributing to the formation of a mineral may be reconstructed from the known stability relationships of the resulting mineralogy. A wide range of sensitivity to specific processes or conditions is found in naturally occurring systems. Highly stable minerals offer little resolution and highly unstable minerals may be altered to new assemblages by small changes in the environment.

DTA is a qualitative and semi-quantitative method of analysis that allows the identification of mineralogy by directly measuring the thermal stability as a function of temperature in various reactive or nonreactive environmental gases. It follows that the nature of this method of analysis is most responsive for those sensitive or unstable minerals that have the highest correlative value for reconstruction of the processes and conditions prevailing during the formation of such mineralogy. In other words, those minerals, which are sensitive to changes in environment and therefore diagnostic of formation under certain conditions, are also sensitive to the rather extreme conditions of thermal analysis and yield thermal reactions amenable to analysis. Even in the extreme case of accretion of random or unreacted nonequilibrium crystalline or amorphous materials of diverse origin, the method allows determination of this situation as these materials would react exothermally with each other tending to produce the

lowest energy state available to the constituent elements.
Also, certain minerals that are found associated with specific or characteristic environments (evaporites, meta-
morphics, precipitates, condensates, etc.) are highly
indicative of formation in such an environment.

Comparative Utility of DTA for Identification of Various Types of Mineralogy

"During recent years, differential thermal analysis
has become a standard analytical procedure for the study
of complex mixtures of minerals when resolution is difficult by conventional microscopic techniques or by X-ray
methods," was stated by Whitehead and Breger, 1950 (8).
One of the most important points concerning geologic processes is that, although a great number of minerals are
chemically possible within a given composition range, only
a very few of those possible are found in any appreciable
abundance. This point is true of igneous, sedimentary,
and metamorphic rocks and it may be stated as a first
principal that nearly all geologic processes tend towards
equilibria which, if allowed to continue for an appreciable
length of time, produce a rather simple assemblage of
minerals. Chemical composition may be commonly rather
complex, but due to a rather large toleration of substitution
of ions within many crystal lattices, the resulting mineralogy is relatively simple. For instance, the very common
igneous mineral hornblende is expressed by the formula
$(Ca, Na)_2 Na_{0-1} Mg_1 (Mg Al)_4 (Al, Si)_2 Si_6 O_{22} (O, OH, F)_2$ with
K replacing Na in part and Fe'', Fe''', Mn, and Ti replacing
more or less Mg and Al (9). This mineralogic simplicity,
and to some extent chemical simplicity, is especially
characteristic of those processes that produce deposits of
large lateral extent. Therefore, in random sampling
(characteristic of planetary probes), there is very little
probability of sampling highly complex mineralogic
assemblages; but rather, the probability is high for sampling simple common mineralogic assemblages, such as
are found covering large areas of the earth. Possible complex assemblages produced by impact mixing of different
genetic assemblages or accretion from divergent sources
without subsequent reaction are a possible exception that
may or may not be amenable to analysis depending upon the
specific mineralogy encountered.

1393

Igneous Minerals

In the determination of the utility of DTA to furnish significant data concerning the environmental indications of life-related processes, it is necessary to consider over-all mineral groups and probable mineralogy that might occur starting from an undifferentiated silicate melt and to indicate where in this sequence DTA is applicable, and further, where in the sequence the resulting mineralogy is capable of giving interpretative data of significance to life-related processes.

Berry and Mason (10) have pointed out that the mineralogy of igneous rocks is comparatively simple: "Only seven minerals or mineral groups — quartz, feldspares, feldspathoids, pyroxenes, hornblende, biotite, and olivine — are commonly present in major amounts in igneous rocks." As early as 1915, Bowen (11) has shown that the generalized course of crystallization of an igneous melt follows two convergent reaction series (Fig. 1). These series show that anhydrous minerals of high melting point crystallize out first and react with the residual melt to form later minerals in the sequence. In nature, the sequence may be interrupted at any point or may continue to react resulting in the end members of the series and a final liquid rich in silica and water.

The most important point of Bowen's reaction series in relation to life-related processes is that a distinctive change occurs in the discontinuous mafic reaction series, which is the change from high-temperature anhydrous mineralogy to hydrated forms at the amphibole stage. The fundamental point here is whether the melt originally contained sufficient water to reach this stage. If a planetary body does not contain sufficient water as an essential constituent to reach this stage, or other conditions (such as, time and pressure) were not favorable, there is little hope for sufficient water to be released by later processes to be available for subsequent life-related processes.

It is also at the amphibole point in the reaction series that DTA becomes usable, since little or no thermal reactions are obtainable from the anhydrous mafic series or the feldspar series. The feldspar series is important petrologically because the feldspars constitute up to 59% of the igneous rocks. However, they are of little interest biologically, since they do not indicate the presence or absence of water in the silicate melt and furnish little, if any, important biologic interactions or information.

As the fractionation or differentiation of the melt proceeds, a higher concentration of volatiles results within the residual melt, which is essentially a siliceous liquid containing water and other volatiles. The later formed minerals show a decreased stability to high temperatures and an increased stability to low temperatures with the result that the mineralogy lower in the series can be disintegrated into fragments of structures higher in the series by heating (10).

Normal Igneous Evolutionary Sequence

DTA has little, if any, analytical capability for the high-temperature anhydrous igneous assemblages that are of great interest to the igneous petrologist, but these minerals indicate little, if any, evidence of interaction with the surface environment or life-related processes; therefore, they have only passive interest to the soil scientist (12). These minerals are the first differentiates in the normal crystallization sequence of magma, which progresses into the high-temperature hydroxyl mineral stage (13).

The high-temperature hydroxyl minerals. These minerals are particularly suited to analysis by DTA and indicate whether the crystallizing magmas originally contained water and/or other volatiles. There has been relatively little application of DTA to these assemblages, since they are readily resolved by microscopic techniques. However, their thermal reactions are large, and the presence of high-temperature hydroxyl groups is readily discernable.

The lower temperature hydroxyl minerals. These minerals merge with and to a large extent include the clay minerals. These minerals indicate either an intense hydrothermal activity or extensive aqueous weathering generally considered to be in part the result of combination with organic acids. Extensive DTA information is available for these minerals and has been the major geologic use of the method. There is intensive interaction of microbiologic activity with these minerals because of ion exchange capability and high surface area, and they are, therefore, of major importance to the soil scientist (12).

Other Minerals

Hydrates, carbonates, halides, sulfates, nitrates, and borates generally have characteristic thermograms. The commonly found impurities in clay minerals are particularly susceptible to detection in small quantities and include gypsum, organic material, sulfides, limonite, chlorite, and carbonate minerals (14).

Thus, the portion of terrestrial mineralogy that is most sensitive to determination by DTA because of marginal stability is of greatest interest in determining environmental reactions with life-related processes. The portion that has little value for interpretation of these factors shows no reaction to DTA and, therefore, does not introduce superfluous or interfering data. The presence of non-thermally reactive mineralogy is readily detected by the absence of reactions, other than baseline offset due to thermal conductivity. Further discrimination of this type of mineralogy is of no consequence to the determination of life-related processes.

Interpretation of Data

Presence of Water

The determination of the presence and state of water, past or present, is of extreme importance in the analysis of the probability of life processes and interpretation of the development of the planetary surface environment. Thermal analysis, especially in conjunction with the highly sensitive water detectors available, is capable of determining the presence of water whether as free pore water, or adsorbed; combined as simple or multiple hydrates; or as hydroxyl water.

The temperature at which the various states of water are released is dependent upon: (a) the total pressure, fixing the boiling point of interstitial or adsorbed water and the majority of simple hydrates; (b) the partial pressure of water in the environment, determining the range of dissociation of some multiple hydrates and especially the hydroxyl minerals; and (c) the range of stability of the specific minerals present under the above conditions.

Physical characteristics of the sample (such as, grain size and packing density in the sample holder) may cause a shift of characteristic temperature, but information concerning partial pressure and total pressure from other instrumentation provide evaluation of these variables. The data on total pressure and partial pressure of water derived from indigenous mineralogy also provide a redundancy or check on the determination of these data from the other instrumentation. Specific chemicals chosen for their sensitivity to these parameters are preloaded as a multiple calibration sample and can serve to measure these quantities with a high degree of accuracy and establish proper operation of the entire experiment should lightweight payload requirements preclude other instrumentation.

The identification of specific water bearing mineralogy can provide highly important indications of the origin and development of the surface characteristics of the planet. The presently estimated low partial pressure of water at the surface of Mars may well have led to the impoverishment of low-temperature forms of water storage. However, if water has been important in forming the surface of the planet, the high-temperature hydroxyl minerals, or other indications or hydrolytic activity, have sufficient stability to record the existence of these processes. The relatively high percentage of volatiles in some of the carbonaceous chondrites indicates that volatiles are not eliminated by even the hard vacuum of space and that extrapolations yielding extremely low volatile content, based only on fugacity of volatiles under such conditions for the length of geologic time, do indeed have unwarranted simplifying assumptions. Volatiles exposed to the much less stringent conditions of a planetary body can be assumed to have a fairly reasonable stability range.

Previous Organic Activity

The most significant data that DTA can contribute to a planetary exploration program oriented toward the detection of life-related processes is to provide interpretative information concerning the physical environment or determine what, if any, relic indications (such as, mineralogy indicative of a previous environment) are present. Factors concerning the present condition of the lithosphere and its capability to support life processes (such as, the presence of water, organic material, or other source of nutrition) are amenable to detection in small quantities by DTA due to the high heat of vaporization of water and the large evolution of heat of combustion of organics in the presence of oxygen.

1397

Perhaps an even more widely applicable method would be one not requiring the chance sampling of material present to a small extent, or the continued viability of a biotic community. Such a method is the investigation of the physical environment for the presence of extensive cumulative products indicative of biotic or life-supporting reactions with the lithosphere.

Such processes of wide lateral distribution include: (a) intense chemical weathering, which occurs only in the presence of organics producing nearly pure silica deserts or characteristic lateritic deposits (nearly pure aluminum or iron oxides); (b) development of a soil profile; (c) deposits of limestone or dolomite; (d) phosphorites; (e) evaporite deposits from the retreat of large bodies of water, or the drying up of previous oceanic basins. Such deposits once formed are exceedingly stable in the absence of water and do not depend upon the preservation of the organic material itself to indicate the presence of biotic activity. The presence of extensive cumulative organogenic products of these processes, which have an extremely low probability or have wide departures from an inorganic steady-state equilibrium of chemical potential, lead to an unequivocal conclusion as to the influence of the biotic activity. Furthermore, many reaction products indicative of a specific environment as represented by a characteristic mineralogic assemblages do not require a strict maintenance of that environment, but have a metastability range many orders of magnitude removed from the conditions of formation.

Carbonates

Williams and Barghoorn (15), in an examination of the biogeochemical aspects of the formation of marine carbonates, have evolved a working hypothesis that generally reflects modern thinking based upon the assumptions that "...purely inorganic precipitation of marine carbonates by solar evaporation of sea water, without the intervention of biotic processes, is rare today and cannot be of significance...virtually all marine carbonates are precipitated directly or indirectly as a result of biological processes in marine waters." The conclusions developed as a result of studies are that "...biological phenomena or biological processes are the principal cause, directly or indirectly, of carbonate precipitation in the oceans and that the sites of precipitation bear recognizable, though complex relations to ocean currents and to physiographic features of the ocean basins. "

Evidence confirming the nature of the role of biotic influence in the precipitation of carbonates is presented by Evans (16) in a study of organic solubilization of minerals in sediments. Adenosine triphosphate (ATP) salts, amino acids, and a wide range of biogenic derivates were found to have a profound effect upon the solubility of an unexpectedly wide range of commonly occurring minerals. The solubility in these media bear little resemblance to the relative solubility of these minerals in inorganic media; "...relatively water-insoluble minerals, such as carbonates, phosphates, and silicates are easily brought into solution by ATP." In contrast hydrated oxides of iron and aluminum were found to be insoluble and in many instances precipitated from solutions of ATP soluble minerals.

The inability to precipitate calcite or dolomite in the laboratory under conditions found in nature is a well known problem in the geochemistry of limestone formation. The decomposition of the relatively unstable ATP, which had dissolved calcium carbonate at a pH of 7.5, resulted in the crystallization of an aggregate of calcite crystals comparing with that of a normal fine-grained limestone.

Fairbridge (17), in the conclusion of a volume devoted to carbonates, states: "five great biologic revolutions have occurred throughout earth's history that have fundamentally shaped the modern geochemical picture. It is significant that organisms have shaped their own environment. Organic CO_2 and the calcium budget have played critical roles. "

Silica and Laterites

The nearly ubiquitous presence of such a high percentage of silica covering such a large percentage of the surface of the earth cannot readily be accounted for, or explained by, any other process than biologic activity. Purely inorganic equilibria relations without the presence of the highly reactive organic products do not produce the required weathering. This problem has not yet received the extensive treatment as the carbonates; however, the work of Evans with ATP shows the solubility of silicates very well. As in the case of the carbonates, when the ATP decomposes, the silica is readily precipitated in a manner that very closely compares with cementation in sandstones.

The solubility of the hydrated oxides of iron and aluminum with ATP is especially relevant, since these are the end products of the most extreme biochemical weathering process of laterization. These deposits of nearly pure iron or aluminum oxides are known to occur only under tropical weathering conditions of high temperature, humidity, and intense biological activity.

Sedimentary Minerals

The stability of minerals in ambient temperatures of planetary surfaces is nearly an identical reverse of Bowen's reaction series and, as pointed out by Mason (18), quartz is the only common mineral of igneous rocks that is highly resistant to weathering processes on earth. The sedimentary minerals are those minerals that are provisionally stable at the terrestrial surface. While the recorded number of minerals in the sedimentary environment is very large, since any minerals may be present for a time dependent upon its stability range and the intensity of weathering processes to which it is exposed, the abundant minerals on earth are essentially quartz, clay minerals, calcite, dolomite, and feldspar. Minerals or mineral groups, such as limonite (hydrated iron), bauxite (hydrates of aluminum) collophane (phosphorite), and glauconite, may be abundant in deposits of restricted extent. Of these groups, only the feldspars do not yield to DTA.

Soil Minerals

Soils differ from sediments in the development of characteristic horizons or layers by the soil-forming process as a result of interaction of biotic activity. Brewer has pointed out that one of the most important pedological applications of mineral analyses is in the study of the genesis of soil profiles as reflected by changes in mineralogical profile with depth due to weathering and leaching. Material released by weathering of primary minerals may occur in the soil as oxides, carbonates, sulfates, and clay minerals through leaching of the upper layers and redeposition in lower layers. Evaporation at the surface in arid environments caused an upward movement of soluble materials resulting in a characteristic "caliche" layer (19).

1400

Jackson and Sherman (20) have developed a weathering sequence for clay size minerals (Fig. 2) in which the degree of weathering increases the kind of weathering product from weathering stage No. 1 gypsum to No. 13 anatase. This weathering stage of minerals in the soil profiles has been used directly as an assessment of the "intensity of weathering;" whereas, "absolute weathering" may be measured simply by the amounts of the specific ratios of the various mineral species in the parent material that have been weathered (19).

Estimates as to the type and degree of weathering that may be deduced from constituent mineralogy of a terrain are most extensively developed in the pedological literature. Brewer (19) indicates that pedologists have had little success in attempting to use petrological classifications of rock types, since they are based upon "normative" minerals, or the stability relationships of the silicate melt, rather than upon the thermodynamic stabilities found at or near atmospheric ambient conditions. Therefore, none of the rock classifications reviewed by Johannsen (21) is satisfactory for pedological relationships. This is not surprising since the silicate melt reaction series of Bowen (11) is nearly the identical reverse of Goldich's (22) stability to weathering series.

Since the most significant difference between the formation of a sediment and a soil is the interaction of biologic activity, it follows that, in the search for the presence of biologic activity or the interpretation of the environment in such terms, the principles used by the pedologist are those that are the most appropriate. It is significant in this regard that Brewer (19), in attempting to establish a pedological classification "based on those characteristics for which there is evidence of significance in the genesis of different kinds of soil profiles," chose as the primary major subdivision the proportion of clay minerals that can be formed from the parent rock. Thus, the clay minerals constitute one of the primary indicators of soil genesis interpretation.

Clay Minerals

The importance of clay mineralogy is particularly stressed as being applicable to the detection of life-related processes. Although sedimentary rocks make up only approximately one-tenth of the earth's crust, they tend

1401

to accumulate near the interface of the crust with the hydrosphere and the atmosphere and, thus, cover approximately three-fourths of the land area of the earth and nearly all of the area covered by the hydrosphere. The clay fraction of soils and sediments is that portion which is of special interest, because many of the most important chemical and physical properties arise in the clay fraction. It is the clay fraction that frequently reflects influences of climate, organisms, topography, and time of soil formation (23).

Normal laboratory procedure for many pedologists is to separate the clay fraction and submit it to X-ray diffraction analysis with and without chemical treatment to identify the clay mineral fractions. However, where separation and chemical treatment are not permissible, the high sensitivity of DTA to these minerals is especially valuable. This point is brought out especially well by Jackson (23): "thus the most reactive and sensitive part of the soil, most characteristic of the soil genesis, is the least reflected in a gross X-ray diffraction analysis of an unseparated soil."

Jackson (24) brings out a very effective argument as to the importance of clay minerals to life-related processes: "it is probable that the accumulation of hydrous minerals in sedimentary muds favored and conditioned the evolutionary development of life forms on earth. Particularly the capacity of fine sediments (primordial soils) to absorb water and readily exchangeable ions in coastal margins encouraged the evolutionary movement of life from sea to land, and thus introduced the biotic factor in soil formation." Under extreme conditions, such as those now found on Mars, it may well be that such favorable sites, such as the clay minerals provide, may well be the only places available capable of supporting life regardless of the mode of its origin.

The present development of clay minerals, except in areas of glaciation, is primarily dependent upon the interaction of biology with the surface to break down primary minerals. Mason (18) has shown the extent to which biology interacts with the surface in that the total annual production of organic carbon has been determined to be $20 \pm 5 \times 10^9$ tons for terrestrial environments, and $126 \pm 82 \times 10^9$ tons for marine environments, resulting in a grand total for the earth of $146 \pm 87 \times 10^9$ tons. The significance of these figures are best realized by Mason's statement (18): "if the mass of the biosphere has been approximately constant over the last 500 million years and if the average life cycle were one year, then the total amount of matter that has passed through the biosphere in that time is comparable with the total mass of the earth." Recycling of this material would concentrate the biogenic reactions at the surface.

Evaporites

The determination of whether or not Mars has passed through a history similar to that of the earth, especially evidence concerning the development of an extensive hydrosphere at some stage, is very critical; not only in the determination of inorganic planetary genesis, but also in determination of the probability of organic development. Inasmuch as present knowledge shows that the surface of Mars now has only a minor surface water content, and theories of planetary evolution show no reasons why water should not have been as abundant on Mars as on the earth during formation, Mars may have had at one time a simi-lar development of a hydrosphere. The presence or absence of differentiation and body degassing is critical in the final determination of planetary evolution.

Retreat of the hydrosphere from land masses on earth has produced extensive sequences throughout the geologic column, which are characteristic of such processes and are readily determined by DTA. As is the situation with igneous and sedimentary rocks, the total number of min-erals recorded from such environments is large (Fig. 3), but the great percentage of the deposits are represented by only a few minerals. Nearly all evaporites show distinc-tive thermal reactions, many have multiple hydrates, distinctive phase change, melting reactions, or a com-bination of these reactions.

The most abundant substances are calcium sulfate and sodium chloride. "Rock salt and anhydrite are found in enormous deposits of the Silurian of New York and Michigan, in the Permian of Kansas, Texas and New Mexico, and in deposits of comparable size on other con-tinents" (25).

More complicated evaporites (such as, chlorides and sulfates of magnesium and potassium) are found in the Permian Zechstein deposits that extend from Holland,

Germany, Poland, and into Northern England. Other Permian potash deposits are found in Texas, New Mexico, and Northern Russia. Large deposits of evaporites also occur in the Pennsylvanian of the Paradox Basin of Utah and the Devonian of North Dakota and Saskatchewan (25).

The complete removal of even a considerably smaller hydrosphere from Mars should lead to the very extensive deposition of an evaporite sequence of considerable thickness and lateral extent. Furthermore, the lack of water would prevent removal or burial by subsequent sedimentation.

The extreme sensitivity of some of these compounds to small changes in partial pressure of water, which is exemplified by the humidity indicator cobalt chloride, may explain in part the wave of darkening that occurs with the movement of water during the change in Martian seasons. Cobalt chloride would certainly not be expected on a geochemical basis. However, the change in physical properties of other similar materials coupled with possible changes in ultraviolet produced color centers, to which the alkali halides are highly liable, could perhaps offer a more plausible explanation than those now advanced. The large lateral area and speed of response of the phenomena is best explained by some process as widespread as large-scale evaporation precipitation.

Discrimination of Meteoritic Material

One of the major problem areas in the detection of life-related compounds is the possible presence of organic material from carbonaceous chondrites. Photographic evidence indicates that the surface topography of Mars has been influenced greatly by meteoric impact. Therefore, the meteorite influence should not only be high, but may be dominant should there have been no effective removal mechanism throughout geologic time.

Mueller, et al. (26) have shown that carbonaceous chondrites consist of anhydrous silicates, troilite, and magnetite embedded in a finely divided volatile containing ground mass consisting of hydrated silicates and of carbonaceous complexes. Total volatiles may be as high as 28%. This type of mineralogy is highly unstable in the presence of oxygen and water, and readily disintegrates in the earth's atmosphere. Therefore, their relative abundance is highly speculative, and effective weathering processes on Mars are not known to be dominant at present.

The true proportions of various types of meteorites are at best only an approximation, especially on Mars. However, the predominantly nickel-iron containing meteorites and the carbonaceous chondrites can readily be detected by DTA-EGA (Fig. 4). Essentially, no information would be obtained on the stoney meteorites, but their influence on life detection is negligible. The fairly large percentage of troilite (FeS) alone results in a high probability of identification of meteorite material, since this mineral has a distinctive endothermic phase transition in the 150°C range, a large oxidative exothermic dissociation at approximately 550°C, and is nearly non-existent as a mineral on earth and by association not a product of thermodynamic equilibria as encountered on the earth. In view of the topography of Mars and the unknown abundance of carbonaceous chondrites, it is extremely important to know if such material is present in samples analyzed by the mass spectrometer in the search of organic material.

References

1. Speed, R. C., ed., Proceedings of Utilization of Extraterrestrial Resources, Jet Propulsion Laboratory, Sept. 25-26, 1962.
2. Speed, R. C., Adams, J. B., and Nash, D. B., Technical Memorandum 33-241, Jet Propulsion Laboratory (1965).
3. Adams, J. B., et al., Technical Memorandum 33-172, Jet Propulsion Laboratory (1964).
4. Bollin, E. M., Space Programs Summary 37-31, IV, 255 (1965).
5. Lovelock, J. E., Nature 207, 568 (1965).
6. Ford, H. W., Margetts, D. R., and Slaughter, D. W., internal document 900-13, Jet Propulsion Laboratory (1967).
7. Staff, internal document 900-44, Jet Propulsion Laboratory (1967).
8. Whitehead, W. L., and Breger, I. A., Science 111, 279 (1950).

9. Wahlstrom, E. E., Theoretical Igneous Petrology, John Wiley and Sons, New York (1950).

10. Berry, L. G., and Mason, B., Mineralogy Concepts Descriptions Determinations, W. H. Freeman and Co., San Francisco (1959).

11. Bowen, N. H., J. Geol. 23, Suppl. 1-89 (1915), and ibid 30, 177 (1922).

12. Jackson, M. L., in Soil Clay Mineralogy, edited by C. I. Rich and G. W. Kunze, Univ. of North Carolina Press, Chapel Hill, 245 (1962).

13. Bowen, N. L., The Evolution of the Igneous Rocks, Princeton Univ. Press (1928).

14. West, R. R., in The Defect Solid State, edited by T. J. Gray, Interscience, 457 (1957).

15. Williams, M., and Borghoorn, E. S., in Organic Geochemistry, edited by I. A. Breger, Pergamon Press, New York, 596 (1963).

16. Evans, W. D., in Advances in Organic Geochemistry, edited by U. Colombo and G. D. Hobson, Pergamon Press, New York, 263 (1964).

17. Fairbridge, R. W., in Carbonite Rocks, edited by G. E. Chilinger, et al., Elsevier, New York, 399 (1967).

18. Mason, B., Principals of Geochemistry, 3rd Ed., John Wiley and Sons, New York (1966).

19. Brewer, R., Fabric and Mineral Analysis of Soils, John Wiley and Sons, New York (1964).

20. Jackson, M. L., and Sherman, G. D., Advan. Agron. 5, 219 (1953).

21. Johannsen, A., A Descriptive Petrography of the Igneous Rocks, 1, Chicago Univ. Press (1939).

22. Goldich, S. S., J. Geol. 46, 17 (1938).

23. Jackson, M. L., in Soil Clay Mineralogy, edited by C. I. Rich and G. W. Kunze, Univ. of North Carolina Press, Chapel Hill, 245 (1964a).

24. Jackson, M. L., in Chemistry of the Soil, 2nd Ed., ACS Monograph Series No. 160, edited by F. E. Bear, Reinhold Publ. Corp., New York (1964).

25. Krauskopf, K. B., Introduction to Geochemistry, McGraw Hill, New York (1967).

26. Mueller, G., et al., Nature 206, 23 (1965).

27. Mason, B., Meteorites, John Wiley and Sons, New York (1962).

STABILITY INCREASING FROM (1) TO (13)

(1) GYPSUM (ALSO HALITE, SODIUM NITRATE, AMMONIUM CHLORIDE, ETC)

(2) CALCITE (ALSO DOLOMITE, ARAGONITE, APATITE, ETC)

(3) OLIVINE-HORNBLENDE (ALSO PYROXENES, DIOPSIDE, ETC)

(4) BIOTITE (ALSO GLAUCONITE, MAGNESIUM CHLORITE, *ANTIGORITE, NONTRONITE, ETC)

(5) ALBITE (ALSO ANORTHITE, STILBITE, MICROCLINE, ORTHOCLASE, ETC)

(6) QUARTZ (ALSO CRISTOBALITE, ETC)

(7) MUSCOVITE (ALSO 10 Å ZONES OF SERICITE, ILLITE, ETC)

(8) INTERSTRATIFIED 2:1 LAYER SILICATES AND VERMICULITE (INCLUDING PARTIALLY
    EXPANDED HYDROUS MICAS, RANDOMLY STRATIFIED 2:1 LAYER SILICATES WITH
    NO BASAL SPACINGS, AND REGULARLY STRATIFIED 2:1 LAYER SILICATES)

(9) MONTMORILLONITE (ALSO BEIDELLITE, SAPONITE, ETC)

(10) KAOLINITE (ALSO HALLOYSITE, ETC)

(11) GIBBSITE (ALSO BOEHMITE, ALLOPHANE, ETC)

(12) HEMATITE (ALSO GOETHITE, LIMONITE, ETC)

(13) ANATASE (ALSO ZIRCON, RUTILE, ILMENITE, LEUCOXENE, CORUNDUM, ETC)

*ADDITIONAL EVIDENCE (JEFFIRES, ROLFE, AND KUNZE, 1953; CAILLERE, HENIN, AND
  MERING, 1947) INDICATES THAT CHLORITE MAY OCCUR AT ANY STAGE FROM (4) TO (9)
  ACCORDING TO ITS COMPOSITION. UNDERSCORING INDICATES MINERALS NOT
  AMENABLE TO DTA.

Fig. 1 Igneous mineralogic reaction series
indicating sequence of crystallization.

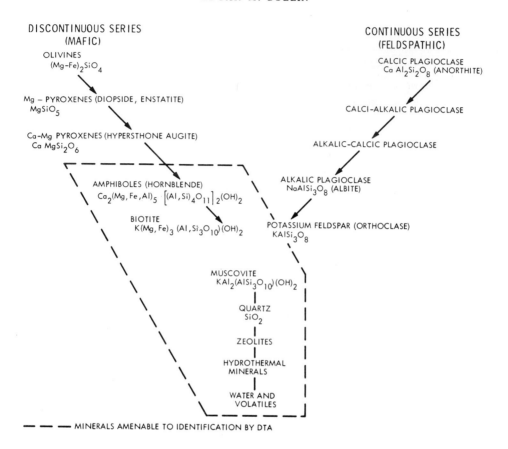

Fig. 2 Weathering sequence for clay size minerals (reprinted from Ref. 19 by permission of John Wiley and Sons).

CHLORIDES
    †HALITE $NaCl$
    †SYLVITE KCl
    BISCHOFITE $MgCl_2\ 6H_2O$
    †CARNALLITE $KMgCl_3\ 6H_2O$

CHLORIDE-SULFATE
    †KAINITE $KMgClSO_4\ 11/4H_2O$

SULFATES CONTAINING Ca
    †ANHYDRITE $CaSO_4$
    †GYPSUM $CaSO_4\ 2H_2O$
    GLAUBERITE $Na_2Ca(SO_4)_2$
    †POLYHALITE $K_2MgCa_2(SO_4)_4\ 2H_2O$

SULFATES OF Na AND K
    THENARDITE Na_2SO_4
    GLASERITE, OR APHTHITALITE $K_3Na(SO_4)_2$

SIMPLE SULFATES OF Mg
    †KIESERITE $MgSO_4\ H_2O$
    HEXAHYDRITE $MgSO_4\ 6H_2O$
    EPSOMITE, OR REICHARDTITE $MgSO_4\ 7H_2O$

SULFATES OF Mg AND Na
    BLOEDITE, OR ASTRAKHANITE $Na_2Mg(SO_4)_2\ 4H_2O$
    LOEWEITE $Na_{12}Mg_7(SO_4)_{13}\ 15H_2O$
    VANTHOFFITE $Na_6Mg(SO_4)_4$

SULFATES OF Mg AND K
    LANGBEINITE $K_2Mg_2(SO_4)_3$
    LEONITE $K_2Mg(SO_4)_2\ 4H_2O$
    PICROMERITE OR SCHOENITE $K_2Mg(SO_4)_2\ 6H_2O$

*FORMULAS FROM BRAITSCH, 1962.
†DAGGERS INDICATE MAJOR CONSTITUENTS.

Fig. 3 Important salts in marine evaporites (reprinted from Ref. 25 by permission of McGraw-Hill Book Co.).

MINERAL	SYMBOL	MINERAL	SYMBOL
NICKEL-IRON	(Fe,Ni)	MAGNESITE	$MgCO_3$
COPPER	Cu	CALCITE	$CaCO_3$
GOLD	Au	DOLOMITE	$CaMg(CO_3)_2$
DIAMOND	C	ILMENITE	$FeTiO_3$
GRAPHITE	C	MAGNETITE	Fe_3O_4
SULFUR	S	CHROMITE	$FeCr_2O_4$
MOISSANITE	SiC	SPINEL	$MgAl_2O_4$
COHENITE	Fe_3C	QUARTZ	SiO_2
*SCHREIBERSITE	$(Fe,Ni)_3P$	TRIDYMITE	SiO_2
*OSBORNITE	TiN	CRISTOBALITE	SiO_2
TROILITE	FeS	APATITE	$Ca_5(PO_4)_3Cl$
*OLDHAMITE	CaS	*MERRILLITE	$Na_2Ca_3(PO_4)_2O(?)$
ALABANDITE	MnS	*FARRINGTONITE	$Mg_3(PO_4)_2$
PENTLANDITE	$(Fe,Ni)_9S_3$	GYPSUM	$CaSO_4\ 2H_2O$
*DAUBREELITE	$FeCr_2S_4$	EPSOMITE	$MgSO_4\ 7H_2O$
CHALCOPYRRHOTITE	$(Cu,Fe)S$	BLOEDITE	$Na_2Mg(SO_4)_2\ 4H_2O$
VALLERIITE	$Cu_3Fe_4S_7(?)$	OLIVINE	$(Mg,Fe)_2SiO_4$
CHALCOPYRITE	$CuFeS_2$	ORTHOPYROXENE	$(Mg,Fe)SiO_3$
PYRITE	FeS_2	CLINOPYROXENE	$(Ca,Mg,Fe)SiO_3$
SPHALCRITE	ZnS	PLAGIOCLASE	$(Na,Ca)(Al,Si)_4O_8$
*LAWRENCITE	$FeCl_2$	SERPENTINE	$Mg_6Si_4O_{10}(OH)_8$

*NOT KNOWN TO OCCUR IN TERRESTRIAL ROCKS
UNDERSCORING INDICATES MINERALS NOT AMENABLE TO DTA.

Fig. 4 The minerals of meteorites (reprinted from Ref. 27 by permission of John Wiley and Sons).

Differential Thermal Analysis Studies of Compound Semiconductors

Alfred C. Glatz*

NASA - Electronics Research Center
Cambridge, Mass. 02139

The use of DTA for phase equilibria studies and determinations of maximum melting compositions is presented with
some of its limitations considered. It is demonstrated that
in systems in which equilibrium is difficult to achieve,
thermal methods of analysis must be treated with caution,
because 'true' equilibrium may not be attained at each
temperature. DTA studies of Bi_2Te_3 grown by Bridgman,
vapor and high pressure techniques are compared to indicate
that crystal perfection may be determined by DTA. Also,
DTA studies of kinetic properties of semiconductors, related
to their preparation and crystal growth are described.
Studies of pyrosynthesis, super-cooling, sluggish phase
changes, and thermal decompositions are presented to
indicate the application of DTA for studying the kinetic
properties of semiconductors.

I. INTRODUCTION

The preparation and crystal growth of compound semiconductors requires a knowledge of the phase transitions
that occur in the materials during these physico-chemical
processes. In order to measure these thermal effects, DTA
provides an invaluable routine, research tool for performing such studies.

DTA is a technique for studying the thermal transitions
that a substance undergoes upon heating or cooling (1,2).
It consists of measuring the energy content of a substance
as a function of temperature. Basically, it is merely
necessary to place the substance in a furnace, the temperature of which can be continuously varied through some
predetermined range, and measure the temperature difference

* Formerly with Carrier Corporation, Syracuse, New York

Δ T, between the sample under investigation and a thermally inert reference standard as a function of temperature. The resulting thermograms indicate the temperatures at which transitions occur by the deviation of Δ T from its near zero value. These thermograms consist of thermal bands and peaks which correspond to the characteristic physicochemical transitions of the substance under investigation. The resulting thermograms indicate temperatures and temperature ranges at which changes in state, chemical composition and molecular reactivity of the substance occur.

The use of DTA for phase equilibria studies of compound semiconductors is becoming recognized as an essential technique in semiconductor research. In general, the preparation of good single crystal specimens of semiconducting compounds requires a detailed knowledge of the equilibrium phase diagram, and there are many reported studies of such investigations in the literature. For many systems it has become apparent that kinetic considerations are also important. For these systems DTA is an invaluable technique, because it is a dynamic rather than an equilibrium method, and it allows investigating the system under nearly identical conditions that exist during synthesis and crystal growth in the laboratory. Some related kinetic effects that may be studied by DTA are: 1) Pyrosynthesis Studies, 2) Super-cooling Effects, 3) Studies of Sluggish Phase Changes, and 4) Thermal Decomposition Studies. Also, it may be possible to obtain some measure of crystal perfection by DTA studies of melting transitions.

In this paper some DTA studies of phase equilibria of semiconductors, including determinations of maximum melting compositions, will be reviewed with some of its limitations considered. The use of DTA for obtaining a qualitative measure of crystal perfection will be explored and studies of some kinetic effects important to the preparation and crystal growth of semiconductors will be described.

1.2 DTA Apparatus

A DTA Apparatus was designed and built for investigating the thermal properties of semiconductors from room temperature to 1000 °C. This apparatus is similar to that described previously (3,4) and is shown diagramatically in Figure 1. In this apparatus an Al_2O_3 standard and the sample are contained in sealed vycor ampoules with concentric thermocouple wells and placed symmetrically in a high thermal capacity Kanthal furnace. The DTA thermo-

1412

grams are obtained by the conventional technique of plotting
the difference in temperature between the sample and the
standard on an X-Y recorder (Honeywell Function Plotter)
versus the temperature of the sample, which is heated at
a controlled rate using a Leeds and Northrup cam-type
Program Controller. The DTA samples were prepared by
adding 750 mg. of the sample under investigation to 250 mg.
of α- Al_2O_3. The aluminum oxide was added to the sample
to minimize base-line drift. The samples were then
evacuated and sealed for the DTA studies. Heating rates
of 5 $^\circ$ C./minute were employed in the operation of the
apparatus.

II. STUDIES OF EQUILIBRIUM PROPERTIES
2.1 Equilibrium Phase Diagrams
The use of DTA, which has been established for some
time in the field of ceramics, minerals and clays and,
to a lesser extent, in metallic alloy systems (1), is
becoming recognized as an essential technique for studying
phase transformations occuring in compounds and mixtures of
semiconductor interest. For semiconductors a detailed
knowledge of the phase diagram in the region near the
compound composition is requisite for selecting the appropriate crystal growth procedure, e.g. the crystal growth
technique is obviously very different for peritectic and
congruently melting compounds. Although the phase diagrams
of the classical III-V and II-VI compounds are relatively
well known (5,6), studies of lesser known and more complicated systems has made phase equilibria studies an important part of semiconductor research. In addition, studies
of deviations from stoichiometry are of great importance
because of their effect on the electrical and thermal
properties of semiconductors.

In general, the preparation of good single crystal
specimens of semiconducting compounds requires a detailed
knowledge of the equilibrium phase diagram and there are
many reported studies of such investigations in the
literature (6). Although thermal methods of analysis
(DTA, TGA, etc.) provide a relatively simple method for
performing such studies, it is important to realize that
in systems in which equilibrium is difficult to achieve,
thermal methods of analysis must be treated with caution
because 'true' equilibrium may not be attained at each
temperature. For such cases, it is better to corroborate
thermal analysis studies with x-ray diffraction and metallo-

graphic studies at appropriate temperatures for establishing the 'true' equilibrium phase boundaries.

A DTA technique that can be used for establishing the
importance of 'equilibrium' is to anneal the samples at the
highest possible temperature in the sub-solidus region for
varying lengths of time and observing the resulting DTA
thermograms. It may be concluded that the sample has reached a 'metastable equilibrium', when there is no change in
the resultant DTA thermograms for sufficiently longer
annealing times. This technique has been used to evaluate
the 'equilibrium' phase diagram of the Bi – Te System (4)
and to interpret the diverse phase diagrams that had been
previously reported for this system. Such studies have
clearly demonstrated that phase equilibria studies of
relatively unknown systems should be cooborated by
several analytical methods, including thermal analysis:
and results of studies performed by a single technique
should be treated with caution.

2.2 Maximum Melting Composition

For congruently melting semiconducting materials, it
is important to know the maximum melting composition
because, if it deviates from the stoichiometric composition,
it can effect the pertinent physical properties by incorporation of defects into the grown crystal. Also, in
crystal growth from the melt, a knowledge of the maximum
melting composition is required in order that minute
portions of other phases will not be incorporated into the
grown crystal.

Offergeld and VanCakenberge reported (7) an ingeneious
technique using quantitative DTA for determining the
maximum melting composition. This technique is based
upon the fact that the phase diagrams of congruently,
melting binary semiconductors are usually characterized by
isothermal transitions (eutectics or peritectics) up to the
phase boundaries of the compound. The amount of heat
involved in these phase transitions is a linear function of
the difference between the actual composition and the
composition at the phase boundary. Using DTA it is
possible to determine the composition for which these
thermal effects disappear at the phase boundary and to
measure the difference between the congruent and stoichiometric compositions. This method for determining the
maximum melting composition, however, has the following

limitations: 1) The phase diagram must conform to that
described., 2) The phase boundaries are determined at the
temperatures of the isothermal transitions, and not at the
melting point. This can be a severe problem, if the
compound has a wide range of stability and the isothermal
transitions are considerably below the melting point.,
and 3) The DTA method must be quantitatively reproducable.

An alternate method for establishing the maximum
melting composition is to determine the composition having
the greatest enthalpy per unit weight for the liquid –
solid equilibrium reaction. This, may be determined by
precise quantitative measurements of DTA transitions as a
function of composition. Although this method determines
the maximum melting composition at the melting point,
it is strongly dependent upon precise quantitative DTA
measurements. A comparsion of the results obtained for
Sb_2Te_3 and Bi_2Te_3 using both of these methods is shown in
Table 1. It may be observed that for Sb_2Te_3 the two
methods yield identical results, but for Bi_2Te_3 there is a
deviation of 0.1 mole per cent Tellurium. This deviation
(approximately 2 parts per 1000) probably represents the
precision that may be obtained by thermal analysis for
determining deviations from stoichiometry, rather than a
limitation of either method.

2.3 Studies of Crystal Perfection

A pure substance should have a sharper melting
transition than an impure substance. This is because at
the transformation temperature all of the solid is transformed isothermally into liquid. Such transitions are
defined, according to the Gibb's Phase Rule, as invariant
transitions. For an impure substance there is a gradation
in the melting transition, which is characteristic of
univariant or higher order transitions. Similarly, the
incorporation of imperfections into a grown crystal can
only be effected at the expense of the internal energy of
the system and will result in a lower and less defined
melting transition. Therefore, it might be possible to
employ DTA for qualitatively determining crystal perfection.

Two Bridgman grown crystals of Bi_2Te_3 were selected
on the basis of optical examination: one, having a well-
defined, mirror-like cleavage plane and the other having
a poor, polycrystalline cleavage surface. Initial DTA's
of both of these crystals are shown in Figures 2 (A) and

1415

2 (B). It may be observed that the sample with the well-defined cleavage plane definitely has a sharper melting transition than that with the poorer cleavage surface. However, the rerun DTA of the sample with the well-defined cleavage surface indicates a negligible difference from the first thermogram of this sample, as shown in Figure 2 (C). It is expected that the conditions for crystal growth in a DTA ampoule (on the cooling cycle) will produce a very polycrystalline, imperfect sample. Therefore, it appears on the basis of these results that it might be extremely difficult to determine crystal perfection by DTA. However, it must be realized that these samples were selected by optical observation, and it is probable that there is very little difference between the two samples on an imperfection level.

It has been shown by Prener (8) that the thermodynamic state of a semiconductor containing imperfections is completely defined by the specification of $Q + 1$ degrees of freedom, where Q is the number of components in a semiconductor. This result states that for a binary compound ($Q = 2$), and the number of degrees of freedom is three. Therefore, if we fix the temperature and pressure and the chemical potential of one of the constituents, then the concentrations of the various imperfections are fixed at their equilibrium values. Although these conditions are not satisfied for Bridgman Crystal Growth, they can be approached in both vapor growth and high pressure crystal growth. Shown in Figure 3 are an initial DTA and a rerun DTA of a sample of Bi_2Te_3 prepared by vapor crystal growth. It may be observed that the initial DTA shows a very sharp knee, which is absent on the rerun DTA of this sample. Shown in Figure 4 are the DTA thermograms (initial and rerun) for a sample of Bi_2Te_3 grown at 20,000 psi (1.4 kilobars). It may also be observed that the initial DTA shows a very sharp melting transition, which is not repeated on the rerun. The DTA's of these high pressure samples show very sharp melting transitions, with negligible super-cooling. This behavior is not observed on the samples prepared by the other techniques. These DTA studies show a definite difference between the samples prepared by Bridgman and vapor or high pressure crystal growth. Whether these differences are indeed due to variations in crystal perfection will require further, more detailed investigation. For example, it would be interesting to correlate DTA with Hall Coefficient studies. However, it does appear on the basis of the preliminary studies reported in this paper, that DTA can be used as a qualitative measure of crystal or specimen perfection.

III. KINETIC STUDIES

Since DTA is a dynamic, rather than a static-equilibrium technique, it allows investigating the system under nearly identical conditions that may exist during synthesis and/or crystal growth in the laboratory. Some kinetic effects that may be studied by DTA are: 1) Pyrosynthesis Studies, 2) Super-cooling Effects, 3) Studies of Sluggish Phase Changes, and 4) Thermal Decomposition Studies.

3.1 Pyrosynthesis of Semiconductors

Many semiconductors can be prepared by thermal reaction of the constituents resulting in the synthesis of the desired compound. However, compounds with constituent elements having significantly lower melting points than that of the desired compound may be difficult to synthesize, especially if the constituents are volatile at the melting point of the compound. Examples of such compounds are the III-V 's, II-VI 's, and many semiconductors containing As, S, Se, and P. DTA studies of the synthesis of CdSe (9) and Bi_2S_3 (10) have demonstrated, for example, that the formation of a low temperature phase prevents the reaction from going to completion with the result that the presence of the volatile constituent at the melting point of the compound results in an explosion. These studies have demonstrated that this mechanism may be elucidated by DTA pyrosynthesis studies using constituent elements of varying particle sizes. It appears that this mechanism is quite general for binary compounds which melt appreciably higher than either of the elemental constituents.

3.2 Super-cooling Effects

Another kinetic effect that can be conveniently studied by DTA is super-cooling. For some systems super-cooling can have a detramental effect on crystal growth from the melt, because of the difficulty in nucleating crystal growth. DTA can be used to determine whether such effects may be a problem, because it is possible to study 'cooling' effects under conditions approaching those

1417

existing during crystal growth in the laboratory.

3.3 Studies of Sluggish Phase Changes

Another kinetic effect that can be conveniently studied by DTA are studies of sluggish phase changes. It has been shown for $Bi_{56}Te_{44}$ (4) that DTA can be used to investigate sluggish phase changes by observing the difference between the heating and cooling curves. This is particularly important for the crystal growth of compounds that undergo sluggish, low temperature phase changes, as for example $AgBiSe_2$ and $AgBiS_2$ (11).

3.4 Studies of Thermal Decompositions

Thermal decompositions can be conveniently studied by DTA by observing whether the thermograms represent reversible transformations. For a reversible transformation the heating and cooling curves should be mirror images. The semiconductor, BiSI, is an example of a compound that thermally decomposes as shown in Figure 5. It may be observed that above the melting point of this compound the thermogram shows a small change in slope on the heating cycle and the cooling curve shows the appearance of two super-cooled phases. The knowledge of these phases is not clearly evident, because it does not appear that they are BiI_3 and Bi_2S_3 which have melting points of 439° (12) and 760° C. (10), respectively. This indicates one of the limitations of DTA - although it provides a profile of the thermal changes that occur upon heating or cooling a sample, it is sometimes difficult to interpret in regard to the actual composition producing the thermal change. Other studies, for example, x-ray diffraction at the appropriate temperature, would be required in order to identify the decomposition products.

IV. CONCLUSIONS

In this paper the use of DTA as an analytical tool for investigating the thermal properties of semiconductors has been explored. It has been demonstrated that it is a very useful technique for investigating the equilibrium and kinetic properties of semiconductors. However, it has been shown that as a routine laboratory tool, its limitations must be realized in order that erroneous conclusions will not be evolved.

V. ACKNOWLEDGEMENT

The author wishes to acknowledge that some of the experimental work described in this paper was performed while the author was employed at Carrier Corporation, Syracuse, New York.

VI. REFERENCES

1. W. J. Smothers and Y. Chiang, "Handbook of Differential Thermal Analysis" (Chemical Publishing Co., New York, 1966).
2. P. D. Garn, "Thermoanalytical Methods of Investigation" (Academic Press, New York, 1965).
3. D. B. Gasson, J. Sci. Instrum., 39, 78, (1962).
4. A. C. Glatz, J. Electrochem. Soc., 112, 1204, (1965).
5. M. Hansen, "Constitution of Binary Alloys", (McGraw-Hill, New York, 1958).
6. J. J. Gilman, "The Art and Science of Growing Crystals", (John Wiley and Sons, New York, 1963) pgs. 365-396.
7. G. Offergeld and J. Van Cakenberghe, J. Phys. Chem. Solids, 11, 310, (1959).
8. J. Prener, J. Appl. Phys., 33, 434, (1962).
9. A. Reisman and M. Berkenblit, J. Phys. Chem., 67, 22, (1963).
10. A. Glatz and V. Meikleham, J. Electrochem. Soc., 110, 1231, (1963).
11. S. Geller and J. Wernick, Acta. Cryst., 12, 46, (1959).
12. W. Latimer and J. Hildebrand, "Reference Book of Inorganic Chemistry", (Macmillan Company, New York, 1951) pg. 580.

TABLE 1

DETERMINATIONS OF MAXIMUM MELTING COMPOSITIONS

MATERIAL	METHOD OF OFFERGELD ET. AL. (7) (MOLE % Te)	METHOD OF MAXIMUM ENTHALPY (MOLE % Te)
Sb_2Te_3	59.6	59.6
Bi_2Te_3	59.6	59.8

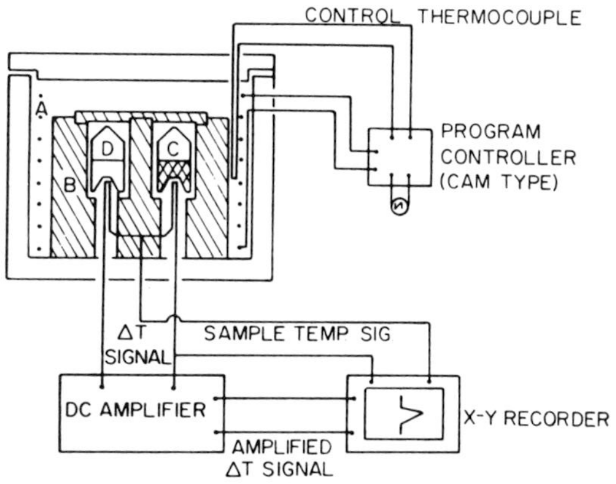

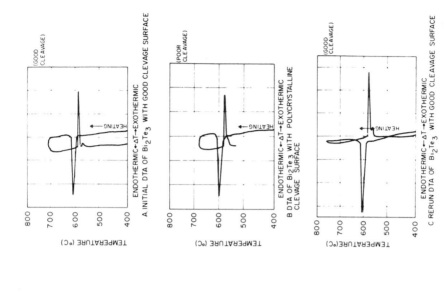

Figure 2 : DTA's for Bridgman Grown Samples of Bi₂Te₃

Figure 1 : DTA Apparatus

A – KANTHAL FURNACE

B – STAINLESS STEEL HEAT SINK

C – SAMPLE UNDER INVESTIGATION

D – α –ALUMINA STANDARD

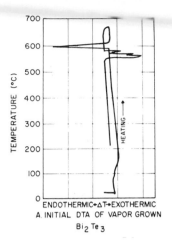

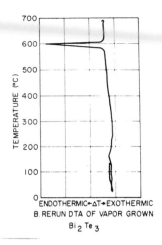

A. INITIAL DTA OF VAPOR GROWN Bi$_2$Te$_3$

B. RERUN DTA OF VAPOR GROWN Bi$_2$Te$_3$

Figure 3 : DTA's for Vapor Grown Bi$_2$Te$_3$

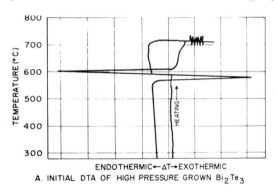

A. INITIAL DTA OF HIGH PRESSURE GROWN Bi$_2$Te$_3$

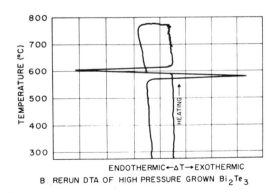

B. RERUN DTA OF HIGH PRESSURE GROWN Bi$_2$Te$_3$

Figure 4 : DTA's for Bi$_2$Te$_3$ Grown at 1.4 Kilobars

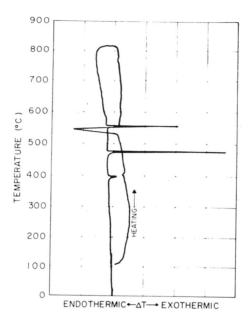

Figure 5 : DTA for BiSI

The formation and surface properties of electron emissive coatings

I. Thermogravimetric and gas evolution studies of alkaline earth carbonates and hydroxides

JUDD, M.D. and POPE, M.I.

Department of Chemistry, College of Technology,
Portsmouth, England.

Abstract.

Although "oxide cathode" electron tubes have been used since 1904, surprisingly little attention has been paid to the nature of the decomposition reactions leading to the formation of the electron emissive coating, or to the surface properties of the coating itself. Accordingly, simultaneous thermogravimetric (TG) and effluent gas analysis (EGA) has been carried out on the hydroxides and carbonates of calcium, strontium and barium; measurements were also made on co-precipitated carbonates, prepared in a manner similar to that used in the manufacture of emissive coatings.

The peaks obtained by EGA coincide well in all cases with the maximum rates of weight loss observed by differential thermogravimetry (DTG). For the single compounds studied, the results show that the temperature (T_D) at which the maximum rate of decomposition occurs, is significantly different in each case. Hence the appearance of DTG or EGA peaks at a given value of T_D, can be used to confirm the presence of a particular compound in a mixture of the hydroxides and carbonates. This data made it possible to interpret the more complex TG, DTG and EGA curves which were obtained with the double and triple carbonates.

1423

Introduction

The use of "oxide cathodes" for electron tubes was first reported[1] in 1904, when they proved so successful that their use subsequently became almost universal. Despite the immense importance of electron tubes during the past half century, surprisingly little attention has been paid to the nature of the decomposition reactions leading to the formation of the emissive coating, or to the surface properties of the coating itself. Although electron tubes are now being superseded for most applications by various solid state devices, it has been estimated[2] that world production of oxide cathode electron tubes is still of the order of one thousand million per annum.

The oxide cathode consists essentially of a layer, about 0.1mm. thick, of mixed alkaline earth oxides coated on a supporting tube, which is usually made of nickel. The coating is originally prepared by co-precipitating alkaline earth carbonates in accurately known proportions from a solution of the corresponding nitrates, by the addition of either sodium or ammonium carbonate solution. After filtration, ball milling and drying, the carbonates may be mixed with a suitable binder and sprayed from a slurry onto the cathode tube; alternatively, the carbonates may be coated electrophoretically onto the cathode from a non-aqueous suspension. During subsequent processing of the electron tube, the carbonate coating is decomposed under vacuum at temperatures in the region 900-1100°C, leading to the formation of an adherent, porous oxide layer, on the cathode surface. The emissive coating is then "activated" so as to form some free barium in the oxide matrix, after which the tube is sealed under vacuum in the presence of a getter. Comprehensive discussions of the manufacture and properties of oxide cathodes may be found in reviews by Wright[3], Nergaard[4] and by Noelcke[5].

Studies of the thermal decomposition of single calcium[6-11], strontium and barium carbonates[12-19] are fairly numerous; but the experimental conditions have varied so widely, that corelation between the results of different workers is seldom possible. For example, Thomas[6]

1424

has clearly demonstrated that decomposition of calcium carbonate is appreciable after heating a sample under vacuum at 570°C; this result contrasts with the observations of Rao et al[7], who found no evidence of thermal decomposition below 1015°C.

By comparison, thermal decomposition of the co-precipitated carbonates has received little attention, apart from the EGA studies of Wolk[20]. Accordingly simultaneous TG and EGA measurements have been carried out, under identical conditions, on the hydroxides and carbonates of calcium, strontium and barium. The results obtained with these single compounds were then used to interpret the more complex curves, obtained by TG and EGA of co-precipitated alkaline earth carbonates, which had been prepared in a manner similar to that used in the manufacture of emissive coatings.

Experimental

The sodium carbonate, barium nitrate and hydroxide used in this work were of "AnalaR" grade, the other chemicals being ordinary laboratory reagents, except for the single alkaline earth carbonates; these carbonates were "Spec Pure" chemicals, supplied by Johnson, Matthey and Co. Ltd, London.

The co-precipitated carbonates were prepared as described below, following closely a technique used in the manufacture of emissive coatings. The quantities stated lead to a precipitate of molecular ratios CaO: SrO: BaO of 10: 43: 47, corresponding to the composition required for maximum pulsed emission, according to the work of Grey[21]. Two solutions were made up, one containing 88g. anhydrous Na_2CO_3 in 1100 ml. distilled water and the other containing 8.2g $Ca(NO_3)_2$ $4H_2O$, 31.7g. $Sr(NO_3)_2$ and 42.7g $Ba(NO_3)_2$ in 3 litres of distilled water. Carbonate solution (3ml) was then added to the 3 litres of nitrate solution; after filtration, the filtrate was made up to 4 litres and heated to boiling. Similarly, 3 ml. nitrate solution was added to the carbonate solution, which was then filtered and heated; the object of this cross-precipitation is to remove impurities. The carbonate solution was poured rapidly into the nitrate solution at ca. 90°C, with rapid stirring,

after which the mixture was allowed to stand for 4 hours.
The precipitate was then separated by filtration (Buchner,
porosity 3), washed with hot distilled water and dried in
air at 80°C. The precipitate was subsequently stirred with
high purity ethanol and again filtered (Buchner, porosity
3) and dried. Finally, 55g co-precipitated carbonate was
dispersed in 500 ml. ethanol and the mixture ball milled at
90 r.p.m. for 24 hours, using a porcelain mill and balls;
the resultant slurry was stored in a polypropylene bottle.

A double carbonate, with a molecular ratio SrO: BaO of
50: 50 was prepared in an exactly similar manner, except
that the nitrate solution contained 44.7g $Sr(NO_3)_2$ and
55.3g $Ba(NO_3)_2$.

Thermal analysis was carried out using a spiral quartz
spring balance (Fig. 1), which was continuously evacuated
by means of a mercury diffusion pump backed by a rotary oil
pump; the vacuum obtained when no thermal decomposition was
taking place was ca 10^{-5} Torr.

A known weight of substance (about 0.6g) was placed in
a nickel bucket, consisting of an anode component from a
Mullard DY 802 valve: this particular bucket was chosen
because the composition of the nickel used corresponds to
that of an active cathode nickel, in accordance with A.S.T.M
specification F 239-61T. The sample was surrounded by an
aluminous porcelain 525 tube (a silica tube was used in
some earlier experiments), which was heated externally by
means of a Kanthal Al furnace. A rate of rise of
temperature of 200°C/hr was maintained up to a maximum of
1250°C using an "Ether" 12-94/8 programme unit with a type
2815 SCR output control. This comparatively slow rate of
rise of temperature was used in order to obtain a minimum
temperature differential between the sample and the
furnace tube. In trial runs, using no sample, with a
thermocouple mounted internally in the sample bucket, the
maximum temperature differential recorded between the
internal and external thermocouples was 40°C under high
vacuum and 10°C at a pressure of 0.05 torr.

Changes in weight of the sample were measured to an

accuracy of $\pm$ 0.1 mg., using a cathetometer, and the pressure in the balance case was recorded by a Pirani gauge. The results obtained with each of the substances studied were represented on three graphs, all plotted against temperature as abscissa: the corresponding ordinates were (TG) per cent weight loss, (DTG) rate of loss of weight in mg/g/hr and (EGA) ambient gas pressure in Torr.

Results and Discussion

The peaks obtained on the EGA curves coincide well in all cases with the DTG peaks, for each of the single compounds studied.

Hydroxides

The TG, DTG and EGA curves for calcium, strontium and barium hydroxides are shown in Figs. 2-4 respectively. It will be seen that decomposition in each case involves more than one stage, some of the observed peaks being due to the presence of impurities. The results obtained with the hydroxides are summarised in Table I, the temperatures recorded for each stage of decomposition representing the onset, maximum rate and completion of that stage. The probable reaction responsible for the observed DTG and EGA peaks, associated with each stage, is indicated below; reactions due to the decomposition of impurities are shown in brackets.

The TG curve for $Sr(OH)_2$. $8H_2O$ indicates the existence of a monohydrate, within the temperature range $100°-200°$, confirming a report by other workers[22]. However, no evidence was obtained for the formation of $Ba(OH)_2$. H_2O, although this compound has also been reported[23] to exist in a similar range of temperature.

Carbonates

Corresponding curves for calcium, strontium and barium carbonates are shown in Figs. 5-7, respectively; again, the decomposition reactions involve a number of stages, which are summarised in Table II. The curves shown are for the "Spec Pure" carbonates, but the behaviour of the "AnalaR" compounds was remarkably similar in all three cases. The sample of calcium carbonate appeared to be surprisingly pure, but the impurities detected in the strontium and barium carbonates fell within the limits set by the maker's specification.

The final stage of the decomposition of barium carbonate resulted in a weight loss which slightly exceeded the theoretical value for decomposition to the oxide. However, on standing overnight under vacuum (ca 10^{-5} Torr), the sample gained weight, so that the final overall weight loss corresponded exactly to the formation of barium oxide. It appears, therefore, that at $1200^{\circ}C$ under vacuum the barium oxide had lost some oxygen, leaving metallic barium in the residue. On cooling, this barium had acted as a getter, reforming the near stoichiometric oxide; evidence of similar behaviour has been reported elsewhere[5].

From the foregoing results, obtained with the hydroxides and carbonates, it is apparent that the temperature at which the maximum rate of decomposition occurs is significantly different for each of the compounds studied. Hence, the appearance of a DTG or EGA peak at this temperature, hereafter referred to as the "characteristic decomposition temperature" (T_D), may be taken as evidence of the presence of this compound in a mixture of alkaline earth hydroxides and carbonates. Values of T_D and the range of temperature within which decomposition occurred are recorded in Table III.

Co-precipitated carbonates

The TG, DTG and EGA curves for the double ($SrCO_3$: $BaCO_3$ 50: 50 mole %) and triple ($CaCO_3$: $SrCO_3$: $BaCO_3$ 10: 43: 47 mole %) carbonates are illustrated in Figs. 8 and 9, respectively.

Neglecting the effect of small amounts of impurities, it is clear that the double carbonate decomposes in two stages, having characteristic decomposition temperatures of

$940^{\circ}C$ and $1055^{\circ}C$. This result is surprising, since the work of Cork and Gerhard[24], of Terrada[25] and of Ostapchenko[26] appears to show that the two carbonates exist as a single solid phase; hence a single decomposition peak might have been expected. The two T_D values for the double carbonate are lower than those of pure strontium (960°) and barium (1130°) carbonates; however, T_D for the calcium carbonate, present as an impurity, remains unaltered at $725^{\circ}C$. These results indicate that calcium carbonate is present as a separate phase and decomposes independently of its surroundings. Conversely, the lowering of the T_D values in the double carbonate, from the values for pure strontium and barium carbonates, suggest that two phases may be present, comprising (a) a dilute solution of barium carbonate in strontium carbonate and (b) a dilute solution of strontium carbonate in barium carbonate.

Decomposition of the triple carbonate shows three T_D values at 685°, 925° and $1045^{\circ}C$, if the effects due to known minor impurities are again ignored. This is even more surprising, since both Terrada[25] and Ostapchenko[26] agree that, at this composition, an aragonite type of solid solution is formed, containing all three components. The fact that the T_D which appears to correspond to calcium carbonate is also lowered, suggests that a phase exists which consists mainly of calcium carbonate, but contains small amounts of either barium and/or strontium carbonates. The two higher T_D values are now still further reduced from the values for pure strontium and barium carbonates, but otherwise the double and triple carbonates decompose in a closely similar manner (cf Figs 8 and 9).

The thermal analysis evidence therefore suggests that both double and triple carbonates do not comprise a single homogenous phase: instead, it appears that they consist of a mixture of particles which contain predominantly one component, but with either or both the other components present in dilute solution. A clue to the explanation of the apparent conflict between the above conclusion and results published by Terrada[25], may well lie in the fact that for the compositions studied here, Terrada obtained needle shaped crystals. By contrast, the samples

1429

prepared by us, as well as a triple carbonate of similar composition supplied by Hopkin and Williams Ltd., all consisted entirely of approximately isodimensional crystals, as is clearly illustrated in Fig. 10.

Acknowlegements

The authors wish to thank Dr. G. Thornhill, Laboratory Manager, Mullard Blackburn, for the supply of DY 802 anodes and much useful information.

Table I

Calcium hydroxide	Stage (I)	Stage (II)	Stage (III)
DTG	up to 250	320/400/540	540/600/700
EGA	70/120-160/220	270/365-430/500	540/600/700
probable reaction	loss H_2O	$Ca(OH)_2 \rightarrow CaO$	$[Ba(OH)_2 \rightarrow BaO]$
Strontium hydroxide			
DTG	50/120/200	390/490/560	-
EGA	-/70/220	350/490/580	-
probable reaction	loss H_2O	$Sr(OH)_2 \rightarrow SrO$	-
Barium hydroxide			
DTG	-/120/170	390/400+495/500	525/600/640
EGA	-/80-120/210	390/495/510	510/595/700
probable reaction	loss H_2O	$[Sr(OH)_2 \rightarrow SrO]$	$Ba(OH)_2 \rightarrow BaO$

References

1. Wehnelt, A., Ann. Physik. 14 425 (1904).
2. Thornhill, G., Private communication to the Authors (1968).
3. Wright, D.A., Proc. Inst. Elect. Engrs. 100 Pt.3 125 (1953).
4. Nergaard, L.S., R.C.A. Rev. 13 464 (1952).
5. Noelcke, C.L.., Arinc Research Monograph No. 6 Arinc Research Corpn. Washington (1958).
6. Thomas, J.M. and Renshaw, G.D., J. Chem. Soc. (A) 2056 (1967).
7. Rao, C.N., Yoganarasimhan, S.R. and Lewis, M.P., Canad. J. Chem. 38 2359 (1960).
8. Ingraham, T.R. and Marier, P., Canad. J. Chem. Eng. 170 (1963).
9. Britton, H.T.S., Gregg, S.J. and Windsor, G.W., Trans. Farad. Soc. 48 63 (1952).
10. Glasson, D.R., S.C.I. Monograph No. 18 p.401 Society of Chemical Industry, London. (1964).
11. Sato, Y. and Yamashita, T., J. Chem. Soc. Japan 56 476 (1953).
12. Proks, I., Chem. Zvesti. 20 697 (1966).
13. Gruver, R.M., J. Amer. Chem. Soc. 33 96 (1950).
14. Zimens, K.E., Z. Physik. Chem. B37 231 (1937).
15. Lander, J., J. Amer. Chem. Soc. 73 5794 (1951).
16. Sargorodskii, S.D. and Shor, O.I., Khim. Zhur. 20 357 (1954).
17. Caillere, S. and Pobeguin, T., Bull. Soc. Franc. Mineral 83 36 (1960).
18. Erdey, L., Liptay, G., Svenca, G. and Paulik, F., Talanta 9 489 (1962).
19. Glasson, D.R., J. Appl. Chem. 13 124 (1963).
20. Wolk, B., J. Electrochem. Soc. 105 89 (1958).
21. Grey, L.E., Nature (Lond) 167 522 (1951).
22. Buriel-Marti, S. and Garcia-Clavel, M.E., 16th Inter. Congr. Pure and Appl. Chem. p.861 Paris (1957).
23. Duval, C., Anal. Chim. Acta. 13 428 (1955).
24. Cork, J.M. and Gerhard, S.L., Amer. Mineral 16 71 (1931)
25. Terrada, J., J. Phys. Soc. Japan. 8 158 (1953) Nature (Lond) 171 517 (1953).
26. Ostapchenko, E.P., Bull Acad. Scien. U.S.S.R. 20 687 (1956).

Table II

	Stage I	Stage II	Stage III	Stage IV
Calcium carbonate				
DTG	up to 500	500/725/950	-	-
EGA	-	510/725/1000	-	-
Probable reaction	loss H_2O	$CaCO_3 \rightarrow CaO$		
Strontium carbonate				
DTG	350/420/450	500/580+640/690	690/740/770	780/960/1050
EGA	370/415/445	515/560+640/700	710/740/770	800/960/1050
Probable reaction	[$Ca(OH)_2 \rightarrow CaO$]	[$Ba(OH)_2 \rightarrow BaO$]	[$CaCO_3 \rightarrow CaO$]	$SrCO_3 \rightarrow SrO$
Barium carbonate				
DTG	350/380/420	670/700/720	900/940/960	960/1120/1200
EGA	350/485/530	670/inflection 700	900/inflection 940	960/1120-1150/1200
Probable reaction	[$Sr(OH)_2 \rightarrow SrO$]	[$CaCO_3 \rightarrow CaO$]	[$SrCO_3 \rightarrow SrO$]	$BaCO_3 \rightarrow BaO$

Table III

Compound	Max. observed rate "T_D" ($^{\circ}$C)	Decomposition range ($^{\circ}$C)
$Ca(OH)_2$	400	270–540
$Sr(OH)_2$	490	350–560
$Ba(OH)_2$	600	510–700
$CaCO_3$	725	500–1000
$SrCO_3$	960	780–1050
$BaCO_3$	1130	960–1200

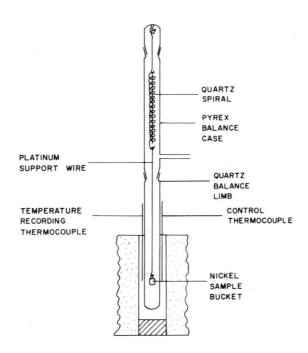

QUARTZ
SPIRAL

PYREX
BALANCE
CASE

PLATINUM
SUPPORT WIRE

QUARTZ
BALANCE
LIMB

TEMPERATURE
RECORDING
THERMOCOUPLE

CONTROL
THERMOCOUPLE

NICKEL
SAMPLE
BUCKET

Fig. 1.   The thermal balance

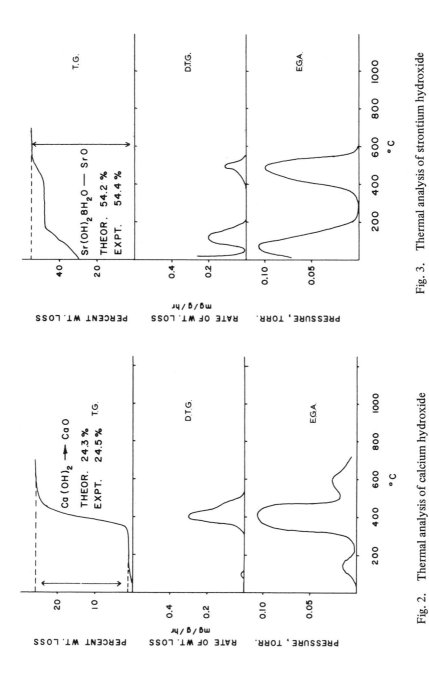

Fig. 3. Thermal analysis of strontium hydroxide

Fig. 2. Thermal analysis of calcium hydroxide

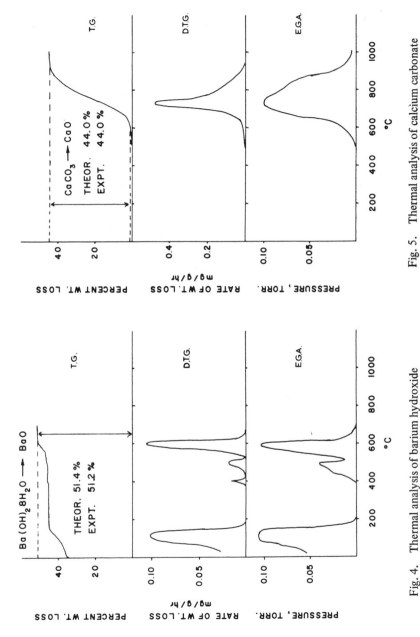

Fig. 5. Thermal analysis of calcium carbonate

Fig. 4. Thermal analysis of barium hydroxide

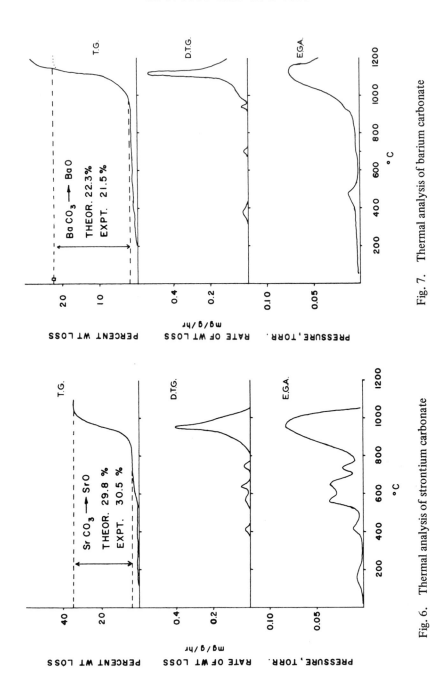

Fig. 7. Thermal analysis of barium carbonate

Fig. 6. Thermal analysis of strontium carbonate

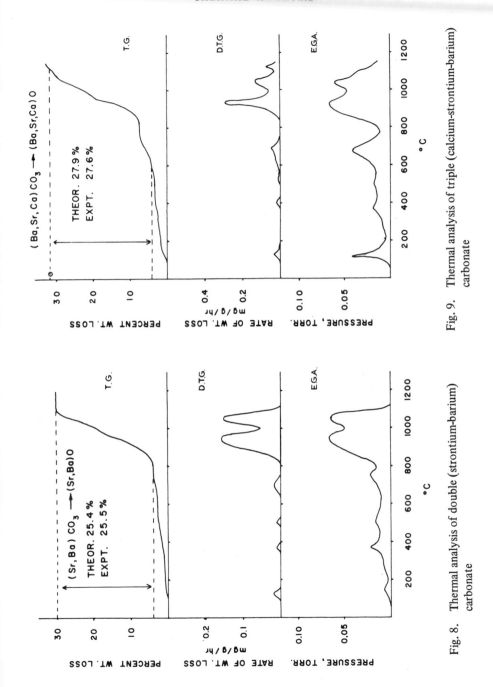

Fig. 9.   Thermal analysis of triple (calcium-strontium-barium) carbonate

Fig. 8.   Thermal analysis of double (strontium-barium) carbonate

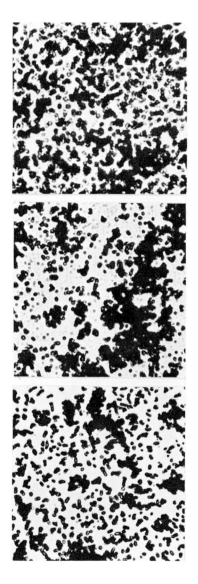

Fig. 10. Photomicrographs of (a) double carbonate (b) triple carbonate and (c) triple carbonate supplied by Hopkin and Williams Ltd. (All x 350 magnification)

TGA MEASUREMENT OF CURIE TEMPERATURE OF SOME COMMERCIAL FERRITES

W. Richard Ott and Malcolm G. McLaren

Rutgers, The State University
New Brunswick, N. J.

Abstract

Thermogravimetric Analysis was used to investigate the Curie point of commercial classes of ferrites. This was accomplished by heating the samples in the presence of a magnetic field. The Curie point was observed by an apparent weight gain when the ferrimagnetic material became paramagnetic.

A comparison is made with other existing methods of measuring the Curie point and the precision of the method is noted. This thermogravimetric procedure was found to provide a convenient and accurate measure of the Curie temperature.

The range of Curie points that were determined was approximately $150^{\circ}C$ to $600^{\circ}C$ for the materials under investigation.

Equipment used was the Mettler Thermoanalyzer with simultaneous DTA, TGA and DTG recording.

Introduction

The Curie temperature of a ferrimagnetic material is a very important material parameter and limits its useful operating temperature. Determination of the Curie Point may be made by one of several methods but, in general, most of these are time consuming. The effort in this experiment was to utilize existing thermogravimetric equipment for a more rapid assessment of the Curie Point of commercial grades of ferrites. This method had been utilized previously in measuring Curie points of nickel metals.[1] Inasmuch as these measurements are related to commercial grades of materials, the Curie temperatures indicated will be those at which there is significant loss of magnetic susceptibility. This would be indicated by drawing a line tangent to the low temperature side of the DTG peak and observing the temperature where this intersects the extension of the DTG base line.

In some cases this could be as much as 15°C lower than the true Curie temperature but is a practical temperature for proper material utilization.

Experimental Method and Procedure

For these experiments the Mettler recording thermoanalyzer with an automatic derivative computer was the basic equipment used.

The sample was placed in a 16mm platinum dish crucible on a TGA sample holder stick with a Pt,Pt/Rh-10 thermocouple. (Fig. 1) A large laboratory horseshoe magnet was placed just above the fused quartz furnace, which was approximately

$3\frac{1}{2}$ inches above the sample itself. (Fig. 2)

The temperature was increased at a programmed linear rate of rise and the Curie Point was
determined by the apparent weight gain which occurred when the sample began to lose its magnetic susceptibility.

A typical run (Fig. 3) used 500 milligrams
of 40 mesh and finer sample, a sensitivity of 1
milligram/in., a DTG sensitivity of 1.0mg/min/in,
a flowing air atmosphere of 5.7 liters/hr, a
heating rate of $4^{\circ}C/min$, a temperature recording
of 2mv full scale, and a chart speed of 12 in/hr.
Temperatures recorded were corrected for $25^{\circ}C$
cold junction on the thermocouples.

Six different commercial ferrite compositions were measured by this method and the results are shown on table I.*

In order to substantiate this method and
compare it to other methods, a number of runs
were made to observe the influence of particle
size, heating rate, sample size, and any possible
hysteresis upon heating and cooling. The precision was indicated by the reproducibility, observed on a number of runs from the same lot of
material.

The effect of heating rate is evident from
the data presented in Fig. 4, where the temperature is plotted vs. the percent apparent weight
gain for rates of heating: 1, 2, 4, 6, 8, and
$15^{\circ}C/min$. At 50% weight change the spread of
data for all heating rates falls between $\pm 2^{\circ}C$.
There is a much larger discrepancy between the
different heating rates at the low end of the
curves but this is undoubtedly due to the poor
thermal conductivity of the ceramics.

In Fig. 5 the results of the effect of heating and cooling were observed on the $4^{\circ}C/min$

*Samples were supplied courtesy of the Indiana
  General Corp., Electronics Div., Keasby, N.J.

heating and cooling rate on the T-1 samples. As
can be seen, there is no appreciable hysteresis
at this programmed rate of heating and cooling.

In order to check the effect of particle
size, the Q-1 sample was run as a solid piece of
500mg and as -100, +200 mesh powder. The maximum
points on the DTG peaks were 394°C for the solid
piece and 395°C for the powdered sample. However, by plotting the percent apparent weight
gain vs. the temperature about a 4°C difference
can be observed due to the difference in thermal
conductivity of the samples. (Fig. 6)

An indication of the precision of the method
was observed by the reproducibility of the DTG
peak on six different T-1 samples. (Table II)
The precision observed was indicated as $< \pm$ 2°C.

To compare this method with other commercially acceptable methods, another laboratory
tested 3 toroids of T-1 material. This was done
by graphing the change in permeability with respect to temperature and extrapolating to 90% loss
of permeability. These measurements were made
using a heated oil bath and an induction bridge.
The toroids were wound with 20 turns of #30 wire
and immersed in the oil bath. The inductance and
series resistance were measured at 100 KH$_z$ at
various temperatures. The percentage change in
permeability from room temperature permeability
was calculated and plotted. This test gave the
Curie Point of 182°C $\pm$ 1.5°C. [2] (Fig. 7)

These toroids were then subsequently tested
on the Mettler Thermoanalyzer by the method previously described with a 4°C/min rate of rise in
temperature. (Fig. 8) It was observed that the
very small toroid samples did not exhibit as well
defined patterns as the other T-1 samples tested.
This was explained easily by the fact that the

other samples tested, although powdered before
measurement, came from solid bars of material and
so in sintering were more uniform in the oxidation state of the iron present in the ferrite.
The toroids, on the other hand, presented a large
surface to weight ratio and were not as uniform
throughout the sample. It can be seen that the
initial loss of permeability by electrical measurement and initial weight gain by TGA analysis
occurred together at approximately 177°C. However, with a sample like the toroid it was difficult to get good definition of the DTG peak.

Summary and Conclusions

The data indicate that it is possible to
utilize recording thermogravimetric equipment as
previously described in order to make measurements of the Curie Point for ferrite materials.
It is particularly useful to have an automatic
derivative computer incorporated in the equipment, as the DTG peak serves as a very good approximation of the Curie temperature. One of the
main advantages to the method is the speed of
determination without suffering any lack of accuracy. Whereas most presently acceptable
methods require approximately 4 hours and quite
some surveillance, this procedure can be completed in about 45 minutes. It also has the advantages that no special shapes are required and very
small samples can be analyzed.
Depending on how the DTG peak is analyzed,
several useful temperatures can be noted. The
corresponding temperature at which a tangent
drawn to the low temperature side of the DTG
peak intersects with the extension of the DTG
base line would be the most useful commercial

figure for the Curie Point. The peak of the DTG seems to be very reproducible and is probably a good material parameter. Finally, the temperature at which the tangent drawn to the high temperature side of the DTG peak intersects with the extension of the DTG base line would, most likely, coincide with the textbook definition of the Curie Point. [3]

It should be noted that the disparity between the commercial literature and the values obtained for the Curie points of the Q series of ferrites tested, can be explained on the basis of the oxidation state of the iron ions in the lattice. During the sintering of these nickel-zinc ferrites preferential atmospheres are used and the state of oxidation of the iron ions is highly dependent on accurate control of atmosphere. Therefore, the commercial producers are quite apt to suggest lower values than are actually obtained.

Acknowledgements

The authors wish to acknowledge helpful discussions and contributions of Dr. Rudolf Tenzer and Mr. Lewis Jones; also the Mettler Instrument Corporation and, in particular, Mr. Hugh P. Vaughan and Mr. Hans J. Hoehn.

Bibliography

1. Vaughan, Hugh P., Mettler Instrument Corporation, Private communication, 1968.
2. Tenzer, Rudolf and Lewis Jones, Indiana General Corporation, Private communication, 1968.
3. Smit, J. and H. P. J. Wijn, Ferrites, John Wiley and Sons, New York, 1959.

Table I

Ferrite Designation	General Composition	Heating Rate °C/min.	Temp. @ Tangent to Low Temp. Side of DTG Peak °C	Temp. of DTG Peak °C	Values of Curie Temp. °C Commercial Lit.	Temp. @ Tangent to High Temp. Side of DTG Peak - °C
T-1	Mn-Zn ferrite	4	181	185	180	193
TC6	Mn-Zn ferrite	4	155	161	160	169
05	Mn-Zn ferrite	4	205	207	215	208
Q1	Ni-Zn ferrite	4	390	394	350	397
Q2	Ni-Zn ferrite	4	455	466	450	474
Q3	Ni-Zn ferrite	4	577	584	500	593

Table II

T-1 Sample No.	DTG Peak °C	Rate of Heating °C/min.
1	185	4
2	186	15
3	187	6
4	185	2
5	185	1
6	187	8

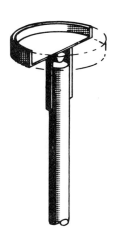

Figure 1.

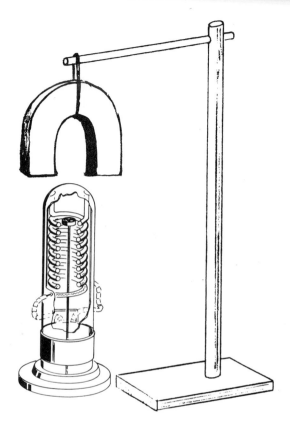

Figure 2.

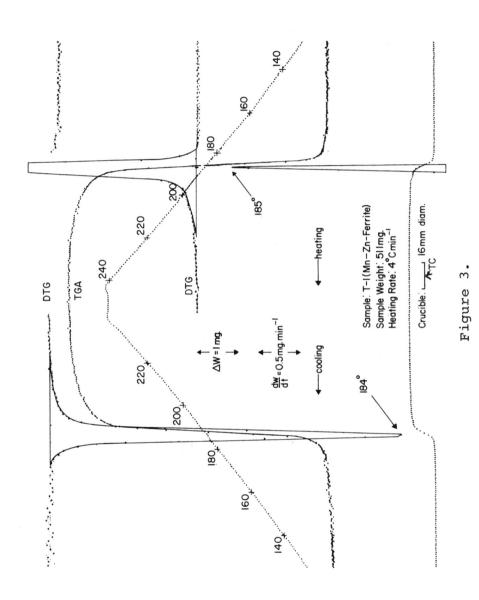

Figure 3.

Sample: T-1 (Mn–Zn–Ferrite)
Sample Weight: 511 mg.
Heating Rate: 4°C min⁻¹

Crucible: TC 16mm diam.

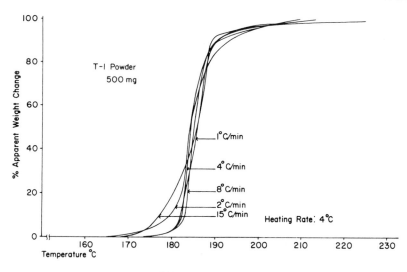

Effect Of Heating Rate

Figure 4.

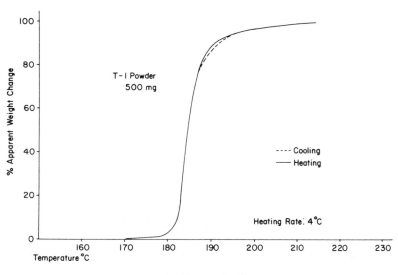

Heating vs Cooling

Figure 5.

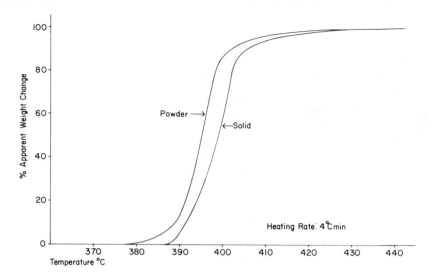

Q-I Solid Piece vs -100+200 Mesh Powder

Figure 6.

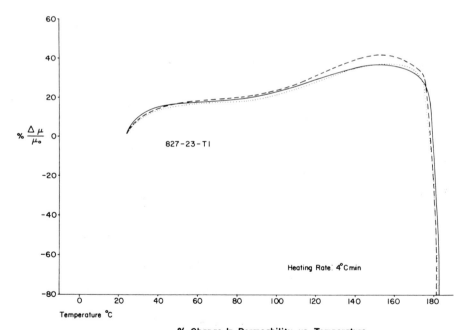

% Change In Permeability vs Temperature

Figure 7.

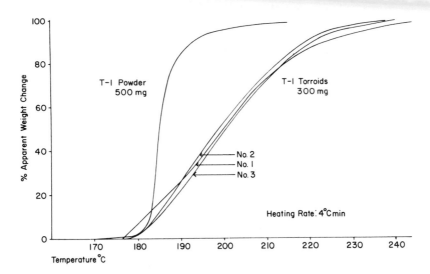

Figure 8.

A MASS-THERMAL METHOD FOR STUDYING ABLATIVE POLYMER DEGRADATION MECHANISMS

C. A. Gaulin, F. M. Wachi and T. H. Johnston

Aerospace Corporation
El Segundo, California

ABSTRACT

A proper evaluation of candidate thermal protection polymers requires a detailed description of the products being introduced into the boundary layer. This information is needed to conduct both an accurate analysis for ablator efficiency and an assessment of the contribution to the observables in the vehicle's wake. A technique to provide this essential information has been developed. The results are directly applicable to ablation and observables analyses. The new technique for coupling a specially designed high vacuum DTA cell to a high resolution mass spectrometer is described. The utility of the method is illustrated by a study of the well-known case of polystyrene sequential depolymerization. Application of the method to reentry thermal protection materials is demonstrated by a detailed study of the mechanism of degradation of polyimide resin. The results of supplementary studies of model compound degradations are described.

Introduction

A proper evaluation of candidate aerospace materials for reentry thermal protection requires a detailed description of the products being introduced into the boundary layer. This information is needed to conduct both an accurate analysis for ablator efficiency and an assessment of the contribution of observables to the vehicle wake. A technique which could rapidly provide this essential information has been needed, particularly in view of the recent development of advanced polymer systems whose elevated temperature chemistry is largely unknown. Several individual methods have been used in the past to provide as yet unrelated fragments of the required information. Thermogravimetry (1,2), differential thermal analysis (3), and mass spectrometry (4) have been given the broadest application. Individually these techniques provide information on the nature of the thermal behavior of polymers without completely elucidating the chemistry related to the observed thermal responses. Frequently unjustified inferences are drawn from such scanty data.

Recently Langer, et.al. (5) introduced the concept of simultaneous DTA and mass spectrometry. However, their apparatus was limited in several respects, e.g., the DTA cell was not designed for high vacuum operation and the spectrometer employed, while of high speed, had quite limited resolution. Their demonstration of the technique was therefore limited to simple reactions such as the dehydration of diphenyltin hydroxide and magnesium chloride hexahydrate while monitoring a single mass unit continuously at $m/e = 18$.

The present report describes the use of the combined techniques of DTA and mass analysis in a manner which can supply the required data for a comprehensive ablation and wake observables analysis. Applicability of the technique to a polymeric system (polystyrene) is demonstrated by correlation between its differential thermogram and the mass spectra of the volatile decomposition products. The utility of the method for describing the mechanism of degradation of an ablative polymer system is demonstrated in its application to a study of a polyimide system. Finished composites of polyimide with carbonaceous reinforcements have given favorable test results when exposed to ground base simulated reentry environments.

The elucidation of chemical decomposition mechanisms of a nitrogen-containing heterocyclic polymer such as a polyimide is needed to provide basic information which has a direct bearing on the ablation performance of the material as a reentry heat shield and permits interpretation of the wake chemistry associated with this material. Supplementary techniques were employed to completely define the decomposition mechanism by controlled degradation of selected model compounds and detailed analysis of the volatile products.

General Considerations

A system for the detection of thermal responses and subsequent analysis and correlation of gaseous decomposition products requires certain equipment specifications. The polymer must be decomposed in a reliably programmed furnace employing a matched thermocouple pair with associated electronics for the amplification and recording of differential emfs. The decomposition products should be supplied rapidly to the electron beam of the spectrometer under high vacuum conditions which will minimize gas-solid reactions between the volatile decomposition products and the decomposing residue or residual char. The mass spectrometer employed must have high resolution to eliminate ambiguities in product identification and must be capable of continuous scanning over a wide mass range at a rate compatible with the programmed rate of the analyzer.

For this work, a high-resolution double-focusing spectrometer (C.E.C. Model 21-110B) was used with a special ion source with a capability of 1:39,000 AMU at $m/e = 142$. In this study the resolution was adjusted to 1:3000 AMU since this resolution sufficed to eliminate potential interferences. The ion source used was the CEC Model #140527 source, designed for Knudsen cell studies. It has not previously been used for analysis of organic materials. Access of the molecular beam to this source is through a 0.010" x 0.65" entrance slit.

The DuPont Model 900 DTA with a modified version of the DuPont 1200°C cell was used to control the temperature program and record the thermogram during decomposition of the sample. The 1200° DTA cell required a completely redesigned housing to meet the condition of high vacuum operation. The details of construction of the high vacuum DTA cell are shown in Figure 1. The gas path above the differential thermocouple assembly containing the polymer sample led directly to a quasimolecular beam-former aligned with the entrance slit of the spectrometer.

The beam-former is critical to this mode of operation and the details of its construction are shown in Figure 2. It consists of a baffled Pyrex sleeve, differentially pumped to operate in high vacuum, leading from the DTA cell. The beam-former attaches to the ion source housing of the spectrometer by means of a 50/30 Pyrex socket joint sealed with black wax. The sleeve is ultransonically drilled at its inner end, on center, to give a 0.015" diameter orifice. This orifice is aligned with the source entrance slit during assembly by visually sighting down the length of the inner tube. The distance from the orifice to the entrance slit is 0.275 in. Differential pumping is achieved through the side arm by attachment to a high speed pumping station, a Veeco Model VS 400. Pressures measured above the pumping station during a mass-DTA run are generally in the low 10^{-8} Torr region.

Under these conditions, a small portion of the decomposition products exit through the orifice and become available for ionization in the spectrometer source. The apparatus has not been calibrated to measure the fraction of vapor passing through the orifice and into the source since this is not essential to the analysis. Under operating conditions, a high velocity beam tends to form a static charge along the glass beam-former. The charge is sufficient to distort the electric field of the repeller electrodes, resulting in a loss of ion beam to the analyzer section of the spectrometer. In this apparatus, the charge is dissipated by baking a platinum coating onto the outer surfaces of the jacket which is grounded with a platinum lead to the source housing. The quasimolecular beam enters the ionizing region of the ion source through a series of 3 collimating slits. The slit dimensions are 0.010" x 0.65", 0.015" x 0.65", and 0.020" x 0.65". These slits are spatially arranged so that those molecules traversing the first entrance slit (0.010" x 0.65") do not encounter any further collisions with the two succeeding slits before entering the ionization zone. In operation, the molecular beam and ion beam are traveling in the same direction. As yet, no evidence has been detected for the occurrence of ion-molecule reactions.

Experimental Procedure

In an experimental run a weighed quantity of polymer (usually on the order of 5 mg) is diluted with an inert material (95 mg). α-Al_2O_3 is used because of its low surface area and lack of catalytic activity. It also undergoes no physical or chemical change in the temperature range of interest. The mixture is homogenized and ground in a Wig-L-Bug and an aliquot (10 mg) is transferred to the platinum sample cup of the measuring thermocouple. The reference cup contains a nearly equivalent amount of Al_2O_3. The DTA furnace assembly is attached through ball and socket joints to the beam-former which is already mounted on the source housing and aligned with the source slit. The differential pumping station and the ion source pump are activated simultaneously. Heat is then applied to the sample to outgas at a temperature below the decomposition point. The mass spectrum is recorded periodically to determine when the degassing operation is complete. Generally, it requires less than one hour. A predetermined temperature program, in the range $5\text{-}25^{o}C/min$, is started and continuous magnetic scan with the mass spectrometer is begun. The molecules are ionized with 70 eV ionization potential electrons. In the event that it is desired to record only the parent ions, controlled low voltage ionization potentials may be used. The applied magnetic field is continuously varied between 1500-5500 gauss, which covers the mass range from 12-200 AMU. A complete mass spectrum may be recorded every 3 minutes at high resolution. At the same time, the differential thermal response of the sample is monitored and recorded as a function of temperature. The initiation of thermal decomposition is thus detected in the DTA by a thermal response and in the mass spectrometer by the appearance of decomposition products. As the cell temperature increases, changes in the decomposition mechanism are defined by differences in the composition of the vapor detected by the spectrometer. During this period it is sometimes desirable to convert to electric scanning while recording a narrower mass range of particular interest.

Discussion & Results

1. Polystyrene Decomposition

To illustrate the utility of the technique a polystyrene polymer whose decomposition behavior is reasonably well known (6) was degraded. A 12 mg sample of 5 wt.% powdered polystyrene in Al_2O_3 was loaded into the sample cup. After outgassing at 150°C on the spectrometer, a DTA heating program of 10°C/min was started. The initial differential pumping station pressure was 2.8×10^{-8} torr and rose at the peak of decomposition to 5.1×10^{-8} torr. The corresponding ion source pressures were 3.6×10^{-7} and 1.5×10^{-6} torr. During the temperature program period, the thermogram in Figure 3 was recorded. The peak decomposition temperature is seen to be approximately 420°C. Decomposition begins at temperatures between 300 and 350°C during what appears to be background noise in the thermogram. This noise is also accompanied by a high incidence of oxygen - containing fragments in the mass spectrum, notably $m/e = 41$ (C_2HO) and 69 (C_4H_5O). These mass units indicate that the polymer contains a minor fraction of oxygenated components which are readily degraded. The impurities peak out at 350°C and the main polymer decomposition sets in at a slightly higher temperature.

From the spectrum taken between 390 and 425°C (reproduced in Figure 4) it is evident that the primary decomposition mechanism is by sequential depolymerization to the monomer. With minor exceptions, the spectrum is consistent with that of the styrene monomer, for which the fragmentation pattern has been determined on this spectrometer at identical instrument conditions. Additional ions are detected at $m/e = 91$, 92 and 106, and a small signal at $m/e = 105$. These are readily attributable respectively to 4.5% toluene, 0.6% ethyl benzene and a trace of isopropyl benzene. These results are consistent with the literature concerning this particular polymer and are included merely to illustrate the applicability of the method to polymer degradation studies.

2. Polyimide Decomposition

A primary objective of this work was to conduct a study of the decomposition mechanism for a polyimide resin system. A specific polyimide, Monsanto Corp. "Skybond 700", was selected because of its favorable processing characteristics in the fabrication of potential heat shield materials for reentry vehicles.

The Skybond 700 resin was obtained from Monsanto Corp. and was cured in an air oven for a total of 16 hours at 25°C increments, between 200 and 372°C. Infrared analysis of the resulting polymer showed that free carboxylic acid was not present and that amide and amine nitrogen to hydrogen bonds were present in a quantity consistent with polymer chain termination groups. The polymer was extracted with dimethylformamide and an infrared spectrum showed that the extracted material was not organic in nature. The cured polymer has the general structure:

The intermediate incompletely cyclyzed form, the polyamic acid, would have the structure:

In previous publications, analysis of the gaseous decomposition products of various polyimides showed that carbon monoxide and carbon dioxide accounted for about 80-90 mole percent of the gases evolved (2, 5, 7, 8, 9). The presence of carbon dioxide after pyrolysis in air is easily explained. This is not the case for thermal decomposition in a vacuum environment. Bruck (7) reported substantial quantities of CO_2 in the pyrolysis of H-film. Bruck's analysis of the condensable decomposition gases shows that water is also a significant product (8.0 mole %). The presumption was that carbon dioxide is solely a by-product from the decomposition of incompletely cyclized polypyromellitamic acid and that it is formed by decarboxylation and by hydrolytic scission of the amide groups. He also assumed that carbon monoxide is the only gaseous oxygen product evolved from the decomposition of the imide groups and other oxygen containing components of the polymer. He reported that the ratio of CO to CO_2 at $610^\circ C$ from purified H-film was three to one. H-film differs from the preceeding two materials shown in having the following structure:

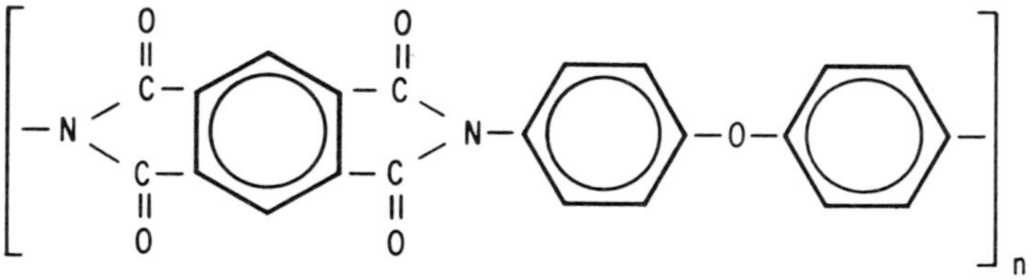

wherein pyromellitic dianhydride replaces the benzophenone dianhydride of Skybond to form the basic imide linkage. The composition of DuPont's H-film has also been studied by others (8). These studies showed that at $540^\circ C$ carbon monoxide and carbon dioxide were the important gaseous products (93 mole %) in a ratio of 1.67 to 1. Water constituted only 1.2 mole %.

In the present study the experimental conditions of the mass thermal analyses of the Skybond 700 were essentially identical with those reported above for polystyrene, with the following exceptions: 1. the degradative temperature program was taken to $1000^{\circ}C$, 2. the high cure temperature of the polymer permitted conditioning or outgassing of the polymer at $200-250^{\circ}C$ without degradation, 3. the sample size was adjusted to provide 10-15 mg of a mixture of Skybond 700 (10 mg in 90 mg of Al_2O_3), 4. in addition to the normal scan covering the mass range 12-200 AMU, separate experiments were carried out at each heating rate with the mass spectrometer focused for mass 2 and scanned electrostatically for detection of hydrogen every two minutes using a 70 eV ionization potential.

The temperature program was varied from $5-25^{\circ}C$ per minute in separate experiments. Variations in heating rates had minor effects on the temperature of the decomposition endotherm, however no appreciable differences in the absolute quantity or nature of the degradation products were detected.

The primary decomposition products, shown in Figure 5 without regard to temperature, were CO, CO_2, H_2O, HCN, hydrogen and small quantities of benzonitrile, benzene, methane and ammonia. The ion currents from the mass spectral data for the major decomposition products are plotted as a function of temperature in Figure 6. The plots indicate that sequential decomposition reactions occur in the degradation of the polymer which involve distinct functional groups. A plot for hydrogen obtained from a separate experiment, is shown in Figure 7. Figure 8 shows the thermogram determined simultaneously with the mass spectrum. This figure also shows a TGA run at the same heating rate to illustrate the correspondence of decomposition temperatures determined by the two methods.

Similarities between the mass spectral intensities and the peaks in the thermogram permit certain correlations between the two sets of data. One of the first products to appear was carbon dioxide. At moderate temperatures (e.g., $300^{\circ}C$ - $500^{\circ}C$) it proved to be only a minor product. Water also appears early as a minor product. At the low temperatures both CO_2 and H_2O probably result, as postulated by Bruck (7) from ring closure and decomposition of polyamic acid groups. This is seen in the mass spectrometry results as a gradual increase in these components

1461

between 300-500°C and similarly in the thermogram as a weak, broad inflection in the same temperature range. From 500° to 605°C, CO and CO_2 are the major products formed, as determined by the mass spectrometer. This temperature range corresponds to that of the major endotherm in the thermogram, which has its maximum intensity at 600°C. Carbon monoxide can arise from degradation of the benzophenone substructure, from the phenyl ether or from the imide ring. Subsequent infrared studies of the degradation of Skybond 700 film at 550°C showed that benzophenone decomposes rapidly in this temperature region, the imide bond slowly decomposes, and the ether linkage remains intact. Assuming that CO_2 arises from decomposition of the imide bond the relative slopes of the CO and CO_2 peaks at 550°C indicate that a bond other than that of the imide is rupturing simultaneously to yield CO. This is in agreement with the infrared study which shows the disappearance of a carbonyl band (6.05μ) in the polymer at 550°C. This reaction is much more rapid than the imide decomposition with the result that the peak for CO is reached at 585°C as opposed to 605° for CO_2. A plot of the relative ion current ratio of CO versus CO_2 (Figure 9) places the decomposition peak for the benzophenone carbonyl at 560°C. Above 600°C the primary products are CO_2, CO, benzonitrile, benzene, hydrogen, ammonia, methane and hydrogen cyanide. At these temperatures, the CO_2 intensity decreases rapidly and disappears at 700°C. The intensity of the carbon monoxide peak diminishes rapidly, rises again as the ether linkages decompose, and continues to evolve past 1000°C. Hydrogen cyanide is a major product which peaks at 650°C and like CO continues to evolve past 1000°C. This is seen in both the mass spectrum and in the thermogram, the latter showing a pronounced inflection at 655°C. Significant quantities of HCN in the volatile product are not surprising since elemental analysis of the residue remaining after treatment at 1000°C shows that the concentration of nitrogen in the char is approximately 50% of its concentration in the polymer. The decomposition products of the aromatic groups also show up in the region 600 to 700°C. The ion current peaks for benzonitrile and ammonia are at 620°C, benzene is at 625°C, methane is at 660°C and hydrogen is a major product at the high temperatures, peaking at 750°C.

The source and mechanism of CO_2 formation from the decomposition of the polymer pose difficult questions which are not clearly answered by the mass spectral studies alone. There are at least three possible mechanisms. CO_2 could be formed in (1) the decomposition of incompletely cyclized polyamic acid as proposed by Bruck, (2) by decomposition of the polyimide through an intermolecular oxygen transfer or (3) an intramolecular rearrangement. Since it would be difficult to characterize the polymer completely, and since multiple sources of oxygen are present, supplementary experiments were carried out using the model compounds phthalimide, N-methyl phthalimide and N-phenyl phthalimide. The results of these studies have been reported elsewhere (10). Essentially the results showed that a unimolecular reaction, following first order kinetics was responsible for production of CO_2. This suggests that an intramolecular oxygen transfer occurs at elevated temperatures in imide compounds and is responsible for evolution of CO_2 in completely cyclyzed imide polymers.

A complete comparative kinetic analysis of the polymer could not be made since two sources of CO were decomposing at the same time and a quantitative analysis of the various oxygen groups in the residue using infrared techniques was not feasible. Accordingly the polymer was decomposed at 550°C for comparison with the N-phenyl phthalimide. The decomposition was carried to completion and for a time period beyond completion to determine if secondary decomposition products were being formed at this temperature. In this way a quantitative analysis of the gaseous oxygen products could be made. The experimental results are given in Table I.

For N-phenyl phthalimide the complete reaction scheme at 550°C most probably occurs as follows:

I.   (I)

Ia. I $\longrightarrow$ CO + CHAR + HCN + H$_2$ + MINOR PRODUCTS

Ib. I + FREE RADICALS $\longrightarrow$ STABILIZED OXYGENATED PRODUCT (II)

2.

Reaction Ia is important in interpreting the results obtained from the degradation of the polymer. In a gas state decomposition, reaction sites are not localized and small changes in temperature markedly affect the lifetime of I. The end result is that a large portion of I thermally decomposes before it can enter into a stabilizing collision reaction. The polymer, being a linear chain and partially crosslinked in the solid state at comparable temperatures, is less affected by these factors. From the data obtained (10), it appears that three initial reactions occur almost simultaneously in the decomposition of Skybond 700.

3.

4.

(III)

5.

Reaction 3 is readily observable in the infrared region at 6.05μ and proceeds at a much faster rate than the
imide decomposition. A reasonable oxygen mass balance can
be obtained by subtracting the mM of CO formed from reaction 3 from the total mM of CO formed. This is possible
since the data at $550^{\circ}C$ shows that the decomposition
reactions of the polymer at this temperature have essentially gone to completion in the allotted time. The total mM
of oxygen present in the polymer were calculated using the
molecular weight of the repeating unit. The remaining CO
versus the CO_2 formed gives a ratio of 0.67 for k_4/k_5.
Essentially complete stabilization of III in reaction 4 is
evident as opposed to only partial stabilization of I in
the model compound vapor. The stabilized intermediate of
reaction 4 is responsible to a great extent for the retention of the polymer configuration until higher temperatures
where the char is formed.
    It is reasonable to assume at this point that the
mechanism for the formation of CO in an imide decomposition
involves scission of the imide ring to release either one
or two of the carbonyl groups. The mechanism for the
formation of CO_2 is not as easy to characterize.

However it has been found that the ratio k_{CO}/k_{CO_2} increases as the nitrogen substituent is changed from H < phenoxy phenyl < phenyl < methyl, phenoxy phenyl being the substituent in the polymer. Of all the imides studied, phthalimide gives the greatest amount of CO_2 when decomposed. Phthalimide differs from the other imides chiefly in the ionic isomeric structures within the imide itself,

$$O = \overset{|}{\underset{R}{C}} - N - \overset{|}{\underset{R}{C}} = O \quad \text{and} \quad O = \overset{|}{\underset{R}{C}} - N = \overset{|}{\underset{R}{C}} - \overset{\ominus}{O} -.$$

We believe that these ionic structures are an intregal part of the mechanism which favors the formation of CO_2. Stabilization of the ionic structures can occur in two ways: free radical stabilization which occurs when the nitrogen substituent bond is broken or stabilization due to the electron donating characteristics of the nitrogen substituent. The principal feature common to both is that each requires an internal oxygen transfer to produce the CO_2.

Regardless of which mechanism is assumed, it appears that the imide ring is a primary source of CO_2 and that this reaction is competitive in rate with CO-producing ring scission according to the nature of the substituent on the imide group.

Summary

A technique of mass thermal analysis has been developed for studying the degradation of ablative polymers. The technique has been applied to studying the degradation of a polyimide resin system. Detailed description of the degradative mechanisms for polyimide have been derived by the application of this technique. The source of CO_2 in the product gases has been shown to result primarily from an intramolecular oxygen rearrangement in the imide ring. Mechanisms have been postulated which explain the high char yield of the polymer and account for the high residual nitrogen content of the char

References

1. R. W. Farmer, "Thermogravimetry of Phenol-Formaldehyde Polycondensates", AFML TR-65-246, January 1966.
2. H. L. Friedman, "The Relationship Between Structure and Thermal Stability of New High Temperature Polymers", AFML, ML-TDR-64-274, August 1964.
3. C. B. Murphy, "Thermal Analysis - Annual Reviews", Anal. Chem. 38, 443-51, April 1966.
4. D. L. Werner and K. A. Lincoln, "Mass Spectrometric Analysis of Ablation Products Produced by High Intensity Thermal Radiation", TR-N2116, United States Naval Radiological Defense Laboratory (December 1966) and H. L. Friedman, loc. cit., Part III, April 1967.
5. H. G. Langer, R. S. Gohlke, and D. H. Smith, "Mass Spectrometric Differential Thermal Analysis", Anal. Chem. 37, 443-4, 1965.
6. S. L. Madorsky, "Thermal Degradation of Organic Polymers", Interscience Publ., 26-92, John Wiley and Sons, New York, 1964.
7. S. D. Bruck, Polymer Preprints, 148, 147th National Meeting, Am. Chem. Soc., Philadelphia, Pa., 5-10 April 1964.
8. J. F. Heacock and C. F. Berr, SPE Transactions, 105-10, April 1965.
9. P. W. Juneau, Jr., Proc. 22nd Ann. Tech. Conf. SPE, Montreal, Mar. 7-10, 66, XVII, Paper #3.
10. T. H. Johnston and C. A. Gaulin, Polymers in Space Symposium, Joint JPL/Southwest ACS Polymer Group, Jet Propulsion Laboratory, Pasadena, California, July 15-17 (1968).

Table I*

Compound	Temp.	Reaction Rate Constants (Sec-1)		Ratio k_{CO}/k_{CO_2}
N-phenyl phthalimide	550°C	$k_{CO}= 5.99 \times 10^{-5}$		
		$k_{CO_2} = 4.23 \times 10^{-5}$		1.42
	575°C	$k_{CO}= 3.37 \times 10^{-4}$		
		$k_{CO_2} = 2.92 \times 10^{-4}$		1.15
(extrapolated)	600°C	$k_{CO}= 1.55 \times 10^{-3}$		
		$k_{CO_2} = 1.8 \times 10^{-3}$		.86
phthalimide	600°C	$k_{CO}= 5.3 \times 10^{-5}$		
		$k_{CO_2} = 2.12 \times 10^{-4}$		0.25
N-methyl phthalimide	600°C	$k_{CO}= 2.69 \times 10^{-4}$		
		$k_{CO_2} = 8.73 \times 10^{-5}$		3.06
Skybond 700	550°C	——————————		0.67

* Ref - 10

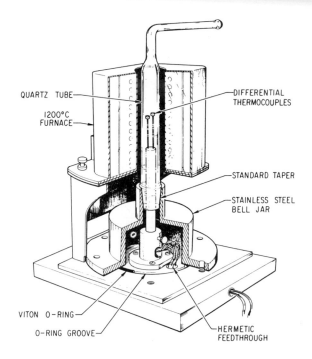

QUARTZ TUBE

1200°C FURNACE

DIFFERENTIAL THERMOCOUPLES

STANDARD TAPER

STAINLESS STEEL BELL JAR

VITON O-RING

O-RING GROOVE

HERMETIC FEEDTHROUGH

Figure 1 - High Vacuum DTA Cell

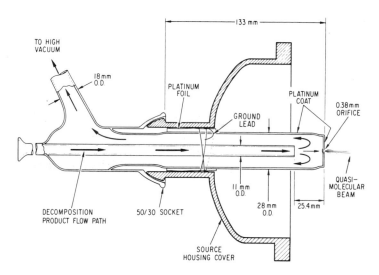

133 mm

TO HIGH VACUUM

18mm O.D.

PLATINUM FOIL

GROUND LEAD

PLATINUM COAT

0.38 mm ORIFICE

QUASI-MOLECULAR BEAM

DECOMPOSITION PRODUCT FLOW PATH

50/30 SOCKET

11 mm O.D.

28 mm O.D.

25.4 mm

SOURCE HOUSING COVER

Figure 2 - Quasi-Molecular Beam Former

1469

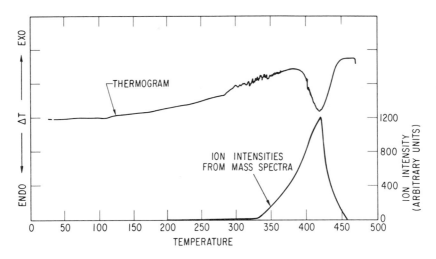

Figure 3 - DTA Thermogram and Mass Spectral Ion Intensities
During Decomposition of Polystyrene

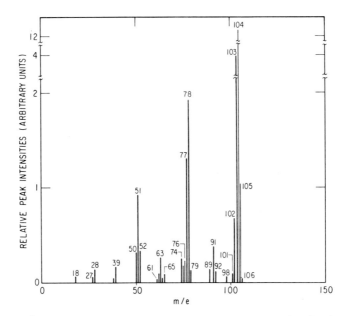

Figure 4 - Mass Spectrum of Decomposition Products of
Polystyrene Between 390-425°C

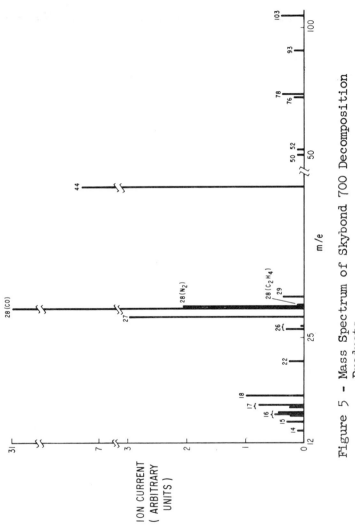

Figure 5 – Mass Spectrum of Skybond 700 Decomposition Products

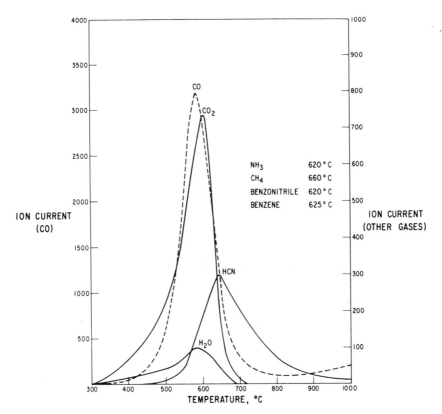

Figure 6 - Mass Spectral Intensities of the Decomposition
Products of Skybond 700 vs Temperature

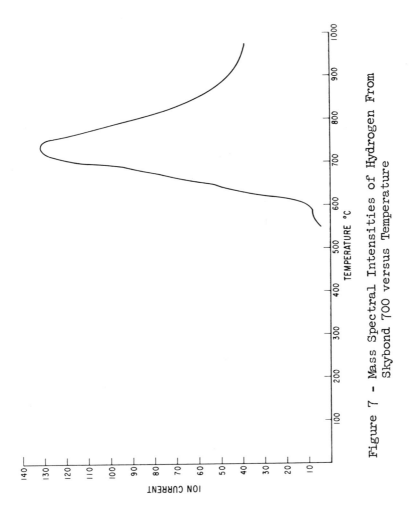

Figure 7 - Mass Spectral Intensities of Hydrogen From Skybond 700 versus Temperature

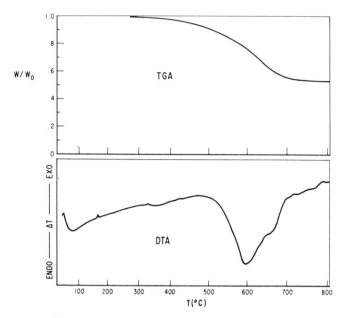

Figure 8 - TGA and DTA of Skybond 700 in Vacuum

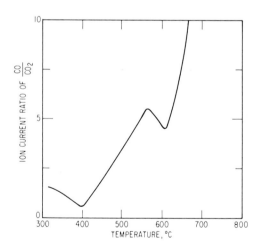

Figure 9 - Ion Current Ratio of $\frac{CO}{CO_2}$ versus Temperature

THE IMPACT OF THERMAL ANALYSES ON NUCLEAR AMMONIUM POLYURANATE PREPARATION

Michel Y. Farah, Mourad R. Zaki
and Sayed A. El-Fekey

Nuclear Chemistry Department
UAR Atomic Energy Establishment

ABSTRACT

The present study sheds light on the controversery pertaining to rigid or tolerant views concerning APU precipitation history and subsequent UO_3 and UO_2 characterisation. TGA, DTA and BET measurements were made as functions of final pH values, aging of powders, nitrates washing, settling, degassing and comparison with TGA plots for denitrated trioxides. The technological basis for production of a multipurpose metal or ceramic uranium dioxide is thus defined.

INTRODUCTION

Several early investigations (1,2,3) had suggested the formation of ammonium diuranate when ammonia is added to uranyl solutions. However, the considerable variations reported in NH_4 : U ratios, as well as the tremendous number of structures proposed, suggested that the additional ammonia may be bound physically by adsorption rather than chemically. Since the precipitates were amorphous they possessed a considerably capacity to adsorb ammonia or ammonium salts. Consequently few authors (4,5,6) recommended that strict conditions of precipitation be followed to reach, by the subsequent calcination and reduction, sinterable uranium dioxide. Philip and Thomas (7) stated, that the assumption of the existence of ammonium diuranate is suspect and that no single well-defined species of $(NH_4)_2U_2O_7$ exists. Decrop and others (8) reaffirmed that diuranate is only stable in the mother liquor, and that it hydrolyses on washing. They stated that it was impossible to obtain even at pH 4.0 a precipitate completely free from ammonia. In 1961 Ainscough (9) stated that the density of uranium dioxide prepared from the presumed ADU does not depend on the history of precipitation as had been thought before. The difference between the precipitated uranates disappears during subsequent processing, since U_3O_8 is a common intermidiary stage in the preparation of dioxide. The calcination temperature on the contrary, plays a determining role in fixing the surface of the dioxide and its behavior on sintering. Some tolerance is therefore allowable during precipitation.

The aim of this work is to discuss, in the light of thermal analyses, the impact on the characterisation of nuclear uranium of rigorous or tolerant conditions of precipitation (pH, temperature, duration, washing by organic reagents, drying, etc.). It will try also to examine the various proposed formations (hydrated oxides, di- or polyuranates, ammoniates) and dissipate the confusion pertaining to subsequent textures and specific surface values.

EXPERIMENTAL

Apparatus and Technique

Uranium refining was effected on a semi-
pilot 10 cm diameter pulsating column "model
Ziehl", whereby the operations of TBP extraction,
scrubbing and stripping were undertaken simultaneously. A stainless steel precipitation tank
and filter-press served for the decantation-
washing and filtering the refined uranium, whose
nuclear purity was ascertained by analysis on a
Jarrel Ash spectrograph.

The thermobalance was a Gebruder Netzch Selb.
The different linear rates of heating were recorded automatically at a heating rate of 5°C. per
minute. A full scale range of 200 mg was recorded
on a 6 inch chart, simultaneously with temperature
up to 1000°C. The temperature of the oven was
regulated by the aid of two thermocouples, a potentiometer, variable transformer, galvanometer,
a photocell and heating device.

The differential thermal analysis apparatus
was provided with two horizontal tubular furnaces
each with an outside nickel-chrome wound wiring
and an inside Pt-10% rhodium tape, both insulated
by calcined alumina. The double junction differential thermocouple consisted of 2 chromel threads
joined by a bridge of alumel wire. The recording
instrument included a D.C. amplifier, sensitivity
selector, recording ammeter, and a second Cambridge
temperature indicator.

For B.E.T. specific surface determination,
nitrogen was used at -195°C. in a Duran-Muller
modified apparatus. Debye Sherrer diagrams were
obtained with the aid of a type 3NH-09 M3 unit

X-ray diffractometer using a copper target operated at 50 Kv and 10 mA. The patterns were
matched with the cards of the American Society
for Testing Materials (10), and also with versatile diagrams reported recently in the literature.

Materials

The crude yellow cake was a Spanish sodium
uranate assaying 67.37% uranium. The relation
between structure of partly or completely refined
APU as deduced from potentiometric titration
curves and settling rates, filtrability and
apparent density was examined before (11).
Ammonia liquid used throughout these studies was
pure B.D.H., while the gas was the product of the
Egyptian Industrial Gas Works. Comparative experiments with hydrazine reported before (12), relied
on diluting to 0.09 - 1.5 normal, the Carlo Erba
85% hydrazine dihydrate.

RESULTS AND DISCUSSION

a) The TGA-DTA analyses of routine refinery APU

Fig. 1, reports the thermograms for the
routine refinery product obtained by precipitation
through air-diluted gaseous ammonia at 50°C., pH
8.0, decantation-washing with deionised water and
final drying to 110°C. of APU, before the runs
were made. The TGA curve represents the percentage weight decrease when the sample was heated
in open air at the rate of 5°C. per minute. Work
was carried out in air since it simulates better
calcination behaviour during production and owing
to the unavailability of an effluent gas analyser
connected to the thermobalance. However, to
minimise overlapping in the loss of water and
ammonia at the start of the thermograms and up to

1478

220°C. as recorded by Szabo (13), an arbitrary temperature of 220°C. was adopted as the initial reading for deducing weight decrease of the samples.

It could be said, that for various batches prepared strictly as detailed above, the thermograms were reproducible and indicating, until U_3O_8 formation around 660°C., a total decrease in weight approximating 12.5%. This cumulates the multistage loss of ammonia with presumably ammonia and water entangled until about 300°C., as well as the subsequent departure of oxygen gas. Numerous intermediate horizontal plateaus are reported due to nitrate contamination. Owing to the lack of a Nutsch filter at the time this study was started, ammonium nitrate could not be completely removed by washing on the filter-press nor by repeated decantation and settling and the loss of fines was otherwise substantial.

It was also shown from the parallel DTA for the same sample, that the first ammonia departure was accompanied by a mild then pronounced exothermic effect around 325°C. and 400°C. respectively, while the second oxygen departure by a less pronounced endothermic effect around 560°C. This latter peak was encountered recently at 550°C. by Kanellakopouls (14), working on chlorides. It corresponds to UO_3 transformation to U_3O_8.

To correlate thermal analyses with texture of the refinery APU, triplicate determinations of specific surface using BET technique were undertaken for each sample, after 120 minutes outgassing at 20°C. and prior to measurement. The mean result for routine APU (Fig. 2: sample a) was 3.5 m^2/gm $\pm$ 10%. Although this value is below that of 6.5 m^2/gm reported by Ainscough (9), it coincides better with Swedish authors. It is

to be noted that although this value indicates a
rather coarse texture, yet some difficulties were
encountered during filtration. These were explained by some workers as due to a change in
crystalline structure and the beginning of nucleation and agglomeration in microscopic grains still
escaping from the filters. Incomplete water washing or outgassing is responsible for apparent
coarser grains - as inferred by B.E.T. - that seem
slightly smaller than the hydrated aggregates
precipitated at pH 6.0, under identical temperature and duration conditions. As will be shown
later, the product at pH 6.0 had a settling rate
around 3.0 m/hr compared to 2.2 m/hr for the pH
8.0 precipitated product. Aging and conditioning
in ammoniacal mother liquor seem to some into play
to various extents. Heating enhances the rate of
decantation - as it also favours aggregation -
particularly with respect to precipitates obtained
in shorter duration of time, as is evident from the
following:

Experi-ment	Conditions			Rate of settling
1	0.33 N U^6,			
	9.0 M Ammonia,	$25^{\circ}C$,	18 mn.,	1.20m/hr
2		$40^{\circ}C$,		2.20m/hr
3		$40^{\circ}C$,	3 mn.,	0.60m/hr
4			10 mn.,	2.34m/hr
5			26 mn.,	2.80m/hr
6		$65^{\circ}C$,	18 mn.,	2.89m/hr
7		$85^{\circ}C$,		2.37m/hr

N.B.: All these experiments were undertaken
       at pH 8.0

All the routine APU satisfied nuclear purity. On rotapping for ten minutes the texture was as follows: $< 37\mu$: 23.53%, $> 37\mu$: 21.95%, $> 53\mu$: 18.44%, $> 74\mu$: 19.25%, $> 105\mu$: 16.79%; when calcined for 3 hours at 350 C., the obtained UO_3 texture became $< 37\mu$: 75%, $> 37\mu$: 5.1%, $> 53\mu$: 5.4%, $> 74\mu$: 5.8%, $> 105\mu$: 8.7%. For comparison, the specific surface and texture of a reference Swedish sample kingly offered by Dr. Svenke (Aktiebolaget Atomenergi, Sweden) is quoted as follows: $26\mu < 10\%$, $46\mu < 50\%$, $64\mu < 90\%$ and specific surface 2.75 m^2/gm.

The routine uranium trioxide was found to reduce readily by cracked ammonia to a passivated, sinterable dioxide conveniently pelletised into compacts of sufficiently high density, as also ascertained by the Staff of the Metallurgy Department, who studied these products concurrently.

b) Thermograms and BET data for pH 6.0 uranates.

The settling rates of uranates precipitated from versatile media at pH values around 6.0 had somehow higher results than those precipitated at pH 8.0. It is believed that polarity of water brings about stronger holding forces than ammoniate aggregations. Variation in decantation rates is evident from the following:

Experiment	Conditions	Rate of settling
1	0.33N U^6nitrate, 9.0 ammonia, 40°C, 18 mn.	2.20m/hr
2	65°C, 26 mn. 6.8 ammonia	2.75m/hr
3	65°C, 26 mn. 6.8 ammonia	2.93m/hr
4	sulphate	2.95m/hr
5	chloride	2.85m/hr

N.B.: Expt. 1 : pH 8.0, and Expts. 2-5 pH 6.6

It was deemed desirable to investigate later
the effect of washing with organic reagents and
prolonged drying in vacuum, since both treatments
may detach the aggregates or affect their reactivity. Fig. 3 is concerned with thermograms of
a typical sample b, obtained by precipitating
from nuclear purity uranyl nitrate solution assaying 72 gm U/l, using dilute ammonia solution 1:1
at 60°C. and a controlled pH of 6.0, followed by
washing with water, acetone spray and rapidly
drying in air on the filter. Between 200°C. and
660°C, a slightly lower cumulative decrease in
weight of about 12% is recorded of which about 4%
is due to oxygen loss above 420°C. The curve also
shows a lower number of horizontal plateaus presumably due to better cleaning from nitrate by
water then acetone spraying, bringing about better
dehydration of coagulated particles, as well as
less ammonia entangled (8.0 instead of 8.5%) as
compared to Fig. 1. Washing with methyl alcohol,
adopted by Jakes (15,16), then drying at 20°C. led
to higher surface areas. To emphasize BET variations for samples a and b in the present study, a
third sample c was concurrently studied, subjected
to copious acetone washing (about six times) and
one week degassing. The results were 16.6 and
38.0 m^2/gm respectively for b and c. The result
of B compares favourably with 18.7 reported for
routine samples of Sauteron (17) at a similar pH
value. Although the treatment to which sample c
was subjected is a usual one in laboratory and
pilot practice, it was motivated by Jakes warning
that several days degassing was unable to give
stable vacuum results in surface measurements.
It is known that his samples contained more ammonia than other workers. As the exchange of NH_3
with water is reversible and fast, it is supposed
that amorphous UO_3 and $UO_3 \cdot 2 H_2O$ reported by
Szabo (13) to be formed at lower pH values, exchange removable NH_3 forming UO_3 ammoniates, where

ammonia is not present as ammonium ion but as removable NH_3. This is presumably accompanied by pH increase, by a change from orthorhombic to hexagonal pattern and, at still higher pH, by polymerisation, ammoniation and fining of the aggregate size (18). All the formed products then could be assimilated to UO_3-hydrates-ammoniates and variants therefrom (19).

c)   TGA of trioxide obtained by denitration.

Fig. 3 shows also, that for uranium trioxide obtained by denitration of uranyl nitrate (Sample d), and equal decrease in weight of 4% is recorded above $660^{\circ}C$. that corresponds to oxygen loss and transformation to violet black U_3O_8. A small number of plateaus are still encountered due to trace nitrate, since the examined trioxide was obtained from analar BDH, not nuclear grade product, and also owing to incomplete aeration of the furance during the thermogravimetric run.

d)   X-ray structural analyses.

The Debye Sherrer diagrams indicated for routine refinery ammonium polyuranate, obtained at pH 8.0, patterns that fairly coincided with those of Debets (20) for compound III i.e. the hexagonal $2UO_3 \cdot NH_3 \cdot 3H_2O$, with the following results:

d	I
7.35	V.S.
4.09	W
3.52	M
3.34	M
2.03	W
1.25	W

The final calcined product of the same polyuranate gave a pattern coinciding with ASTM card
8-244, i.e. the hexagonal U_3O_8, with the following
data:

d	I
4.10	V.S.
3.37	S
3.31	S
2.61	V.S.
1.76	V.S.

For uranates obtained at pH 6.0, compared to
uranium trioxide obtained by calcining APU, (precipitated at pH 8.0) to 350°C., the intensities
were nearly identical, indicating the efficiency
of washing with organic liquids as well as of
prolonged degassing, in obtaining a product practically free of entangled ammonia. The following
results are quoted for comparison:

d	I	
	(pH 6.0 product)	(calcined UO_3)
7.35	V.S.	V.S.
7.823	S	W
3.608	S	S
3.246	V.S.	V.S.
3.112	W	S
2.560	M	–

CONCLUSIONS

The refinery APU obtained by precipitation
at pH 8.0 using air-diluted gaseous ammonia at
50°C. satisfied nuclear purity standards and

physical character specifications. To facilitate
filtrability and minimise the loss of fines, it
is equally recommended to undertake precipitation
at pH 6.0. Wash with deionised water then spray
with organic reagents (acetone or alcohol), dry
by suction or aeration to get a product with at
least 16 m^2/gm specific surface, possessing high
reactivity and as free as possible from nitrate
or ammonia. This procedure is convenient for
both : fluorination-metallothermy to U or reduc-
tion-passivation-pelletising-sintering to ceramic
UO_2 fuel.

REFERENCES

1. J. A. Arfvedson, Sevenska Akad. 404, (1822).
2. A. J. Carson and T. H. Norton, Amer. Chem.
   Journ. 10, 219 (1888).
3. P. Jolibois and F. Bossuet, Compt. Rend. 174,
   1625, (1922).
4. B. A. J. Lister and G. M. Gilles, in Progress
   in Nuclear Energy, Series III, Process Chemistry, 1, edited by Pergamon Press Ltd., London
   1956.
5. L. Wirth and L. Ziehl, in Proceedings 2nd.
   Geneva Conference, P/1001, (1958).
6. E. Yatabe and L. C. Watson, CRCE-716, (1958).
7. S. Philips et al., NLCO-645, (1959).
8. J. Decrop et al., in Proceedings 2nd Geneva
   Conference, P/1252, (1958).
9. J. B. Ainscough, TID-7637, (1961).
10. A.S.T.M., in Alphabetical and Grouped Numeri-
    cal of X-ray.
11. M. Y. Farah, M. R. Zaki and S. A. El-Fekey,
    in Proceedings of Fifth Arab Science Confer-
    ence, Bagdad, 231, (1966).
12. M. R. Zaki, S. A. El-Fekey and M. Y. Farah,
    in VIII International Mineral Processing
    Congress E-3, Leningrad, (1968).

13. E. Szabo, in *Proceedings 3rd Geneva Conference* P/450, (1964)

14. B. Kanellakopouls and H. Parthey, *J. Inorg. Nucl. Chem.*, **28**, 2541, (1965)

15. D. Jakes and H. Landspersky, in *Proceedings 3rd Geneva Conference* P/530, (1964) and UJV, 1332, (1965)

16. Ibid., *Collect. Czechoslov. Chem. Comm.*, **31**, 1677, (1966)

17. J. Sauteron, Note *CEA*, *Le Bouchet*, **326** (1960)

18. S. A. El-Fekey, *M. Sc. Dissertation*, Cairo University June (1967)

19. M. E. A. Hermans, *Ph.D. Dissertation*, Delft University (1964)

20. P. C. Debets and B. O. Loopstra, *J. Inorg. Nucl. Chem.* **25**, 945, (1963)

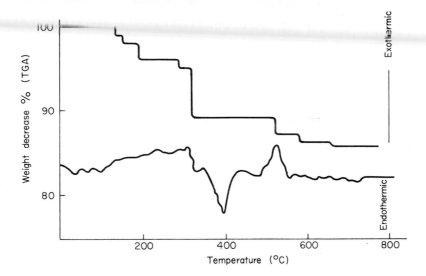

Fig. 1 – DTA & TGA of refinery APU

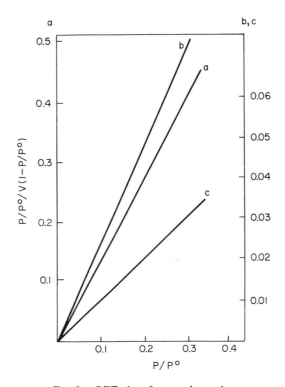

Fig. 2 – BET plots for samples, *a, b, c*

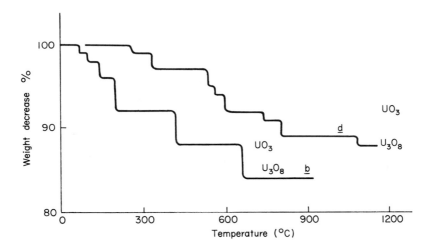

Fig. 3 – TGA of samples b & d

APPENDIX 1

RECOMMENDATIONS FOR REPORTING THERMAL ANALYSIS DATA

SIR: Because thermal analysis involves dynamic techniques, it is essential that all pertinent experimental detail accompany the actual experimental records to allow their critical assessment. This was emphasized by Newkirk and Simons (*1*) who offered some suggestions for the information required with curves obtained by Thermogravimetry (TG). Publication of data obtained by other dynamic thermal methods, particularly differential thermal analysis (DTA), requires equal but occasionally different detail, and this letter is intended to present comprehensive recommendations regarding both DTA and TG.

In 1965 the First International Conference on Thermal Analysis (ICTA) established a Committee on Standardization charged with the task of studying how and where standardization might further the value of these methods. One area of concern was with the uniform reporting of data, in view of the profound lack of essential experimental information occurring in much of the thermal analysis literature. The following recommendations are now put forward by the Committee on Standardization, in the hope that authors, editors, and referees will be guided to give their readers full but concise detail. The actual format for communicating these details, of course, will depend upon a combination of the author's preference, the purpose for which the experiments are reported, and the policy of the particular publishing medium.

To accompany each DTA or TG record, the following information should be reported:

1. Identification of all substances (sample, reference, diluent) by a definitive name, an empirical formula, or equivalent compositional data.

2. A statement of the source of all substances, details of their histories, pre-treatments, and chemical purities, so far as these are known.

3. Measurement of the average rate of linear temperature change over the temperature range involving the phenomena of interest.

4. Identification of the sample atmosphere by pressure, composition, and purity; whether the atmosphere is static, self-generated, or dynamic through or over the sample. Where applicable the ambient atmospheric pressure and humidity should be specified. If the pressure is other than atmospheric, full details of the method of control should be given.

5. A statement of the dimensions, geometry, and materials of the sample holder; the method of loading the sample where applicable.

(*1*) A.E. Newkirk and E.L. Simons, *Talanta*, **10**, 1199 (1963).

6. Identification of the abscissa scale in terms of time or of temperature at a specified location. Time or temperature should be plotted to increase from left to right.

7. A statement of the methods used to identify intermediates or final products.

8. Faithful reproduction of all original records.

9. Wherever possible, each thermal effect should be identified and supplementary supporting evidence stated.

In the reporting of TG Data, the following additional details are also necessary:

10. Identification of the thermobalance, including the location of the temperature-measuring thermocouple.

11. A statement of the sample weight and weight scale for the ordinate. Weight loss should be plotted as a downward trend and deviations from this practice should be clearly marked. Additional scales (e.g., fractional decomposition, molecular composition) may be used for the ordinate where desired.

12. If derivative thermogravimetry is employed, the method of obtaining the derivative should be indicated and the units of the ordinate specified.

When reporting DTA traces, these specific details should also be presented:

10. Sample weight and dilution of the sample.

11. Identification of the apparatus, including the geometry and materials of the thermocouples and the locations of the differential and temperature-measuring thermocouples.

12. The ordinate scale should indicate deflection per degree Centigrade at a specified temperature. Preferred plotting will indicate upward deflection as a positive temperature differential, and downward deflection as a negative temperature differential, with respect to the reference. Deviations from this practice should be clearly marked.

Members of the Committee on Standardization of ICTA are: Professor C. Mazieres (France), Professor T. Sudo (Japan), Mr. R.S. Forsyth (Sweden), Mr. H.G. Wiedemann (Switzerland), Dr. I.S. Rassonskaya (U.S.S.R.), Mr. C.J. Keattch (United Kingdom), and Dr. P.D. Garn (United States). Other delegates to the Committee include Professor L.G. Berg (U.S.S.R.), Dr. R.C. Mackenzie (United Kingdom), Dr. J.P. Redfern (United Kingdom) and Dr. S. Gordon (United States). The Chairman is Dr. H.G. McAdie from Canada.

H.G. McAdie

Ontario Research Foundation
43 Queen's Park Crescent East
Toronto, 5, Canada

RECEIVED for review January 18, 1967. Accepted February 10, 1967.

APPENDIX 2

RECOMMENDATIONS FOR NOMENCLATURE IN THERMAL ANALYSIS

I. INTRODUCTION

Nomenclature in thermal analysis is neither uniform nor consistent and can at times be confusing. Because of this, the First International Conference on Thermal Analysis set up a Committee to examine the whole question and to report to the Second Conference.

During the period between the two Conferences the Committee have been able to prepare a definitive list of recommendations for nomenclature in English. These recommendations have been approved in principle by the Business Session at the Second Conference and consequently the Council of the International Confederation for Thermal Analysis have directed that they be published. In doing so the Council are well aware that new developments in the science and further consideration of certain points raised in discussion may lead to minor revision, but meantime the report is offered as a definitive document, the recommendations in which ought to be adhered to in all publications on thermal analysis in the English language.

Linguistic considerations naturally render difficult any universal application of terms, and it may well be that names unacceptable in one language are normal usage in another. It must be stressed therefore that the present document refers to the English language *only,* and that thermal analysts in all major English-speaking countries were consulted before it was finalized. Similar documents for French, German, Japanese, and Russian are currently being compiled by Sub-Committees in the areas within which these languages are spoken. It is anticipated that the deliberations of these Committees will result in recommendations similar in general principle to, although undoubtedly different in detail from, those listed here. These documents will be published in due course. In this connection, there is considerable merit in the suggestion made during discussion of this report that the limited number of abbreviations regarded as permissible should be adopted internationally, irrespective of language.

Subsequent developments in the field of nomenclature will be reported from time to time in the *ICTA Newsletter.*

1491

II. GENERAL RECOMMENDATIONS

(a) *Thermal analysis* and *not* 'thermography' should be the acceptable name in English, since the latter has at least two other meanings in this language, the major one being medical (*Science Progress*, 1967, **55**, 167). The adjective should then be *thermoanalytical* (cf. physical chemistry and physicochemical): the term 'thermoanalysis' was not supported (on the same logical basis).

(b) *Differential* should be the adjectival form of *difference; derivative* should be used for the first derivative (mathematical) of any curve.

(c) The term 'analysis' should be avoided as far as possible since the methods considered do not comprise analysis as generally understood chemically: terms like *differential thermal analysis* are too widely accepted, however, to be changed.

(d) The term *curve* is preferred to 'thermogram' for the following reasons:

1. 'Thermogram' is used for the results obtained by the medical technique of thermography – see (a).

2. If applied to certain curves (e.g. thermogravimetric curves), 'thermogram' would not be consistent with the dictionary definition.

3. For clarity one would frequently have to use terms like differential thermogram, thermogravimetric thermogram, etc., which are not only cumbersome but also confusing.

(e) In multiple techniques, *simultaneous* should be used for the application of two or more techniques to the same sample at the same time: *combined* would then indicate the use of separate samples for each technique.

(f) *Thermal decomposition* and similar terms are being further considered by the Committee.

III. TERMINOLOGY

The names accepted after much discussion are listed in Table 1, together with acceptable abbreviations and names which were, for one reason or another, rejected. The aim has been to obtain a *logical* classification and some recently introduced names have been rejected on this ground.

The committee decided that it was not its function to pronounce on borderline techniques (such as thermometric titrimetry or enthalpimetry) or on calorimetric terms, which are, to its knowledge, being considered by other bodies. Consideration of techniques not yet extensively employed has also been deferred.

IV. DEFINITIONS AND CONVENTIONS

A. GENERAL

Thermal Analysis. A general term covering a group of related techniques whereby the dependence of the parameters of any physical property of a substance on temperature is measured.

B. METHODS ASSOCIATED WITH WEIGHT CHANGES

1. Static

Isobaric Weight-Change Determination. A technique of obtaining a record of the equilibrium weight of a substance as a function of temperature (T) at a constant partial pressure of the volatile product, or products.

The record is the isobaric weight-change curve; it is normal to plot weight on the ordinate with weight decreasing downwards and T on the abscissa increasing from left to right.

Isothermal Weight-Change Determination. A technique of obtaining a record of the dependence of the weight of a substance on time (t) at constant temperature.

The record is the isothermal weight-change curve; it is normal to plot weight on the ordinate with weight decreasing downwards and t on the abscissa increasing from left to right.

2. Dynamic

Thermogravimetry (TG). A technique whereby the weight of a substance, in an environment heated or cooled at a controlled rate, is recorded as a function of time or temperature.

The record is the thermogravimetric or TG curve; the weight should be plotted on the ordinate with weight decreasing downwards and t or T on the abscissa increasing from left to right.

Derivative Thermogravimetry (DTG). A technique yielding the first derivative of the thermogravimetric curve with respect to either time or temperature.

The curve is the derivative thermogravimetric or DTG curve; the derivative should be plotted on the ordinate with weight losses downwards and t or T on the abscissa increasing from left to right.

TABLE 1

Recommended Terminology

Acceptable Name	Acceptable Abbreviation*	Rejected Name (s)
A. General		
Thermal Analysis		Thermography Thermoanalysis
B. Methods Associated with Weight Change		
1. Static		
Isobaric Weight-Change Determination		
Isothermal Weight-Change Determination		Isothermal Thermogravimetric Analysis
2. Dynamic		
Thermogravimetry	TG	Thermogravimetric Analysis Dynamic Thermogravimetric Analysis
Derivative Thermogravimetry	DTG	Differential Thermogravimetry Differential Thermogravimetric Analysis Derivative Thermogravimetric Analysis
C. Methods Associated with Energy Change		
Heating Curves (1)		
Heating-Rate Curves (1)		
Inverse Heating-Rate Curves (1)		
Differential Thermal Analysis	DTA	Thermal Analysis Derivative Thermal Analysis
Derivative Differential Thermal Analysis		
Differential Scanning Calorimetry	DSC	Dynamic Differential Calorimetry

D. Methods Associated with Evolved Volatiles

Evolved Gas Detection	EGD	Effluent Gas Detection
Evolved Gas Analysis (2)	EGA	Effluent Gas Analysis
		Thermovaporimetric Analysis

E. Methods Associated with Dimensional Change

Dilatometry
Derivative Dilatometry
Differential Dilatometry

F. Multiple Techniques

Simultaneous TG and DTA, etc.

DATA (Differential and Thermo-gravimetric Analysis)
Derivatography
Derivatographic Analysis

---

* Abbreviations should be in capital letters without full-stops, and should be kept to the minimum to avoid confusion.

(1) When determinations are performed during the cooling cycle these become *Cooling Curves*, *Cooling-Rate Curves* and *Inverse Cooling-Rate Curves*, respectively.

(2) The method of analysis should be clearly stated and abbreviations such as MTA (mass-spectrometric thermal analysis) and MDTA (mass spectrometry and differential thermal analysis) avoided.

C. METHODS ASSOCIATED WITH ENERGY CHANGES

Heating Curves. These are records of the temperature of a substance against time in an environment heated at a controlled rate.

T should be plotted on the ordinate increasing upwards and t on the abscissa increasing from left to right.

Heating-Rate Curves. These are records of the first derivative of the heating curve with respect to time (i.e. dT/dt) plotted against time or temperature.

The function dT/dt should be plotted on the ordinate and t or T on the abscissa increasing from left to right.

Inverse Heating-Rate Curves. These are records of the first derivative of the heating curve with respect to temperature (i.e. dt/dT) plotted against either time or temperature.

The function dt/dT should be plotted on the ordinate and t or T on the abscissa increasing from left to right.

Differential Thermal Analysis (DTA). A technique of recording the difference in temperature between a substance and a reference material against either time or temperature as the two specimens are subjected to identical temperature regimes in an environment heated or cooled at a controlled rate.

The record is the differential thermal or DTA curve; the temperature difference ($\triangle T$) should be plotted on the ordinate with endothermic reactions downwards and t or T on the abscissa increasing from left to right.

Derivative Differential Thermal Analysis. A technique yielding the first derivative of the differential thermal curve with respect to either time or temperature.

The record is the derivative differential thermal or derivative DTA curve; the derivative should be plotted on the ordinate and t or T on the abscissa increasing from left to right.

Differential Scanning Calorimetry (DSC). A technique of recording the energy necessary to establish zero temperature difference between a substance and a reference material against either time or temperature as the two specimens are subjected to identical temperature regimes in an environment heated or cooled at a controlled rate.

The record is the DSC curve; it represents the amount of heat applied per unit time as ordinate against either t or T as abscissa.

D. METHODS ASSOCIATED WITH EVOLVED VOLATILES

Evolved Gas Detection (EGD). This term covers any technique of detecting whether or not a volatile product is formed during thermal analysis.

Evolved Gas Analysis (EGA). A technique of determining the nature and/or amount of volatile product or products formed during thermal analysis.

E. METHODS ASSOCIATED WITH DIMENSIONAL CHANGES

Dilatometry. A technique whereby changes in dimension(s) of a substance are measured as a function of temperature.

The record is the dilatometric curve.

Derivative Dilatometry	These terms carry the connotations
Differential Dilatometry	given in Paragraph II(b) above.

F. MULTIPLE TECHNIQUES

This term covers simultaneous DTA and TG, etc., and definitions follow from the above.

V. ACKNOWLEDGEMENTS

The Committee, consisting of Dr. R.C. Mackenzie (Chairman), Mr. C.J. Keattch (Secretary), Dr. J.P. Redfern and Dr. A.A. Hodgson, wish to express their thanks to the Committee of the Thermal Analysis Group of the Society for Analytical Chemistry for assistance during their deliberations, to the Society for Analytical Chemistry for providing accommodation for meetings and secretarial facilities, and to thermal analysts in many countries for co-operation in providing comments at various stages of the programme.

R.C. Mackenzie

The Macaulay Institute for Soil Research,
Craigiebuckler, ABERDEEN, Scotland.

APPENDIX 3

PROGRESS TOWARDS THERMAL ANALYSIS STANDARDS

A REPORT FROM THE COMMITTEE ON STANDARDIZATION INTERNATIONAL CONFEDERATION FOR THERMAL ANALYSIS

H.G. McAdie

Ontario Research Foundation
Sheridan Park, Ontario, Canada.

ABSTRACT

A number of areas within thermal analysis require standardization in order that workers may properly relate their findings to one another and to information obtained from other techniques. Progress by ICTA towards such standardization is now well advanced. Recommendations for the reporting of DTA and TG data have been published and eight solid I $\rightleftharpoons$ solid II type transitions have been selected provisionally as temperature standards for DTA based on an international laboratory evaluation. Details of this evaluation and the conclusions therefrom are presented. Future ICTA programmes to complete the evaluation of these DTA standards, extend the range of provisionally acceptable DTA temperature standards, to provide systems for evaluating instrument resolution, and to provide temperature standards for thermogravimetry are described.

THE NEED FOR STANDARDS

Modern thermoanalytical methods today routinely characterize the thermal properties of materials allowing scientists to operate with ease outside previous semiisothermal restrictions. However, the diversity of instrumentation available for thermal analysis makes it necessary to prevent purely procedural effects from confusing, or even obscuring, the physical and chemical processes under study. Unless each worker who uses thermal analysis can place his data in proper relation to those obtained elsewhere, and to known phenomena characterized by independent means, he will continue to work in partial isolation from his colleagues and from other methods of investigation. Standards are therefore required in thermal analysis:

(i) to define good practice, both in experimentation and reporting, so that information obtained and communicated is of maximum value;

(ii) to provide a common basis for relating independently acquired data;

(iii) to provide means for comparing and calibrating all available instrumentation;

(iv) to promote ease of communication through common nomenclature and presentation of data.

1499

Such broad standards in thermal analysis must be applicable within the requirements of the experiment to be performed. Any attempt to define a certain procedure or instrumental design as "standard" would defeat one of the strong advantages of thermoanalytical methods, viz. adaptability to the system under study and to a wide range of procedural variations. It is only suitable to consider closely defined technique and instrumentation for test methods having a specific purpose and, generally, of applicability to specific types of materials.

The use of dynamic heating and cooling generally introduces deviations from equilibrium values in the temperatures at which processes occur. There is a need to be able to correct for these procedural deviations, i.e. to be able to construct a "calibration curve" relating dynamic procedural temperatures to equilibrium temperatures. Of equal importance is the need to know the limits of consistency achievable between individual workers, thus establishing the extent of the scatter within which all results are valid. Such limits cannot properly be inferred from the reproducibility within a given laboratory, or from experiments designed specifically to test the effects of instrumental variables, due to the different systematic bias which frequently exists over a group of laboratories.

HISTORICAL

Consideration of broad standards for thermal analysis is comparatively recent. For many years certain of the laboratories more involved in thermal analysis have selected one or two materials, based on their particular requirements and experience, and these have become "in-house" reference materials largely to assure that instruments are functioning reproducibly.

On a broader base, a number of programmes began over a comparatively short period of time during 1964-65 as the need for standards having more general applicability became evident to several groups at once. One of the first of these, begun under Dr. S. Gordon in 1964, was a programme to assess the reproducibility with which the temperature of a number of solid I $\rightleftharpoons$ solid II, first-order phase transitions could be measured by DTA. Teams of three laboratories investigated selected transitions, with only one team eventually reporting in detail on two systems.

In October, 1964, ISO Committee TC-61 (Plastics) organized task group WG 4 to explore the possibility of arriving at useful international recommendations for the thermal analysis of high polymers. An early step was to circulate a sample of poly(vinyl chloride) for examination according to "national practice". None of the eight countries circulated are known to have such practice, and it is uncertain how many laboratories eventually participated in this test. In 1966 WG 4 also circulated a list of nomenclature and definitions concerning the thermal analysis of plastics, revisions to which are now under study by other working groups within ISO prior to preparing a draft proposal.

Another group concerned with the application of thermal analysis in the field of plastics has been ASTM Committee D-20, Sub-Committee 3b. Interest here is to develop appropriate thermoanalytical test methods, the initial effort being to set forth a series of definitions and nomenclature.

In 1967 the ASTM recognized that test methods involving thermal analysis apply more widely than to plastics. A provisional sub-committee on thermoanalytical test methods was constituted under Committee E-1 (Methods of Testing) and is currently devising a programme, in cooperation with other ASTM committees and international bodies, having the objective of defining more general test methods employing thermal analysis. Initial areas of activity include nomenclature, standard materials, and test methods and recommended practices.

It is apparent that some duplication of effort exists, particularly with regard to nomenclature. However, the major activity is concerned with *test methods* as opposed to standards useful in all applications of thermal analysis. To fill this need, an extensive international programme was begun in 1965 under the auspices of the International Confederation for Thermal Analysis.

ICTA COMMITTEE ON STANDARDIZATION

Formation

The Committee on Standardization was established by approval of the Executive Committee and delegates at First ICTA. In order to maintain a Committee sufficiently small to function effectively, national delegates were invited from a number of the regions in which thermal analysis is most active. Subsequent to Second ICTA, representation has been invited from further areas. In addition to national delegates, many of whom function also as observers for national standards bodies and/or thermal analysis societies, representation was invited from the ASTM and National Bureau of Standards in the United States, and from ISO TC-61.

Objectives

The Committee on Standardization sought to define those areas within the techniques of thermal analysis, with initial emphasis on DTA and TG, where standard practices are most important:

(i)   Recommendations for good practice in the reporting of thermoanalytical data.

(ii) Provision of a common basis

- to which all thermoanalytical data can be referred;

- by which a particular technique can be calibrated in terms of established thermodynamic phenomena;

- by which instrument performance can be assessed in terms of reproducibility, accuracy, sensitivity and resolution.

As part of objective (ii) the Committee is seeking to recommend a series of secondary temperature standards and to establish the reproducibility within which these temperatures can be measured in a thermal analysis experiment. The actual temperature observed is procedurally dependent and must be related to temperatures obtained by other physical methods through a form of calibration curve. In addition to recommending a series of standards, the Committee is seeking to establish the degree of scatter about the calibration curve.

Progress

The Committee has met for 2-3 days each year beginning in 1966. Details of their accomplishments are reviewed in the following sections. Brief summaries of the Committee's objectives and programme have appeared (1, 2), while more detailed discussions have been presented to the 5th and 6th Thermoanalysis Institutes (1966, 1967), the Second Toronto Symposium on Thermal Analysis (1967), and the Pittsburgh Conference on Analytical Chemistry (1968). The contribution from the U.S. National Bureau of Standards has also been reviewed (3).

RECOMMENDATIONS FOR THE REPORTING OF THERMAL ANALYSIS DATA

The literature of thermal analysis frequently suffers from a lack of experimental detail which renders the published curves of little value, makes their critical assessment difficult, if not impossible, and gives rise to needless discrepancies and repetition. Such oversight may be the fault of the author, the result of a superficial review, or due to a lack of appreciation of essentials by editors striving to conserve space.

While a number of recommendations had been made concerning the publication of TG data (4), no reasonably complete and consistent set of guidelines existed for DTA and TG to which any of these groups could refer. It was also obvious that national practices varied widely. The Committee on Standardization therefore agreed upon twelve areas of detail which are essential in any paper on DTA and TG (5). This international consensus will be supplemented from time to time as technology develops.

These Recommendations have now been published in English (5), French (6-8), German (9), Japanese (10), Russian (11), and Spanish (12), while they will receive mention in the Czechoslovak, Hungarian and Italian technical literature. l'Association Française de Normalization (AFNOR) recently has accepted these Recommendations, while endorsation by other groups is under active study.

In each of the language areas mentioned above, the Recommendations have been circulated to editors of major journals publishing papers involving thermal analysis, with the request that they be brought to the attention of authors and reviewers and, insofar as journal policy permits, adopted as journal practice. The English-language area has been most extensively covered, with more than 100 journals having been contacted. Comments were received from over one-third of these, virtually all of whom have heartily endorsed the Recommendations and intended to implement them. Since it is all too easy in a rapidly developing field to have the quality of papers inversely proportional to their quantity, the Committee is hopeful that these Recommendations will assist in improving the value of the literature.

STANDARD MATERIALS FOR DTA

Definition of Activity

The object of this programme is to provide a common basis on which all DTA results can be assessed, instrument performance evaluated, and essential calibration made. Thus, not only can meaningful calibration and evaluation of reproducibility and resolution be undertaken, but the inclusion of one or two curves of standard materials *obtained under the conditions of a particular study* will allow the reader to relate the subject matter to the performance of his own instrumentation, and to evaluate the quality of the published data.

As its first concern, the Committee is preparing a series of standards for the calibration of the temperature axis in DTA. Initial guidelines included:

(i)   establishment of standards first for the range 0–1000°C., this being the range which includes the largest proportion of current interest;

(ii)   more specialized study of standards outside this range;

(iii)   immediate development of an international test programme on selected materials.

While melting or freezing points have traditionally been employed in temperature standardization, the Committee considered that solid I ⇌ solid II first–order phase transitions were more appropriate in dynamic DTA studies. Among the factors contributing to this decision were:

(i)   not all instrumentation is adapted to melting samples unless considerable diluent is present;

(ii)   changes in other physical properties, e.g. heat capacity, thermal conductivity, specific volume, are often large when accompanying solid ⇌ solid phase transitions and thus less likely to complicate or restrict the use of a standard;

(iii)   atmosphere control is not a stringent requirement and there is less likelihood of decomposition following melting, sublimation, or other adverse happenings.

Selection of Systems for Study

From a group of more than 200 solid ⇌ solid phase transitions whose thermodynamic properties have been reported (13), 12 systems were selected based on a number of factors:

(i)   chemical stability — the material should not change on storage;

(ii)   chemical inertness — the material should not attack materials normally employed in instrument construction;

(iii)   transitions should be characterized adequately by equilibrium thermodynamic methods;

(iv)   materials should not require pretreatment;

(v)   materials can be heated in inert atmospheres without secondary effects;

(vi)   any other thermal effects should occur at temperatures removed from the transition of interest;

(vii)   materials possessing more than one suitable transition at well-separated temperatures would be desirable;

(viii)   potential suitability as a temperature standard for TG or other thermal methods would be desirable;

(ix)   materials should be commercially available in high purity;

(x)   naturally occurring materials were not favoured because of inhomogeneity;

(xi)   expensive and relatively rare materials would be unsuitable for eventual large-scale distribution.

For each system selected, a large master sample was obtained, from which smaller samples were distributed to all participants, together with all available physical and chemical characterization.

Conditions of Study

To provide a measure of consistency between the various laboratories, certain common experimental conditions were agreed upon:

(i)   the operating conditions of each instrument should be those normally employed;

(ii)   the temperature-measuring thermocouple should be calibrated if possible;

(iii)   the reference alumina supplied should be calcined to at least $1200°C$. and stored over P_2O_5;

(iv)   samples should be used as received and not pre-treated in any way;

(v)   samples should not be diluted;

(vi)   maximum sample size should be approximately 300 mg.;

(vii)   each sample should be examined at heating rates of $3°C.min.^{-1}$ and $10°C.min.^{-1}$, or as near to these values as the apparatus permits;

(viii)   both programmed heating and cooling should be employed as the apparatus permits;

(ix)   sample atmosphere should be flowing nitrogen at 1 atm. pressure;

(x)   three curves should be run on each material but not consecutively;

(xi)   one curve of the reference material against the reference material should be supplied with the other curves;

(xii)   typical temperature–time curves should be included if possible;

(xiii)   results should be reported according to recommendations for good practice defined by the Committee.

Each national delegate undertook to secure the assistance of at least two other laboratories in the same country or geographic area. Invitations were extended on the basis of the competence of the worker, rather than on the equipment available, while maintaining as broad a selection of instrumentation as possible.

Response to these invitations was both willing and enthusiastic and data were compiled from 25 workers using a total of 18 commercial and laboratory instruments.

Temperature Measurement

The Committee defined three points on each thermal effect at which temperatures were to be reported (Fig. 1):

(i)   the departure point, or first detectable deviation from the baseline;

(ii)   the intersection of the forward-extrapolated baseline with the backward-extrapolated initial side of the peak;

(iii)   the peak temperature.

The same time sequence was maintained for these points regardless of the direction of temperature change.

Each investigator measured temperatures from their individual curves, applied any appropriate correction factors before transmitting the data, with copies of all curves, for compilation.

Preliminary Evaluation

Based on comments received from the various participants and its initial review of the data, the Committee agreed to reject four of the twelve materials as potentially suitable standards.

$KHSO_4$	–	decomposition partially overlaps the transition of interest
Na_2SO_4	–	thermograms are not reproducible and depend strongly upon pretreatment of the sample
K_2CO_3 and Na_2CO_3	–	small thermal effects given by these materials were below the limit of resolution of some instruments
	–	effects appear frequently as steps on the experimental record rather than true peaks typical of first-order transitions
	–	materials tend to lose CO_2 at comparatively low temperatures.

Following this review, the Committee appointed a task group to subject the information to computer analysis. A FORTRAN IV programme was designed to extract the means and standard deviations for each of the three temperatures measured during heating and cooling. For each set of data the number of observations, the maximum and minimum values included, the variance, the sum of all observations and the sum of their squares were also calculated. Although some workers reported temperature measurements to the nearest $0.1°C.$, others did not; so that analysis was made only to the nearest $1°C.$

From the data contributed it was possible to examine the effects of some instrumental parameters upon the reported temperatures. Due to the variety of equipment employed, a particular description of some parameter occasionally was unique to a single worker and hence not necessarily representative of the influence of that parameter. The Committee chose, therefore:

(i)   to group results into two classes of temperature programme: $\leqslant 4.9°C.min.^{-1}$ and $\geqslant 5.0°C.min.^{-1}$;

(ii) to examine data without regard to differences in other parameters;

(iii) to further separate the data of workers employing externally calibrated T thermocouples from those using uncalibrated T thermocouples;

(iv) to examine the influence of the point of T measurement within the apparatus;

(v)   to examine the influence of the sample holder configuration (implicit in this is a contribution from sample size which can vary over a considerable range within a particular configuration);

(vi) to examine the influence of sample size.

In this preliminary evaluation, no attempt was made to refine the data for the individual bias of any laboratory.

Conclusions

Limitations of space prevent a detailed report of numerical data from the first evaluation programme. Table I summarizes the mean temperatures obtained by all investigators, divided only according to the rate of temperature change, serving to illustrate the consistency currently possible between competent workers investigating the same sample using different instrumentation. *At the present stage in its investigation the Committee does not wish to attach any significance to the absolute values reported here.*

TABLE I

Mean Temperature Data in Two Programme Classes

Compound	$\Delta T/\Delta t$ °C.min.$^{-1}$	n	Departure	Heating (°C.) Intersection	Peak
KNO_3 127.7° (13)	⩽4.9	36	128 ± 4	128 ± 4	134 ± 5
	⩾5.0	62	127 ± 5	129 ± 5	137 ± 6
$KClO_4$ 299.5° (13)	⩽4.9	41	297 ± 6	299 ± 6	304 ± 6
	⩾5.0	62	298 ± 5	300 ± 5	309 ± 6
Ag_2SO_4 412° (13)	⩽4.9	40	425 ± 6	426 ± 7	433 ± 7
	⩾5.0	67	424 ± 8	429 ± 6	438 ± 6
SiO_2 573° (13)	⩽4.9	39	567 ± 7	572 ± 5	575 ± 5
	⩾5.0	71	543 ± 38	569 ± 6	575 ± 4
K_2SO_4 583° (13)	⩽4.9	38	576 ± 11	584 ± 4	588 ± 4
	⩾5.0	66	558 ± 29	583 ± 4	589 ± 5
K_2CrO_4 665° (13)	⩽4.9	37	663 ± 12	668 ± 5	671 ± 4
	⩾5.0	59	657 ± 14	668 ± 5	674 ± 5
$BaCO_3$ 810° (13)	⩽4.9	72	802 ± 8	807 ± 6	815 ± 7
	⩾5.0	41	800 ± 7	809 ± 4	819 ± 8
$SrCO_3$ 925° (13)	⩽4.9	37	922 ± 7	928 ± 6	934 ± 5
	⩾5.0	57	921 ± 10	928 ± 6	938 ± 7

n = minimum number of observations contributing to each set of temperature measurements

TABLE I (Cont'd)

Mean Temperature Data in Two Programme Classes

Compound	$\Delta T/\Delta t$ °C.min.$^{-1}$	n	Departure	Cooling (°C.) Intersection	Peak
KNO_3 127.7° (13)	$\leqslant 4.9$	27	121 ± 6	120 ± 7	118 ± 7
	$\geqslant 5.0$	34	122 ± 5	122 ± 5	119 ± 7
$KClO_4$ 299.5° (13)	$\leqslant 4.9$	32	293 ± 7	292 ± 6	288 ± 7
	$\geqslant 5.0$	38	292 ± 7	291 ± 7	286 ± 9
Ag_2SO_4 412° (13)	$\leqslant 4.9$	27	401 ± 11	399 ± 12	402 ± 12
	$\geqslant 5.0$	45	389 ± 19	388 ± 19	389 ± 20
SiO_2 573° (13)	$\leqslant 4.9$	27	578 ± 6	573 ± 4	571 ± 3
	$\geqslant 5.0$	48	580 ± 8	573 ± 6	569 ± 6
K_2SO_4 583° (13)	$\leqslant 4.9$	27	587 ± 7	585 ± 4	581 ± 5
	$\geqslant 5.0$	45	584 ± 8	583 ± 7	578 ± 8
K_2CrO_4 665° (13)	$\leqslant 4.9$	28	668 ± 10	666 ± 6	663 ± 7
	$\geqslant 5.0$	44	668 ± 8	667 ± 8	663 ± 9
$BaCO_3$ 810° (13)	$\leqslant 4.9$	49	768 ± 16	766 ± 16	759 ± 17
	$\geqslant 5.0$	23	766 ± 12	763 ± 12	764 ± 16
$SrCO_3$ 925° (13)	$\leqslant 4.9$	24	909 ± 13	905 ± 12	900 ± 12
	$\geqslant 5.0$	39	900 ± 12	898 ± 11	891 ± 12

n = minimum number of observations contributing to each set of temperature measurements

Based on the overall analysis of its data, the Committee offers the following comments:

(i) Over a representative selection of instrumentation, used by experienced workers, the present optimum consistency of temperature measurement is ± 5-6°C., irrespective of temperature over the range 100-950°C., the rate of temperature programme, and of any previous calibration of the temperature-measuring thermocouple by other means. This optimum consistency applies *only* to relatively simple thermal processes exemplified by solid I $\rightleftharpoons$ solid II transitions and would not necessarily be expected for more complex processes and less experienced workers.

(ii) Excluding data samples containing results from only one or two workers, the optimum consistency achieved within a group of workers using similar sample holder configurations and measuring temperature at similar points in each instrument was $\pm 2.5^{\circ}$C. *Individual* workers may achieve higher precision.

(iii) For the practical application of DTA temperature standards, the difficulties inherent in the supercooling of materials, and in the selection and control of cooling rates, make it advisable to recommend that these standards be used only in the heating mode at the present time.

(iv) The point at which a thermal effect first deviates from the base line is subject to considerable irreproducibility in judgement between different operators and, possibly, in the same operator over a series of replicate experiments.

(v) In the heating mode, temperatures at the intersection point generally correspond most closely with the reported (13) equilibrium transition temperature.

(vi) The mean temperature for each of the three measured points *generally* increases with heating rate. Exceptions were noted.

(vii) An examination of the influence of sample holder geometry, sample size, and the location of the temperature-measuring thermocouple failed to indicate any consistent and statistically significant bias attributable to these parameters.

(viii) KNO_3, $KClO_4$, Ag_2SO_4, SiO_2, K_2SO_4, K_2CrO_4, $BaCO_3$ and $SrCO_3$ have been selected as provisional temperature standards pending further international testing. This test programme will involve more acceptable specimens of each material and somewhat more closely specified conditions.

(ix) Recommendations are sought for systems having suitable transitions in the temperature ranges: below ambient; 128-300°; 412-573°; 665-810°; and $>$1000°C.

FUTURE PROGRAMME FOR DTA STANDARDS

A number of the specimens examined in the first evaluation programme did not produce the unique and sharply defined thermal effects desirable in a DTA temperature standard. Examination of further specimens of eight provisional standard substances has led to a revision of the previous selections. The necessity for, and effect of, thermal pretreatment has also been evaluated. The revised selection of substances will be submitted to a further international test programme during 1969. Concurrently a system for distributing approved standards will be developed by ICTA with the objective of offering these at nominal cost no later than 1971.

The Committee is also investigating systems potentially suitable for defining the resolution obtainable from a particular instrument. At present, one system, a physical mixture of SiO_2 and K_2SO_4, appears suitable for establishing resolution in the 550-600°C. range.

TG TEMPERATURE STANDARDS

Programme

A preliminary evaluation has been made of the feasibility of certain compounds to be potential TG temperature standards. The principal criteria for selecting systems were:

(i) that the weight change process should become measurable over as narrow a range of temperature as possible;

(ii) that successive weight change processes should be clearly separated.

An earlier report (14) suggested a number of systems which might be used as the basis for common reference in cases where controversies >25°C. existed between workers. The Committee selected certain of these suggestions, together with other materials and circulated common samples to a limited group of workers for preliminary study at a single heating rate (approx. 3°C.min.$^{-1}$) under dynamic air atmosphere. The system studied included:

ammonium dihydrogen phosphate
ammonium molybdate
barium acetate
boric acid
cupric oxide
magnesium acetate
potassium hydrogen tartrate
silver carbonate
sucrose

Temperatures were measured at the point of first detectable deviation from the base line, 10% decomposition, 50% decomposition, and at the point where further weight change no longer was detectable.

Conclusions

On the basis of presently available information the Committee offers the following comment:

(i) The temperature of first detectable deviations from the base line, frequently referred to as T_i or the "procedural decomposition temperature", depends upon the inertia of the detecting system and is therefore of restricted value in the calibration and comparison of experimental work involving diverse instrumentation.

(ii) A number of the systems studied do not possess simple, single-stage decompositions. Because of the complexity of the decomposition mechanism, the experimental record obtained frequently shows gross variation, suggestive of differences in the decomposition process arising from differences in instrumental parameters, rendering difficult the estimation of temperatures corresponding to a fraction of a specific decomposition process.

(iii) At the present time the Committee is not prepared to recommend any decomposition process as being potentially suitable for the exact calibration of the temperature axis in thermogravimetry. The possible application of other physical methods and the use of DTA temperature standards in certain equipment is under review.

A REQUEST

The Committee invites comment, constructive criticism and suggestions, from all workers in thermal analysis. In turn, it commends its findings and actions to their careful consideration with the hope that these may serve individual as well as collective needs.

ACKNOWLEDGEMENTS

The Committee on Standardization wishes to record its sincere appreciation to all who have participated in its programme thus far, and to the organizations represented by these participants for their financial support. Particular gratitude is expressed to the Ontario Research Foundation for the substantial support of the Chairman, and to the University of Akron for making available computer facilities and personnel to undertake the extensive data analysis programme. The kindness of Northern Polytechnic, London, England, and Massachusetts Institute of Technology, Boston, U.S.A., in providing accommodations for Committee meetings is gratefully acknowledged.

The Committee also wishes to thank Mr. D. Holub of the University of Akron for his valuable contribution to the development of the computer programme and its execution.

Finally, the Chairman wishes to record his personal thanks to the individual members of the Committee for their support, effort and enthusiasm, without which thermal analysis standards today would still be a vague uncertainty.

REFERENCES

1. Nature *217*, 507 (1968).
2. Chemistry in Canada *20*(5), 11 (1968).
3. U.S. Dept. of Commerce, N.B.S. Technical Note 424 (1968).
4. Talanta *10*, 1199 (1963).
5. Anal. Chem. *39*, 543 (1967).
6. Bull. Soc. Chim. France *1967*, 3583.
7. Chimie Analytique. (In press.)
8. Revue des Hautes Temperatures. (In press.)
9. Z. anal. Chem. *231*, 35 (1967).
10. Bull. Ceram. Assoc. Japan *2*(9), 749 (1967).
11. Zhur. Neorg. Khim. *19*, 909 (1968).
12. Bol. R. Soc. Espanola Hist. Nat. (Geol.) *65*, 331 (1967).
13. Selected Values of Chemical Thermodynamic Properties, U.S. National Bureau of Standards Circular 500 (and Supplements).
14. Talanta *14*, 77 (1964).

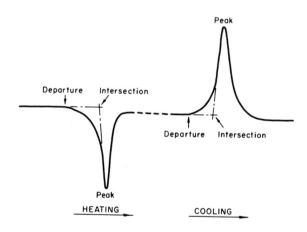

Figure 1

SUBJECT INDEX

Pages 1-706 refer to Volume 1, 707-1512 refer to Volume 2

1

2

D

4